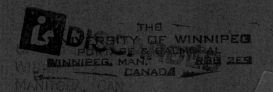

THE MEMOIRS
OF JACQUES CASANOVA
DE SEINGALT

The Memoirs of
JACQUES
CASANOVA
DE SEINGALT

VENETIAN YEARS

---

*The first complete and
unabridged English translation*

BY

ARTHUR MACHEN

Illustrated with Old Engravings

G. P. PUTNAM'S SONS, NEW YORK
ELEK BOOKS, LONDON

Published in England by
ELEK BOOKS LIMITED
14 Great James Street
London, W.C.1

Published in the United States of America by
G. P. PUTNAM'S SONS
210 Madison Avenue
New York City 16
New York

Published in Canada by
LONGMANS, GREEN AND COMPANY
Toronto

Printed in the United States of America

CONTENTS

CONTENTS

CONTENTS

CASANOVA AT DUX

An Unpublished Chapter of History, By Arthur Symons

I

THE *Memoirs* of Casanova, though they have enjoyed the popularity of a bad reputation, have never had justice done to them by serious students of literature, of life, and of history. One English writer, indeed, Mr. Havelock Ellis, has realised that 'there are few more delightful books in the world,' and he has analysed them in an essay on Casanova, published in *Affirmations*, with extreme care and remarkable subtlety. But this essay stands alone, at all events in English, as an attempt to take Casanova seriously, to show him in his relation to his time, and in his relation to human problems. And yet these *Memoirs* are perhaps the most valuable document which we possess on the society of the eighteenth century; they are the history of a unique life, a unique personality, one of the greatest of autobiographies; as a record of adventures, they are more entertaining than *Gil Blas*, or *Monte Cristo*, or any of the imaginary travels, and escapes, and masquerades in life, which have been written in imitation of them. They tell the story of a man who loved life passionately for its own sake: one to whom woman was, indeed, the most important thing in the world, but to whom nothing in the world was indifferent. The bust which gives us the most lively notion of him shows us a great, vivid, intellectual face, full of fiery energy and calm resource, the face of a thinker and a fighter in one. A scholar, an adventurer, perhaps a Cabalist, a busy stirrer in politics, a gamester, one 'born for the fairer sex,' as he tells us, and born also to be a vagabond; this man, who is remembered now for his written account of his own life, was that rarest kind of autobiographer, one who did not live to write, but wrote because he had lived, and when he could live no longer.

And his *Memoirs* take one all over Europe, giving sidelights, all the more valuable in being almost accidental, upon many of the affairs and people most interesting to us during two-thirds of the eighteenth century. Giacomo Casanova was born in Venice, of Spanish and Italian parentage, on April 2, 1725; he died at the Château of Dux, in Bohemia, on June 4, 1798. In that lifetime of seventy-three years he travelled, as his *Memoirs* show us, in Italy, France, Germany, Austria, England, Switzerland, Belgium, Russia, Poland, Spain, Holland, Turkey; he met Voltaire at Ferney, Rousseau at Montmorency, Fontenelle, d'Alembert and Crébillon at Paris, George III. in London, Louis XV. at Fontainebleau, Catherine the Great at St. Petersburg, Benedict XII. at Rome, Joseph II. at Vienna, Frederick the Great at Sans-Souci. Imprisoned by the Inquisitors of State in the *Piombi* at Venice, he made, in 1755, the most famous escape in history. His *Memoirs*, as we have them, break off abruptly at the moment when he is expecting a safe conduct, and the permission to return to Venice after twenty years' wanderings. He did return, as we know from documents in the Venetian archives; he returned as secret agent of the Inquisitors, and remained in their service from 1774 until 1782. At the end of 1782 he left Venice; and next year we find him in Paris, where, in 1784, he met Count Waldstein at the

Venetian Ambassador's, and was invited by him to become his librarian at Dux. He accepted, and for the fourteen remaining years of his life lived at Dux, where he wrote his *Memoirs*.

Casanova died in 1798, but nothing was heard of the *Memoirs* (which the Prince de Ligne, in his own *Memoirs*, tells us that Casanova had read to him, and in which he found *du dramatique, de la rapidité, du comique, de la philosophie, des choses neuves, sublimes, inimitables même*) until the year 1820, when a certain Carlo Angiolini brought to the publishing house of Brockhaus, in Leipzig, a manuscript entitled *Histoire de ma vie jusqu'à l'an* 1797, in the handwriting of Casanova. This manuscript, which I have examined at Leipzig, is written on foolscap paper, rather rough and yellow; it is written on both sides of the page, and in sheets or quires; here and there the paging shows that some pages have been omitted, and in their place are smaller sheets of thinner and whiter paper, all in Casanova's handsome, unmistakable handwriting. The manuscript is done up in twelve bundles, corresponding with the twelve volumes of the original edition; and only in one place is there a gap. The fourth and fifth chapters of the twelfth volume are missing, as the editor of the original edition points out, adding: 'It is not probable that these two chapters have been withdrawn from the manuscript of Casanova by a strange hand; everything leads us to believe that the author himself suppressed them, in the intention, no doubt, of re-writing them, but without having found time to do so.' The manuscript ends abruptly with the year 1774, and not with the year 1797, as the title would lead us to suppose.

This manuscript, in its original state, has never been printed. Herr Brockhaus, on obtaining possession of the manuscript, had it translated into German by Wilhelm Schütz, but with many omissions and alterations, and published this translation, volume by volume, from 1822 to 1828, under the title, *Aus den Memoiren des Venetianers Jacob Casanova de Seingalt*. While the German edition was in course of publication, Herr Brockhaus employed a certain Jean Laforgue, a professor of the French language at Dresden, to revise the original manuscript, correcting Casanova's vigorous, but at times incorrect, and often somewhat Italian, French according to his own notions of elegant writing, suppressing passages which seemed too free-spoken from the point of view of morals and of politics, and altering the names of some of the persons referred to, or replacing those names by initials. This revised text was published in twelve volumes, the first two in 1826, the third and fourth in 1828, the fifth to the eighth in 1832, and the ninth to the twelfth in 1837; the first four bearing the imprint of Brockhaus at Leipzig and Ponthieu et Cie at Paris; the next four the imprint of Heideloff et Campé at Paris; and the last four nothing but *A Bruxelles*. The volumes are all uniform, and were all really printed for the firm of Brockhaus. This, however far from representing the real text, is the only authoritative edition, and my references throughout this article will always be to this edition.

In turning over the manuscript at Leipzig, I read some of the suppressed passages, and regretted their suppression; but Herr Brockhaus, the present head of the firm, assured me that they are not really very considerable in number. The damage, however, to the vivacity of the whole narrative, by the persistent alterations of M. Laforgue, is incalculable. I compared many passages, and found scarcely three consecutive sentences untouched. Herr Brockhaus (whose courtesy I cannot sufficiently acknowledge) was kind enough to have a passage copied out for me, which I afterwards read over, and checked word by word. In this passage Casanova says, for instance: *Elle venoit presque tous les jours lui faire une belle visite.* This is altered into: *Cependant chaque jour Thérèse venait lui faire une visite.* Casanova says that some one *avoit, comme de raison, formé le projet d'allier Dieu avec le diable.* This is made to read: *Qui, comme de raison, avait saintement formé le projet d'allier les intérêts du ciel aux œuvres de ce monde.* Casanova tells us that Thérèse would not commit a mortal sin *pour devenir reine du monde: pour une couronne,* corrects the indefatigable Laforgue. *Il ne savoit que lui dire* becomes *Dans cet état de perplexité;* and so forth. It must, therefore, be realized that the *Memoirs,* as we have them, are only a kind of pale tracing of the vivid colours of the original.

When Casanova's *Memoirs* were first published, doubts were expressed as to their authenticity, first by Ugo Foscolo (in the *Westminster Review,* 1827), then by Quérard, supposed to be an authority in regard to anonymous and pseudonymous writings, finally by Paul Lacroix, *le bibliophile Jacob,* who suggested, or rather expressed his 'certainty,' that the real author of the *Memoirs* was Stendhal, whose 'mind, character, ideas and style' he seemed to recognise on every page. This theory, as foolish and as unsupported as the Baconian theory of Shakespeare, has been carelessly accepted, or at all events accepted as possible, by many good scholars who have never taken the trouble to look into the matter for themselves. It was finally disproved by a series of articles of Armand Baschet, entitled *Preuves curieuses de l'authenticité des Mémoires de Jacques Casanova de*

Seingalt, in *Le Livre,* January, February, April and May,
1881; and these proofs were further corroborated by two
articles of Alessandro d'Ancona, entitled *Un Avventuriere
del Secolo XVIII.,* in the *Nuova Antologia,* February 1
and August 1, 1882. Baschet had never himself seen the
manuscript of the *Memoirs,* but he had learnt all the facts
about it from Messrs. Brockhaus, and he had himself
examined the numerous papers relating to Casanova in
the Venetian archives. A similar examination was made
at the Frari at about the same time by the Abbé Fulin;
and I myself, in 1894, not knowing at the time that the
discovery had been already made, made it over again
for myself. There the arrest of Casanova, his imprisonment in the *Piombi,* the exact date of his escape, the
name of the monk who accompanied him, are all au-
thenticated by documents contained in the *riferte* of the
Inquisition of State; there are the bills for the repairs of
the roof and walls of the cell from which he escaped;
there are the reports of the spies on whose information
he was arrested, for his too dangerous free-spokenness in
matters of religion and morality. The same archives
contain forty-eight letters of Casanova to the Inquisitors
of State, dating from 1763 to 1782, among the *Riferte
dei Confidenti,* or reports of secret agents; the earliest
asking permission to return to Venice, the rest giving
information in regard to the immoralities of the city,
after his return there; all in the same handwriting as
the *Memoirs.* Further proof could scarcely be needed,
but Baschet has done more than prove the authenticity,
he has proved the extraordinary veracity, of the *Memoirs.*
F. W. Barthold, in *Die Geschichtlichen Persönlichkeiten
in J. Casanova's Memoiren,* 2 vols., 1846, had already examined about a hundred of Casanova's allusions to well-
known people, showing the perfect exactitude of all but

six or seven, and out of these six or seven inexactitudes ascribing only a single one to the author's intention. Baschet and d'Ancona both carry on what Barthold had begun; other investigators, in France, Italy and Germany, have followed them; and two things are now certain, first, that Casanova himself wrote the *Memoirs* published under his name, though not textually in the precise form in which we have them; and, second, that as their veracity becomes more and more evident as they are confronted with more and more independent witnesses, it is only fair to suppose that they are equally truthful where the facts are such as could only have been known to Casanova himself.

II

For more than two-thirds of a century it has been known that Casanova spent the last fourteen years of his life at Dux, that he wrote his *Memoirs* there, and that he died there. During all this time people have been discussing the authenticity and the truthfulness of the *Memoirs,* they have been searching for information about Casanova in various directions, and yet hardly any one has ever taken the trouble, or obtained the permission, to make a careful examination in precisely the one place where information was most likely to be found. The very existence of the manuscripts at Dux was known only to a few, and to most of these only on hearsay; and thus the singular good fortune was reserved for me, on my visit to Count Waldstein in September 1899, to be the first to discover the most interesting things contained in these manuscripts. M. Octave Uzanne, though he had not himself visited Dux, had indeed procured copies of some of the manuscripts, a few of which were published by him in *Le Livre,* in 1887 and 1889. But with the

death of *Le Livre* in 1889 the *Casanova inédit* came to an
end, and has never, so far as I know, been continued elsewhere. Beyond the publication of these fragments,
nothing has been done with the manuscripts at Dux, nor
has an account of them ever been given by any one who
has been allowed to examine them.

For five years, ever since I had discovered the documents in the Venetian archives, I had wanted to go to
Dux; and in 1899, when I was staying with Count
Lützow at Zampach, in Bohemia, I found the way kindly
opened for me. Count Waldstein, the present head of
the family, with extreme courtesy, put all his manuscripts at my disposal, and invited me to stay with him.
Unluckily, he was called away on the morning of the day
that I reached Dux. He had left everything ready for
me, and I was shown over the castle by a friend of his,
Dr. Kittel, whose courtesy I should like also to acknowledge. After a hurried visit to the castle we started on
the long drive to Oberleutensdorf, a smaller Schloss near
Komotau, where the Waldstein family was then staying.
The air was sharp and bracing; the two Russian horses
flew like the wind; I was whirled along in an unfamiliar
darkness, through a strange country, black with coal
mines, through dark pine woods, where a wild peasantry
dwelt in little mining towns. Here and there, a few
men and women passed us on the road, in their Sunday
finery; then a long space of silence, and we were in the
open country, galloping between broad fields; and always in a haze of lovely hills, which I saw more distinctly
as we drove back next morning.

The return to Dux was like a triumphal entry, as we
dashed through the market-place filled with people come
for the Monday market, pots and pans and vegetables
strewn in heaps all over the ground, on the rough paving

stones, up to the great gateway of the castle, leaving but just room for us to drive through their midst. I had the sensation of an enormous building: all Bohemian castles are big, but this one was like a royal palace. Set there in the midst of the town, after the Bohemian fashion, it opens at the back upon great gardens, as if it were in the midst of the country. I walked through room after room, along corridor after corridor; everywhere there were pictures, everywhere portraits of Wallenstein, and battle-scenes in which he led on his troops. The library, which was formed, or at least arranged, by Casanova, and which remains as he left it, contains some 25,000 volumes, some of them of considerable value; one of the most famous books in Bohemian literature, Skála's *History of the Church,* exists in manuscript at Dux, and it is from this manuscript that the two published volumes of it were printed. The library forms part of the Museum, which occupies a ground-floor wing of the castle. The first room is an armoury, in which all kinds of arms are arranged, in a decorative way, covering the ceiling and the walls with strange patterns. The second room contains pottery, collected by Casanova's Waldstein on his Eastern travels. The third room is full of curious mechanical toys, and cabinets, and carvings in ivory. Finally, we come to the library, contained in the two innermost rooms. The book-shelves are painted white, and reach to the low-vaulted ceilings, which are whitewashed. At the end of a bookcase, in the corner of one of the windows, hangs a fine engraved portrait of Casanova.

After I had been all over the castle, so long Casanova's home, I was taken to Count Waldstein's study, and left there with the manuscripts. I found six huge cardboard cases, large enough to contain foolscap paper, lettered on the back: *Gräfl.. Waldstein-Wartenberg'sches Real Fideicommiss. Dux-Oberleutensdorf: Handschriftlicher Nachlass Casanova.* The cases were arranged so as to stand like books; they opened at the side; and on opening them, one after another, I found series after series of manuscripts roughly thrown together, after some pretence at arrangement, and lettered with a very generalised description of contents. The greater part of the manuscripts were in Casanova's handwriting, which I could see gradually beginning to get shaky with years. Most were written in French, a certain number in Italian. The beginning of a catalogue in the library, though said to be by him, was not in his handwriting. Perhaps it was taken down at his dictation. There were also some copies of Italian and Latin poems not written by him. Then there were many big bundles of letters addressed to him, dating over more than thirty years. Almost all the rest was in his own handwriting.

I came first upon the smaller manuscripts, among which I found, jumbled together on the same and on separate scraps of paper, washing-bills, accounts, hotel bills, lists of letters written, first drafts of letters with many erasures, notes on books, theological and mathematical notes, sums, Latin quotations, French and Italian verses, with variants, a long list of classical names which have and have not been *francisés*, with reasons for and against; 'what I must wear at Dresden'; headings without anything to follow, such as: 'Reflexions on respiration, on the true cause of youth—the crows'; a new method of winning the lottery at Rome; recipes, among which is a long printed list of perfumes sold at Spa; a newspaper cutting, dated Prague, 25th October 1790, on the thirty-seventh balloon ascent of Blanchard; thanks to some 'noble donor' for the gift of a dog called

'Finette'; a passport for *Monsieur de Casanova, Véni-tien, allant d'ici en Hollande,* October 13, 1758 (*Ce Passeport bon pour quinze jours*), together with an *order* for post-horses, gratis, from Paris to Bordeaux and Bayonne.[1]

Occasionally, one gets a glimpse into his daily life at Dux, as in this note, scribbled on a fragment of paper (here and always I translate the French literally): 'I beg you to tell my servant what the biscuits are that I like to eat, dipped in wine, to fortify my stomach. I believe that they can all be found at Roman's.' Usually, however, these notes, though often suggested by some-thing closely personal, branch off into more general con-siderations; or else begin with general considerations, and end with a case in point. Thus, for instance, a frag-ment of three pages begins: 'A compliment which is only made to gild the pill is a positive impertinence, and Monsieur Bailli is nothing but a charlatan; the monarch ought to have spit in his face, but the monarch trembled with fear.' A manuscript entitled *Essai d'Égoïsme,* dated, 'Dux, this 27th June, 1769,' contains, in the midst of various reflections, an offer to let his *appartement* in return for enough money to 'tranquillise for six months two Jew creditors at Prague.' Another manuscript is headed 'Pride and Folly,' and begins with a long series of antitheses, such as: 'All fools are not proud, and all proud men are fools. Many fools are happy, all proud men are unhappy.' On the same sheet follows this in-stance or application:

Whether it is possible to compose a Latin distich of the greatest beauty without knowing either the Latin language or prosody. We must examine the possibility and the impossibility, and after-wards see who is the man who says he is the author of the dis-

[1] See the account of this visit to Holland, and the reference to taking a passport, *Memoirs,* v. 238.

tich, for there are extraordinary people in the world. My brother, in short, ought to have composed the distich, because he says so, and because he confided it to me tête-à-tête. I had, it is true, difficulty in believing him; but what is one to do? Either one must believe, or suppose him capable of telling a lie which could only be told by a fool; and that is impossible, for all Europe knows that my brother is not a fool.

Here, as so often in these manuscripts, we seem to see Casanova thinking on paper. He uses scraps of paper (sometimes the blank page of a letter, on the other side of which we see the address) as a kind of informal diary; and it is characteristic of him, of the man of infinitely curious mind, which this adventurer really was, that there are so few merely personal notes among these casual jottings. Often, they are purely abstract; at times, metaphysical *jeux d'esprit,* like the sheet of fourteen 'Different Wagers,' which begins:

I wager that it is not true that a man who weighs a hundred pounds will weigh more if you kill him. I wager that if there is any difference, he will weigh less. I wager that diamond powder has not sufficient force to kill a man.

Side by side with these fanciful excursions into science, come more serious ones, as in the note on Algebra, which traces its progress since the year 1494, before which 'it had only arrived at the solution of problems of the second degree, inclusive.' A scrap of paper tells us that Casanova 'did not like regular towns.' 'I like,' he says, 'Venice, Rome, Florence, Milan, Constantinople, Genoa.' Then he becomes abstract and inquisitive again, and writes two pages, full of curious, out-of-the-way learning, on the name of Paradise:

The name of Paradise is a name in Genesis which indicates a place of pleasure (*lieu voluptueux*): this term is Persian. This place of pleasure was made by God before he had created man.

It may be remembered that Casanova quarrelled with Voltaire, because Voltaire had told him frankly that his translation of *L'Écossaise* was a bad translation. It is piquant to read another note written in this style of righteous indignation:

Voltaire, the hardy Voltaire, whose pen is without bit or bridle; Voltaire, who devoured the Bible, and ridiculed our dogmas, doubts, and after having made proselytes to impiety, is not ashamed, being reduced to the extremity of life, to ask for the sacraments, and to cover his body with more relics than St. Louis had at Amboise.

Here is an argument more in keeping with the tone of the *Memoirs:*

A girl who is pretty and good, and as virtuous as you please, ought not to take it ill that a man, carried away by her charms, should set himself to the task of making their conquest. If this man cannot please her by any means, even if his passion be criminal, she ought never to take offence at it, nor treat him unkindly; she ought to be gentle, and pity him, if she does not love him, and think it enough to keep invincibly hold upon her own duty.

Occasionally he touches upon æsthetical matters, as in a fragment which begins with this liberal definition of beauty:

Harmony makes beauty, says M. de S. P. (Bernardin de St. Pierre), but the definition is too short, if he thinks he has said everything. Here is mine. Remember that the subject is metaphysical. An object really beautiful ought to seem beautiful to all whose eyes fall upon it. That is all; there is nothing more to be said.

At times we have an anecdote and its commentary, perhaps jotted down for use in that latter part of the *Memoirs* which was never written, or which has been lost. Here is a single sheet, dated 'this 2nd September, 1791,' and headed *Souvenir:*

The Prince de Rosenberg said to me, as we went down stairs, that Madame de Rosenberg was dead, and asked me if the Comte de Waldstein had in the library the illustration of the Villa d'Altichiero, which the Emperor had asked for in vain at the city library of Prague, and when I answered 'yes,' he gave an equivocal laugh. A moment afterwards, he asked me if he might tell the Emperor. 'Why not, monseigneur? It is not a secret.' 'Is His Majesty coming to Dux?' 'If he goes to Oberlaitensdorf (*sic*) he will go to Dux, too; and he may ask you for it, for there is a monument there which relates to him when he was Grand Duke.' 'In that case,

xxii CASANOVA AT DUX

His Majesty can also see my critical remarks on the Egyptian prints.'

The Emperor asked me this morning, 6th October, how I employed my time at Dux, and I told him that I was making an Italian anthology. 'You have all the Italians, then?' 'All, sire.' See what a lie leads to. If I had not lied in saying that I was making an anthology, I should not have found myself obliged to lie again in saying that we have all the Italian poets. If the Emperor comes to Dux, I shall kill myself.

'They say that this Dux is a delightful spot,' says Casanova in one of the most personal of his notes, 'and I see that it might be for many; but not for me, for what delights me in my old age is independent of the place which I inhabit. When I do not sleep I dream, and when I am tired of dreaming I blacken paper, then I read, and most often reject all that my pen has vomited.' Here we see him blackening paper, on every occasion, and for every purpose. In one bundle I found an unfinished story about Roland, and some adventure with women in a cave; then a 'Meditation on arising from sleep, 19th May 1789'; then a 'Short Reflection of a Philosopher who finds himself thinking of procuring his own death. At Dux, on getting out of bed on 13th October 1793, day dedicated to St. Lucy, memorable in my too long life.' A big budget, containing cryptograms, is headed 'Grammatical Lottery'; and there is the title-page of a treatise on *The Duplication of the Hexahedron, demonstrated geometrically to all the Universities and all the Academies of Europe.*[1] There are innumerable verses, French and Italian, in all stages, occasionally attaining the finality of these lines, which appear in half a dozen tentative forms:

> *Sans mystère point de plaisirs,*
> *Sans silence point de mystère.*
> *Charme divin de mes loisirs,*
> *Solitude! que tu m'es chère!*

[1] See Charles Henry, *Les Connaissances Mathématiques de Casanova.* Rome, 1883.

Then there are a number of more or less complete manuscripts of some extent. There is the manuscript of the translation of Homer's *Iliad, in ottava rima* (published in Venice, 1775-8); of the *Histoire de Venise,* of the *Icosameron,* a curious book published in 1787, purporting to be 'translated from English,' but really an original work of Casanova; *Philocalies sur les Sottises des Mortels,* a long manuscript never published; the sketch and beginning of *Le Polémarque, ou la Calomnie démasquée par la présence d'esprit. Tragicomédie en trois actes, composée à Dux dans le mois de Juin de l'Année,* 1791, which recurs again under the form of the *Polémoscopé: La Lorgnette menteuse ou la Calomnie démasquée,* acted before the Princess de Ligne, at her château at Teplitz, 1791. There is a treatise in Italian, *Delle Passioni;* there are long dialogues, such as *Le Philosophe et le Théologien,* and *Rêve: Dieu-Moi;* there is the *Songe d'un Quart d'Heure,* divided into minutes; there is the very lengthy criticism of *Bernardin de Saint-Pierre;* there is the *Confutation d'une Censure indiscrète qu'on lit dans la Gazette de Iéna,* 19 *Juin* 1789; with another large manuscript, unfortunately imperfect, first called *L'Insulte,* and then *Placet au Public,* dated 'Dux, this 2nd March, 1790,' referring to the same criticism on the *Icosameron* and the *Fuite des Prisons. L'Histoire de ma Fuite des Prisons de la République de Venise, qu'on appelle les Plombs,* which is the first draft of the most famous part of the *Memoirs,* was published at Leipzig in 1788; and, having read it in the Marcian Library at Venice, I am not surprised to learn from this indignant document that it was printed 'under the care of a young Swiss, who had the talent to commit a hundred faults of orthography.'

III

We come now to the documents directly relating to the *Memoirs,* and among these are several attempts at a preface, in which we see the actual preface coming gradually into form.   One is entitled *Casanova au Lecteur,* another *Histoire de mon Existence,* and a third *Preface.*   There is also a brief and characteristic *Précis de ma vie,* dated November 17, 1797.   Some of these have been printed in *Le Livre,* 1887.   But by far the most important manuscript that I discovered, one which, apparently, I am the first to discover, is a manuscript entitled *Extrait du Chapitre 4 et 5.*   It is written on paper similar to that on which the *Memoirs* are written; the pages are numbered 104-148; and though it is described as *Extrait,* it seems to contain, at all events, the greater part of the missing chapters to which I have already referred, Chapters IV. and V. of the last volume of the *Memoirs.*   In this manuscript we find Armelline and Scolastica, whose story is interrupted by the abrupt ending of Chapter III.; we find Mariuccia of Vol. VII., Chapter IX., who married a hairdresser; and we find also Jaconine, whom Casanova recognises as his daughter, 'much prettier than Sophia, the daughter of Thérèse Pompeati, whom I had left at London.'[1]   It is curious that this very important manuscript, which supplies the one missing link in the *Memoirs,* should never have been discovered by any of the few people who have had the opportunity of looking over the Dux manuscripts.   I am inclined to explain it by the fact that the case in which I found this manuscript contains some papers not relating to Casanova.   Probably, those who looked into this

---

[1] See *memoirs,* ix. 272, *et seq.*

case looked no further. I have told Herr Brockhaus of my discovery, and I hope to see Chapters IV. and V. in their places when the long-looked-for edition of the complete text is at length given to the world.

Another manuscript which I found tells with great piquancy the whole story of the Abbé de Brosses' ointment, the curing of the Princess de Conti's pimples, and the birth of the Duc de Montpensier, which is told very briefly, and with much less point, in the *Memoirs* (vol. iii., p. 327). Readers of the *Memoirs* will remember the duel at Warsaw with Count Branicki in 1766 (vol. x., pp. 274-320), an affair which attracted a good deal of attention at the time, and of which there is an account in a letter from the Abbé Taruffi to the dramatist, Francesco Albergati, dated Warsaw, March 19, 1766, quoted in Ernesto Masi's *Life of Albergati,* Bologna, 1878. A manuscript at Dux in Casanova's handwriting gives an account of this duel in the third person; it is entitled, *Description de l'affaire arrivée à Varsovie le 5 Mars, 1766.* D'Ancona, in the *Nuova Antologia* (vol. lxvii., p. 412), referring to the Abbé Taruffi's account, mentions what he considers to be a slight discrepancy: that Taruffi refers to the *danseuse,* about whom the duel was fought, as La Casacci, while Casanova refers to her as La Catai. In this manuscript Casanova always refers to her as La Casacci; La Catai is evidently one of M. Laforgue's arbitrary alterations of the text.

In turning over another manuscript, I was caught by the name Charpillon, which every reader of the *Memoirs* will remember as the name of the harpy by whom Casanova suffered so much in London, in 1763-4. This manuscript begins by saying: 'I have been in London for six months and have been to see them (that is, the mother and daughter) in their own house,' where he finds nothing but 'swindlers, who cause all who go there to lose their money in gambling.' This manuscript adds some details to the story told in the ninth and tenth volumes of the *Memoirs,* and refers to the meeting with the Charpillons four and a half years before, described in Volume V., pages 428-485. It is written in a tone of great indignation. Elsewhere, I found a letter written by Casanova, but not signed, referring to an anonymous letter which he had received in reference to the Charpillons, and ending: 'My handwriting is known.' It was not until the last that I came upon great bundles of letters addressed to Casanova, and so carefully preserved that little scraps of paper, on which postscripts are written, are still in their places. One still sees the seals on the backs of many of the letters, on paper which has slightly yellowed with age, leaving the ink, however, almost always fresh. They come from Venice, Paris, Rome, Prague, Bayreuth, The Hague, Genoa, Fiume, Trieste, etc., and are addressed to as many places, often *poste restante.* Many are letters from women, some in beautiful handwriting, on thick paper; others on scraps of paper, in painful hands, ill-spelt. A Countess writes pitifully, imploring help; one protests her love, in spite of the 'many chagrins' he has caused her; another asks 'how they are to live together'; another laments that a report has gone about that she is secretly living with him, which may harm *his* reputation. Some are in French, more in Italian. *Mon cher Giacometto,* writes one woman, in French; *Carissimo e Amatissimo,* writes another, in Italian. These letters from women are in some confusion, and are in need of a good deal of sorting over and rearranging before their full extent can be realised. Thus I found letters in the same handwriting separated by letters in other handwritings; many are

unsigned, or signed only by a single initial; many are un-
dated, or dated only with the day of the week or month.
There are a great many letters, dating from 1779 to 1786,
signed 'Francesca Buschini,' a name which I cannot
identify; they are written in Italian, and one of them
begins: *Unico Mio vero Amico* ('my only true friend').
Others are signed 'Virginia B.'; one of these is dated,
'Forli, October 15, 1773.' There is also a 'Theresa B.,'
who writes from Genoa. I was at first unable to identify
the writer of a whole series of letters in French, very
affectionate and intimate letters, usually unsigned, occasionally signed 'B.' She calls herself *votre petite amie;*
or she ends with a half-smiling, half-reproachful 'good-
night, and sleep better than I.' In one letter, sent from
Paris in 1759, she writes: 'Never believe me, but when
I tell you that I love you, and that I shall love you
always.' In another letter, ill-spelt, as her letters often
are, she writes: 'Be assured that evil tongues, vapours,
calumny, nothing can change my heart, which is yours
entirely, and has no will to change its master.' Now,
it seems to me that these letters must be from Manon
Baletti, and that they are the letters referred to in the
sixth volume of the *Memoirs.* We read there (page 60)
how on Christmas Day, 1759, Casanova receives a letter
from Manon in Paris, announcing her marriage with 'M.
Blondel, architect to the King, and member of his
Academy'; she returns him his letters, and begs him to
return hers, or burn them. Instead of doing so he allows
Esther to read them, intending to burn them afterwards.
Esther begs to be allowed to keep the letters, promising
to 'preserve them religiously all her life.' 'These letters,'
he says, 'numbered more than two hundred, and the
shortest were of four pages.' Certainly there are not
two hundred of them at Dux, but it seems to me highly

probable that Casanova made a final selection from Manon's letters, and that it is these which I have found.

But, however this may be, I was fortunate enough to find the set of letters which I was most anxious to find: the letters from Henriette, whose loss every writer on Casanova has lamented. Henriette, it will be remembered, makes her first appearance at Cesena, in the year 1748; after their meeting at Geneva, she reappears, romantically *à propos,* twenty-two years later, at Aix in Provence; and she writes to Casanova proposing *un commerce épistolaire,* asking him what he has done since his escape from prison, and promising to do her best to tell him all that has happened to her during the long interval. After quoting her letter, he adds: 'I replied to her, accepting the correspondence that she offered me, and telling her briefly all my vicissitudes. She related to me in turn, in some forty letters, all the history of her life. If she dies before me, I shall add these letters to these *Memoirs;* but to-day she is still alive, and always happy, though now old.' It has never been known what became of these letters, and why they were not added to the *Memoirs.* I have found a great quantity of them, some signed with her married name in full, 'Henriette de Schnetzmann,' and I am inclined to think that she survived Casanova, for one of the letters is dated Bayreuth, 1798, the year of Casanova's death. They are remarkably charming, written with a mixture of piquancy and distinction; and I will quote the characteristic beginning and end of the last letter I was able to find. It begins: 'No, it is impossible to be sulky with you!' and ends: 'If I become vicious, it is you, my Mentor, who make me so, and I cast my sins upon you. Even if I were damned I should still be your most devoted friend, Henriette de Schnetzmann.' Casanova was

twenty-three when he met Henriette; now, herself an
old woman, she writes to him when he is seventy-three,
as if the fifty years that had passed were blotted out
in the faithful affection of her memory. How many
more discreet and less changing lovers have had the
quality of constancy in change, to which this life-long
correspondence bears witness? Does it not suggest a
view of Casanova not quite the view of all the world?
To me it shows the real man, who perhaps of all others
best understood what Shelley meant when he said:

> True love in this differs from gold or clay,
> That to divide is not to take away.

But, though the letters from women naturally interested me the most, they were only a certain proportion
of the great mass of correspondence which I turned over.
There were letters from Carlo Angiolini, who was afterwards to bring the manuscript of the *Memoirs* to Brockhaus; from Balbi, the monk with whom Casanova
escaped from the *Piombi;* from the Marquis Albergati,
playwright, actor, and eccentric, of whom there is some
account in the *Memoirs;* from the Marquis Mosca, 'a
distinguished man of letters whom I was anxious to see,'
Casanova tells us in the same volume in which he de-
scribes his visit to the Moscas at Pesaro; from Zulian,
brother of the Duchess of Fiano; from Richard Lorrain,
*bel homme, ayant de l'esprit, le ton et le goût de la
bonne société,* who came to settle at Gorizia in 1773,
while Casanova was there; from the Procurator Moro-
sini, whom he speaks of in the *Memoirs* as his 'protector,' and as one of those through whom he obtained permission to return to Venice. His other 'protector,' the
avogador Zaguri, had, says Casanova, 'since the affair
of the Marquis Albergati, carried on a most interesting
correspondence with me'; and in fact I found a bundle

of no less than a hundred and thirty-eight letters from
him, dating from 1784 to 1798. Another bundle contains one hundred and seventy-two letters from Count
Lamberg. In the *Memoirs* Casanova says, referring to
his visit to Augsburg at the end of 1761:

> I used to spend my evenings in a very agreeable manner at the
> house of Count Max de Lamberg, who resided at the court of the
> Prince-Bishop with the title of Grand Marshal. What particularly
> attached me to Count Lamberg was his literary talent. A first-rate
> scholar, learned to a degree, he has published several much esteemed
> works. I carried on an exchange of letters with him which ended
> only with his death four years ago in 1792.

Casanova tells us that, at his second visit to Augsburg
in the early part of 1767, he 'supped with Count Lamberg two or three times a week,' during the four months
he was there. It is with this year that the letters I
have found begin: they end with the year of his death,
1792. In his *Mémorial d'un Mondain* Lamberg refers
to Casanova as 'a man known in literature, a man of
profound knowledge.' In the first edition of 1774, he
laments that 'a man such as M. de S. Galt' should not
yet have been taken back into favour by the Venetian
government, and in the second edition, 1775, rejoices
over Casanova's return to Venice. Then there are letters from Da Ponte, who tells the story of Casanova's
curious relations with Mme. d'Urfé, in his *Memorie
scritte da esso*, 1829; from Pittoni, Bono, and others
mentioned in different parts of the *Memoirs*, and from
some dozen others who are not mentioned in them. The
only letters in the whole collection that have been published are those from the Prince de Ligne and from
Count Koenig.

IV

Casanova tells us in his *Memoirs* that, during his
later years at Dux, he had only been able to 'hinder

black melancholy from devouring his poor existence, or
sending him out of his mind,' by writing ten or twelve
hours a day. The copious manuscripts at Dux show us
how persistently he was at work on a singular variety
of subjects, in addition to the *Memoirs,* and to the various books which he published during those years. We
see him jotting down everything that comes into his
head, for his own amusement, and certainly without any
thought of publication; engaging in learned contro-
versies, writing treatises on abstruse mathematical problems, composing comedies to be acted before Count
Waldstein's neighbours, practising verse-writing in two
languages, indeed with more patience than success,
writing philosophical dialogues in which God and himself are the speakers, and keeping up an extensive correspondence, both with distinguished men and with
delightful women. His mental activity, up to the age of
seventy-three, is as prodigious as the activity which he
had expended in living a multiform and incalculable
life. As in life everything living had interested him,
so in his retirement from life every idea makes its separate appeal to him; and he welcomes ideas with the
same impartiality with which he had welcomed adventures. Passion has intellectualised itself, and remains
not less passionate. He wishes to do everything, to
compete with every one; and it is only after having
spent seven years in heaping up miscellaneous learning,
and exercising his faculties in many directions, that he
turns to look back over his own past life, and to live
it over again in memory, as he writes down the narrative of what had interested him most in it. 'I write in
the hope that my history will never see the broad daylight of publication,' he tells us, scarcely meaning it,
we may be sure, even in the moment of hesitancy which

may naturally come to him. But if ever a book was written for the pleasure of writing it, it was this one; and an autobiography written for oneself is not likely to be anything but frank.

'Truth is the only God I have ever adored,' he tells us: and we now know how truthful he was in saying so. I have only summarised in this article the most important confirmations of his exact accuracy in facts and dates; the number could be extended indefinitely. In the manuscripts we find innumerable further confirmations; and their chief value as testimony is that they tell us nothing which we should not have already known, if we had merely taken Casanova at his word. But it is not always easy to take people at their own word, when they are writing about themselves; and the world has been very loth to believe in Casanova as he represents himself. It has been specially loth to believe that he is telling the truth when he tells us about his adventures with women. But the letters contained among these manuscripts shows us the women of Casanova writing to him with all the fervour and all the fidelity which he attributes to them; and they show him to us in the character of as fervid and faithful a lover. In every fact, every detail, and in the whole mental impression which they convey, these manuscripts bring before us the Casanova of the *Memoirs*. As I seemed to come upon Casanova at home, it was as if I came upon old friend, already perfectly known to me, before I had made my pilgrimage to Dux.

1902.

TRANSLATOR'S PREFACE

A SERIES of adventures wilder and more fantastic than the wildest of romances, written down with the exactitude of a business diary; a view of men and cities from Naples to Berlin, from Madrid and London to Constantinople and St. Petersburg; the *vie intime* of the eighteenth century depicted by a man, who to-day sat with cardinals and saluted crowned heads, and to-morrow lurked in dens of profligacy and crime; a book of confessions penned without reticence and without penitence; a record of forty years of "occult" charlatanism; a collection of tales of successful imposture, of *bonnes fortunes,* of marvellous escapes, of transcendent audacity, told with the humour of Smollett and the delicate wit of Voltaire. Who is there interested in men and letters, and in the life of the past, who would not cry, "Where can such a book as this be found?"

Yet the above catalogue is but a brief outline, a bare and meagre summary, of the book known as "THE MEMOIRS OF CASANOVA"; a work absolutely unique in literature. He who opens these wonderful pages is as one who sits in a theatre and looks across the gloom, not on a stage-play, but on another and a vanished world. The curtain draws up, and suddenly a hundred and fifty years are rolled away, and in bright light stands out before us the whole life of the past; the gay dresses, the polished wit, the careless morals, and all the revel and dancing of those merry years before the mighty deluge

of the Revolution. The palaces and marble stairs of old
Venice are no longer desolate, but thronged with scarlet-
robed senators, prisoners with the doom of the Ten upon
their heads cross the Bridge of Sighs, at dead of night
the nun slips out of the convent gate to the dark canal
where a gondola is waiting, we assist at the *parties fines*
of cardinals, and we see the bank made at faro. Venice
gives place to the assembly rooms of Mrs. Cornely and
the fast taverns of the London of 1760; we pass from
Versailles to the Winter Palace of St. Petersburg in the
days of Catherine, from the policy of the Great Frederick
to the lewd mirth of strolling-players, and the presence-
chamber of the Vatican is succeeded by an intrigue in a
garret. It is indeed a new experience to read this history
of a man who, refraining from nothing, has concealed
nothing; of one who stood in the courts of Louis the
Magnificent before Madame de Pompadour and the
nobles of the *Ancien Régime,* and had an affair with an
adventuress of Denmark Street, Soho; who was bound
over to keep the peace by Fielding, and knew Cagliostro.
The friend of popes and kings and noblemen, and of all
the male and female ruffians and vagabonds of Europe,
abbé, soldier, charlatan, gamester, financier, diplomatist,
viveur, philosopher, virtuoso, "chemist, fiddler, and buf-
foon," each of these, and all of these was Giacomo Casanova, Chevalier de Seingalt, Knight of the Golden Spur.

And not only are the Memoirs a literary curiosity;
they are almost equally curious from a bibliographical
point of view. The manuscript was written in French
and came into the possession of the publisher Brockhaus,
of Leipzig, who had it translated into German, and
printed. From this German edition, M. Aubert de Vitry
re-translated the work into French, but omitted about
a fourth of the matter, and this mutilated and worthless

version is frequently purchased by unwary bibliophiles. In the year 1826, however, Brockhaus, in order presumably to protect his property, printed the entire text of the original MS. in French, for the first time, and in this complete form, containing a large number of anecdotes and incidents not to be found in the spurious version, the work was not acceptable to the authorities, and was consequently rigorously suppressed. Only a few copies sent out for presentation or for review are known to have escaped, and from one of these rare copies the present translation has been made strictly and solely for private circulation.

In conclusion, both translator and *éditeur* have done their utmost to present the English Casanova in a dress worthy of the wonderful and witty original.

AUTHOR'S PREFACE

I WILL begin with this confession: whatever I have done in the course of my life, whether it be good or evil, has been done freely; I am a free agent.

The doctrine of the Stoics or of any other sect as to the force of Destiny is a bubble engendered by the imagination of man, and is near akin to Atheism. I not only believe in one God, but my faith as a Christian is also grafted upon that tree of philosophy which has never spoiled anything.

I believe in the existence of an immaterial God, the Author and Master of all beings and all things, and I feel that I never had any doubt of His existence, from the fact that I have always relied upon His providence, prayed to Him in my distress, and that He has always granted my prayers. Despair brings death, but prayer does away with despair; and when a man has prayed he feels himself supported by new confidence and endowed with power to act. As to the means employed by the Sovereign Master of human beings to avert impending dangers from those who beseech His assistance, I confess that the knowledge of them is above the intelligence of man, who can but wonder and adore. Our ignorance becomes our only resource, and happy, truly happy, are those who cherish their ignorance! Therefore must we pray to God, and believe that He has granted the favour we have been praying for, even when in appearance it seems the reverse. As to the position which our body ought to assume when we address ourselves to the Creator, a line of Petrarch settles it:

Con le ginocchia della mente inchine.

Man is free, but his freedom ceases when he has no faith in it; and the greater power he ascribes to faith, the more he deprives himself of that power which God has given to him when He endowed him with the gift of reason. Reason is a particle of the Creator's divinity. When we use it with a spirit of humility and justice we are certain to please the Giver of that precious gift. God ceases to be God only for those who can admit the possibility of His non-existence, and that conception is in itself the most severe punishment they can suffer.

Man is free; yet we must not suppose that he is at liberty to do everything he pleases, for he becomes a slave the moment he allows his actions to be ruled by passion. The man who has sufficient power over himself to wait until his nature has recovered its even balance is the truly wise man, but such beings are seldom met with.

The reader of these Memoirs will discover that I never had any fixed aim before my eyes, and that my system, if it can be called a system, has been to glide away unconcernedly on the stream of life, trusting to the wind wherever it led. How many changes arise from such an independent mode of life! My success and my misfortunes, the bright and the dark days I have gone through, everything has proved to me that in this world, either physical or moral, good comes out of evil just as well as evil comes out of good. My errors will point to thinking men the various roads, and will teach them the great art of treading on the brink of the precipice without falling into it. It is only necessary to have courage, for strength without self-confidence is useless. I have often met with happiness after some imprudent step which ought to have brought ruin upon me, and although passing a vote of censure upon myself I would thank God for his mercy. But, by way of compensation, dire misfortune has befallen me in consequence of actions prompted by the most cautious wisdom. This would humble me; yet conscious that I had acted rightly I would easily derive comfort from that conviction.

In spite of a good foundation of sound morals, the natural offspring of the Divine principles which had been early rooted in my heart, I have been throughout my life the victim of my senses; I have found delight in losing the right path, I have constantly lived in the midst of error, with no consolation but the consciousness of my being mistaken. Therefore, dear reader, I trust that, far from attaching to my history the character of impudent boasting, you will find in my Memoirs only the characteristic proper to a general confession, and that my narratory style will be the manner neither of a repenting sinner, nor of a man ashamed to acknowledge his frolics. They are the follies inherent to youth; I make sport of them, and, if you are kind, you will not yourself refuse them a good-natured smile. You will be amused when you see that I have more than once deceived without the slightest qualm of conscience, both knaves and fools. As to the deceit perpetrated upon women, let it pass, for, when love is in the way, men and women as a general rule dupe each other. But on the score of fools it is a very different matter. I always feel the greatest bliss when I recollect those I have caught in my snares, for they generally are insolent, and so self-conceited that they challenge wit. We avenge intellect when we dupe a fool, and it is a victory not to be despised, for a fool is covered with steel, and it is often very hard to find his vulnerable part. In fact, to gull a fool seems to me an exploit worthy of a witty man. I have felt in my very blood, ever since I was born, a most unconquerable hatred towards the whole tribe of fools, and it arises from the fact that I feel myself a blockhead whenever I am in their company. I am very far from placing them in the same class with those men whom we call stupid, for the latter are stupid only from deficient education, and I rather like them. I have met with some of them—very honest fellows, who, with all their stupidity, had a kind of intelligence and an upright good sense, which cannot be the characteristics of fools. They are like eyes veiled with the cataract, which, if the disease could be removed, would be very beautiful.

Dear reader, examine the spirit of this preface, and you will at once guess at my purpose. I have written a preface because I wish you to know me thoroughly before you begin the reading of my Memoirs. It is only in a coffee-room or at a *table d'hôte* that we like to converse with strangers.

I have written the history of my life, and I have a perfect right to do so; but am I wise in throwing it before a public of which I know nothing but evil? No, I am aware it is sheer folly, but I want to be busy, I want to laugh, and why should I deny myself this gratification?

Expulit elleboro morbum bilemque mero.

An ancient author tells us somewhere, with the tone of a pedagogue, if you have not done anything worthy of being recorded, at least write something worthy of being read. It is a precept as beautiful as a diamond of the first water cut in England, but it cannot be applied to me, because I have not written either a novel, or the life of an illustrious character. Worthy or not, my life is my subject, and my subject is my life. I have lived without dreaming that I should ever take a fancy to write the history of my life, and, for that very reason, my Memoirs may claim from the reader an interest and a sympathy which they would not have obtained, had I always entertained the design to write them in my old age, and, still more, to publish them.

I have reached, in 1797, the age of three-score years and twelve; I can not say, *Vixi*, and I could not procure a more agreeable pastime than to relate my own adventures, and to cause pleasant laughter amongst the good company listening to me, from which I have received so many tokens of friendship, and in the midst of which I have ever lived. To enable me to write well, I have only to think that my readers will belong to that polite society:

Quæcunque dixi, si placuerint, dictavit auditor.

Should there be a few intruders whom I can not prevent from perusing my Memoirs, I must find comfort in the idea that my history was not written for them.

By recollecting the pleasures I have had formerly, I renew them, I enjoy them a second time, while I laugh at the remembrance of troubles now past, and which I no longer feel. A member of this great universe, I speak to the air, and I fancy myself rendering an account of my administration, as a steward is wont to do before leaving his situation. For my future I have no concern, and as a true philosopher, I never would have any, for I know not what it may be: as a Christian, on the other hand, faith must believe without discussion, and the stronger it is, the more it keeps silent. I know that I have lived because I have felt, and, feeling giving me the knowledge of my existence, I know likewise that I shall exist no more when I shall have ceased to feel.

Should I perchance still feel after my death, I would no longer have any doubt, but I would most certainly give the lie to anyone asserting before me that I was dead.

The history of my life must begin by the earliest circumstance which my memory can evoke; it will therefore commence when I had attained the age of eight years and four months. Before that time, if *to think is to live* be a true axiom, I did not live, I could only lay claim to a state of vegetation. The mind of a human being is formed only of comparisons made in order to examine analogies, and therefore cannot precede the existence of memory. The mnemonic organ was developed in my head only eight years and four months after my birth; it is then that my soul began to be susceptible of receiving impressions. How is it possible for an immaterial substance, which can neither touch nor be touched to receive impressions? It is a mystery which man cannot unravel.

A certain philosophy, full of consolation, and in perfect accord with religion, pretends that the state of dependence in which the soul stands in relation to the senses and to the organs, is only incidental and transient, and that it will reach a condition of freedom and happiness when the death of the body shall have delivered it from that state of tyrannic subjection. This is very fine, but, apart from religion, where is the proof of it all? Therefore, as I cannot, from my own information, have a perfect certainty of my being immortal until the dissolution of my body has actually taken place, people must kindly bear with me, if I am in no hurry to obtain that certain knowledge, for, in my estimation, a knowledge to be gained at the cost of life is a rather expensive piece of information. In the mean time I worship God, laying every wrong action under an interdict which I endeavour to respect, and I loathe the wicked without doing them any injury. I only abstain from doing them any good, in the full belief that we ought not to cherish serpents.

As I must likewise say a few words respecting my nature and my temperament, I premise that the most indulgent of my readers is not likely to be the most dishonest or the least gifted with intelligence.

I have had in turn every temperament; phlegmatic in my infancy; sanguine in my youth; later on, bilious; and now I have a disposition which engenders melancholy, and most likely will never change. I always made my food congenial to my constitution, and my health was always excellent. I learned very early that our health is always impaired by some excess either of food or abstinence, and I never had any physician except myself. I am bound to add that the excess in *too little* has ever proved in me more dangerous than the excess in *too much;* the last may cause indigestion, but the first causes death.

Now, old as I am, and although enjoying good digestive organs, I must have only one meal every day; but I find a set-off to that privation in my delightful sleep, and in the ease which I experience in writing down my thoughts without having recourse to paradox or sophism, which would be calculated to deceive myself even more than my readers, for I never could make up my mind to palm counterfeit coin upon them if I knew it to be such.

The sanguine temperament rendered me very sensible to the attractions of voluptuousness: I was always cheerful and ever ready to pass from one enjoyment to another, and I was at the same time very skillful in inventing new pleasures. Thence, I suppose, my natural disposition to make fresh acquaintances, and to break with them so readily, although always for a good reason, and never through mere fickleness. The errors caused by temperament are not to be corrected, because our temperament is perfectly independent of our strength: it is not the case with our character. Heart and head are the constituent parts of character; temperament has almost nothing to do with it, and, therefore, character is dependent upon education, and is susceptible of being corrected and improved.

I leave to others the decision as to the good or evil tendencies of my character, but such as it is it shines upon my countenance, and there it can easily be detected by any physiognomist. It is only on the fact that character can be read; there it lies exposed to the view. It is worthy of remark that men who have no peculiar cast of countenance, and there are a great many such men, are likewise totally deficient in peculiar characteristics, and we may establish the rule that the varieties in physiognomy are equal to the differences in character. I am aware that throughout my life my actions have received their impulse more from the force of feeling than from the wisdom of reason, and this has led me to acknowledge that my conduct has been dependent upon my nature more than upon my mind; both are generally at war, and in the midst of their continual collisions I have never found in me sufficient mind to balance my nature, or enough strength in my nature to counteract the power of my mind. But enough of this, for there is truth in the old saying: *Si brevis esse volo, obscurus fio,* and I believe that, without offending against

modesty, I can apply to myself the following words of
my dear Virgil:

Nec sum adeo informis: nuper me in littore vidi
Cum placidum ventis staret mare.

The chief business of my life has always been to indulge my senses; I never knew anything of greater importance. I felt myself born for the fair sex, I have
ever loved it dearly, and I have been loved by it as
often and as much as I could. I have likewise always
had a great weakness for good living, and I ever felt
passionately fond of every object which excited my
curiosity.

I have had friends who have acted kindly towards
me, and it has been my good fortune to have it in my
power to give them substantial proofs of my gratitude.
I have had also bitter enemies who have persecuted me,
and whom I have not crushed simply because I could
not do it. I never would have forgiven them, had I not
lost the memory of all the injuries they had heaped
upon me. The man who forgets does not forgive, he
only loses the remembrance of the harm inflicted upon
him; forgiveness is the offspring of a feeling of heroism,
of a noble heart, of a generous mind, whilst forgetfulness
is only the result of a weak memory, or of an easy carelessness, and still oftener of a natural desire for calm
and quietness. Hatred, in the course of time, kills the
unhappy wretch who delights in nursing it in his bosom.

Should anyone bring against me an accusation of
sensuality he would be wrong, for all the fierceness of
my senses never caused me to neglect any of my duties.
For the same excellent reason, the accusation of drunkenness ought not to have been brought against Homer:

Laudibus arguitur vini vinosus Homerus.

I have always been fond of highly-seasoned, rich dishes, such as macaroni prepared by a skilful Neapolitan cook, the olla-podrida of the Spaniards, the glutinous codfish from Newfoundland, game with a strong flavour, and cheese the perfect state of which is attained when the tiny animaculæ formed from its very essence begin to shew signs of life. As for women, I have always found the odour of my beloved ones exceeding pleasant.

What depraved tastes! some people will exclaim. Are you not ashamed to confess such inclinations without blushing! Dear critics, you make me laugh heartily. Thanks to my coarse tastes, I believe myself happier than other men, because I am convinced that they enhance my enjoyment. Happy are those who know how to obtain pleasures without injury to anyone; insane are those who fancy that the Almighty can enjoy the sufferings, the pains, the fasts and abstinences which they offer to Him as a sacrifice, and that His love is granted only to those who tax themselves so foolishly. God can only demand from His creatures the practice of virtues the seed of which He has sown in their soul, and all He has given unto us has been intended for our happiness; self-love, thirst for praise, emulation, strength, courage, and a power of which nothing can deprive us— the power of self-destruction, if, after due calculation, whether false or just, we unfortunately reckon death to be advantageous. This is the strongest proof of our moral freedom so much attacked by sophists. Yet this power of self-destruction is repugnant to nature, and has been rightly opposed by every religion.

A so-called free-thinker told me at one time that I could not consider myself a philosopher if I placed any faith in revelation. But when we accept it readily in physics, why should we reject it in religious matters? The form alone is the point in question. The spirit speaks to the spirit, and not to the ears. The principles of everything we are acquainted with must necessarily have been revealed to those from whom we have received them by the great, supreme principle, which contains them all. The bee erecting its hive, the swallow building its nest, the ant constructing its cave, and the spider warping its web, would never have done anything but for a previous and everlasting revelation. We must either believe that it is so, or admit that matter is endowed with thought. But as we dare not pay such a compliment to matter, let us stand by revelation.

The great philosopher, who having deeply studied nature, thought he had found the truth because he acknowledged nature as God, died too soon. Had he lived a little while longer, he would have gone much farther, and yet his journey would have been but a short one, for finding himself in his Author, he could not have denied Him: *In Him we move and have our being.* He would have found Him inscrutable, and thus would have ended his journey.

God, great principle of all minor principles, God, who is Himself without a principle, could not conceive Himself, if, in order to do it, He required to know His own principle.

Oh, blissful ignorance! Spinosa, the virtuous Spinosa, died before he could possess it. He would have died a learned man and with a right to the reward his virtue deserved, if he had only supposed his soul to be immortal!

It is not true that a wish for reward is unworthy of real virtue, and throws a blemish upon its purity. Such a pretension, on the contrary, helps to sustain virtue,

man being himself too weak to consent to be virtuous
only for his own gratification. I hold as a myth that
Amphiaraüs who preferred to be good than to seem good.
In fact, I do not believe there is an honest man alive
without some pretension, and here is mine.

I pretend to the friendship, to the esteem, to the gratitude of my readers. I claim their gratitude, if my Memoirs can give them instruction and pleasure; I claim
their esteem if, rendering me justice, they find more
good qualities in me than faults, and I claim their friendship as soon as they deem me worthy of it by the candour and the good faith with which I abandon myself
to their judgment, without disguise and exactly as I am
in reality. They will find that I have always had such
sincere love for truth, that I have often begun by telling
stories for the purpose of getting truth to enter the
heads of those who could not appreciate its charms.
They will not form a wrong opinion of me when they
see me emptying the purse of my friends to satisfy my
fancies, for those friends entertained idle schemes, and
by giving them the hope of success I trusted to disappointment to cure them. I would deceive them to make
them wiser, and I did not consider myself guilty, for
I applied to my own enjoyment sums of money which
would have been lost in the vain pursuit of possessions
denied by nature; therefore I was not actuated by any
avaricious rapacity. I might think myself guilty if I
were rich now, but I have nothing. I have squandered
everything; it is my comfort and my justification. The
money was intended for extravagant follies, and by applying it to my own frolics I did not turn it into a very
different channel.

If I were deceived in my hope to please, I candidly
confess I would regret it, but not sufficiently so to repent

having written my Memoirs, for, after all, writing them has given me pleasure. Oh, cruel *ennui!* It must be by mistake that those who have invented the torments of hell have forgotten to ascribe thee the first place among them. Yet I am bound to own that I entertain a great fear of hisses; it is too natural a fear for me to boast of being insensible to them, and I cannot find any solace in the idea that, when these Memoirs are published, I shall be no more. I cannot think without a shudder of contracting any obligation towards death: I hate death; for, happy or miserable, life is the only blessing which man possesses, and those who do not love it are unworthy of it. If we prefer honour to life, it is because life is blighted by infamy; and if, in the alternative, man sometimes throws away his life, philosophy must remain silent.

Oh, death, cruel death! Fatal law which nature necessarily rejects because thy very office is to destroy nature! Cicero says that death frees us from all pains and sorrows, but this great philosopher books all the expense without taking the receipts into account. I do not recollect if, when he wrote his *Tusculan Disputations,* his own Tullia was dead. Death is a monster which turns away from the great theatre an attentive hearer before the end of the play which deeply interests him, and this is reason enough to hate it.

All my adventures are not to be found in these Memoirs; I have left out those which might have offended the persons who have played a sorry part therein. In spite of this reserve, my readers will perhaps often think me indiscreet, and I am sorry for it. Should I perchance become wiser before I give up the ghost, I might burn every one of these sheets, but now I have not courage enough to do it.

It may be that certain love scenes will be considered too explicit, but let no one blame me, unless it be for lack of skill, for I ought not to be scolded because, in my old age, I can find no other enjoyment but that which recollections of the past afford to me. After all, virtuous and prudish readers are at liberty to skip over any offensive pictures, and I think it my duty to give them this piece of advice; so much the worse for those who may not read my preface; it is no fault of mine if they do not, for everyone ought to know that a preface is to a book what the play-bill is to a comedy; both must be read.

My Memoirs are not written for young persons who, in order to avoid false steps and slippery roads, ought to spend their youth in blissful ignorance, but for those who, having thorough experience of life, are no longer exposed to temptation, and who, having but too often gone through the fire, are like salamanders, and can be scorched by it no more. True virtue is but a habit, and I have no hesitation in saying that the really virtuous are those persons who can practice virtue without the slightest trouble; such persons are always full of toleration, and it is to them that my Memoirs are addressed.

I have written in French, and not in Italian, because the French language is more universal than mine, and the purists, who may criticise in my style some Italian turns will be quite right, but only in case it should prevent them from understanding me clearly. The Greeks admired Theophrastus in spite of his Eresian style, and the Romans delighted in their Livy in spite of his Patavinity. Provided I amuse my readers, it seems to me that I can claim the same indulgence. After all, every Italian reads Algarotti with pleasure, although his works are full of French idioms.

There is one thing worthy of notice: of all the living languages belonging to the republic of letters, the French tongue is the only one which has been condemned by its masters never to borrow in order to become richer, whilst all other languages, although richer in words than the French, plunder from it words and constructions of sentences, whenever they find that by such robbery they add something to their own beauty. Yet those who borrow the most from the French, are the most forward in trumpeting the poverty of that language, very likely thinking that such an accusation justifies their depredations. It is said that the French language has attained the apogee of its beauty, and that the smallest foreign loan would spoil it, but I make bold to assert that this is prejudice, for, although it certainly is the most clear, the most logical of all languages, it would be great temerity to affirm that it can never go farther or higher than it has gone. We all recollect that, in the days of Lulli, there was but one opinion of his music, yet Rameau came and everything was changed. The new impulse given to the French nation may open new and unexpected horizons, and new beauties, fresh perfections, may spring up from new combinations and from new wants.

The motto I have adopted justifies my digressions, and all the commentaries, perhaps too numerous, in which I indulge upon my various exploits: *Nequidquam sapit qui sibi non sapit.* For the same reason I have always felt a great desire to receive praise and applause from polite society:

Excitat auditor studium, laudataque virtus
Crescit, et immensum gloria calcar habet.

I would willingly have displayed here the proud axiom: *Nemo læditur nisi a se ipso,* had I not feared to offend the immense number of persons who, whenever anything goes wrong with them, are wont to exclaim, "It is no fault of mine!" I cannot deprive them of that small particle of comfort, for, were it not for it, they would soon feel hatred for themselves, and self-hatred often leads to the fatal idea of self-destruction.

As for myself, I always willingly acknowledge my own self as the principal cause of every good or of every evil which may befall me; therefore I have always found myself capable of being my own pupil, and ready to love my teacher.

The Memoirs of

JACQUES CASANOVA

CHAPTER I

My Family Pedigree—My Childhood

DON JACOB CASANOVA, the illegitimate son of
Don Francisco Casanova, was a native of Sara-
gosa, the capital of Aragon, and in the year of 1428 he
carried off Dona Anna Palofax from her convent, on the
day after she had taken the veil. He was secretary to
King Alfonso. He ran away with her to Rome, where,
after one year of imprisonment, the pope, Martin III.,
released Anna from her vows, and gave them the nuptial
blessing at the instance of Don Juan Casanova, major-
domo of the Vatican, and uncle of Don Jacob. All the
children born from that marriage died in their infancy,
with the exception of Don Juan, who, in 1475, married
Donna Eleonora Albini, by whom he had a son, Marco
Antonio.

In 1481, Don Juan, having killed an officer of the king
of Naples, was compelled to leave Rome, and escaped to
Como with his wife and his son; but having left that
city to seek his fortune, he died while traveling with
Christopher Columbus in the year 1493.

Marco Antonio became a noted poet of the school of
Martial, and was secretary to Cardinal Pompeo Colonna.

1

The satire against Giulio de Medicis, which we find in his works, having made it necessary for him to leave Rome, he returned to Como, where he married Abondia Rezzonica. The same Giulio de Medicis, having become pope under the name of Clement VII., pardoned him and called him back to Rome with his wife. The city having been taken and ransacked by the Imperialists in 1526, Marco Antonio died there from an attack of the plague; otherwise he would have died of misery, the soldiers of Charles V. having taken all he possessed. Pierre Valérien speaks of him in his work *de infelicitate litteratorum.*

Three months after his death, his wife gave birth to Jacques Casanova, who died in France at a great age, colonel in the army commanded by Farnèse against Henri, king of Navarre, afterwards king of France. He had left in the city of Parma a son who married Theresa Conti, from whom he had Jacques, who, in the year 1681, married Anna Roli. Jacques had two sons, Jean-Baptiste and Gaëtan-Joseph-Jacques. The eldest left Parma in 1712, and was never heard of; the other also went away in 1715, being only nineteen years old.

This is all I have found in my father's diary: from my mother's lips I have heard the following particulars:—

Gaëtan-Joseph-Jacques left his family, madly in love with an actress named Fragoletta, who performed the chambermaids. In his poverty, he determined to earn a living by making the most of his own person. At first he gave himself up to dancing, and five years afterwards became an actor, making himself conspicuous by his conduct still more than by his talent.

Whether from fickleness or from jealousy, he abandoned the Fragoletta, and joined in Venice a troop of comedians then giving performances at the Saint-Samuel Theatre. Opposite the house in which he had taken his lodging resided a shoemaker, by name Jerome Farusi, with his wife Marzia, and Zanetta, their only daughter —a perfect beauty sixteen years of age. The young actor fell in love with this girl, succeeded in gaining her affection, and in obtaining her consent to a runaway match. It was the only way to win her, for, being an actor, he never could have had Marzia's consent, still less Jerome's, as in their eyes a player was a most awful individual. The young lovers, provided with the necessary certificates and accompanied by two witnesses, presented themselves before the Patriarch of Venice, who performed over them the marriage ceremony. Marzia, Zanetta's mother, indulged in a good deal of exclamation, and the father died broken-hearted.

I was born nine months afterwards, on the 2nd of April, 1725.

The following April my mother left me under the care of her own mother, who had forgiven her as soon as she had heard that my father had promised never to compel her to appear on the stage. This is a promise which all actors make to the young girls they marry, and which they never fulfil, simply because their wives never care much about claiming from them the performance of it. Moreover, it turned out a very fortunate thing for my mother that she had studied for the stage, for nine years later, having been left a widow with six children, she could not have brought them up if it had not been for the resources she found in that profession.

I was only one year old when my father left me to go to London, where he had an engagement. It was in that great city that my mother made her first appearance on the stage, and in that city likewise that she gave birth to my brother François, a celebrated painter of battles, now residing in Vienna, where he has followed his profession since 1783.

Towards the end of the year 1728 my mother returned to Venice with her husband, and as she had become an actress she continued her artistic life. In 1730 she was delivered of my brother Jean, who became Director of the Academy of painting at Dresden, and died there in 1795; and during the three following years she became the mother of two daughters, one of whom died at an early age, while the other married in Dresden, where she still lived in 1798. I had also a posthumous brother, who became a priest; he died in Rome fifteen years ago.

Let us now come to the dawn of my existence in the character of a thinking being.

The organ of memory began to develop itself in me at the beginning of August, 1733. I had at that time reached the age of eight years and four months. Of what may have happened to me before that period I have not the faintest recollection. This is the circumstance.

I was standing in the corner of a room bending towards the wall, supporting my head, and my eyes fixed upon a stream of blood flowing from my nose to the ground. My grandmother, Marzia, whose pet I was, came to me, bathed my face with cold water, and, unknown to everyone in the house, took me with her in a gondola as far as Muran, a thickly-populated island only half a league distant from Venice.

Alighting from the gondola, we enter a wretched hole, where we find an old woman sitting on a rickety bed, holding a black cat in her arms, with five or six more purring around her. The two old cronies held together a long discourse of which, most likely, I was the subject.

At the end of the dialogue, which was carried on in the *patois* of Forli, the witch having received a silver ducat from my grandmother, opened a box, took me in her arms, placed me in the box and locked me in it, telling me not to be frightened—a piece of advice which would certainly have had the contrary effect, if I had had any wits about me, but I was stupefied. I kept myself quiet in a corner of the box, holding a handkerchief to my nose because it was still bleeding, and otherwise very indifferent to the uproar going on outside. I could hear in turn, laughter, weeping, singing, screams, shrieks, and knocking against the box, but for all that I cared nought. At last I am taken out of the box; the blood stops flowing. The wonderful old witch, after lavishing caresses upon me, takes off my clothes, lays me on the bed, burns some drugs, gathers the smoke in a sheet which she wraps around me, pronounces incantations, takes the sheet off me, and gives me five sugar-plums of a very agreeable taste. Then she immediately rubs my temples and the nape of my neck with an ointment exhaling a delightful perfume, and puts my clothes on me again. She told me that my hæmorrhage would little by little leave me, provided I should never disclose to any one what she had done to cure me, and she threatened me, on the other hand, with the loss of all my blood and with death, should I ever breathe a word concerning those mysteries. After having thus taught me my lesson, she informed me that a beautiful lady would pay me a visit during the following night, and that she would make me happy, on condition that I should have sufficient control over myself never to mention to anyone my having received such a visit. Upon this we left and returned home.

I fell asleep almost as soon as I was in bed, without giving a thought to the beautiful visitor I was to receive; but, waking up a few hours afterwards, I saw, or fancied I saw, coming down the chimney, a dazzling woman, with immense hoops, splendidly attired, and wearing on her head a crown set with precious stones, which seemed to me sparkling with fire. With slow steps, but with a majestic and sweet countenance, she came forward and sat on my bed; then taking several small boxes from her pocket, she emptied their contents over my head, softly whispering a few words, and after giving utterance to a long speech, not a single word of which I understood, she kissed me and disappeared the same way she had come. I soon went again to sleep.

The next morning, my grandmother came to dress me, and the moment she was near my bed, she cautioned me to be silent, threatening me with death if I dared to say anything respecting my night's adventures. This command, laid upon me by the only woman who had complete authority over me, and whose orders I was accustomed to obey blindly, caused me to remember the vision, and to store it, with the seal of secrecy, in the inmost corner of my dawning memory. I had not, however, the slightest inclination to mention the circumstances to anyone; in the first place, because I did not suppose it would interest anybody, and in the second because I would not have known whom to make a confidant of. My disease had rendered me dull and retired; everybody pitied me and left me to myself; my life was considered likely to be but a short one, and as to my parents, they never spoke to me.

After the journey to Muran, and the nocturnal visit of the fairy, I continued to have bleeding at the nose, but less from day to day, and my memory slowly developed itself. I learned to read in less than a month.

It would be ridiculous, of course, to attribute this cure

to such follies, but at the same time I think it would
be wrong to assert that they did not in any way con-
tribute to it. As far as the apparition of the beautiful
queen is concerned, I have always deemed it to be a
dream, unless it should have been some masquerade got
up for the occasion, but it is not always in the druggist's
shop that are found the best remedies for severe diseases.
Our ignorance is every day proved by some wonderful
phenomenon, and I believe this to be the reason why it
is so difficult to meet with a learned man entirely un-
tainted with superstition. We know, as a matter of
course, that there never have been any sorcerers in this
world, yet it is true that their power has always existed
in the estimation of those to whom crafty knaves have
passed themselves off as such.

Somnio nocturnos lemures portentaque Thessalia vides.

Many things become real which, at first, had no existence but in our imagination, and, as a natural consequence, many facts which have been attributed to
Faith may not always have been miraculous, although
they are true miracles for those who lend to Faith a
boundless power.

The next circumstance of any importance to myself
which I recollect happened three months after my trip
to Muran, and six weeks before my father's death. I
give it to my readers only to convey some idea of the
manner in which my nature was expanding.

One day, about the middle of November, I was with
my brother François, two years younger than I, in my
father's room, watching him attentively as he was working at optics. A large lump of crystal, round and cut
into facets, attracted my attention. I took it up, and
having brought it near my eyes I was delighted to see

that it multiplied objects. The wish to possess myself of it at once got hold of me, and seeing myself unobserved I took my opportunity and hid it in my pocket.

A few minutes after this my father looked about for his crystal, and unable to find it, he concluded that one of us must have taken it. My brother asserted that he had not touched it, and I, although guilty, said the same; but my father, satisfied that he could not be mistaken, threatened to search us and to thrash the one who had told him a story. I pretended to look for the crystal in every corner of the room, and, watching my opportunity I slyly slipped it in the pocket of my brother's jacket. At first I was sorry for what I had done, for I might as well have feigned to find the crystal somewhere about the room; but the evil deed was past recall. My father, seeing that we were looking in vain, lost patience, searched us, found the unlucky ball of crystal in the pocket of the innocent boy, and inflicted upon him the promised thrashing. Three or four years later I was foolish enough to boast before my brother of the trick I had then played on him; he never forgave me, and has never failed to take his revenge whenever the opportunity offered.

However, having at a later period gone to confession, and accused myself to the priest of the sin with every circumstance surrounding it, I gained some knowledge which afforded me great satisfaction. My confessor, who was a Jesuit, told me that by that deed I had verified the meaning of my first name, Jacques, which, he said, meant, in Hebrew, *"supplanter,"* and that God had changed for that reason the name of the ancient patriarch into that of Israel, which meant *"knowing."* He had deceived his brother Esau.

Six weeks after the above adventure my father was

attacked with an abscess in the head, which carried him off in a week. Dr. Zambelli first gave him oppilative remedies, and, seeing his mistake, he tried to mend it by administering castoreum, which sent his patient into convulsions and killed him. The abscess broke out through the ear one minute after his death, taking its leave after killing him, as if it had no longer any business with him. My father departed this life in the very prime of his manhood. He was only thirty-six years of age, but he was followed to his grave by the regrets of the public, and more particularly of all the patricians amongst whom he was held as above his profession, not less on account of his gentlemanly behaviour than on account of his extensive knowledge in mechanics.

Two days before his death, feeling that his end was at hand, my father expressed a wish to see us all around his bed, in the presence of his wife and of the Messieurs Grimani, three Venetian noblemen whose protection he wished to entreat in our favour. After giving us his blessing, he requested our mother, who was drowned in tears, to give her sacred promise that she would not educate any of us for the stage, on which he never would have appeared himself had he not been led to it by an unfortunate attachment. My mother gave her promise, and the three noblemen said that they would see to its being faithfully kept. Circumstances helped our mother to fulfill her word.

At that time my mother had been pregnant for six months, and she was allowed to remain away from the stage until after Easter. Beautiful and young as she was, she declined all the offers of marriage which were made to her, and, placing her trust in Providence, she courageously devoted herself to the task of bringing up her young family.

She considered it a duty to think of me before the others, not so much from a feeling of preference as in consequence of my disease, which had such an effect upon me that it was difficult to know what to do with me. I was very weak, without any appetite, unable to apply myself to anything, and I had all the appearance of an idiot. Physicians disagreed as to the cause of the disease. He loses, they would say, two pounds of blood every week; yet there cannot be more than sixteen or eighteen pounds in his body. What, then, can cause so abundant a bleeding? One asserted that in me all the chyle turned into blood; another was of opinion that the air I was breathing must, at each inhalation, increase the quantity of blood in my lungs, and contended that this was the reason for which I always kept my mouth open. I heard of it all six years afterward from M. Baffo, a great friend of my late father.

This M. Baffo consulted the celebrated Doctor Macop, of Padua, who sent him his opinion by writing. This consultation, which I have still in my possession, says that our blood is an elastic fluid which is liable to diminish or to increase in thickness, but never in quantity, and that my hæmorrhage could only proceed from the thickness of the mass of my blood, which relieved itself in a natural way in order to facilitate circulation. The doctor added that I would have died long before, had not nature, in its wish for life, assisted itself, and he concluded by stating that the cause of the thickness of my blood could only be ascribed to the air I was breathing and that consequently I must have a change of air, or every hope of cure be abandoned. He thought likewise, that the stupidity so apparent on my countenance was caused by nothing else but the thickness of my blood.

M. Baffo, a man of sublime genius, a most lascivious, yet a great and original poet, was therefore instrumental in bringing about the decision which was then taken to send me to Padua, and to him I am indebted for my life. He died twenty years after, the last of his ancient patrician family, but his poems, although obscene, will give everlasting fame to his name. The state-inquisitors of Venice have contributed to his celebrity by their mistaken strictness. Their persecutions caused his manuscript works to become precious. They ought to have been aware that despised things are forgotten.

As soon as the verdict given by Professor Macop had been approved of, the Abbé Grimani undertook to find a good boarding-house in Padua for me, through a chemist of his acquaintance who resided in that city. His name was Ottaviani, and he was also an antiquarian of some repute. In a few days the boarding-house was found, and on the 2nd day of April, 1734, on the very day I had accomplished my ninth year, I was taken to Padua in a *burchiello,* along the Brenta Canal. We embarked at ten o'clock in the evening, immediately after supper.

The *burchiello* may be considered a small floating house. There is a large saloon with a smaller cabin at each end, and rooms for servants fore and aft. It is a long square with a roof, and cut on each side by glazed windows with shutters. The voyage takes eight hours. M. Grimani, M. Baffo, and my mother accompanied me. I slept with her in the saloon, and the two friends passed the night in one of the cabins. My mother rose at daybreak, opened one of the windows facing the bed, and the rays of the rising sun, falling on my eyes, caused me to open them. The bed was too low for me to see the land; I could see through the window only the tops of the trees along the river. The boat was sailing with such an even movement that I could not realize the fact of our moving, so that the trees, which, one after the other, were rapidly disappearing from my sight, caused me an extreme surprise. "Ah, dear mother!" I exclaimed, "what is this? the trees are walking!" At that very moment the two noblemen came in, and reading astonishment on my countenance, they asked me what my thoughts were so busy about. "How is it," I answered, "that the trees are walking."

They all laughed, but my mother, heaving a great sigh, told me, in a tone of deep pity, "The boat is moving, the trees are not. Now dress yourself."

I understood at once the reason of the phenomenon. "Then it may be," said I, "that the sun does not move, and that we, on the contrary, are revolving from west to east." At these words my good mother fairly screamed. M. Grimani pitied my foolishness, and I remained dismayed, grieved, and ready to cry. M. Baffo brought me life again. He rushed to me, embraced me tenderly, and said, "Thou are right, my child. The sun does not move; take courage, give heed to your reasoning powers and let others laugh."

My mother, greatly surprised, asked him whether he had taken leave of his senses to give me such lessons; but the philosopher, not even condescending to answer her, went on sketching a theory in harmony with my young and simple intelligence. This was the first real pleasure I enjoyed in my life. Had it not been for M. Baffo, this circumstance might have been enough to degrade my understanding; the weakness of credulity would have become part of my mind. The ignorance of the two others would certainly have blunted in me the edge of a faculty which, perhaps, has not carried me very far in my after life, but to which alone I feel that I am indebted for every particle of happiness I enjoy when I look into myself.

We reached Padua at an early hour and went to Ottaviani's house; his wife loaded me with caresses. I found there five or six children, amongst them a girl of eight years, named Marie, and another of seven, Rose, beautiful as a seraph. Ten years later Marie became the wife of the broker Colonda, and Rose, a few years afterwards, married a nobleman, Pierre Marcello, and had one son and two daughters, one of whom was wedded to M. Pierre Moncenigo, and the other to a nobleman of the Carrero family. This last marriage was afterwards nullified. I shall have, in the course of events, to speak of all these persons, and that is my reason for mentioning their names here.

Ottaviani took us at once to the house where I was to board. It was only a few yards from his own residence, at Sainte-Marie d'Advance, in the parish of Saint-Michel, in the house of an old Sclavonian woman, who let the first floor to Signora Mida, wife of a Sclavonian colonel. My small trunk was laid open before the old woman, to whom was handed an inventory of all its contents, together with six sequins for six months paid in advance. For this small sum she undertook to feed me, to keep me clean, and to send me to a day-school. Protesting that it was not enough, she accepted these terms. I was kissed and strongly commanded to be always obedient and docile, and I was left with her.

In this way did my family get rid of me.

CHAPTER II

My Grandmother Comes to Padua, and Takes Me to Dr.
Gozzi's School—My First Love Affair

AS soon as I was left alone with the Sclavonian woman, she took me up to the garret, where she pointed out my bed in a row with four others, three of which belonged to three young boys of my age, who at that moment were at school, and the fourth to a servant girl whose province it was to watch us and to prevent the many peccadilloes in which school-boys are wont to indulge. After this visit we came downstairs, and I was taken to the garden with permission to walk about until dinner-time.

I felt neither happy nor unhappy; I had nothing to say. I had neither fear nor hope, nor even a feeling of curiosity; I was neither cheerful nor sad. The only thing which grated upon me was the face of the mistress of the house. Although I had not the faintest idea either of beauty or of ugliness, her face, her countenance, her tone of voice, her language, everything in that woman was repulsive to me. Her masculine features repelled me every time I lifted my eyes towards her face to listen to what she said to me. She was tall and coarse like a trooper; her complexion was yellow, her hair black, her eyebrows long and thick, and her chin gloried in a respectable bristly beard: to complete the picture, her hideous, half-naked bosom was hanging half-way down her long chest; she may have been about fifty. The servant was a stout country girl, who did all the work of the house; the garden was a square of some thirty feet, which had no other beauty than its green appearance.

Towards noon my three companions came back from school, and they at once spoke to me as if we had been old acquaintances, naturally giving me credit for such intelligence as belonged to my age, but which I did not possess. I did not answer them, but they were not baffled, and they at last prevailed upon me to share their innocent pleasures. I had to run, to carry and be carried, to turn head over heels, and I allowed myself to be initiated into those arts with a pretty good grace until we were summoned to dinner. I sat down to the table; but seeing before me a wooden spoon, I pushed it back, asking for my silver spoon and fork to which I was much attached, because they were a gift from my good old granny. The servant answered that the mistress wished to maintain equality between the boys, and I had to submit, much to my disgust. Having thus learned that equality in everything was the rule of the house, I went to work like the others and began to eat the soup out of the common dish, and if I did not complain of the rapidity with which my companions made it disappear, I could not help wondering at such inequality being allowed. To follow this very poor soup, we had a small portion of dried cod and one apple each, and dinner was over: it was in Lent. We had neither glasses nor cups, and we all helped ourselves out of the same earthen pitcher to a miserable drink called *graspia*, which is made by boiling in water the stems of grapes stripped of their fruit. From the following day I drank nothing but water. This way of living surprised me, for I did not know whether I had a right to complain of it.

After dinner the servant took me to the school, kept by a young priest, Doctor Gozzi, with whom the Sclavonian woman had bargained for my schooling at the rate of forty sous a month, or the eleventh part of a sequin.

The first thing to do was to teach me writing, and I was placed amongst children of five and six years, who did not fail to turn me into ridicule on account of my age.

On my return to the boarding-house I had my supper, which, as a matter of course, was worse than the dinner, and I could not make out why the right of complaint should be denied me. I was then put to bed, but there three well-known species of vermin kept me awake all night, besides the rats, which, running all over the garret, jumped on my bed and fairly made my blood run cold with fright. This is the way in which I began to feel misery, and to learn how to suffer it patiently. The vermin, which feasted upon me, lessened my fear of the rats, and by a very lucky system of compensation, the dread of the rats made me less sensitive to the bites of the vermin. My mind was reaping benefit from the very struggle fought between the evils which surrounded me. The servant was perfectly deaf to my screaming.

As soon as it was daylight I ran out of the wretched garret, and, after complaining to the girl of all I had endured during the night, I asked her to give me a clean shirt, the one I had on being disgusting to look at, but she answered that I could only change my linen on a Sunday, and laughed at me when I threatened to complain to the mistress. For the first time in my life I shed tears of sorrow and of anger, when I heard my companions scoffing at me. The poor wretches shared my unhappy condition, but they were used to it, and that makes all the difference.

Sorely depressed, I went to school, but only to sleep soundly through the morning. One of my comrades, in the hope of turning the affair into ridicule at my expense, told the doctor the reason of my being so sleepy. The good priest, however, to whom without doubt Providence had guided me, called me into his private room, listened to all I had to say, saw with his own eyes the proofs of my misery, and moved by the sight of the blisters which disfigured my innocent skin, he took up his cloak, went with me to my boarding-house, and shewed the woman the state I was in. She put on a look of great astonishment, and threw all the blame upon the servant. The doctor being curious to see my bed, I was, as much as he was, surprised at the filthy state of the sheets in which I had passed the night. The accursed woman went on blaming the servant, and said that she would discharge her; but the girl, happening to be close by, and not relishing the accusation, told her boldly that the fault was her own, and she then threw open the beds of my companions to shew us that they did not experience any better treatment. The mistress, raving, slapped her on the face, and the servant, to be even with her, returned the compliment and ran away. The doctor left me there, saying that I could not enter his school unless I was sent to him as clean as the other boys. The result for me was a very sharp rebuke, with the threat, as a finishing stroke, that if I ever caused such a broil again, I would be ignominiously turned out of the house.

I could not make it out; I had just entered life, and I had no knowledge of any other place but the house in which I had been born, in which I had been brought up, and in which I had always seen cleanliness and honest comfort. Here I found myself ill-treated, scolded, although it did not seem possible that any blame could be attached to me. At last the old shrew tossed a shirt in my face, and an hour later I saw a new servant changing the sheets, after which we had our dinner.

My schoolmaster took particular care in instructing me. He gave me a seat at his own desk, and in order to shew my proper appreciation of such a favour, I gave myself up to my studies; at the end of the first month I could write so well that I was promoted to the grammar class.

The new life I was leading, the half-starvation system to which I was condemned, and most likely more than everything else, the air of Padua, brought me health such as I had never enjoyed before, but that very state of blooming health made it still more difficult for me to bear the hunger which I was compelled to endure; it became unbearable. I was growing rapidly; I enjoyed nine hours of deep sleep, unbroken by any dreams, save that I always fancied myself sitting at a well-spread table, and gratifying my cruel appetite, but every morning I could realize in full the vanity and the unpleasant disappointment of flattering dreams! This ravenous appetite would at last have weakened me to death, had I not made up my mind to pounce upon, and to swallow, every kind of eatables I could find, whenever I was certain of not being seen.

Necessity begets ingenuity. I had spied in a cupboard of the kitchen some fifty red herrings; I devoured them all one after the other, as well as all the sausages which were hanging in the chimney to be smoked; and in order to accomplish those feats without being detected, I was in the habit of getting up at night and of undertaking my foraging expeditions under the friendly veil of darkness. Every new-laid egg I could discover in the poultry-yard, quite warm and scarcely dropped by the hen, was a most delicious treat. I would even go as far as the kitchen of the schoolmaster in the hope of pilfering something to eat.

The Sclavonian woman, in despair at being unable to catch the thieves, turned away servant after servant. But, in spite of all my expeditions, as I could not always find something to steal, I was as thin as a walking skeleton.

My progress at school was so rapid during four or five months that the master promoted me to the rank of dux. My province was to examine the lessons of my thirty school-fellows, to correct their mistakes and report to the master with whatever note of blame or of approval I thought they deserved; but my strictness did not last long, for idle boys soon found out the way to enlist my sympathy. When their Latin lesson was full of mistakes, they would buy me off with cutlets and roast chickens; they even gave me money. These proceedings excited my covetousness, or, rather, my gluttony, and, not satisfied with levying a tax upon the ignorant, I became a tyrant, and I refused well-merited approbation to all those who declined paying the contribution I demanded. At last, unable to bear my injustice any longer, the boys accused me, and the master, seeing me convicted of extortion, removed me from my exalted position. I would very likely have fared badly after my dismissal, had not Fate decided to put an end to my cruel apprenticeship.

Doctor Gozzi, who was attached to me, called me privately one day into his study, and asked me whether I would feel disposed to carry out the advice he would give me in order to bring about my removal from the

house of the Sclavonian woman, and my admission in
his own family.   Finding me delighted at such an offer,
he caused me to copy three letters which I sent, one to
the Abbé Grimani, another to my friend Baffo, and the
last to my excellent grandam.   The half-year was nearly
out, and my mother not being in Venice at that period
there was no time to lose.

In my letters I gave a description of all my sufferings,
and I prognosticated my death were I not immediately
removed from my boarding-house and placed under the
care of my school-master, who was disposed to receive
me; but he wanted two sequins a month.

M. Grimani did not answer me, and commissioned
his friend Ottaviani to scold me for allowing myself to
be ensnared by the doctor; but M. Baffo went to consult with my grandmother, who could not write, and in
a letter which he addressed to me he informed me that
I would soon find myself in a happier situation.   And,
truly, within a week the excellent old woman, who loved
me until her death, made her appearance as I was sitting
down to my dinner.   She came in with the mistress of
the house, and the moment I saw her I threw my arms
around her neck, crying bitterly, in which luxury the
old lady soon joined me.   She sat down and took me on
her knees; my courage rose again.   In the presence of
the Sclavonian woman I enumerated all my grievances,
and after calling her attention to the food, fit only for
beggars, which I was compelled to swallow, I took her
upstairs to shew her my bed.   I begged her to take me
out and give me a good dinner after six months of such
starvation.   The boarding-house keeper boldly asserted
that she could not afford better for the amount she had
received, and there was truth in that, but she had no
business to keep house and to become the tormentor of

poor children who were thrown on her hands by stingi-
ness, and who required to be properly fed.

My grandmother very quietly intimated her intention
to take me away forthwith, and asked her to put all my
things in my trunk. I cannot express my joy during
these preparations. For the first time I felt that kind
of happiness which makes forgiveness compulsory upon
the being who enjoys it, and causes him to forget all
previous unpleasantness. My grandmother took me to
the inn, and dinner was served, but she could hardly
eat anything in her astonishment at the voracity with
which I was swallowing my food. In the meantime Doctor Gozzi, to whom she had sent notice of her arrival,
came in, and his appearance soon prepossessed her in
his favour. He was then a fine-looking priest, twenty-
six years of age, chubby, modest, and respectful. In less
than a quarter of an hour everything was satisfactorily
arranged between them. The good old lady counted out
twenty-four sequins for one year of my schooling, and
took a receipt for the same, but she kept me with her
for three days in order to have me clothed like a priest,
and to get me a wig, as the filthy state of my hair made
it necessary to have it all cut off.

At the end of the three days she took me to the doctor's house, so as to see herself to my installation and to
recommend me to the doctor's mother, who desired her
to send or to buy in Padua a bedstead and bedding; but
the doctor having remarked that, his own bed being very
wide, I might sleep with him, my grandmother expressed
her gratitude for all his kindness, and we accompanied
her as far as the *burchiello* she had engaged to return to
Venice.

The family of Doctor Gozzi was composed of his
mother, who had great reverence for him, because, a

peasant by birth, she did not think herself worthy of having a son who was a priest, and still more a doctor in divinity; she was plain, old, and cross; and of his father, a shoemaker by trade, working all day long and never addressing a word to anyone, not even during the meals. He only became a sociable being on holidays, on which occasions he would spend his time with his friends in some tavern, coming home at midnight as drunk as a lord and singing verses from Tasso. When in this blissful state the good man could not make up his mind to go to bed, and became violent if anyone attempted to compel him to lie down. Wine alone gave him sense and spirit, for when sober he was incapable of attending to the simplest family matter, and his wife often said that he never would have married her had not his friends taken care to give him a good breakfast before he went to the church.

But Doctor Gozzi had also a sister, called Bettina, who at the age of thirteen was pretty, lively, and a great reader of romances. Her father and mother scolded her constantly because she was too often looking out of the window, and the doctor did the same on account of her love for reading. This girl took at once my fancy without my knowing why, and little by little she kindled in my heart the first spark of a passion which, afterwards became in me the ruling one.

Six months after I had been an inmate in the house, the doctor found himself without scholars; they all went away because I had become the sole object of his affection. He then determined to establish a college, and to receive young boys as boarders; but two years passed before he met with any success. During that period he taught me everything he knew; true, it was not much; yet it was enough to open to me the high road to all sciences. He likewise taught me the violin, an accomplishment which proved very useful to me in a peculiar circumstance, the particulars of which I will give in good time. The excellent doctor, who was in no way a philosopher, made me study the logic of the Peripatetics, and the cosmography of the ancient system of Ptolemy, at which I would laugh, teasing the poor doctor with theorems to which he could find no answer. His habits, moreover, were irreproachable, and in all things connected with religion, although no bigot, he was of the greatest strictness, and, admitting everything as an article of faith, nothing appeared difficult to his conception. He believed the deluge to have been universal, and he thought that, before that great cataclysm, men lived a thousand years and conversed with God, that Noah took one hundred years to build the ark, and that the earth, suspended in the air, is firmly held in the very centre of the universe which God had created from nothing. When I would say and prove that it was absurd to believe in the existence of nothingness, he would stop me short and call me a fool.

He could enjoy a good bed, a glass of wine, and cheerfulness at home. He did not admire fine wits, good jests or criticism, because it easily turns to slander, and he would laugh at the folly of men reading newspapers which, in his opinion, always lied and constantly repeated the same things. He asserted that nothing was more troublesome than incertitude, and therefore he condemned thought because it gives birth to doubt.

His ruling passion was preaching, for which his face and his voice qualified him; his congregation was almost entirely composed of women of whom, however, he was the sworn enemy; so much so, that he would not look them in the face even when he spoke to them. Weakness of the flesh and fornication appeared to him the most monstrous of sins, and he would be very angry if I dared to assert that, in my estimation, they were the most venial of faults. His sermons were crammed with passages from the Greek authors, which he translated into Latin. One day I ventured to remark that those passages ought to be translated into Italian because women did not understand Latin any more than Greek, but he took offence, and I never had afterwards the courage to allude any more to the matter. Moreover he praised me to his friends as a wonder, because I had learned to read Greek alone, without any assistance but a grammar.

During Lent, in the year 1736, my mother wrote to the doctor; and, as she was on the point of her departure for St. Petersburg, she wished to see me, and requested him to accompany me to Venice for three or four days. This invitation set him thinking, for he had never seen Venice, never frequented good company, and yet he did not wish to appear a novice in anything. We were soon ready to leave Padua, and all the family escorted us to the *burchiello*.

My mother received the doctor with a most friendly welcome; but she was strikingly beautiful, and my poor master felt very uncomfortable, not daring to look her in the face, and yet called upon to converse with her. She saw the dilemma he was in, and thought she would have some amusing sport about it should opportunity present itself. I, in the meantime, drew the attention of everyone in her circle; everybody had known me as a fool, and was amazed at my improvement in the short space of two years. The doctor was overjoyed, because he saw that the full credit of my transformation was given to him.

The first thing which struck my mother unpleasantly was my light-coloured wig, which was not in harmony with my dark complexion, and contrasted most woefully with my black eyes and eyebrows. She inquired from the doctor why I did not wear my own hair, and he answered that, with a wig, it was easier for his sister to keep me clean. Everyone smiled at the simplicity of the answer, but the merriment increased when, to the question made by my mother whether his sister was married, I took the answer upon myself, and said that Bettina was the prettiest girl of Padua, and was only fourteen years of age. My mother promised the doctor a splendid present for his sister on condition that she would let me wear my own hair, and he promised that her wishes would be complied with. The peruke-maker was then called, and I had a wig which matched my complexion.

Soon afterwards all the guests began to play cards, with the exception of my master, and I went to see my brothers in my grandmother's room. François shewed me some architectural designs which I pretended to admire; Jean had nothing to shew me, and I thought him a rather insignificant boy. The others were still very young.

At the supper-table, the doctor, seated next to my mother, was very awkward. He would very likely not have said one word, had not an Englishman, a writer of talent, addressed him in Latin; but the doctor, being unable to make him out, modestly answered that he did not understand English, which caused much hilarity. M. Baffo, however, explained the puzzle by telling us that Englishmen read and pronounced Latin in the same way that they read and spoke their own language, and I remarked that Englishmen were wrong as much as we would be, if we pretended to read and to pronounce their language according to Latin rules. The Englishman, pleased with my reasoning, wrote down the following old couplet, and gave it to me to read:

> *Dicite, grammatici, cur mascula nomina cunnus,*
> *Et cur femineum mentula nomen habet.*

After reading it aloud, I exclaimed, "This is Latin indeed."

"We know that," said my mother, "but can you explain it,"

"To explain it is not enough," I answered; "it is a question which is worthy of an answer." And after considering for a moment, I wrote the following pentameter:

> *Disce quod à domino nomina servus habet.*

This was my first literary exploit, and I may say that in that very instant the seed of my love for literary fame was sown in my breast, for the applause lavished upon me exalted me to the very pinnacle of happiness. The Englishman, quite amazed at my answer, said that no boy of eleven years had ever accomplished such a feat, embraced me repeatedly, and presented me with his watch. My mother, inquisitive like a woman, asked M. Grimani to tell her the meaning of the lines, but as the abbé was not any wiser than she was M. Baffo translated it in a whisper. Surprised at my knowledge, she rose from her chair to get a valuable gold watch and presented to my master, who, not knowing how to express his deep gratitude, treated us to the most comic scene. My mother, in order to save him from the difficulty of paying her a compliment, offered him her cheek. He had only to give her a couple of kisses, the easiest and the most innocent thing in good company; but the poor man was on burning coals, and so completely out of countenance that he would, I truly believe, rather have died than give the kisses. He drew back with his head down, and he was allowed to remain in peace until we retired for the night.

When we found ourselves alone in our room, he poured out his heart, and exclaimed that it was a pity he could not publish in Padua the distich and my answer.

"And why not?" I said.

"Because both are obscene."

"But they are sublime."

"Let us go to bed and speak no more on the subject. Your answer was wonderful, because you cannot possibly know anything of the subject in question, or of the manner in which verses ought to be written."

As far as the subject was concerned, I knew it by theory; for, unknown to the doctor, and because he had forbidden it, I had read Meursius, but it was natural that he should be amazed at my being able to write verses, when he, who had taught me prosody, never could compose a single line. *Nemo dat quod non habet* is a false axiom when applied to mental acquirements.

Four days afterwards, as we were preparing for our departure, my mother gave me a parcel for Bettina, and M. Grimani presented me with four sequins to buy books. A week later my mother left for St. Petersburg.

After our return to Padua, my good master for three or four months never ceased to speak of my mother, and Bettina, having found in the parcel five yards of black silk and twelve pairs of gloves, became singularly attached to me, and took such good care of my hair that

in less than six months I was able to give up wearing
the wig. She used to comb my hair every morning, often
before I was out of bed, saying that she had not time
to wait until I was dressed. She washed my face, my
neck, my chest; lavished on me childish caresses which
I thought innocent, but which caused me to be angry
with myself, because I felt that they excited me. Three
years younger than she was, it seemed to me that she
could not love me with any idea of mischief, and the
consciousness of my own vicious excitement put me out
of temper with myself. When, seated on my bed, she
would say that I was getting stouter, and would have
the proof of it with her own hands, she caused me the
most intense emotion; but I said nothing, for fear she
would remark my sensitiveness, and when she would go
on saying that my skin was soft, the tickling sensation
made me draw back, angry with myself that I did not
dare to do the same to her, but delighted at her not
guessing how I longed to do it. When I was dressed,
she often gave me the sweetest kisses, calling me her
darling child, but whatever wish I had to follow her
example, I was not yet bold enough. After some time,
however, Bettina laughing at my timidity, I became more
daring and returned her kisses with interest, but I always
gave way the moment I felt a wish to go further; I
then would turn my head, pretending to look for something, and she would go away. She was scarcely out of
the room before I was in despair at not having followed
the inclination of my nature, and, astonished at the fact
that Bettina could do to me all she was in the habit of
doing without feeling any excitement from it, while I
could hardly refrain from pushing my attacks further,
I would every day determine to change my way of
acting.

In the early part of autumn, the doctor received three new boarders; and one of them, who was fifteen years old, appeared to me in less than a month on very friendly terms with Bettina.

This circumstance caused me a feeling of which until then I had no idea, and which I only analyzed a few years afterwards. It was neither jealousy nor indignation, but a noble contempt which I thought ought not to be repressed, because Cordiani, an ignorant, coarse boy, without talent or polite education, the son of a simple farmer, and incapable of competing with me in anything, having over me but the advantage of dawning manhood, did not appear to me a fit person to be preferred to me; my young self-esteem whispered that I was above him. I began to nurse a feeling of pride mixed with contempt which told against Bettina, whom I loved unknown to myself. She soon guessed it from the way I would receive her caresses, when she came to comb my hair while I was in bed; I would repulse her hands, and no longer return her kisses. One day, vexed at my answering her question as to the reason of my change towards her by stating that I had no cause for it, she told me in a tone of commiseration that I was jealous of Cordiani. This reproach sounded to me like a debasing slander. I answered that Cordiani was, in my estimation, as worthy of her as she was worthy of him. She went away smiling, but, revolving in her mind the only way by which she could be revenged, she thought herself bound to render me jealous. However, as she could not attain such an end without making me fall in love with her, this is the policy she adopted.

One morning she came to me as I was in bed and brought me a pair of white stockings of her own knitting. After dressing my hair, she asked my permission to try the stockings on herself, in order to correct any deficiency in the other pairs she intended to knit for me. The doctor had gone out to say his mass. As she was putting on the stocking, she remarked that my legs were not clean, and without any more ado she immediately began to wash them. I would have been ashamed to let her see my bashfulness; I let her do as she liked, not foreseeing what would happen. Bettina, seated on my bed, carried too far her love for cleanliness, and her curiosity caused me such intense voluptuousness that the feeling did not stop until it could be carried no further. Having recovered my calm, I bethought myself that I was guilty and begged her forgiveness. She did not expect this, and, after considering for a few moments, she told me kindly that the fault was entirely her own, but that she never would again be guilty of it. And she went out of the room, leaving me to my own thoughts.

They were of a cruel character. It seemed to me that I had brought dishonour upon Bettina, that I had betrayed the confidence of her family, offended against the sacred laws of hospitality, that I was guilty of a most wicked crime, which I could only atone for by marrying her, in case Bettina could make up her mind to accept for her husband a wretch unworthy of her.

These thoughts led to a deep melancholy which went on increasing from day to day, Bettina having entirely ceased her morning visits by my bedside. During the first week, I could easily account for the girl's reserve, and my sadness would soon have taken the character of the warmest love, had not her manner towards Cordiani inoculated in my veins the poison of jealousy, although I never dreamed of accusing her of the same crime towards him that she had committed upon me.

I felt convinced, after due consideration, that the

act she had been guilty of with me had been deliberately done, and that her feelings of repentance kept her away from me. This conviction was rather flattering to my vanity, as it gave me the hope of being loved, and the end of all my communings was that I made up my mind to write to her, and thus to give her courage.

I composed a letter, short but calculated to restore peace to her mind, whether she thought herself guilty, or suspected me of feelings contrary to those which her dignity might expect from me. My letter was, in my own estimation, a perfect masterpiece, and just the kind of epistle by which I was certain to conquer her very adoration, and to sink for ever the sun of Cordiani, whom I could not accept as the sort of being likely to make her hesitate for one instant in her choice between him and me. Half-an-hour after the receipt of my letter, she told me herself that the next morning she would pay me her usual visit, but I waited in vain. This conduct provoked me almost to madness, but my surprise was indeed great when, at the breakfast table, she asked me whether I would let her dress me up as a girl to accompany her five or six days later to a ball for which a neighbour of ours, Doctor Olivo, had sent letters of invitation. Everybody having seconded the motion, I gave my consent. I thought this arrangement would afford a favourable opportunity for an explanation, for mutual vindication, and would open a door for the most complete reconciliation, without fear of any surprise arising from the proverbial weakness of the flesh. But a most unexpected circumstance prevented our attending the ball, and brought forth a comedy with a truly tragic turn.

Doctor Gozzi's godfather, a man advanced in age, and in easy circumstances, residing in the country, thought

himself, after a severe illness, very near his end, and
sent to the doctor a carriage with a request to come to
him at once with his father, as he wished them to be
present at his death, and to pray for his departing soul.
The old shoemaker drained a bottle, donned his Sunday
clothes, and went off with his son.

I thought this a favourable opportunity and determined to improve it, considering that the night of the
ball was too remote to suit my impatience. I therefore
managed to tell Bettina that I would leave ajar the door
of my room, and that I would wait for her as soon as
everyone in the house had gone to bed. She promised
to come. She slept on the ground floor in a small closet
divided only by a partition from her father's chamber;
the doctor being away, I was alone in the large room.
The three boarders had their apartment in a different
part of the house, and I had therefore no mishap to
fear. I was delighted at the idea that I had at last
reached the moment so ardently desired.

The instant I was in my room I bolted my door and
opened the one leading to the passage, so that Bettina
should have only to push it in order to come in; I then
put my light out, but did not undress.

When we read of such situations in a romance we
think they are exaggerated; they are not so, and the
passage in which Ariosto represents Roger waiting for
Alcine is a beautiful picture painted from nature.

Until midnight I waited without feeling much anxiety;
but I heard the clock strike two, three, four o'clock in
the morning without seeing Bettina; my blood began
to boil, and I was soon in a state of furious rage. It
was snowing hard, but I shook from passion more than
from cold. One hour before day-break, unable to master
any longer my impatience, I made up my mind to go

downstairs with bare feet, so as not to wake the dog, and to place myself at the bottom of the stairs within a yard of Bettina's door, which ought to have been opened if she had gone out of her room. I reached the door; it was closed, and as it could be locked only from inside I imagined that Bettina had fallen asleep. I was on the point of knocking at the door, but was prevented by fear of rousing the dog, as from that door to that of her closet there was a distance of three or four yards. Overwhelmed with grief, and unable to take a decision, I sat down on the last step of the stairs; but at day-break, chilled, benumbed, shivering with cold, afraid that the servant would see me and would think I was mad, I determined to go back to my room. I arise, but at that very moment I hear some noise in Bettina's room. Certain that I am going to see her, and hope lending me new strength, I draw nearer to the door. It opens; but instead of Bettina coming out I see Cordiani, who gives me such a furious kick in the stomach that I am thrown at a distance deep in the snow. Without stopping a single instant Cordiani is off, and locks himself up in the room which he shared with the brothers Feltrini.

I pick myself up quickly with the intention of taking my revenge upon Bettina, whom nothing could have saved from the effects of my rage at that moment. But I find her door locked; I kick vigorously against it, the dog starts a loud barking, and I make a hurried retreat to my room, in which I lock myself up, throwing myself in bed to compose and heal up my mind and body, for I was half dead.

Deceived, humbled, ill-treated, an object of contempt to the happy and triumphant Cordiani, I spent three hours ruminating the darkest schemes of revenge. To poison them both seemed to me but a trifle in that ter-

rible moment of bitter misery. This project gave way
to another as extravagant, as cowardly—namely, to go
at once to her brother and disclose everything to him.
I was twelve years of age, and my mind had not yet
acquired sufficient coolness to mature schemes of heroic
revenge, which are produced by false feelings of honour;
this was only my apprenticeship in such adventures.

I was in that state of mind when suddenly I heard
outside of my door the gruff voice of Bettina's mother,
who begged me to come down, adding that her daughter
was dying. As I would have been very sorry if she had
departed this life before she could feel the effects of my
revenge, I got up hurriedly and went downstairs. I
found Bettina lying in her father's bed writhing with
fearful convulsions, and surrounded by the whole family.
Half dressed, nearly bent in two, she was throwing her
body now to the right, now to the left, striking at random with her feet and with her fists, and extricating
herself by violent shaking from the hands of those who
endeavoured to keep her down.

With this sight before me, and the night's adventure
still in my mind, I hardly knew what to think. I had no
knowledge of human nature, no knowledge of artifice
and tricks, and I could not understand how I found myself coolly witnessing such a scene, and composedly calm
in the presence of two beings, one of whom I intended
to kill and the other to dishonour. At the end of an
hour Bettina fell asleep.

A nurse and Doctor Olivo came soon after. The first
said that the convulsions were caused by hysterics, but
the doctor said no, and prescribed rest and cold baths.
I said nothing, but I could not refrain from laughing at
them, for I knew, or rather guessed, that Bettina's sickness was the result of her nocturnal employment, or of

the fright which she must have felt at my meeting with Cordiani. At all events, I determined to postpone my revenge until the return of her brother, although I had not the slightest suspicion that her illness was all sham, for I did not give her credit for so much cleverness.

To return to my room I had to pass through Bettina's closet, and seeing her dress handy on the bed I took it into my head to search her pockets. I found a small note, and recognizing Cordiani's handwriting, I took possession of it to read it in my room. I marvelled at the girl's imprudence, for her mother might have discovered it, and being unable to read would very likely have given it to the doctor, her son. I thought she must have taken leave of her senses, but my feelings may be appreciated when I read the following words: "As your father is away it is not necessary to leave your door ajar as usual. When we leave the supper-table I will go to your closet; you will find me there."

When I recovered from my stupor I gave way to an irresistible fit of laughter, and seeing how completely I had been duped I thought I was cured of my love. Cordiani appeared to me deserving of forgiveness, and Bettina of contempt. I congratulated myself upon having received a lesson of such importance for the remainder of my life. I even went so far as to acknowledge to myself that Bettina had been quite right in giving the preference to Cordiani, who was fifteen years old, while I was only a child. Yet, in spite of my good disposition to forgiveness, the kick administered by Cordiani was still heavy upon my memory, and I could not help keeping a grudge against him.

At noon, as we were at dinner in the kitchen, where we took our meals on account of the cold weather, Bettina began again to raise piercing screams. Everybody rushed to her room, but I quietly kept my seat and finished my dinner, after which I went to my studies. In the evening when I came down to supper I found that Bettina's bed had been brought to the kitchen close by her mother's; but it was no concern of mine, and I remained likewise perfectly indifferent to the noise made during the night, and to the confusion which took place in the morning, when she had a fresh fit of convulsions.

Doctor Gozzi and his father returned in the evening. Cordiani, who felt uneasy, came to inquire from me what my intentions were, but I rushed towards him with an open penknife in my hand, and he beat a hasty retreat. I had entirely abandoned the idea of relating the night's scandalous adventure to the doctor, for such a project I could only entertain in a moment of excitement and rage. The next day the mother came in while we were at our lesson, and told the doctor, after a lengthened preamble, that she had discovered the character of her daughter's illness; that it was caused by a spell thrown over her by a witch, and that she knew the witch well.

"It may be, my dear mother, but we must be careful not to make a mistake. Who is the witch?"

"Our old servant, and I have just had a proof of it."

"How so?"

"I have barred the door of my room with two broomsticks placed in the shape of a cross, which she must have undone to go in; but when she saw them she drew back, and she went round by the other door. It is evident that, were she not a witch, she would not be afraid of touching them."

"It is not complete evidence, dear mother; send the woman to me."

The servant made her appearance.

"Why," said the doctor, "did you not enter my mother's room this morning through the usual door?"

"I do not know what you mean."

"Did you not see the St. Andrew's cross on the door?"

"What cross is that?"

"It is useless to plead ignorance," said the mother; "where did you sleep last Thursday night?"

"At my niece's, who had just been confined."

"Nothing of the sort. You were at the witches' Sabbath; you are a witch, and have bewitched my daughter."

The poor woman, indignant at such an accusation, spits at her mistress's face; the mistress, enraged, gets hold of a stick to give the servant a drubbing; the doctor endeavours to keep his mother back, but he is compelled to let her loose and to run after the servant, who was hurrying down the stairs, screaming and howling in order to rouse the neighbours; he catches her, and finally succeeds in pacifying her with some money.

After this comical but rather scandalous exhibition, the doctor donned his vestments for the purpose of exorcising his sister and of ascertaining whether she was truly possessed of an unclean spirit. The novelty of this mystery attracted the whole of my attention. All the inmates of the house appeared to me either mad or stupid, for I could not, for the life of me, imagine that diabolical spirits were dwelling in Bettina's body. When we drew near her bed, her breathing had, to all appearance, stopped, and the exorcisms of her brother did not restore it. Doctor Olivo happened to come in at that moment, and inquired whether he would be in the way; he was answered in the negative, provided he had faith.

Upon which he left, saying that he had no faith in any miracles except in those of the Gospel.

Soon after Doctor Gozzi went to his room, and finding myself alone with Bettina I bent down over her bed and whispered in her ear:

"Take courage, get well again, and rely upon my discretion."

She turned her head towards the wall and did not answer me, but the day passed off without any more convulsions. I thought I had cured her, but on the following day the frenzy went up to the brain, and in her delirium she pronounced at random Greek and Latin words without any meaning, and then no doubt whatever was entertained of her being possessed of the evil spirit. Her mother went out and returned soon, accompanied by the most renowned exorcist of Padua, a very ill-featured Capuchin, called Friar Prospero da Bovolenta.

The moment Bettina saw the exorcist, she burst into loud laughter, and addressed to him the most offensive insults, which fairly delighted everybody, as the devil alone could be bold enough to address a Capuchin in such a manner; but the holy man, hearing himself called an obtrusive ignoramus and a stinkard, went on striking Bettina with a heavy crucifix, saying that he was beating the devil. He stopped only when he saw her on the point of hurling at him the chamber utensil which she had just seized. "If it is the devil who has offended thee with his words," she said, "resent the insult with words likewise, jackass that thou art, but if I have offended thee myself, learn, stupid booby, that thou must respect me, and be off at once."

I could see poor Doctor Gozzi blushing; the friar, however, held his ground, and, armed at all points, began to read a terrible exorcism, at the end of which he commanded the devil to state his name.

"My name is Bettina."

"It cannot be, for it is the name of a baptized girl."

"Then thou art of opinion that a devil must rejoice in a masculine name? Learn, ignorant friar, that a devil is a spirit, and does not belong to either sex. But as thou believest that a devil is speaking to thee through my lips, promise to answer me with truth, and I will engage to give way before thy incantations."

"Very well, I agree to this."

"Tell me, then, art thou thinking that thy knowledge is greater than mine?"

"No, but I believe myself more powerful in the name of the holy Trinity, and by my sacred character."

"If thou art more powerful than I, then prevent me from telling thee unpalatable truths. Thou art very vain of thy beard, thou art combing and dressing it ten times a day, and thou would'st not shave half of it to get me out of this body. Cut off thy beard, and I promise to come out."

"Father of lies, I will increase thy punishment a hundred fold."

"I dare thee to do it."

After saying these words, Bettina broke into such a loud peal of laughter, that I could not refrain from joining in it. The Capuchin, turning towards Doctor Gozzi, told him that I was wanting in faith, and that I ought to leave the room; which I did, remarking that he had guessed rightly. I was not yet out of the room when the friar offered his hand to Bettina for her to kiss, and I had the pleasure of seeing her spit upon it.

This strange girl, full of extraordinary talent, made rare sport of the friar, without causing any surprise to anyone, as all her answers were attributed to the devil. I could not conceive what her purpose was in playing such a part.

The Capuchin dined with us, and during the meal he uttered a good deal of nonsense. After dinner, he returned to Bettina's chamber, with the intention of blessing her, but as soon as she caught sight of him, she took up a glass full of some black mixture sent from the apothecary, and threw it at his head. Cordiani, being close by the friar, came in for a good share of the liquid —an accident which afforded me the greatest delight. Bettina was quite right to improve her opportunity, as everything she did was, of course, put to the account of the unfortunate devil. Not overmuch pleased, Friar Prospero, as he left the house, told the doctor that there was no doubt of the girl being possessed, but that another exorcist must be sent for, since he had not, himself, obtained God's grace to eject the evil spirit.

After he had gone, Bettina kept very calm for six hours, and in the evening, to our great surprise, she joined us at the supper table. She told her parents that she felt quite well, spoke to her brother, and then, addressing me, she remarked that, the ball taking place on the morrow, she would come to my room in the morning to dress my hair like a girl's. I thanked her, and said that, as she had been so ill, she ought to nurse herself. She soon retired to bed, and we remained at the table, talking of her.

When I was undressing for the night, I took up my night-cap, and found in it a small note with these words: "You must accompany me to the ball, disguised as a girl, or I will give you a sight which will cause you to weep."

I waited until the doctor was asleep, and I wrote the

following answer: "I cannot go to the ball, because I have fully made up my mind to avoid every opportunity of being alone with you. As for the painful sight with which you threaten to entertain me, I believe you capable of keeping your word, but I entreat you to spare my heart, for I love you as if you were my sister. I have forgiven you, dear Bettina, and I wish to forget everything. I enclose a note which you must be delighted to have again in your possession. You see what risk you were running when you left it in your pocket. This restitution must convince you of my friendship."

CHAPTER III

Bettina Is Supposed to Go Mad—Father Mancia—The
Small-pox—I Leave Padua

BETTINA must have been in despair, not knowing into whose hands her letter had fallen; to return it to her and thus to allay her anxiety, was therefore a great proof of friendship; but my generosity, at the same time that it freed her from a keen sorrow, must have caused her another quite as dreadful, for she knew that I was master of her secret. Cordiani's letter was perfectly explicit; it gave the strongest evidence that she was in the habit of receiving him every night, and therefore the story she had prepared to deceive me was useless. I felt it was so, and, being disposed to calm her anxiety as far as I could, I went to her bedside in the morning, and I placed in her hands Cordiani's note and my answer to her letter.

The girl's spirit and talent had won my esteem; I could no longer despise her; I saw in her only a poor creature seduced by her natural temperament. She loved man, and was to be pitied only on account of the consequences. Believing that the view I took of the situation was a right one, I had resigned myself like a reasonable being, and not like a disappointed lover. The shame was for her and not for me. I had only one wish, namely, to find out whether the two brothers Feltrini,

Cordiani's companions, had likewise shared Bettina's favours.

Bettina put on throughout the day a cheerful and happy look. In the evening she dressed herself for the ball; but suddenly an attack of sickness, whether feigned or real I did not know, compelled her to go to bed, and frightened everybody in the house. As for myself, knowing the whole affair, I was prepared for new scenes, and indeed for sad ones, for I felt that I had obtained over her a power repugnant to her vanity and self-love. I must, however, confess that, in spite of the excellent school in which I found myself before I had attained manhood, and which ought to have given me experience as a shield for the future, I have through the whole of my life been the dupe of women. Twelve years ago, if it had not been for my guardian angel, I would have foolishly married a young, thoughtless girl, with whom I had fallen in love. Now that I am seventy-two years old I believe myself no longer susceptible of such follies; but, alas! that is the very thing which causes me to be miserable.

The next day the whole family was deeply grieved because the devil of whom Bettina was possessed had made himself master of her reason. Doctor Gozzi told me that there could not be the shadow of a doubt that his unfortunate sister was possessed, as, if she had only been mad, she never would have so cruelly ill-treated the Capuchin, Prospero, and he determined to place her under the care of Father Mancia.

This Mancia was a celebrated Jacobin (or Dominican) exorcist, who enjoyed the reputation of never having failed to cure a girl possessed of the demon.

Sunday had come; Bettina had made a good dinner, but she had been frantic all through the day. Towards midnight her father came home, singing Tasso as usual, and so drunk that he could not stand. He went up to Bettina's bed, and after kissing her affectionately he said to her: "Thou art not mad, my girl."

Her answer was that he was not drunk.

"Thou art possessed of the devil, my dear child."

"Yes, father, and you alone can cure me."

"Well, I am ready."

Upon this our shoemaker begins a theological discourse, expatiating upon the power of faith and upon the virtue of the paternal blessing. He throws off his cloak, takes a crucifix with one hand, places the other over the head of his daughter, and addresses the devil in such an amusing way that even his wife, always a stupid, dull, cross-grained old woman, had to laugh till the tears came down her cheeks. The two performers in the comedy alone were not laughing, and their serious countenance added to the fun of the performance. I marvelled at Bettina (who was always ready to enjoy a good laugh) having sufficient control over herself to remain calm and grave. Doctor Gozzi had also given way to merriment; but begged that the farce should come to an end, for he deemed that his father's eccentricities were as many profanations against the sacredness of exorcism. At last the exorcist, doubtless tired out, went to bed saying that he was certain that the devil would not disturb his daughter during the night.

On the morrow, just as we had finished our breakfast, Father Mancia made his appearance. Doctor Gozzi, followed by the whole family, escorted him to his sister's bedside. As for me, I was entirely taken up by the face of the monk. Here is his portrait. His figure was tall and majestic, his age about thirty; he had light hair and blue eyes; his features were those of Apollo, but without his pride and assuming haughtiness; his complexion, dazzling white, was pale, but that paleness seemed to have been given for the very purpose of showing off the red coral of his lips, through which could be seen, when they opened, two rows of pearls. He was neither thin nor stout, and the habitual sadness of his countenance enhanced its sweetness. His gait was slow, his air timid, an indication of the great modesty of his mind.

When we entered the room Bettina was asleep, or pretended to be so. Father Mancia took a sprinkler and threw over her a few drops of holy water; she opened her eyes, looked at the monk, and closed them immediately; a little while after she opened them again, had a better look at him, laid herself on her back, let her arms droop down gently, and with her head prettily bent on one side she fell into the sweetest of slumbers.

The exorcist, standing by the bed, took out his pocket ritual and the stole which he put round his neck, then a reliquary, which he placed on the bosom of the sleeping girl, and with the air of a saint he begged all of us to fall on our knees and to pray, so that God should let him know whether the patient was possessed or only labouring under a natural disease. He kept us kneeling for half an hour, reading all the time in a low tone of voice. Bettina did not stir.

Tired, I suppose, of the performance, he desired to speak privately with Doctor Gozzi. They passed into the next room, out of which they emerged after a quarter of an hour, brought back by a loud peal of laughter from the mad girl, who, when she saw them, turned her back on them. Father Mancia smiled, dipped the sprinkler over and over in the holy water, gave us all a generous shower, and took his leave.

Doctor Gozzi told us that the exorcist would come again on the morrow, and that he had promised to deliver Bettina within three hours if she were truly possessed of the demon, but that he made no promise if it should turn out to be a case of madness. The mother exclaimed that he would surely deliver her, and she poured out her thanks to God for having allowed her the grace of beholding a saint before her death.

The following day Bettina was in a fine frenzy. She began to utter the most extravagant speeches that a poet could imagine, and did not stop when the charming exorcist came into her room; he seemed to enjoy her foolish talk for a few minutes, after which, having armed himself *cap-à-pie*, he begged us to withdraw. His order was obeyed instantly; we left the chamber, and the door remained open. But what did it matter? Who would have been bold enough to go in?

During three long hours we heard nothing; the stillness was unbroken. At noon the monk called us in. Bettina was there sad and very quiet while the exorcist packed up his things. He took his departure, saying he had very good hopes of the case, and requesting that the doctor would send him news of the patient. Bettina partook of dinner in her bed, got up for supper, and the next day behaved herself rationally; but the following circumstance strengthened my opinion that she had been neither insane nor possessed.

It was two days before the Purification of the Holy Virgin. Doctor Gozzi was in the habit of giving us the sacrament in his own church, but he always sent us for our confession to the church of Saint-Augustin, in which the Jacobins of Padua officiated. At the supper table, he told us to prepare ourselves for the next day, and his mother, addressing us, said: "You ought, all of you, to confess to Father Mancia, so as to obtain absolution from that holy man. I intend to go to him myself." Cordiani and the two Feltrini agreed to the proposal; I remained silent, but as the idea was unpleasant to me, I concealed the feeling, with a full determination to prevent the execution of the project.

I had entire confidence in the secrecy of confession, and I was incapable of making a false one, but knowing that I had a right to choose my confessor, I most certainly never would have been so simple as to confess to Father Mancia what had taken place between me and a girl, because he would have easily guessed that the girl could be no other but Bettina. Besides, I was satisfied that Cordiani would confess everything to the monk, and I was deeply sorry.

Early the next morning, Bettina brought me a band for my neck, and gave me the following letter: "Spurn me, but respect my honour and the shadow of peace to which I aspire. No one from this house must confess to Father Mancia; you alone can prevent the execution of that project, and I need not suggest the way to succeed. It will prove whether you have some friendship for me."

I could not express the pity I felt for the poor girl, as I read that note. In spite of that feeling, this is what I answered: "I can well understand that, notwithstanding the inviolability of confession, your mother's proposal should cause you great anxiety; but I cannot see why, in order to prevent its execution, you should depend upon me rather than upon Cordiani who has expressed his acceptance of it. All I can promise you is that I will not be one of those who may go to Father Mancia; but I have no influence over your lover; you alone can speak to him."

She replied: "I have never addressed a word to Cordiani since the fatal night which has sealed my misery, and I never will speak to him again, even if I could by so doing recover my lost happiness. To you alone I wish to be indebted for my life and for my honour."

This girl appeared to me more wonderful than all the heroines of whom I had read in novels. It seemed to me that she was making sport of me with the most barefaced effrontery. I thought she was trying to fetter me again with her chains; and although I had no inclination for them, I made up my mind to render her the service she claimed at my hands, and which she believed I alone could compass. She felt certain of her success, but in what school had she obtained her experience of the human heart? Was it in reading novels? Most likely the reading of a certain class of novels causes the ruin of a great many young girls, but I am of opinion that from good romances they acquire graceful manners and a knowledge of society.

Having made up my mind to shew her every kindness in my power, I took an opportunity, as we were undressing for the night, of telling Doctor Gozzi that, for conscientious motives, I could not confess to Father Mancia, and yet that I did not wish to be an exception in that matter. He kindly answered that he understood my reasons, and that he would take us all to the church of Saint-Antoine. I kissed his hand in token of my gratitude.

On the following day, everything having gone according to her wishes, I saw Bettina sit down to the table with a face beaming with satisfaction. In the afternoon I had to go to bed in consequence of a wound in my foot; the doctor accompanied his pupils to church; and Bettina being alone, availed herself of the opportunity,

came to my room and sat down on my bed. I had
expected her visit, and I received it with pleasure, as it
heralded an explanation for which I was positively
longing.

She began by expressing a hope that I would not be
angry with her for seizing the first opportunity she had
of some conversation with me.

'No," I answered, "for you thus afford me an occasion
of assuring you that, my feelings towards you being
those of a friend only, you need not have any fear of my
causing you any anxiety or displeasure. Therefore Bettina, you may do whatever suits you; my love is no
more. You have at one blow given the death-stroke to
the intense passion which was blossoming in my heart.
When I reached my room, after the ill-treatment I had
experienced at Cordiani's hands, I felt for you nothing
but hatred; that feeling soon merged into utter contempt, but that sensation itself was in time, when my
mind recovered its balance, changed for a feeling of the
deepest indifference, which again has given way when
I saw what power there is in your mind. I have now become your friend; I have conceived the greatest esteem
for your cleverness. I have been the dupe of it, but no
matter; that talent of yours does exist, it is wonderful,
divine, I admire it, I love it, and the highest homage
I can render to it is, in my estimation, to foster for the
possessor of it the purest feelings of friendship. Reciprocate that friendship, be true, sincere, and plain dealing.
Give up all nonsense, for you have already obtained from
me all I can give you. The very thought of love is
repugnant to me; I can bestow my love only where I
feel certain of being the only one loved. You are at
liberty to lay my foolish delicacy to the account of my
youthful age, but I feel so, and I cannot help it. You

have written to me that you never speak to Cordiani; if I am the cause of that rupture between you, I regret it, and I think that, in the interest of your honour, you would do well to make it up with him; for the future I must be careful never to give him any grounds for umbrage or suspicion. Recollect also that, if you have tempted him by the same manœuvres which you have employed towards me, you are doubly wrong, for it may be that, if he truly loves you, you have caused him to be miserable."

"All you have just said to me," answered Bettina, "is grounded upon false impressions and deceptive appearances. I do not love Cordiani, and I never had any love for him; on the contrary, I have felt, and I do feel, for him a hatred which he has richly deserved, and I hope to convince you, in spite of every appearance which seems to convict me. As to the reproach of seduction, I entreat you to spare me such an accusation. On our side, consider that, if you had not yourself thrown temptation in my way, I never would have committed towards you an action of which I have deeply repented, for reasons which you do not know, but which you must learn from me. The fault I have been guilty of is a serious one only because I did not foresee the injury it would do me in the inexperienced mind of the ingrate who dares to reproach me with it."

Bettina was shedding tears: all she had said was not unlikely and rather complimentary to my vanity, but I had seen too much. Besides, I knew the extent of her cleverness, and it was very natural to lend her a wish to deceive me; how could I help thinking that her visit to me was prompted only by her self-love being too deeply wounded to let me enjoy a victory so humiliating to herself? Therefore, unshaken in my preconceived opinion, I told her that I placed implicit confidence in all she had just said respecting the state of her heart previous to the playful nonsense which had been the origin of my love for her, and that I promised never in the future to allude again to my accusation of seduction. "But," I continued, "confess that the fire at that time burning in your bosom was only of short duration, and that the slightest breath of wind had been enough to extinguish it. Your virtue, which went astray for only one instant, and which has so suddenly recovered its mastery over your senses, deserves some praise. You, with all your deep adoring love for me, became all at once blind to my sorrow, whatever care I took to make it clear to your sight. It remains for me to learn how that virtue could be so very dear to you, at the very time that Cordiani took care to wreck it every night."

Bettina eyed me with the air of triumph which perfect confidence in victory gives to a person, and said: "You have just reached the point where I wished you to be. You shall now be made aware of things which I could not explain before, owing to your refusing the appointment which I then gave you for no other purpose than to tell you all the truth. Cordiani declared his love for me a week after he became an inmate in our house; he begged my consent to a marriage, if his father made the demand of my hand as soon as he should have completed his studies. My answer was that I did not know him sufficiently, that I could form no idea on the subject, and I requested him not to allude to it any more. He appeared to have quietly given up the matter, but soon after, I found out that it was not the case; he begged me one day to come to his room now and then to dress his hair; I told him I had no time to spare, and he remarked that you were more fortunate. I laughed at this reproach, as everyone here knew that I had the care of you. It was a fortnight after my refusal to Cordiani, that I unfortunately spent an hour with you in that loving nonsense which has naturally given you ideas until then unknown to your senses. That hour made me very happy: I loved you, and having given way to very natural desires, I revelled in my enjoyment without the slightest remorse of conscience. I was longing to be again with you the next morning, but after supper, misfortune laid for the first time its hand upon me. Cordiani slipped in my hands this note and this letter which I have since hidden in a hole in the wall, with the intention of shewing them to you at the first opportunity."

Saying this, Bettina handed me the note and the letter; the first ran as follows: "Admit me this evening in your closet, the door of which, leading to the yard, can be left ajar, or prepare yourself to make the best of it with the doctor, to whom I intend to deliver, if you should refuse my request, the letter of which I enclose a copy."

The letter contained the statement of a cowardly and enraged informer, and would certainly have caused the most unpleasant results. In that letter Cordiani informed the doctor that his sister spent her mornings with me in criminal connection while he was saying his mass, and he pledged himself to enter into particulars which would leave him no doubt.

"After giving to the case the consideration it required," continued Bettina, "I made up my mind to hear that monster; but my determination being fixed, I put in my pocket my father's stilletto, and holding my door ajar I waited for him there, unwilling to let him come in, as my closet is divided only by a thin partition from the room of my father, whom the slightest noise might have roused up. My first question to Cordiani was in reference to the slander contained in the letter he threatened to deliver to my brother: he answered that it was no slander, for he had been a witness to everything that had taken place in the morning through a hole he had bored in the garret just above your bed, and to which he would apply his eye the moment he knew that I was in your room. He wound up by threatening to discover everything to my brother and to my mother, unless I granted him the same favours I had bestowed upon you. In my just indignation I loaded him with the most bitter insults, I called him a cowardly spy and slanderer, for he could not have seen anything but childish playfulness, and I declared to him that he need not flatter himself that any threat would compel me to give the slightest compliance to his wishes. He then begged and begged my pardon a thousand times, and went on assuring me that I must lay to my rigour the odium of the step he had taken, the only excuse for it being in the fervent love I had kindled in his heart, and which made him miserable. He acknowledged that his letter might be a slander, that he had acted treacherously, and he pledged his honour never to attempt obtaining from me by violence favours which he desired to merit only by the constancy of his love. I then thought myself to some extent compelled to say that I might love him at some future time, and to promise that I would not again come near your bed during the absence of my brother. In this way I dismissed him satisfied, without his daring to beg for so much as a kiss, but with the promise that we might now and then have some conversation in the same place. As soon as he left me I went to bed, deeply grieved that I could no longer see you in the absence of my brother, and that I was unable, for fear of consequences, to let you know the reason of my change. Three weeks passed off in that position, and I cannot express what have been my sufferings, for you, of course, urged me to come, and I was always under the painful necessity of disappointing you. I even feared to find myself alone with you, for I felt certain that I could not have refrained from telling you the cause of the change in my conduct. To crown my misery, add that I found myself compelled, at least once a week, to receive the vile Cordiani outside of my room, and to speak to him, in order to check his impatience with a few words. At last, unable to bear up any longer under such misery, threatened likewise by you, I determined to end my agony. I wished to disclose to you all this intrigue, leaving to you the care of bringing a change for the better, and for that purpose I proposed that you should accompany me to the ball disguised as a girl, although I knew it would enrage Cordiani; but my mind was made up. You know how my scheme fell to the ground. The unexpected departure of my brother with my father suggested to both of you the same idea, and it was before receiving Cordiani's letter that I promised to come to you. Cordiani did not ask for an appointment; he only stated that he would be waiting for me in my closet, and I had no opportunity of telling him that I could not allow him to come, any more than I could find time to let you know that I would be with you only after midnight, as I intended to do, for I reckoned that after an hour's talk I would dismiss the wretch to his room. But my reckoning was wrong; Cordiani had conceived a scheme, and I could not help listening to all he had to say about it. His whining and exaggerated complaints had no end. He upbraided me for refusing to further the plan he had concocted, and which he thought I would accept with rapture if I loved him. The scheme was for me to elope with him during holy week, and to run away to Ferrara, where he had an uncle who would have given us a kind welcome, and would soon have brought his father to forgive him and to insure our happiness for life. The objections I made, his answers, the details to be entered into, the explanations and the ways and means to be examined to obviate the difficulties of the project, took up the whole night. My heart was bleeding as I thought of you; but my conscience is at rest, and I did nothing that could render me unworthy of your esteem. You cannot refuse it to me, unless you believe that the confession I have just made is untrue; but you would be both mistaken and unjust. Had I made up my mind to sacrifice myself and to grant favours which love alone ought to obtain, I might have got rid of the treacherous wretch within one hour, but death seemed preferable to such a dreadful expedient. Could I in any way suppose that you were outside of my door, exposed to the wind and to the snow? Both of us were deserving of pity, but my misery was still greater than yours. All these fearful circumstances were written in the book of fate, to make me lose my reason, which now returns only at intervals, and I am in constant dread of a fresh attack of those awful convulsions. They say I am bewitched, and possessed of the demon; I do not know anything about it, but if it should be true I am the most miserable creature in existence."

Bettina ceased speaking, and burst into a violent storm of tears, sobs, and groans. I was deeply moved, although I felt that all she had said might be true, and yet was scarcely worthy of belief:

Forse era ver, mà non pero credibile
A chi del senso suo fosse signor.

But she was weeping, and her tears, which at all events were not deceptive, took away from me the faculty of doubt. Yet I put her tears to the account of her wounded self-love; to give way entirely I needed a thorough conviction, and to obtain it evidence was necessary, probability was not enough. I could not admit either Cordiani's moderation or Bettina's patience, or the fact of seven hours employed in innocent conversation. In spite of all these considerations, I felt a sort of pleasure in accepting for ready cash all the counterfeit coins that she had spread out before me.

After drying her tears, Bettina fixed her beautiful eyes upon mine, thinking that she could discern in them evident signs of her victory; but I surprised her much by alluding to one point which, with all her cunning, she had neglected to mention in her defence. Rhetoric makes use of nature's secrets in the same way as painters who try to imitate it: their most beautiful work is false. This young girl, whose mind had not been refined by study, aimed at being considered innocent and artless, and she did her best to succeed, but I had seen too good a specimen of her cleverness.

"Well, my dear Bettina," I said, "your story has affected me; but how do you think I am going to accept your convulsions as natural, and to believe in the demoniac symptoms which came on so seasonably during the exorcisms, although you very properly expressed your doubts on the matter?"

Hearing this, Bettina stared at me, remaining silent for a few minutes, then casting her eyes down she gave way to fresh tears, exclaiming now and then: "Poor me! oh, poor me!" This situation, however, becoming most painful to me, I asked what I could do for her. She answered in a sad tone that if my heart did not suggest to me what to do, she did not herself see what she could demand of me.

"I thought," said she, "that I would reconquer my lost influence over your heart, but, I see it too plainly, you no longer feel an interest in me. Go on treating me harshly; go on taking for mere fictions sufferings which are but too real, which you have caused, and which you will now increase. Some day, but too late, you will be sorry, and your repentance will be bitter indeed."

As she pronounced these words she rose to take her leave; but judging her capable of anything I felt afraid, and I detained her to say that the only way to regain my affection was to remain one month without convulsions and without handsome Father Mancia's presence being required.

"I cannot help being convulsed," she answered, "but what do you mean by applying to the Jacobin that epithet of handsome? Could you suppose——?"

"Not at all, not at all—I suppose nothing; to do so would be necessary for me to be jealous. But I cannot help saying that the preference given by your devils to the exorcism of that handsome monk over the incantations of the ugly Capuchin is likely to give birth to remarks rather detrimental to your honour. Moreover, you are free to do whatever pleases you."

Thereupon she left my room, and a few minutes later everybody came home.

After supper the servant, without any question on my part, informed me that Bettina had gone to bed with violent feverish chills, having previously had her bed carried into the kitchen beside her mother's. This attack of fever might be real, but I had my doubts. I felt certain that she would never make up her mind to be well, for her good health would have supplied me with too strong an argument against her pretended innocence, even in the case of Cordiani; I likewise considered her idea of having her bed placed near her mother's nothing but artful contrivance.

The next day Doctor Olivo found her very feverish, and told her brother that she would most likely be excited and delirious, but that it would be the effect of the fever and not the work of the devil. And truly, Bettina was raving all day, but Dr. Gozzi, placing implicit confidence in the physician, would not listen to his mother, and did not send for the Jacobin friar. The fever increased in violence, and on the fourth day the small-pox broke out. Cordiani and the two brothers Feltrini, who had so far escaped that disease, were immediately sent away, but as I had had it before I remained at home.

The poor girl was so fearfully covered with the loathsome eruption, that on the sixth day her skin could not be seen on any part of her body. Her eyes closed, and her life was despaired of, when it was found that her mouth and throat were obstructed to such a degree that she could swallow nothing but a few drops of honey. She was perfectly motionless; she breathed and that was all. Her mother never left her bedside, and I was thought a saint when I carried my table and my books into the patient's room. The unfortunate girl had become a fearful sight to look upon; her head was dreadfully swollen, the nose could no longer be seen, and much fear was entertained for her eyes, in case her life should be spared. The odour of her perspiration was most offensive, but I persisted in keeping my watch by her.

On the ninth day, the vicar gave her absolution, and

after administering extreme unction, he left her, as he said, in the hands of God. In the midst of so much sadness, the conversation of the mother with her son, would, in spite of myself, cause me some amount of merriment. The good woman wanted to know whether the demon who was dwelling in her child could still influence her to perform extravagant follies, and what would become of the demon in the case of her daughter's death, for, as she expressed it, she could not think of his being so stupid as to remain in so loathsome a body. She particularly wanted to ascertain whether the demon had power to carry off the soul of her child. Doctor Gozzi, who was an ubiquitarian, made to all those questions answers which had not even the shadow of good sense, and which of course had no other effect than to increase a hundred-fold the perplexity of his poor mother.

During the tenth and eleventh days, Bettina was so bad that we thought every moment likely to be her last. The disease had reached its worst period; the smell was unbearable; I alone would not leave her, so sorely did I pity her. The heart of man is indeed an unfathomable abyss, for, however incredible it may appear, it was while in that fearful state that Bettina inspired me with the fondness which I showed her after her recovery.

On the thirteenth day the fever abated, but the patient began to experience great irritation, owing to a dreadful itching, which no remedy could have allayed as effectually as these powerful words which I kept constantly pouring into her ear: "Bettina, you are getting better; but if you dare to scratch yourself, you will become such a fright that nobody will ever love you." All the physicians in the universe might be challenged to

prescribe a more potent remedy against itching for a
girl who, aware that she has been pretty, finds herself
exposed to the loss of her beauty through her own fault,
if she scratches herself.

At last her fine eyes opened again to the light of
heaven; she was moved to her own room, but she had
to keep her bed until Easter. She inoculated me with
a few pocks, three of which have left upon my face
everlasting marks; but in her eyes they gave me credit
for great devotedness, for they were a proof of my
constant care, and she felt that I indeed deserved her
whole love. And she truly loved me, and I returned her
love, although I never plucked a flower which fate and
prejudice kept in store for a husband. But what a contemptible husband!

Two years later she married a shoemaker, by name
Pigozzo—a base, arrant knave who beggared and ill-
treated her to such an extent that her brother had to
take her home and to provide for her. Fifteen years
afterwards, having been appointed arch-priest at Saint-
George de la Vallée, he took her there with him, and
when I went to pay him a visit eighteen years ago, I
found Bettina old, ill, and dying. She breathed her last
in my arms in 1776, twenty-four hours after my arrival.
I will speak of her death in good time.

About that period, my mother returned from St.
Petersburg, where the Empress Anne Iwanowa had not
approved of the Italian comedy. The whole of the
troop had already returned to Italy, and my mother had
travelled with Carlin Bertinazzi, the harlequin, who died
in Paris in the year 1783. As soon as she had reached
Padua, she informed Doctor Gozzi of her arrival, and he
lost no time in accompanying me to the inn where she
had put up. We dined with her, and before bidding us

adieu, she presented the doctor with a splendid fur, and gave me the skin of a lynx for Bettina. Six months afterwards she summoned me to Venice, as she wished to see me before leaving for Dresden, where she had contracted an engagement for life in the service of the Elector of Saxony, Augustus III., King of Poland. She took with her my brother Jean, then eight years old, who was weeping bitterly when he left; I thought him very foolish, for there was nothing very tragic in that departure. He is the only one in the family who was wholly indebted to our mother for his fortune, although he was not her favourite child.

I spent another year in Padua, studying law, in which I took the degree of Doctor in my sixteenth year, the subject of my thesis being in the civil law, *de testamentis,* and in the canon law, *utrum Hebræi possint construere novas synagogas.*

My vocation was to study medicine, and to practice it, for I felt a great inclination for that profession, but no heed was given to my wishes, and I was compelled to apply myself to the study of the law, for which I had an invincible repugnance. My friends were of opinion that I could not make my fortune in any profession but that of an advocate, and, what is still worse, of an ecclesiastical advocate. If they had given the matter proper consideration, they would have given me leave to follow my own inclinations, and I would have been a physician—a profession in which quackery is of still greater avail than in the legal business. I never became either a physician or an advocate, and I never would apply to a lawyer, when I had any legal business, nor call in a physician when I happened to be ill. Lawsuits and pettifoggery may support a good many families, but a greater proportion is ruined by them, and those

who perish in the hands of physicians are more numerous by far than those who get cured—strong evidence,
in my opinion, that mankind would be much less miserable without either lawyers or doctors.

To attend the lectures of the professors, I had to go
to the university called *the Bo,* and it became necessary
for me to go out alone. This was a matter of great
wonder to me, for until then I had never considered
myself a free man; and in my wish to enjoy fully the
liberty I thought I had just conquered, it was not long
before I had made the very worst acquaintances amongst
the most renowned students. As a matter of course, the
most renowned were the most worthless, dissolute fellows, gamblers, frequenters of disorderly houses, hard
drinkers, debauchees, tormentors and suborners of honest
girls, liars, and wholly incapable of any good or virtuous feeling. In the company of such men did I begin my apprenticeship of the world, learning my lesson
from the book of experience.

The theory of morals and its usefulness through the
life of man can be compared to the advantage derived
by running over the index of a book before reading it:
when we have perused that index we know nothing but
the subject of the work. This is like the school for
morals offered by the sermons, the precepts, and the tales
which our instructors recite for our especial benefit. We
lend our whole attention to those lessons, but when an
opportunity offers of profiting by the advice thus bestowed upon us, we feel inclined to ascertain for ourselves whether the result will turn out as predicted; we
give way to that very natural inclination, and punishment speedily follows with concomitant repentance.
Our only consolation lies in the fact that in such moments we are conscious of our own knowledge, and con-

sider ourselves as having earned the right to instruct others; but those to whom we wish to impart our experience act exactly as we have acted before them, and, as a matter of course, the world remains in *statu quo*, or grows worse and worse.

When Doctor Gozzi granted me the privilege of going out alone, he gave me an opporunity for the discovery of several truths which, until then, were not only unknown to me, but the very existence of which I had never suspected. On my first appearance, the boldest scholars got hold of me and sounded my depth. Finding that I was a thorough freshman, they undertook my education, and with that worthy purpose in view they allowed me to fall blindly into every trap. They taught me gambling, won the little I possessed, and then they made me play upon trust, and put me up to dishonest practices in order to procure the means of paying my gambling debts; but I acquired at the same time the sad experience of sorrow! Yet these hard lessons proved useful, for they taught me to mistrust the impudent sycophants who openly flatter their dupes, and never to rely upon the offers made by fawning flatterers. They taught me likewise how to behave in the company of quarrelsome duellists, the society of whom ought to be avoided, unless we make up our mind to be constantly in the very teeth of danger. I was not caught in the snares of professional lewd women, because not one of them was in my eyes as pretty as Bettina, but I did not resist so well the desire for that species of vain glory which is the reward of holding life at a cheap price.

In those days the students in Padua enjoyed very great privileges, which were in reality abuses made legal through prescription, the primitive characteristic of privileges, which differ essentially from prerogatives. In fact, in order to maintain the legality of their privileges, the students often committed crimes. The guilty were dealt with tenderly, because the interest of the city demanded that severity should not diminish the great influx of scholars who flocked to that renowned university from every part of Europe. The practice of the Venetian government was to secure at a high salary the most celebrated professors, and to grant the utmost freedom to the young men attending their lessons. The students acknowledged no authority but that of a chief, chosen among themselves, and called syndic. He was usually a foreign nobleman, who could keep a large establishment, and who was responsible to the government for the behaviour of the scholars. It was his duty to give them up to justice when they transgressed the laws, and the students never disputed his sentence, because he always defended them to the utmost, when they had the slightest shadow of right on their side.

The students, amongst other privileges, would not suffer their trunks to be searched by customhouse authorities, and no ordinary policeman would have dared to arrest one of them. They carried about them forbidden weapons, seduced helpless girls, and often disturbed the public peace by their nocturnal broils and impudent practical jokes; in one word, they were a body of young fellows, whom nothing could restrain, who would gratify every whim, and enjoy their sport without regard or consideration for any human being.

It was about that time that a policeman entered a coffee-room, in which were seated two students. One of them ordered him out, but the man taking no notice of it, the student fired a pistol at him, and missed his aim. The policeman returned the fire, wounded the aggressor, and ran away. The students immediately mustered to-

gether at *the Bo,* divided into bands, and went over the
city, hunting the policemen to murder them, and avenge
the insult they had received. In one of the encounters
two of the students were killed, and all the others, as-
sembling in one troop, swore never to lay their arms
down as long as there should be one policeman alive in
Padua. The authorities had to interfere, and the syndic
of the students undertook to put a stop to hostilities provided proper satisfaction was given, as the police were in
the wrong. The man who had shot the student in the
coffee-room was hanged, and peace was restored; but
during the eight days of agitation, as I was anxious not
to appear less brave than my comrades who were pa-
trolling the city, I followed them in spite of Doctor
Gozzi's remonstrances. Armed with a carbine and a pair
of pistols, I ran about the town with the others, in quest
of the enemy, and I recollect how disappointed I was
because the troop to which I belonged did not meet one
policeman. When the war was over, the doctor laughed
at me, but Bettina admired my valour.

Unfortunately, I indulged in expenses far above my
means, owing to my unwillingness to seem poorer than
my new friends. I sold or pledged everything I possessed, and I contracted debts which I could not possibly pay. This state of things caused my first sorrows,
and they are the most poignant sorrows under which a
young man can smart. Not knowing which way to turn,
I wrote to my excellent grandmother, begging her assistance, but instead of sending me some money, she
came to Padua on the 1st of October, 1739, and, after
thanking the doctor and Bettina for all their affectionate
care, she bought me back to Venice. As he took leave
of me, the doctor, who was shedding tears, gave me what
he prized most on earth; a relic of some saint, which

perhaps I might have kept to this very day, had not the
setting been of gold. It performed only one miracle, that
of being of service to me in a moment of great need.
Whenever I visited Padua, to complete my study of the
law, I stayed at the house of the kind doctor, but I was
always grieved at seeing near Bettina the brute to whom
she was engaged, and who did not appear to me deserving of such a wife. I have always regretted that a prejudice, of which I soon got rid, should have made me
preserve for that man a flower which I could have
plucked so easily.

CHAPTER IV

*I receive the minor orders from the patriarch of Venice
—I get acquainted with Senator Malipiero, with
Thérèse Imer, with the niece of the Curate, with Ma-
dame Orio, with Nanette and Marton, and with the
Cavamacchia—I become a preacher—my adventure
with Lucie at Pasean—a rendezvous on the third story.*

H E comes from Padua, where he has completed his
studies." Such were the words by which I was
everywhere introduced, and which, the moment they were
uttered, called upon me the silent observation of every
young man of my age and condition, the compliments
of all fathers, and the caresses of old women, as well as
the kisses of a few who, although not old, were not sorry
to be considered so for the sake of embracing a young
man without impropriety. The curate of Saint-Samuel,
the Abbé Josello, presented me to Monsignor Correre,
Patriarch of Venice, who gave me the tonsure, and who,
four months afterwards, by special favour, admitted me
to the four minor orders. No words could express the
joy and the pride of my grandmother. Excellent masters
were given to me to continue my studies, and M. Baffo
chose the Abbé Schiavo to teach me a pure Italian
style, especially poetry, for which I had a decided talent.
I was very comfortably lodged with my brother François, who was studying theatrical architecture. My
sister and my youngest brother were living with our
grandam in a house of her own, in which it was her

wish to die, because her husband had there breathed his last. The house in which I dwelt was the same in which my father had died, and the rent of which my mother continued to pay. It was large and well furnished.

Although Abbé Grimani was my chief protector, I seldom saw him, and I particularly attached myself to M. de Malipiero, to whom I had been presented by the Curate Josello. M. de Malipiero was a senator, who was unwilling at seventy years of age to attend any more to State affairs, and enjoyed a happy, sumptuous life in his mansion, surrounded every evening by a well-chosen party of ladies who had all known how to make the best of their younger days, and of gentlemen who were always acquainted with the news of the town. He was a bachelor and wealthy, but, unfortunately, he had three or four times every year severe attacks of gout, which always left him crippled in some part or other of his body, so that all his person was disabled. His head, his lungs, and his stomach had alone escaped this cruel havoc. He was still a fine man, a great epicure, and a good judge of wine; his wit was keen, his knowledge of the world extensive, his eloquence worthy of a son of Venice, and he had that wisdom which must naturally belong to a senator who for forty years has had the management of public affairs, and to a man who has bid farewell to women after having possessed twenty mistresses, and only when he felt himself compelled to acknowledge that he could no longer be accepted by any woman. Although almost entirely crippled, he did not appear to be so when he was seated, when he talked, or when he was at table. He had only one meal a day, and always took it alone because, being toothless and unable to eat otherwise than very slowly, he did not wish to hurry himself out of compliment to his guests, and would have been sorry to see them waiting for him. This feeling deprived him of the pleasure he would have enjoyed in entertaining at his board friendly and agreeable guests, and caused great sorrow to his excellent cook.

The first time I had the honour of being introduced to him by the curate, I opposed earnestly the reason which made him eat his meals in solitude, and I said that his excellency had only to invite guests whose appetite was good enough to enable them to eat a double share.

"But where can I find such table companions?" he asked.

"It is rather a delicate matter," I answered; "but you must take your guests on trial, and after they have been found such as you wish them to be, the only difficulty will be to keep them as your guests without their being aware of the real cause of your preference, for no respectable man could acknowledge that he enjoys the honour of sitting at your excellency's table only because he eats twice as much as any other man."

The senator understood the truth of my argument, and asked the curate to bring me to dinner on the following day. He found my practice even better than my theory, and I became his daily guest.

This man, who had given up everything in life except his own self, fostered an amorous inclination, in spite of his age and of his gout. He loved a young girl named Thérèse Imer, the daughter of an actor residing near his mansion, her bedroom window being opposite to his own. This young girl, then in her seventeenth year, was pretty, whimsical, and a regular coquette. She was practising music with a view to entering the theatrical profession, and by showing herself constantly at the window she had intoxicated the old senator, and was playing with him cruelly. She paid him a daily visit, but always escorted by her mother, a former actress, who had retired from the stage in order to work out her salvation, and who, as a matter of course, had made up her mind to combine the interests of heaven with the works of this world. She took her daughter to mass every day and compelled her to go to confession every week; but every afternoon she accompanied her in a visit to the amorous old man, the rage of whom frightened me when she refused him a kiss under the plea that she had performed her devotions in the morning, and that she could not reconcile herself to the idea of offending the God who was still dwelling in her.

What a sight for a young man of fifteen like me, whom the old man admitted as the only and silent witness of these erotic scenes! The miserable mother applauded her daughter's reserve, and went so far as to lecture the elderly lover, who, in his turn, dared not refute her maxims, which savoured either too much or too little of Christianity, and resisted a very strong inclination to hurl at her head any object he had at hand. Anger would then take the place of lewd desires, and after they had retired he would comfort himself by exchanging with me philosophical considerations.

Compelled to answer him, and not knowing well what to say, I ventured one day upon advising a marriage. He struck me with amazement when he answered that she refused to marry him from fear of drawing upon herself the hatred of his relatives.

"Then make her the offer of a large sum of money, or a position."

"She says that she would not, even for a crown, commit a deadly sin."

"In that case, you must either take her by storm, or banish her for ever from your presence."

"I can do neither one nor the other; physical as well as moral strength is deficient in me."

"Kill her, then."

"That will very likely be the case unless I die first."

"Indeed I pity your excellency."

"Do you sometimes visit her?"

"No, for I might fall in love with her, and I would be miserable."

"You are right."

Witnessing many such scenes, and taking part in many similar conversations, I became an especial favourite with the old nobleman. I was invited to his evening assemblies which were, as I have stated before, frequented by superannuated women and witty men. He told me that in this circle I would learn a science of greater import than Gassendi's philosophy, which I was then studying by his advice instead of Aristotle's, which he turned into ridicule. He laid down some precepts for my conduct in those assemblies, explaining the necessity of my observing them, as there would be some wonder at a young man of my age being received at such parties. He ordered me never to open my lips except to answer direct questions, and particularly enjoined me never to pass an opinion on any subject, because at my age I could not be allowed to have any opinions.

I faithfully followed his precepts, and obeyed his orders so well, that in a few days I had gained his esteem, and become the child of the house, as well as the favourite of all the ladies who visited him. In my character of a young and innocent ecclesiastic, they would ask me to accompany them in their visits to the convents where their daughters or their nieces were educated; I was at all hours received at their houses without even being announced; I was scolded if a week elapsed without my calling upon them, and when I went to the apartments reserved for the young ladies, they would run away, but the moment they saw that the intruder was only I, they would return at once, and their confidence was very charming to me.

Before dinner, M. de Malipiero would often inquire from me what advantages were accruing to me from the welcome I received at the hands of the respectable ladies I had become acquainted with at his house, taking care to tell me, before I could have time to answer, that they were all endowed with the greatest virtue, and that I would give everybody a bad opinion of myself, if I ever breathed one word of disparagement to the high reputation they all enjoyed. In this way he would inculcate in me the wise precept of reserve and discretion.

It was at the senator's house that I made the acquaintance of Madame Manzoni, the wife of a notary public, of whom I shall have to speak very often. This worthy lady inspired me with the deepest attachment, and she gave me the wisest advice. Had I followed it, and profited by it, my life would not have been exposed to so many storms; it is true that, in that case, my life would not be worth writing.

All these fine acquaintances amongst women who enjoyed the reputation of being high-bred ladies, gave me a very natural desire to shine by my good looks and by the elegance of my dress; but my father confessor, as well as my grandmother, objected very strongly to this feeling of vanity. On one occasion, taking me apart, the curate told me, with honeyed words, that in the profession to which I had devoted myself my thoughts ought to dwell upon the best means of being agreeable to God, and not on pleasing the world by my fine appearance. He condemned my elaborate curls, and the exquisite perfume of my pomatum. He said that the devil had got hold of me by the hair, that I would be excommunicated if I continued to take such care of it, and concluded by quoting for my benefit these words from an œcumenical council: *clericus qui nutrit coman, anathema sit.* I answered him with the names of several fashionable perfumed abbots, who were not threatened with excommunication, who were not interfered with, although they wore four times as much powder as I did—for I only used a slight sprinkling—who perfumed their hair with a certain amber-scented pomatum which brought women to the very point of fainting, while mine, a jessamine pomade, called forth the compliment of every circle in which I was received. I added that I could not, much to my regret, obey him, and that if I had meant to live in slovenliness, I would have become a Capuchin and not an abbé.

My answer made him so angry that, three or four days afterwards, he contrived to obtain leave from my grandmother to enter my chamber early in the morning, before I was awake, and, approaching my bed on tiptoe with a sharp pair of scissors, he cut off unmercifully all my front hair, from one ear to the other. My brother François was in the adjoining room and saw him, but he did not interfere as he was delighted at my misfortune. He wore a wig, and was very jealous of my beautiful head of hair. François was envious through the whole of his life; yet he combined this feeling of envy with friendship; I never could understand him; but this vice of his, like my own vices, must by this time have died of old age.

After his great operation, the abbé left my room quietly, but when I woke up shortly afterwards, and realized all the horror of this unheard-of execution, my rage and indignation were indeed wrought to the highest pitch.

What wild schemes of revenge my brain engendered while, with a looking-glass in my hand, I was groaning over the shameful havoc performed by this audacious priest! At the noise I made my grandmother hastened to my room, and amidst my brother's laughter the kind old woman assured me that the priest would never have been allowed to enter my room if she could have foreseen his intention, and she managed to soothe my passion to some extent by confessing that he had over-stepped the limits of his right to administer a reproof.

But I was determined upon revenge, and I went on dressing myself and revolving in my mind the darkest plots. It seemed to me that I was entitled to the most cruel revenge, without having anything to dread from the terrors of the law. The theatres being open at that time, I put on a mask to go out, and I went to the advocate Carrare, with whom I had become acquainted at the senator's house, to inquire from him whether I could bring a suit against the priest. He told me that, but a short time since, a family had been ruined for having sheared the moustache of a Sclavonian—a crime not nearly so atrocious as the shearing of all my front locks, and that I had only to give him my instructions to begin a criminal suit against the abbé, which would make him tremble. I gave my consent, and begged that he would tell M. de Malipiero in the evening the reason for which I could not go to his house, for I did not feel any inclination to show myself anywhere until my hair had grown again.

I went home and partook with my brother of a repast which appeared rather scanty in comparison to the dinners I had with the old senator. The privation of the delicate and plentiful fare to which his excellency had accustomed me was most painful, besides all the enjoyments from which I was excluded through the atrocious conduct of the virulent priest, who was my godfather. I wept from sheer vexation; and my rage was increased by the consciousness that there was in this insult a certain dash of comical fun which threw over me a ridicule more disgraceful in my estimation than the greatest crime.

I went to bed early, and, refreshed by ten hours of profound slumber, I felt in the morning somewhat less angry, but quite as determined to summon the priest before a court. I dressed myself with the intention of calling upon my advocate, when I received the visit of a skilful hair-dresser whom I had seen at Madame Cantarini's house. He told me that he was sent by M. de Malipiero to arrange my hair so that I could go out, as the senator wished me to dine with him on that very day. He examined the damage done to my head, and said, with a smile, that if I would trust to his art, he would undertake to send me out with an appearance of even greater elegance than I could boast of before; and truly, when he had done, I found myself so good-looking that I considered my thirst for revenge entirely satisfied.

Having thus forgotten the injury, I called upon the lawyer to tell him to stay all proceedings, and I hastened to M. de Malipiero's palace, where, as chance would have it, I met the abbé. Notwithstanding all my joy, I could not help casting upon him rather unfriendly looks, but not a word was said about what had taken place. The senator noticed everything, and the priest took his leave, most likely with feelings of mortified repentance, for this time I most verily deserved excommunication by the extreme studied elegance of my curling hair.

When my cruel godfather had left us, I did not dissemble with M. de Malipiero; I candidly told him that I would look out for another church, and that nothing would induce me to remain under a priest who, in his wrath, could go the length of such proceedings. The wise old man agreed with me, and said that I was quite right: it was the best way to make me do ultimately whatever he liked. In the evening everyone in our circle, being well aware of what had happened, complimented me, and assured me that nothing could be handsomer than my new head-dress. I was delighted, and was still more gratified when, after a fortnight had elapsed, I found that M. de Malipiero did not broach the subject of my returning to my godfather's church. My grandmother alone constantly urged me to return. But this calm was the harbinger of a storm. When my mind was thoroughly at rest on that subject, M. de Malipiero threw me into the greatest astonishment by suddenly telling me that an excellent opportunity offered itself for me to reappear in the church and to secure ample satisfaction from the abbé.

"It is my province," added the senator, "as president of the Confraternity of the Holy Sacrament, to choose the preacher who is to deliver the sermon on the fourth Sunday of this month, which happens to be the second Christmas holiday. I mean to appoint you, and I am certain that the abbé will not dare to reject my choice. What say you to such a triumphant reappearance? Does it satisfy you?"

This offer caused me the greatest surprise, for I had never dreamt of becoming a preacher, and I had never been vain enough to suppose that I could write a sermon and deliver it in the church. I told M. de Malipiero that he must surely be enjoying a joke at my expense, but he answered that he had spoken in earnest, and he soon contrived to persuade me and to make me believe that I was born to become the most renowned preacher of our age as soon as I should have grown fat—a quality which I certainly could not boast of, for at that time I was extremely thin. I had not the shadow of a fear as to my voice or to my elocution, and for the matter of composing my sermon I felt myself equal to the production of a masterpiece.

I told M. de Malipiero that I was ready, and anxious to be at home in order to go to work; that, although no theologian, I was acquainted with my subject, and would compose a sermon which would take everyone by surprise on account of its novelty.

On the following day, when I called upon him, he informed me that the abbé had expressed unqualified delight at the choice made by him, and at my readiness in accepting the appointment; but he likewise desired that I should submit my sermon to him as soon as it was written, because the subject belonging to the most sublime theology he could not allow me to enter the pulpit without being satisfied that I would not utter any heresies. I agreed to this demand, and during the week I gave birth to my masterpiece. I have now that first sermon in my possession, and I cannot help saying that, considering my tender years, I think it a very good one.

I could not give an idea of my grandmother's joy; she wept tears of happiness at having a grandson who

had become an apostle. She insisted upon my reading
my sermon to her, listened to it with her beads in her
hands, and pronounced it very beautiful. M. de Malipiero, who had no rosary when I read it to him, was of
opinion that it would not prove acceptable to the parson. My text was from Horace: *Ploravere suis non re-
spondere favorem speratum meritis;* and I deplored the
wickedness and ingratitude of men, through which had
failed the design adopted by Divine wisdom for the re-
demption of humankind. But M. de Malipiero was
sorry that I had taken my text from any heretical poet,
although he was pleased that my sermon was not interlarded with Latin quotations.

I called upon the priest to read my production; but
as he was out I had to wait for his return, and during
that time I fell in love with his niece, Angela. She was
busy upon some tambour work; I sat down close by her,
and telling me that she had long desired to make my acquaintance, she begged me to relate the history of the
locks of hair sheared by her venerable uncle.

My love for Angela proved fatal to me, because from
it sprang two other love affairs which, in their turn, gave
birth to a great many others, and caused me finally to
renounce the Church as a profession. But let us proceed quietly, and not encroach upon future events.

On his return home the abbé found me with his niece,
who was about my age, and he did not appear to be
angry. I gave him my sermon: he read it over, and told
me that it was a beautiful academical dissertation, but
unfit for a sermon from the pulpit, and he added,——

"I will give you a sermon written by myself, which
I have never delivered; you will commit it to memory,
and I promise to let everybody suppose that it is of your
own composition."

"I thank you, very reverend father, but I will preach my own sermon, or none at all."

"At all events, you shall not preach such a sermon as this in my church."

"You can talk the matter over with M. de Malipiero. In the meantime I will take my work to the censorship, and to His Eminence the Patriarch, and if it is not accepted I shall have it printed."

"All very well, young man. The patriarch will coincide with me."

In the evening I related my discussion with the parson before all the guests of M. de Malipiero. The reading of my sermon was called for, and it was praised by all. They lauded me for having with proper modesty refrained from quoting the holy fathers of the Church, whom at my age I could not be supposed to have sufficiently studied, and the ladies particularly admired me because there was no Latin in it but the text from Horace, who, although a great libertine himself, has written very good things. A niece of the patriarch, who was present that evening, promised to prepare her uncle in my favour, as I had expressed my intention to appeal to him; but M. de Malipiero desired me not to take any steps in the matter until I had seen him on the following day, and I submissively bowed to his wishes.

When I called at his mansion the next day he sent for the priest, who soon made his appearance. As he knew well what he had been sent for, he immediately launched out into a very long discourse, which I did not interrupt, but the moment he had concluded his list of objections I told him that there could not be two ways to decide the question; that the patriarch would either approve or disapprove my sermon.

"In the first case," I added, "I can pronounce it in

your church, and no responsibility can possibly fall
upon your shoulders; in the second, I must, of course,
give way."

The abbé was struck by my determination and he
said,——

"Do not go to the patriarch; I accept your sermon;
I only request you to change your text. Horace was a
villain."

"Why do you quote Seneca, Tertullian, Origen, and
Boethius? They were all heretics, and must, consequently, be considered by you as worse wretches than
Horace, who, after all, never had the chance of becoming
a Christian!"

However, as I saw it would please M. de Malipiero,
I finally consented to accept, as a substitute for mine, a
text offered by the abbé, although it did not suit in any
way the spirit of my production; and in order to get an
opportunity for a visit to his niece, I gave him my
manuscript, saying that I would call for it the next day.
My vanity prompted me to send a copy to Doctor
Gozzi, but the good man caused me much amusement
by returning it and wrting that I must have gone mad,
and that if I were allowed to deliver such a sermon from
the pulpit I would bring dishonour upon myself as well
as upon the man who had educated me.

I cared but little for his opinion, and on the appointed
day I delivered my sermon in the Church of the Holy
Sacrament in the presence of the best society of Venice.
I received much applause, and every one predicted that
I would certainly become the first preacher of our century, as no young ecclesiastic of fifteen had ever been
known to preach as well as I had done. It is customary
for the faithful to deposit their offerings for the preacher
in a purse which is handed to them for that purpose.

The sexton who emptied it of its contents found in it more than fifty sequins, and several billets-doux, to the great scandal of the weaker brethren. An anonymous note amongst them, the writer of which I thought I had guessed, let me into a mistake which I think better not to relate. This rich harvest, in my great penury, caused me to entertain serious thoughts of becoming a preacher, and I confided my intention to the parson, requesting his assistance to carry it into execution. This gave me the privilege of visiting at his house every day, and I improved the opportunity of conversing with Angela, for whom my love was daily increasing. But Angela was virtuous. She did not object to my love, but she wished me to renounce the Church and to marry her. In spite of my infatuation for her, I could not make up my mind to such a step, and I went on seeing her and courting her in the hope that she would alter her decision.

The priest, who had at last confessed his admiration for my first sermon, asked me, some time afterwards, to prepare another for St. Joseph's Day, with an invitation to deliver it on the 19th of March, 1741. I composed it, and the abbé spoke of it with enthusiasm, but fate had decided that I should never preach but once in my life. It is a sad tale, unfortunately for me very true, which some persons are cruel enough to consider very amusing.

Young and rather self-conceited, I fancied that it was not necessary for me to spend much time in committing my sermon to memory. Being the author, I had all the ideas contained in my work classified in my mind, and it did not seem to me within the range of possibilities that I could forget what I had written. Perhaps I might not remember the exact words of a sentence, but I was at liberty to replace them by other expressions as good, and as I never happened to be at a loss, or to be struck dumb, when I spoke in society, it was not likely that such an untoward accident would befall me before an audience amongst whom I did not know anyone who could intimidate me and cause me suddenly to lose the faculty of reason or of speech. I therefore took my pleasure as usual, being satisfied with reading my sermon morning and evening, in order to impress it upon my memory which until then had never betrayed me.

The 19th of March came, and on that eventful day at four o'clock in the afternoon I was to ascend the pulpit; but, believing myself quite secure and thoroughly master of my subject, I had not the moral courage to deny myself the pleasure of dining with Count Mont-Réal, who was then residing with me, and who had invited the patrician Barozzi, engaged to be married to his daughter after the Easter holidays.

I was still enjoying myself with my fine company, when the sexton of the church came in to tell me that they were waiting for me in the vestry. With a full stomach and my head rather heated, I took my leave, ran to the church, and entered the pulpit. I went through the exordium with credit to myself, and I took breathing time; but scarcely had I pronounced the first sentences of the narration, before I forgot what I was saying, what I had to say, and in my endeavours to proceed, I fairly wandered from my subject and I lost myself entirely. I was still more discomforted by a half-repressed murmur of the audience, as my deficiency appeared evident. Several persons left the church, others began to smile, I lost all presence of mind and every hope of getting out of the scrape.

I could not say whether I feigned a fainting fit, or whether I truly swooned; all I know is that I fell down on the floor of the pulpit, striking my head against the wall, with an inward prayer for annihilation.

Two of the parish clerks carried me to the vestry, and after a few moments, without addressing a word to anyone, I took my cloak and my hat, and went home to lock myself in my room. I immediately dressed myself in a short coat, after the fashion of travelling priests, I packed a few things in a trunk, obtained some money from my grandmother, and took my departure for Padua, where I intended to pass my third examination. I reached Padua at midnight, and went to Doctor Gozzi's house, but I did not feel the slightest temptation to mention to him my unlucky adventure.

I remained in Padua long enough to prepare myself for the doctor's degree, which I intended to take the following year, and after Easter I returned to Venice, where my misfortune was already forgotten; but preaching was out of the question, and when any attempt was made to induce me to renew my efforts, I manfully kept to my determination never to ascend the pulpit again.

On the eve of Ascension Day M. Manzoni introduced me to a young courtesan, who was at that time in great repute at Venice, and was nick-named Cavamacchia, because her father had been a scourer. This named vexed her a great deal, she wished to be called Preati, which was her family name, but it was all in vain, and the only concession her friends would make was to call her by her Christian name of Juliette. She had been introduced to fashionable notice by the Marquis de Sanvitali, a nobleman from Parma, who had given her one hundred thousand ducats for her favours. Her beauty was then the talk of everybody in Venice, and it was fashionable to call upon her. To converse with her, and especially to be admitted into her circle, was considered a great boon.

As I shall have to mention her several times in the course of my history, my readers will, I trust, allow me to enter into some particulars about her previous life.

Juliette was only fourteen years of age when her father sent her one day to the house of a Venetian nobleman, Marco Muazzo, with a coat which he had cleaned for him. He thought her very beautiful in spite of the dirty rags in which she was dressed, and he called to see her at her father's shop, with a friend of his, the celebrated advocate, Bastien Uccelli, who, struck by the romantic and cheerful nature of Juliette still more than by her beauty and fine figure, gave her an apartment, made her study music, and kept her as his mistress. At the time of the fair, Bastien took her with him to various public places of resort; everywhere she attracted general attention, and secured the admiration of every lover of the sex. She made rapid progress in music, and at the end of six months she felt sufficient confidence in herself to sign an engagement with a theatrical manager who took her to Vienna to give her a *castrato* part in one of Metastasio's operas.

The advocate had previously ceded her to a wealthy Jew who, after giving her splendid diamonds, left her also.

In Vienna, Juliette appeared on the stage, and her beauty gained for her an admiration which she would never have conquered by her very inferior talent. But the constant crowd of adorers who went to worship the goddess, having sounded her exploits rather too loudly, the august Maria-Theresa objected to this new creed being sanctioned in her capital, and the beautfiul actress received an order to quit Vienna forthwith.

Count Spada offered her his protection, and brought her back to Venice, but she soon left for Padua where she had an engagement. In that city she kindled the fire of love in the breast of Marquis Sanvitali, but the marchioness having caught her once in her own box, and Juliette having acted disrespectfully to her, she slapped her face, and the affair having caused a good deal of noise, Juliette gave up the stage altogether. She came back to Venice, where, made conspicuous by her banishment from Vienna, she could not fail to make her fortune. Expulsion from Vienna, for this class of women, had become a title to fashionable favour, and when there was a wish to depreciate a singer or a dancer, it was said of her that she had not been sufficiently prized to be expelled from Vienna.

After her return, her first lover was Steffano Querini de Papozzes, but in the spring of 1740, the Marquis de Sanvitali came to Venice and soon carried her off. It was indeed difficult to resist this delightful marquis! His first present to the fair lady was a sum of one hundred thousand ducats, and, to prevent his being accused of weakness or of lavish prodigality, he loudly proclaimed that the present could scarcely make up for the insult Juliette had received from his wife—an insult, however, which the courtesan never admitted, as she felt that there would be humiliation in such an acknowledgment, and she always professed to admire with gratitude her lover's generosity. She was right; the admission of the blow received would have left a stain upon her charms, and how much more to her taste to allow those charms to be prized at such a high figure!

It was in the year 1741 that M. Manzoni introduced me to this new Phryne as a young ecclesiastic who was beginning to make a reputation. I found her surrounded by seven or eight well-seasoned admirers, who were burning at her feet the incense of their flattery. She was carelessly reclining on a sofa near Querini. I was much struck with her appearance. She eyed me from head to foot, as if I had been exposed for sale, and telling me, with the air of a princess, that she was not sorry to make my acquaintance, she invited me to take a seat. I began then, in my turn, to examine her closely and deliberately, and it was an easy matter, as the room, although small, was lighted with at least twenty wax candles.

Juliette was then in her eighteenth year; the freshness of her complexion was dazzling, but the carnation tint of her cheeks, the vermilion of her lips, and the dark, very narrow curve of her eyebrows, impressed me as being produced by art rather than nature. Her teeth— two rows of magnificent pearls—made one overlook the fact that her mouth was somewhat too large, and whether from habit, or because she could not help it, she seemed to be ever smiling. Her bosom, hid under a light gauze, invited the desires of love; yet I did not surrender to her charms. Her bracelets and the rings which covered her fingers did not prevent me from noticing that her hand was too large and too fleshy, and in spite of her carefully hiding her feet, I judged, by a telltale slipper lying close by her dress, that they were well proportioned to the height of her figure—a proportion which is unpleasant not only to the Chinese and Spaniards, but likewise to every man of refined taste. We want a tall women to have a small foot, and certainly it is not a modern taste, for Holofernes of old was of the same opinion; otherwise he would not have thought Judith so charming: *et sandalia ejus rapuerunt oculos ejus*. Altogether I found her beautiful, but when I compared her beauty and the price of one hundred thousand ducats paid for it, I marvelled at my remaining so cold, and at my not being tempted to give even one sequin for the privilege of making from nature a study of the charms which her dress concealed from my eyes.

I had scarcely been there a quarter of an hour when the noise made by the oars of a gondola striking the water heralded the prodigal marquis. We all rose from our seats, and M. Querini hastened, somewhat blushing, to quit his place on the sofa. M. de Sanvitali, a man of middle age, who had travelled much, took a seat near Juliette, but not on the sofa, so she was compelled to turn round. It gave me the opportunity of seeing her full front, while I had before only a side view of her face.

After my introduction to Juliette, I paid her four or five visits, and I thought myself justified, by the care I had given to the examination of her beauty, in saying in M. de Malipiero's draw-room, one evening, when my opinion about her was asked, that she could please only a glutton with depraved tastes; that she had neither the fascination of simple nature nor any knowledge of society, that she was deficient in well-bred, easy manners as well as in striking talents, and that those were the qualities which a thorough gentleman liked to find in a woman. This opinion met the general approbation of his friends, but M. de Malipiero kindly whispered to me that Juliette would certainly be informed of the portrait I had drawn of her, and that she would become my sworn enemy. He had guessed rightly.

I thought Juliette very singular, for she seldom spoke to me, and whenever she looked at me she made use of an eye-glass, or she contracted her eye-lids, as if she wished to deny me the honour of seeing her eyes, which were beyond all dispute very beautiful. They were blue, wondrously large and full, and tinted with that unfathomable variegated iris which nature only gives to youth, and which generally disappears, after having worked miracles, when the owner reaches the shady side of forty. Frederick the Great preserved it until his death. Juliette was informed of the portrait I had given of her to M. de Malipiero's friends by the indiscreet pensioner, Xavier Cortantini. One evening I called upon her with M. Manzoni, and she told him that a wonderful judge of beauty had found flaws in hers, but she took good care not to specify them. It was not difficult to make out that she was indirectly firing at me, and I prepared myself for the ostracism which I was expecting, but which, however, she kept in abeyance fully for an hour. At last, our conversation falling upon a concert given a few days before by Imer, the actor, and in which his daughter, Thérèse, had taken a brilliant part, Juliette turned round to me and inquired what M. de Malipiero did for Thérèse. I said that he was educating her. "He can well do it," she answered, "for he is a man of talent; but I should like to know what he can do with you?"

"Whatever he can."

"I am told that he thinks you rather stupid."

As a matter of course, she had the laugh on her side, and I, confused, uncomfortable and not knowing what to say, took leave after having cut a very sorry figure, and determined never again to darken her door. The next day at dinner the account of my adventure caused much amusement to the old senator.

Throughout the summer, I carried on a course of Platonic love with my charming Angela at the house of her teacher of embroidery, but her extreme reserve excited me, and my love had almost become a torment to myself. With my ardent nature, I required a mistress like Bettina, who knew how to satisfy my love without wearing it out. I still retained some feelings of purity, and I entertained the deepest veneration for Angela. She was in my eyes the very palladium of Cecrops. Still very innocent, I felt some disinclination towards women, and I was simple enough to be jealous of even their husbands.

Angela would not grant me the slightest favour, yet she was no flirt; but the fire beginning in me parched and withered me. The pathetic entreaties which I poured out of my heart had less effect upon her than upon two young sisters, her companions and friends: had I not concentrated every look of mine upon the heartless girl, I might have discovered that her friends excelled her in beauty and in feeling, but my prejudiced eyes saw no one but Angela. To every outpouring of my love she answered that she was quite ready to become my wife, and that such was to be the limit of my wishes; when she condescended to add that she suffered as much as I did myself, she thought she had bestowed upon me the greatest of favours.

Such was the state of my mind, when, in the first days of autumn, I received a letter from the Countess de Mont-Réal with an invitation to spend some time at her beautiful estate at Paséan. She expected many guests, and among them her own daughter, who had married a Venetian nobleman, and who had a great reputation for wit and beauty, although she had but one eye; but it was so beautiful that it made up for the loss of the other. I accepted the invitation, and Paséan offering me a constant round of pleasures, it was easy enough for me to enjoy myself, and to forget for the time the rigours of the cruel Angela.

I was given a pretty room on the ground floor, opening upon the gardens of Paséan, and I enjoyed its comforts without caring to know who my neighbours were.

The morning after my arrival, at the very moment I awoke, my eyes were delighted with the sight of the charming creature who brought me my coffee. She was a very young girl, but as well formed as a young person of seventeen; yet she had scarcely completed her fourteenth year. The snow of her complexion, her hair as dark as the raven's wing, her black eyes beaming with fire and innocence, her dress composed only of a chemise and a short petticoat which exposed a well-turned leg and the prettiest tiny foot, every detail I gathered in one instant presented to my looks the most original and the most perfect beauty I had ever beheld. I looked at her with the greatest pleasure, and her eyes rested upon me as if we had been old acquaintances.

"How did you find your bed?" she asked.

"Very comfortable; I am sure you made it. Pray, who are you?"

"I am Lucie, the daughter of the gate-keeper: I have neither brothers nor sisters, and I am fourteen years old. I am very glad you have no servant with you; I will be your little maid, and I am sure you will be pleased with me."

Delighted at this beginning, I sat up in my bed and she helped me to put on my dressing-gown, saying a hundred things which I did not understand. I began to drink my coffee, quite amazed at her easy freedom, and struck with her beauty, to which it would have been impossible to remain indifferent. She had seated herself on my bed, giving no other apology for that liberty than the most delightful smile.

I was still sipping my coffee, when Lucie's parents came into my room. She did not move from her place on the bed, but she looked at them, appearing very proud of such a seat. The good people kindly scolded her, begged my forgiveness in her favour, and Lucie left the room to attend to her other duties. The moment she had gone her father and mother began to praise their daughter.

"She is," they said, "our only child, our darling pet, the hope of our old age. She loves and obeys us, and fears God; she is as clean as a new pin, and has but one fault."

"What is that?"

"She is too young."

"That is a charming fault which time will mend."

I was not long in ascertaining that they were living specimens of honesty, of truth, of homely virtues, and of real happiness. I was delighted at this discovery, when Lucie returned as gay as a lark, prettily dressed, her hair done in a peculiar way of her own, and with well-fitting shoes. She dropped a simple courtesy before me, gave a couple of hearty kisses to both her parents, and jumped on her father knees. I asked her to come and sit on my bed, but she answered that she could not take such a liberty now that she was dressed. The simplicity, artlessness, and innocence of the answer seemed to me very enchanting, and brought a smile on my lips. I examined her to see whether she was prettier in her new dress or in the morning's *negligée,* and I decided in favour of the latter. To speak the truth, Lucie was, I thought, superior in everything, not only to Angela, but even to Bettina.

The hair-dresser made his appearance, and the honest family left my room. When I was dressed I went to meet the countess and her amiable daughter. The day passed off very pleasantly, as is generally the case in the country, when you are amongst agreeable people.

In the morning, the moment my eyes were opened,

I rang the bell, and pretty Lucie came in, simple and natural as before, with her easy manners and wonderful remarks. Her candour, her innocence shone brilliantly all over her person. I could not conceive how, with her goodness, her virtue and her intelligence, she could run the risk of exciting me by coming into my room alone, and with so much familiarity. I fancied that she would not attach much importance to certain slight liberties, and would not prove over-scrupulous, and with that idea I made up my mind to shew her that I fully understood her. I felt no remorse of conscience on the score of her parents, who, in my estimation, were as careless as herself; I had no dread of being the first to give the alarm to her innocence, or to enlighten her mind with the gloomy light of malice, but, unwilling either to be the dupe of feeling or to act against it, I resolved to reconnoitre the ground. I extend a daring hand towards her person, and by an involuntary movement she withdraws, blushes, her cheerfulness disappears, and, turning her head aside as if she were in search of something, she waits until her agitation has subsided. The whole affair had not lasted one minute. She came back, abashed at the idea that she had proved herself rather knowing, and at the dread of having perhaps given a wrong interpretation to an action which might have been, on my part, perfectly innocent, or the result of politeness. Her natural laugh soon returned, and, having rapidly read in her mind all I have just described, I lost no time in restoring her confidence, and, judging that I would venture too much by active operations, I resolved to employ the following morning in a friendly chat during which I could make her out better.

In pursuance of that plan, the next morning, as we were talking, I told her that it was cold, but that

she would not feel it if she would lie down near me.
"Shall I disturb you?" she said.

"No; but I am thinking that if your mother happened
to come in, she would be angry."

"Mother would not think of any harm."

"Come, then. But Lucie, do you know what danger
you are exposing yourself to?"

"Certainly I do; but you are good, and, what is more,
you are a priest."

"Come; only lock the door."

"No, no, for people might think. . . . I do not know
what." She laid down close by me, and kept on her
chatting, although I did not understand a word of what
she said, for in that singular position, and unwilling to
give way to my ardent desires, I remained as still as a
log.

Her confidence in her safety, confidence which was
certainly not feigned, worked upon my feelings to such
an extent that I would have been ashamed to take any
advantage of it. At last she told me that nine o'clock
had struck, and that if old Count Antonio found us as
we were, he would tease her with his jokes. "When I
see that man," she said, "I am afraid and I run away."
Saying these words, she rose from the bed and left the
room.

I remained motionless for a long while, stupefied, benumbed, and mastered by the agitation of my excited
senses as well as by my thoughts. The next morning,
as I wished to keep calm, I only let her sit down on my
bed, and the conversation I had with her proved without
the shadow of a doubt that her parents had every reason to idolize her, and that the easy freedom of her mind
as well as of her behaviour with me was entirely owing
to her innocence and to her purity. Her artlessness, her

vivacity, her eager curiosity, and the bashful blushes
which spread over her face whenever her innocent or
jesting remarks caused me to laugh, everything, in fact,
convinced me that she was an angel destined to become
the victim of the first libertine who would undertake to
seduce her. I felt sufficient control over my own feelings
to resist any attempt against her virtue which my conscience might afterwards reproach me with. The mere
thought of taking advantage of her innocence made me
shudder, and my self-esteem was a guarantee to her
parents, who abandoned her to me on the strength of the
good opinion they entertained of me, that Lucie's honour
was safe in my hands. I thought I would have despised
myself if I had betrayed the trust they reposed in me.
I therefore determined to conquer my feelings, and, with
perfect confidence in the victory, I made up my mind
to wage war against myself, and to be satisfied with her
presence as the only reward of my heroic efforts. I was
not yet acquainted with the axiom that "as long as the
fighting lasts, victory remains uncertain."

As I enjoyed her conversation much, a natural instinct prompted me to tell her that she would afford me
great pleasure if she could come earlier in the morning,
and even wake me up if I happened to be asleep, adding,
in order to give more weight to my request, that the less
I slept the better I felt in health. In this manner I contrived to spend three hours instead of two in her society,
although this cunning contrivance of mine did not prevent the hours flying, at least in my opinion, as swift
as lightning.

Her mother would often come in as we were talking,
and when the good woman found her sitting on my bed
she would say nothing, only wondering at my kindness.
Lucie would then cover her with kisses, and the kind

old soul would entreat me to give her child lessons of goodness, and to cultivate her mind; but when she had left us Lucie did not think herself more unrestrained, and whether in or out of her mother's presence, she was always the same without the slightest change.

If the society of this angelic child afforded me the sweetest delight, it also caused me the most cruel suffering. Often, very often, when her face was close to my lips, I felt the most ardent temptation to smother her with kisses, and my blood was at fever heat when she wished that she had been a sister of mine. But I kept sufficient command over myself to avoid the slightest contact, for I was conscious that even one kiss would have been the spark which would have blown up all the edifice of my reserve. Every time she left me I remained astounded at my own victory, but, always eager to win fresh laurels, I longed for the following morning, panting for a renewal of this sweet yet very dangerous contest.

At the end of ten or twelve days, I felt that there was no alternative but to put a stop to this state of things, or to become a monster in my own eyes; and I decided for the moral side of the question all the more easily that nothing insured me success, if I chose the second alternative. The moment I placed her under the obligation to defend herself Lucie would become a heroine, and the door of my room being open, I might have been exposed to shame and to a very useless repentance. This rather frightened me. Yet, to put an end to my torture, I did not know what to decide. I could no longer resist the effect made upon my senses by this beautiful girl, who, at the break of day and scarcely dressed, ran gaily into my room, came to my bed enquiring how I had slept, bent familiarly her head towards me, and, so to speak, dropped her words on my lips. In those dangerous moments I would turn my head aside; but in her innocence she would reproach me for being afraid when she felt herself so safe, and if I answered that I could not possibly fear a child, she would reply that a difference of two years was of no account.

Standing at bay, exhausted, conscious that every instant increased the ardour which was devouring me, I resolved to entreat from herself the discontinuance of her visits, and this resolution appeared to me sublime and infallible; but having postponed its execution until the following morning, I passed a dreadful night, tortured by the image of Lucie, and by the idea that I would see her in the morning for the last time. I fancied that Lucie would not only grant my prayer, but that she would conceive for me the highest esteem. In the morning, it was barely day-light, Lucie beaming, radiant with beauty, a happy smile brightening her pretty mouth, and her splendid hair in the most fascinating disorder, bursts into my room, and rushes with open arms towards my bed; but when she sees my pale, dejected, and unhappy countenance, she stops short, and her beautiful face taking an expression of sadness and anxiety:

"What ails you?" she asks, with deep sympathy.

"I have had no sleep through the night."

"And why?"

"Because I have made up my mind to impart to you a project which, although fraught with misery to myself, will at least secure me your esteem."

"But if your project is to insure my esteem it ought to make you very cheerful. Only tell me, reverend sir, why, after calling me 'thou' yesterday, you treat me to-day respectfully, like a lady? What have I done? I will get your coffee, and you must tell me everything after you have drunk it; I long to hear you."

She goes and returns, I drink the coffee, and seeing that my countenance remains grave she tries to enliven me, contrives to make me smile, and claps her hands for joy. After putting everything in order, she closes the door because the wind is high, and in her anxiety not to lose one word of what I have to say, she entreats artlessly a little place near me. I cannot refuse her, for I feel almost lifeless.

I then begin a faithful recital of the fearful state in which her beauty has thrown me, and a vivid picture of all the suffering I have experienced in trying to master my ardent wish to give her some proof of my love; I explain to her that, unable to endure such torture any longer, I see no other safety but in entreating her not to see me any more. The importance of the subject, the truth of my love, my wish to present my expedient in the light of the heroic effort of a deep and virtuous passion, lend me a peculiar eloquence. I endeavour above all to make her realize the fearful consequences which might follow a course different to the one I was proposing, and how miserable we might be.

At the close of my long discourse Lucie, seeing my eyes wet with tears, throws off the bed-clothes to wipe them, without thinking that in so doing she uncovers two globes, the beauty of which might have caused the wreck of the most experienced pilot. After a short silence, the charming child tells me that my tears make her very unhappy, and that she had never supposed that she could cause them.

"All you have just told me," she added, "proves the sincerity of your great love for me, but I cannot imagine why you should be in such dread of a feeling which affords me the most intense pleasure. You wish to banish me from your presence because you stand in fear of your love, but what would you do if you hated me? Am I guilty because I have pleased you? If it is a crime to have won your affection, I can assure you that I did not think I was committing a criminal action, and therefore you cannot conscientiously punish me. Yet I cannot conceal the truth; I am very happy to be loved by you. As for the danger we run, when we love, danger which I can understand, we can set it at defiance, if we choose, and I wonder at my not fearing it, ignorant as I am, while you, a learned man, think it so terrible. I am astonished that love, which is not a disease, should have made you ill, and that it should have exactly the opposite effect upon me. Is it possible that I am mistaken, and that my feeling towards you should not be love? You saw me very cheerful when I came in this morning; it is because I have been dreaming all night, but my dreams did not keep me awake; only several times I woke up to ascertain whether my dream was true, for I thought I was near you; and every time, finding that it was not so, I quickly went to sleep again in the hope of continuing my happy dream, and every time I succeeded. After such a night, was it not natural for me to be cheerful this morning? My dear abbé, if love is a torment for you I am very sorry, but would it be possible for you to live without love? I will do anything you order me to do, but, even if your cure depended upon it, I would not cease to love you, for that would be impossible. Yet if to heal your sufferings it should be necessary for you to love me no more, you must do your utmost to succeed, for I would much rather see you alive without love, than dead for having loved too much. Only try to find some other plan, for the one you have proposed makes me very miserable. Think of it, there may be some other way which will be less painful. Suggest one more practicable, and depend upon Lucie's obedience."

These words, so true, so artless, so innocent, made me realize the immense superiority of nature's eloquence over that of philosophical intellect. For the first time I folded this angelic being in my arms, exclaiming, "Yes, dearest Lucie, yes, thou hast it in thy power to afford the sweetest relief to my devouring pain; abandon to my ardent kisses thy divine lips which have just assured me of thy love."

An hour passed in the most delightful silence, which nothing interrupted except these words murmured now and then by Lucie, "Oh, God! is it true? is it not a dream?" Yet I respected her innocence, and the more readily that she abandoned herself entirely and without the slightest resistance. At last, extricating herself gently from my arms, she said, with some uneasiness, "My heart begins to speak, I must go;" and she instantly rose. Having somewhat rearranged her dress she sat down, and her mother, coming in at that moment, complimented me upon my good looks and my bright countenance, and told Lucie to dress herself to attend mass. Lucie came back an hour later, and expressed her joy and her pride at the wonderful cure she thought she had performed upon me, for the healthy appearance I was then shewing convinced her of my love much better than the pitiful state in which she had found me in the morning. "If your complete happiness," she said, "rests in my power, be happy; there is nothing that I can refuse you."

The moment she left me, still wavering between hap-

piness and fear, I understood that I was standing on
the very brink of the abyss, and that nothing but a most
extraordinary determination could prevent me from
falling headlong into it.

I remained at Paséan until the end of September,
and the last eleven nights of my stay were passed in the
undisturbed possession of Lucie, who, secure in her
mother's profound sleep, came to my room to enjoy in
my arms the most delicious hours. The burning ardour
of my love was increased by the abstinence to which I
condemned myself, although Lucie did everything in her
power to make me break through my determination.
She could not fully enjoy the sweetness of the forbidden
fruit unless I plucked it without reserve, and the effect
produced by our constantly lying in each other's arms
was too strong for a young girl to resist. She tried
everything she could to deceive me, and to make me believe that I had already, and in reality, gathered the
whole flower, but Bettina's lessons had been too efficient to allow me to go on a wrong scent, and I reached
the end of my stay without yielding entirely to the
temptation she so fondly threw in my way. I promised
her to return in the spring; our farewell was tender and
very sad, and I left her in a state of mind and of body
which must have been the cause of her misfortunes,
which, twenty years after, I had occasion to reproach
myself with in Holland, and which will ever remain upon
my conscience.

A few days after my return to Venice, I had fallen
back into all my old habits, and resumed my courtship
of Angela in the hope that I would obtain from her, at
least, as much as Lucie had granted to me. A certain
dread which to-day I can no longer trace in my nature, a
sort of terror of the consequences which might have a

blighting influence upon my future, prevented me from giving myself up to complete enjoyment. I do not know whether I have ever been a truly honest man, but I am fully aware that the feelings I fostered in my youth were by far more upright than those I have, as I lived on, forced myself to accept. A wicked philosophy throws down too many of these barriers which we call prejudices.

The two sisters who were sharing Angela's embroidery lessons were her intimate friends and the confidantes of all her secrets. I made their acquaintance, and found that they disapproved of her extreme reserve towards me. As I usually saw them with Angela and knew their intimacy with her, I would, when I happened to meet them alone, tell them all my sorrows, and, thinking only of my cruel sweetheart, I never was conceited enough to propose that these young girls might fall in love with me; but I often ventured to speak to them with all the blazing inspiration which was burning in me—a liberty I would not have dared to take in the presence of her whom I loved. True love always begets reserve; we fear to be accused of exaggeration if we should give utterance to feelings inspired by passion, and the modest lover, in his dread of saying too much, very often says too little.

The teacher of embroidery, an old bigot, who at first appeared not to mind the attachment I shewed for Angela, got tired at last of my too frequent visits, and mentioned them to the abbé, the uncle of my fair lady. He told me kindly one day that I ought not to call at that house so often, as my constant visits might be wrongly construed, and prove detrimental to the reputation of his niece. His words fell upon me like a thunder-bolt, but I mastered my feelings sufficiently to leave him without incurring any suspicion, and I promised to follow his good advice.

Three or four days afterwards, I paid a visit to the teacher of embroidery, and, to make her believe that my visit was only intended for her, I did not stop one instant near the young girls; yet I contrived to slip in the hand of the eldest of the two sisters a note enclosing another for my dear Angela, in which I explained why I had been compelled to discontinue my visits, entreating her to devise some means by which I could enjoy the happiness of seeing her and of conversing with her. In my note to Nanette, I only begged her to give my letter to her friend, adding that I would see them again the day after the morrow, and that I trusted to her to find an opportunity for delivering me the answer. She managed it all very cleverly, and, when I renewed my visit two days afterwards, she gave me a letter without attracting the attention of anyone.

Nanette's letter enclosed a very short note from Angela, who, disliking letter-writing, merely advised me to follow, if I could, the plan proposed by her friend. Here is the copy of the letter written by Nanette, which I have always kept, as well as all other letters which I give in these Memoirs:

"There is nothing in the world, reverend sir, that I would not readily do for my friend. She visits at our house every holiday, has supper with us, and sleeps under our roof. I will suggest the best way for you to make the acquaintance of Madame Orio, our aunt; but, if you obtain an introduction to her, you must be very careful not to let her suspect your preference for Angela, for our aunt would certainly object to her house being made a place of rendezvous to facilitate your interviews with a stranger to her family. Now for the plan

I propose, and in the execution of which I will give you every assistance in my power. Madame Orio, although a woman of good station in life, is not wealthy, and she wishes to have her name entered on the list of noble widows who receive the bounties bestowed by the Confraternity of the Holy Sacrament, of which M. de Malipiero is president. Last Sunday, Angela mentioned that you are in the good graces of that nobleman, and that the best way to obtain his patronage would be to ask you to entreat it in her behalf. The foolish girl added that you were smitten with me, that all your visits to our mistress of embroidery were made for my special benefit and for the sake of entertaining me, and that I would find it a very easy task to interest you in her favour. My aunt answered that, as you are a priest, there was no fear of any harm, and she told me to write to you with an invitation to call on her; I refused. The procurator Rosa, who is a great favourite of my aunt's, was present; he approved of my refusal, saying that the letter ought to be written by her and not by me, that it was for my aunt to beg the honour of your visit on business of real importance, and that, if there was any truth in the report of your love for me, you would not fail to come. My aunt, by his advice, has therefore written the letter which you will find at your house. If you wish to meet Angela, postpone your visit to us until next Sunday. Should you succeed in obtaining M. de Malipiero's good will in favour of my aunt, you will become the pet of the household, but you must forgive me if I appear to treat you with coolness, for I have said that I do not like you. I would advise you to make love to my aunt, who is sixty years of age; M. Rosa will not be jealous, and you will become dear to everyone. For my part, I will manage for you an opportunity for some

private conversation with Angela, and I will do anything
to convince you of my friendship. Adieu."

This plan appeared to me very well conceived, and,
having the same evening received Madame Orio's letter,
I called upon her on the following day, Sunday. I
was welcomed in a very friendly manner, and the lady,
entreating me to exert in her behalf my influence with
M. de Malipiero, entrusted me with all the papers which
I might require to succeed. I undertook to do my utmost, and I took care to address only a few words to Angela, but I directed all my gallant attentions to Nanette,
who treated me as coolly as could be. Finally, I won
the friendship of the old procurator Rosa, who, in after
years, was of some service to me.

I had so much at stake in the success of Madame
Orio's petition, that I thought of nothing else, and knowing all the power of the beautiful Thérèse Imer over
our amorous senator, who would be but too happy to
please her in anything, I determined to call upon her the
next day, and I went straight to her room without being announced. I found her alone with the physician
Doro, who, feigning to be on a professional visit, wrote
a prescription, felt her pulse, and went off. This Doro
was suspected of being in love with Thérèse; M. de
Malipiero, who was jealous, had forbidden Thérèse to
receive his visits, and she had promised to obey him.
She knew that I was acquainted with those circumstances, and my presence was evidently unpleasant to
her, for she had certainly no wish that the old man
should hear how she kept her promise. I thought that
no better opportunity could be found of obtaining from
her everything I wished.

I told her in a few words the object of my visit, and
I took care to add that she could rely upon my discre-

tion, and that I would not for the world do her any injury. Thérèse, grateful for this assurance, answered that she rejoiced at finding an occasion to oblige me, and, asking me to give her the papers of my *protégé*, she shewed me the certificates and testimonials of another lady in favour of whom she had undertaken to speak, and whom, she said, she would sacrifice to the person in whose behalf I felt interested. She kept her word, for the very next day she placed in my hands the brevet, signed by his excellency as president of the confraternity. For the present, and with the expectation of further favours, Madame Orio's name was put down to share the bounties which were distributed twice a year.

Nanette and her sister Marton were the orphan daughters of a sister of Madame Orio. All the fortune of the good lady consisted in the house which was her dwelling, the first floor being let, and in a pension given to her by her brother, member of the council of ten. She lived alone with her two charming nieces, the eldest sixteen, and the youngest fifteen years of age. She kept no servant, and only employed an old woman, who, for one crown a month, fetched water, and did the rough work. Her only friend was the procurator Rosa; he had, like her, reached his sixtieth year, and expected to marry her as soon as he should become a widower.

The two sisters slept together on the third floor in a large bed, which was likewise shared by Angela every Sunday.

As soon as I found myself in possession of the deed for Madame Orio, I hastened to pay a visit to the mistress of embroidery, in order to find an opportunity of acquainting Nanette with my success, and in a short note which I prepared, I informed her that in two days I would call to give the brevet to Madame Orio, and I begged her earnestly not to forget her promise to contrive a private interview with my dear Angela.

When I arrived, on the appointed day, at Madame Orio's house, Nanette, who had watched for my coming, dexterously conveyed to my hand a billet, requesting me to find a moment to read it before leaving the house. I found Madame Orio, Angela, the old procurator, and Marton in the room. Longing to read the note, I refused the seat offered to me, and presenting to Madame Orio the deed she had so long desired, I asked, as my only reward, the pleasure of kissing her hand, giving her to understand that I wanted to leave the room immediately.

"Oh, my dear abbé!" said the lady, "you shall have a kiss, but not on my hand, and no one can object to it, as I am thirty years older than you."

She might have said forty-five without going much astray. I gave her two kisses, which evidently satisfied her, for she desired me to perform the same ceremony with her nieces, but they both ran away, and Angela alone stood the brunt of my hardihood. After this the widow asked me to sit down.

"I cannot, Madame."

"Why, I beg?"

"I have——."

"I understand. Nanette, shew the way."

"Dear aunt, excuse me."

"Well, then, Marton——."

"Oh! dear aunt, why do you not insist upon my sister obeying your orders?"

"Alas! madame, these young ladies are quite right. Allow me to retire."

"No, my dear abbé, my nieces are very foolish; M. Rosa, I am sure, will kindly——."

The good procurator takes me affectionately by the

hand, and leads me to the third story, where he leaves me. The moment I am alone I open my letter, and I read the following:

"My aunt will invite you to supper; do not accept. Go away as soon as we sit down to table, and Marton will escort you as far as the street door, but do not leave the house. When the street door is closed again, everyone thinking you are gone, go upstairs in the dark as far as the third floor, where you must wait for us. We will come up the moment M. Rosa has left the house, and our aunt has gone to bed. Angela will be at liberty to grant you throughout the night a *tête-à-tête* which, I trust, will prove a happy one."

Oh! what joy—what gratitude for the lucky chance which allowed me to read this letter on the very spot where I was to expect the dear object of my love! Certain of finding my way without the slightest difficulty, I returned to Madame Orio's sitting-room, overwhelmed with happiness.

CHAPTER V

*An Unlucky Night—I Fall in Love with the Two Sisters,
and Forget Angela—A Ball at My House—Juliette's
Humiliation—My Return to Paséan—Lucie's Misfortune—A Propitious Storm*

O N my reappearance, Madame Orio told me, with
many heart-felt thanks, that I must for the future
consider myself as a privileged and welcome friend, and
the evening passed off very pleasantly. As the hour for
supper drew near, I excused myself so well that Madame
Orio could not insist upon my accepting her invitation
to stay. Marton rose to light me out of the room,
but her aunt, believing Nanette to be my favourite, gave
her such an imperative order to accompany me that she
was compelled to obey. She went down the stairs rapidly, opened and closed the street door very noisily, and
putting her light out, she reëntered the sitting room,
leaving me in darkness. I went upstairs softly: when I
reached the third landing I found the chamber of the
two sisters, and, throwing myself upon a sofa, I waited
patiently for the rising of the star of my happiness. An
hour passed amidst the sweetest dreams of my imagination; at last I hear the noise of the street door opening
and closing, and, a few minutes after, the two sisters
come in with my Angela. I draw her towards me, and
caring for nobody else, I keep up for two full hours my
conversation with her. The clock strikes midnight; I

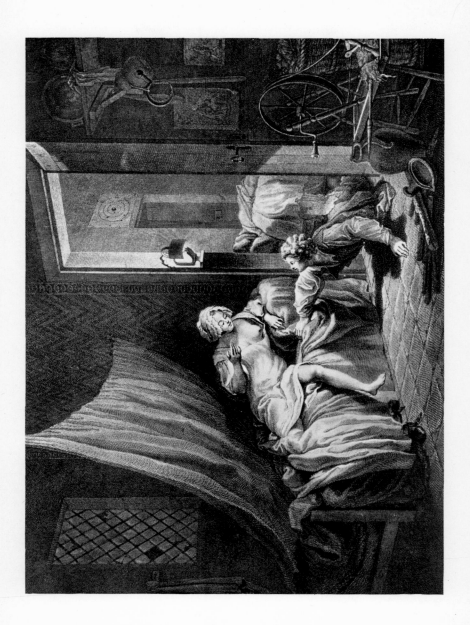

am pitied for having gone so late supperless, but I am
shocked at such an idea; I answer that, with such happiness as I am enjoying, I can suffer from no human
want. I am told that I am a prisoner, that the key of
the house door is under the aunt's pillow, and that it
is opened only by herself as she goes in the morning
to the first mass. I wonder at my young friends imagin-
ing that such news can be anything but delightful to me.
I express all my joy at the certainty of passing the next
five hours with the beloved mistress of my heart. Another hour is spent, when suddenly Nanette begins to
laugh, Angela wants to know the reason, and Marton
whispering a few words to her, they both laugh likewise.
This puzzles me. In my turn, I want to know what
causes this general laughter, and at last Nanette, putting on an air of anxiety, tells me that they have no
more candle, and that in a few minutes we shall be
in the dark. This is a piece of news particularly agreeable to me, but I do not let my satisfaction appear on
my countenance, and saying how truly I am sorry for
their sake, I propose that they should go to bed and
sleep quietly under my respectful guardianship. My
proposal increases their merriment.

"What can we do in the dark?"

"We can talk."

We were four; for the last three hours we had been
talking, and I was the hero of the romance. Love is a
great poet, its resources are inexhaustible, but if the
end it has in view is not obtained, it feels weary and remains silent. My Angela listened willingly, but little
disposed to talk herself, she seldom answered, and she
displayed good sense rather than wit. To weaken the
force of my arguments, she was often satisfied with
hurling at me a proverb, somewhat in the fashion of the

Romans throwing the catapult. Every time that my poor hands came to the assistance of love, she drew herself back or repulsed me. Yet, in spite of all, I went on talking and using my hands without losing courage, but I gave myself up to despair when I found that my rather artful arguing astounded her without bringing conviction to her heart, which was only disquieted, never softened. On the other hand, I could see with astonishment upon their countenances the impression made upon the two sisters by the ardent speeches I poured out to Angela. This metaphysical curve struck me as unnatural, it ought to have been an angle; I was then, unhappily for myself, studying geometry. I was in such a state that, notwithstanding the cold, I was perspiring profusely. At last the light was nearly out, and Nanette took it away.

The moment we were in the dark, I very naturally extended my arms to seize her whom I loved; but I only met with empty space, and I could not help laughing at the rapidity with which Angela had availed herself of the opportunity of escaping me. For one full hour I poured out all the tender, cheerful words that love inspired me with, to persuade her to come back to me; I could only suppose that it was a joke to tease me. But I became impatient.

"The joke," I said, "has lasted long enough; it is foolish, as I could not run after you, and I am surprised to hear you laugh, for your strange conduct leads me to suppose that you are making fun of me. Come and take your seat near me, and if I must speak to you without seeing you let my hands assure me that I am not addressing my words to the empty air. To continue this game would be an insult to me, and my love does not deserve such a return."

"Well, be calm. I will listen to every word you may say, but you must feel that it would not be decent for me to place myself near you in this dark room."

"Do you want me to stand where I am until morning?"

"Lie down on the bed, and go to sleep."

"In wonder, indeed, at your thinking me capable of doing so in the state I am in. Well, I suppose we must play at blind man's buff."

Thereupon, I began to feel right and left, everywhere, but in vain. Whenever I caught anyone it always turned out to be Nanette or Marton, who at once discovered themselves, and I, stupid Don Quixote, instantly would let them go! Love and prejudice blinded me, I could not see how ridiculous I was with my respectful reserve. I had not yet read the anecdotes of Louis XIII., king of France, but I had read Boccacio. I kept on seeking in vain, reproaching her with her cruelty, and entreating her to let me catch her; but she would only answer that the difficulty of meeting each other was mutual. The room was not large, and I was enraged at my want of success.

Tired and still more vexed, I sat down, and for the next hour I told the history of Roger, when Angelica disappears through the power of the magic ring which the loving knight had so imprudently given her:

> *Cosi dicendo, intorno à la fortuna*
> *Brancolando n'andava come cieco.*
> *O quante volte abbraccio l'aria vana*
> *Sperando la donzella abbracciar seco.*

Angela had not read Ariosto, but Nanette had done so several times. She undertook the defence of Angelica, and blamed the simplicity of Roger, who, if he had been wise, would never have trusted the ring to a coquette. I was delighted with Nanette, but I was yet too much of a novice to apply her remarks to myself.

Only one more hour remained, and I was to leave before the break of day, for Madame Orio would have died rather than give way to the temptation of missing the early mass. During that hour I spoke to Angela, trying to convince her that she ought to come and sit by me. My soul went through every gradation of hope and despair, and the reader cannot possibly realize it unless he has been placed in a similar position. I exhausted the most convincing arguments; then I had recourse to prayers, and even to tears; but, seeing all was useless, I gave way to that feeling of noble indignation which lends dignity to anger. Had I not been in the dark, I might, I truly believe, have struck the proud monster, the cruel girl, who had thus for five hours condemned me to the most distressing suffering. I poured out all the abuse, all the insulting words that despised love can suggest to an infuriated mind; I loaded her with the deepest curses; I swore that my love had entirely turned into hatred, and, as a *finale*, I advised her to be careful, as I would kill her the moment I would set my eyes on her.

My invectives came to an end with the darkness. At the first break of day, and as soon as I heard the noise made by the bolt and the key of the street door, which Madame Orio was opening to let herself out, that she might seek in the church the repose of which her pious soul was in need, I got myself ready and looked for my cloak and for my hat. But how can I ever portray the consternation in which I was thrown when, casting a sly glance upon the young friends, I found the three bathed in tears! In my shame and despair I thought of committing suicide, and sitting down again, I recollected my brutal speeches, and upbraided myself for having wantonly caused them to weep. I could not say one word; I felt choking; at last tears came to my assistance, and I gave way to a fit of crying which relieved me. Nanette then remarked that her aunt would soon return home; I dried my eyes, and, not venturing another look at Angela or at her friends, I ran away without uttering a word, and threw myself on my bed, where sleep would not visit my troubled mind.

At noon, M. de Malipiero, noticing the change in my countenance, enquired what ailed me, and longing to unburden my heart, I told him all that had happened. The wise old man did not laugh at my sorrow, but by his sensible advice he managed to console me and to give me courage. He was in the same predicament with the beautiful Thérèse. Yet he could not help giving way to his merriment when at dinner he saw me, in spite of my grief, eat with increased appetite; I had gone without my supper the night before; he complimented me upon my happy constitution.

I was determined never to visit Madame Orio's house, and on that very day I held an argument in metaphysics, in which I contended that any being of whom we had only an abstract idea, could only exist abstractedly, and I was right; but it was a very easy task to give to my thesis an irreligious turn, and I was obliged to recant. A few days afterwards I went to Padua, where I took my degree of doctor *utroque jure*.

When I returned to Venice, I received a note from M. Rosa, who entreated me to call upon Madame Orio; she wished to see me, and, feeling certain of not meeting Angela, I paid her a visit the same evening. The two graceful sisters were so kind, so pleasant, that they scattered to the winds the shame I felt at seeing them after the fearful night I had passed in their room two months before. The labours of writing my thesis and passing my examination were of course sufficient excuses for Madame Orio, who only wanted to reproach me for having remained so long away from her house.

As I left, Nanette gave me a letter containing a note from Angela, the contents of which ran as follows:

"If you are not afraid of passing another night with me you shall have no reason to complain of me, for I love you, and I wish to hear from your own lips whether you would still have loved me if I had consented to become contemptible in your eyes."

This is the letter of Nanette, who alone had her wits about her:

"M. Rosa having undertaken to bring you back to our house, I prepare these few lines to let you know that Angela is in despair at having lost you. I confess that the night you spent with us was a cruel one, but I do not think that you did rightly in giving up your visits to Madame Orio. If you still feel any love for Angela, I advise you to take your chances once more. Accept a rendezvous for another night; she may vindicate herself, and you will be happy. Believe me; come. Farewell."

Those two letters afforded me much gratification, for I had it in my power to enjoy my revenge by shewing to Angela the coldest contempt. Therefore, on the following Sunday I went to Madame Orio's house, having provided myself with a smoked tongue and a couple of bottles of Cyprus wine; but to my great surprise my cruel mistress was not there. Nanette told me that she had met her at church in the morning, and that she would not be able to come before supper-time. Trusting to that promise I declined Madam Orio's invitation, and before the family sat down to supper I left the room as I had done on the former occasion, and slipped upstairs. I longed to represent the character I had prepared myself for, and feeling assured that Angela, even if she should prove less cruel, would only grant me insignificant favours, I despised them in anticipation, and resolved to be avenged.

After waiting three quarters of an hour the street door was locked, and a moment later Nanette and Marton entered the room.

"Where is Angela?" I enquired.

"She must have been unable to come, or to send a message. Yet she knows you are here."

"She thinks she has made a fool of me; but I suspected she would act in this way. You know her now. She is trifling with me, and very likely she is now revelling in her triumph. She has made use of you to allure me in the snare, and it is all the better for her; had she come, I meant to have had my turn, and to have laughed at her."

"Ah! you must allow me to have my doubts as to that."

"Doubt me not, beautiful Nanette; the pleasant night we are going to spend without her must convince you."

"That is to say that, as a man of sense, you can accept us as a makeshift; but you can sleep here, and my sister can lie with me on the sofa in the next room."

"I cannot hinder you, but it would be great unkindness on your part. At all events, I do not intend to go to bed."

"What! you would have the courage to spend seven hours alone with us? Why, I am certain that in a short time you will be at a loss what to say, and you will fall asleep."

"Well, we shall see. In the mean-time here are provisions. You will not be so cruel as to let me eat alone? Can you get any bread?"

"Yes, and to please you we must have a second supper."

"I ought to be in love with you. Tell me, beautiful Nanette, if I were as much attached to you as I was to Angela, would you follow her example and make me unhappy?"

"How can you ask such a question? It is worthy of a conceited man. All I can answer is, that I do not know what I would do."

They laid the cloth, brought some bread, some Parmesan cheese and water, laughing all the while, and then we went to work. The wine, to which they were not accustomed, went to their heads, and their gaiety was soon delightful. I wondered, as I looked at them, at my having been blind enough not to see their merit.

After our supper, which was delicious, I sat between them, holding their hands, which I pressed to my lips, asking them whether they were truly my friends, and whether they approved of Angela's conduct towards me. They both answered that it had made them shed many tears. "Then let me," I said, "have for you the tender feelings of a brother, and share those feelings yourselves as if you were my sisters; let us exchange, in all innocence, proofs of our mutual affection, and swear to each other an eternal fidelity."

The first kiss I gave them was prompted by entirely harmless motives, and they returned the kiss, as they assured me a few days afterwards only to prove to me that they reciprocated my brotherly feelings; but those innocent kisses, as we repeated them, very soon became ardent ones, and kindled a flame which certainly took us by surprise, for we stopped, as by common consent, after a short time, looking at each other very much astonished and rather serious. They both left me without affectation, and I remained alone with my thoughts. Indeed, it was natural that the burning kisses I had given and received should have sent through me the fire of passion, and that I should suddenly have fallen madly in love with the two amiable sisters. Both were handsomer than Angela, and they were superior to her—Nanette by her charming wit, Marton by her sweet and simple nature; I could not understand how I had been so long in rendering them the justice they deserved, but they were the innocent daughters of a noble family, and the lucky chance which had thrown them in my way ought not to prove a calamity for them. I was not vain enough to suppose that they loved me, but I could well enough admit that my kisses had influenced them in the same manner that their kisses had influenced me, and, believing this to be the case, it was evident that, with a little cunning on my part, and of sly practices of which they were ignorant, I could easily, during the long night I was going to spend with them, obtain favours, the consequences of which might be very positive. The very thought made me shudder, and I firmly resolved to respect their virtue, never dreaming that circumstances might prove too strong for me.

When they returned, I read upon their countenances perfect security and satisfaction, and I quickly put on the same appearance, with a full determination not to expose myself again to the danger of their kisses.

For one hour we spoke of Angela, and I expressed my determination never to see her again, as I had every proof that she did not care for me. "She loves you," said the artless Marton; "I know she does, but if you do not mean to marry her, you will do well to give up all intercourse with her, for she is quite determined not to grant you even a kiss as long as you are not her acknowledged suitor. You must therefore either give up the acquaintance altogether, or make up your mind that she will refuse you everything."

"You argue very well, but how do you know that she loves me?"

"I am quite sure of it, and as you have promised to be our brother, I can tell you why I have that conviction. When Angela is in bed with me, she embraces me lovingly and calls me her dear abbé."

The words were scarcely spoken when Nanette, laughing heartily, placed her hand on her sister's lips, but the innocent confession had such an effect upon me that I could hardly control myself.

Marton told Nanette that I could not possibly be ignorant of what takes place between young girls sleeping together.

"There is no doubt," I said, "that everybody knows those trifles, and I do not think, dear Nanette, that you ought to reproach your sister with indiscretion for her friendly confidence."

"It cannot be helped now, but such things ought not to be mentioned. If Angela knew it!"

"She would be vexed, of course; but Marton has given me a mark of her friendship which I never can forget. But it is all over; I hate Angela, and I do not mean to speak to her any more! she is false, and she wishes my ruin."

"Yet, loving you, is she wrong to think of having you for her husband?"

"Granted that she is not; but she thinks only of her own self, for she knows what I suffer, and her conduct would be very different if she loved me. In the mean time, thanks to her imagination, she finds the means of satisfying her senses with the charming Marton who kindly performs the part of her husband."

Nanette laughed louder, but I kept very serious, and I went on talking to her sister, and praising her sincerity. I said that very likely, and to reciprocate her kindness, Angela must likewise have been her husband, but she answered, with a smile, that Angela played husband only to Nanette, and Nanette could not deny it.

"But," said I, "what name did Nanette, in her rapture, give to her husband?"

"Nobody knows."

"Do you love anyone, Nanette?"

"I do; but my secret is my own."

This reserve gave me the suspicion that I had something to do with her secret, and that Nanette was the rival of Angela. Such a delightful conversation caused me to lose the wish of passing an idle night with two girls so well made for love.

"It is very lucky," I exclaimed, "that I have for you only feelings of friendship; otherwise it would be very hard to pass the night without giving way to the temptation of bestowing upon you proofs of my affection, for you are both so lovely, so bewitching, that you would turn the brains of any man."

As I went on talking, I pretended to be somewhat sleepy; Nanette being the first to notice it, said, "Go to bed without any ceremony, we will lie down on the sofa in the adjoining room."

"I would be a very poor-spirited fellow indeed, if I agreed to this; let us talk; my sleepiness will soon pass off, but I am anxious about you. Go to bed yourselves, my charming friends, and I will go into the next room. If you are afraid of me, lock the door, but you would do me an injustice, for I feel only a brother's yearnings towards you."

"We cannot accept such an arrangement," said Nanette, "but let me persuade you; take this bed."

"I cannot sleep with my clothes on."

"Undress yourself; we will not look at you."

"I have no fear of it, but how could I find the heart to sleep, while on my account you are compelled to sit up?"

"Well," said Marton, "we can lie down, too, without undressing."

"If you shew me such distrust, you will offend me. Tell me, Nanette, do you think I am an honest man?"

"Most certainly."

"Well, then, give me a proof of your good opinion; lie down near me in the bed, undressed, and rely on my word of honour that I will not even lay a finger upon you. Besides, you are two against one, what can you fear? Will you not be free to get out of the bed in case I should not keep quiet? In short, unless you consent to give me this mark of your confidence in me, at least when I have fallen asleep, I cannot go to bed."

I said no more, and pretended to be very sleepy. They exchanged a few words, whispering to each other, and Marton told me to go to bed, that they would follow me as soon as I was asleep. Nanette made me the same promise, I turned my back to them, undressed myself quickly, and wishing them good night, I went to bed. I immediately pretended to fall asleep, but soon I dozed in good earnest, and only woke when they came to bed. Then, turning round as if I wished to resume my slumbers, I remained very quiet until I could suppose them fast asleep; at all events, if they did not sleep, they were at liberty to pretend to do so. Their backs were towards me, and the light was out; therefore I could only act at random, and I paid my first compliments to the one who was lying on my right, not knowing whether she was Nanette or Marton. I find her bent in two, and wrapped up in the only garment she had kept on. Taking my time, and sparing her modesty, I compel her by degrees to acknowledge her defeat, and convince her that it is better to feign sleep and to let me proceed. Her natural instincts soon working in concert with mine, I reach the goal; and my efforts, crowned with the most complete success, leave me not the shadow of a doubt that I have gathered those first-fruits to which our prejudice makes us attach so great an importance. Enraptured at having enjoyed my manhood completely and for the first time, I quietly leave my beauty in order to do homage to the other sister. I find her motionless, lying on her back like a person wrapped in profound and undisturbed slumber. Carefully managing my advance, as if I were afraid of waking her up, I begin by gently gratifying her senses, and I ascertain the delightful fact that, like her sister, she is still in possession of her maidenhood. As soon as a natural movement proves to me that love accepts the offering, I take my measures to consummate the sacrifice. At that moment, giving way suddenly to the violence of her feelings, and tired of her assumed dissimulation, she warmly locks me in her arms at the very instant of the voluptuous crisis, smothers me with kisses, shares my raptures, and love blends our souls in the most ecstatic enjoyment.

Guessing her to be Nanette, I whisper her name.

"Yes, I am Nanette," she answers; "and I declare

myself happy, as well as my sister, if you prove yourself true and faithful."

"Until death, my beloved ones, and as everything we
have done is the work of love, do not let us ever mention the name of Angela."

After this, I begged that she would give us a light;
but Marton, always kind and obliging, got out of bed
leaving us alone. When I saw Nanette in my arms,
beaming with love, and Marton near the bed, holding a
candle, with her eyes reproaching us with ingratitude
because we did not speak to her, who, by accepting my
first caresses, had encouraged her sister to follow her
example, I realized all my happiness.

"Let us get up, my darlings," said I, "and swear to
each other eternal affection."

When we had risen we performed, all three together,
ablutions which made them laugh a good deal, and
which gave a new impetus to the ardour of our feelings.
Sitting up in the simple costume of nature, we ate the
remains of our supper, exchanging those thousand trifling
words which love alone can understand, and we again
retired to our bed, where we spent a most delightful
night giving each other mutual and oft-repeated proofs
of our passionate ardour. Nanette was the recipient
of my last bounties, for Madame Orio having left the
house to go to church, I had to hasten my departure,
after assuring the two lovely sisters that they had effectually extinguished whatever flame might still have flick-
ered in my heart for Angela. I went home and slept
soundly until dinner-time.

M. de Malipiero passed a remark upon my cheerful
looks and the dark circles around my eyes, but I kept
my own counsel, and I allowed him to think whatever
he pleased. On the following day I paid a visit to Ma-

dame Orio, and Angela not being of the party, I remained to supper and retired with M. Rosa. During the
evening Nanette contrived to give me a letter and a small
parcel. The parcel contained a small lump of wax with
the stamp of a key, and the letter told me to have a key
made, and to use it to enter the house whenever I wished
to spend the night with them. She informed me at the
same time that Angela had slept with them the night
following our adventures, and that, thanks to their
mutual and usual practices, she had guessed the real
state of things, that they had not denied it, adding that
it was all her fault, and that Angela, after abusing them
most vehemently, had sworn never again to darken their
doors; but they did not care a jot.

A few days afterwards our good fortune delivered us
from Angela; she was taken to Vicenza by her father,
who had removed there for a couple of years, having
been engaged to paint frescoes in some houses in that
city. Thanks to her absence, I found myself undisturbed
possessor of the two charming sisters, with whom I spent
at least two nights every week, finding no difficulty in
entering the house with the key which I had speedily
procured.

Carnival was nearly over, when M. Manzoni informed
me one day that the celebrated Juliette wished to see
me, and regretted much that I had ceased to visit her.
I felt curious as to what she had to say to me, and accompanied him to her house. She received me very
politely, and remarking that she had heard of a large
hall I had in my house, she said she would like to give
a ball there, if I would give her the use of it. I readily
consented, and she handed me twenty-four sequins for
the supper and for the band, undertaking to send people
to place chandeliers in the hall and in my other rooms.

M. de Sanvitali had left Venice, and the Parmesan
government had placed his estates in chancery in consequence of his extravagant expenditure. I met him at
Versailles ten years afterwards. He wore the insignia
of the king's order of knighthood, and was grand equerry
to the eldest daughter of Louis XV., Duchess of Parma,
who, like all the French princesses, could not be reconciled to the climate of Italy.

The ball took place, and went off splendidly. All
the guests belonged to Juliette's set, with the exception
of Madame Orio, her nieces, and the procurator Rosa,
who sat together in the room adjoining the hall, and
whom I had been permitted to introduce as persons of
no consequence whatever.

While the after-supper minuets were being danced
Juliette took me apart, and said, "Take me to your bedroom; I have just got an amusing idea."

My room was on the third story; I shewed her the
way. The moment we entered she bolted the door, much
to my surprise. "I wish you," she said, "to dress me
up in your ecclesiastical clothes, and I will disguise you
as a woman with my own things. We will go down and
dance together. Come, let us first dress our hair."

Feeling sure of something pleasant to come, and delighted with such an unusual adventure, I lose no time
in arranging her hair, and I let her afterwards dress
mine. She applies rouge and a few beauty spots to my
face; I humour her in everything, and to prove her
satisfaction, she gives me with the best of grace a very
loving kiss, on condition that I do not ask for anything
else.

"As you please, beautiful Juliette, but I give you due
notice that I adore you!"

I place upon my bed a shirt, an abbé's neckband, a

pair of drawers, black silk stockings—in fact, a complete
fit-out. Coming near the bed, Juliette drops her skirt,
and cleverly gets into the drawers, which were not a bad
fit, but when she comes to the breeches there is some
difficulty; the waistband is too narrow, and the only
remedy is to rip it behind or to cut it, if necessary. I
undertake to make everything right, and, as I sit on the
foot of my bed, she places herself in front of me, with
her back towards me. I begin my work, but she thinks
that I want to see too much, that I am not skilful
enough, and that my fingers wander in unnecessary
places; she gets fidgety, leaves me, tears the breeches,
and manages in her own way. Then I help her to put
her shoes on, and I pass the shirt over her head, but as
I am disposing the ruffle and the neck-band, she com-
plains of my hands being too curious; and in truth, her
bosom was rather scanty. She calls me a knave and
rascal, but I take no notice of her. I was not going to
be duped, and I thought that a woman who had been
paid one hundred thousand ducats was well worth some
study. At last, her toilet being completed, my turn
comes. In spite of her objections I quickly get rid of
my breeches, and she must put on me the chemise, then
a skirt, in a word she has to dress me up. But all at
once, playing the coquette, she gets angry because I
do not conceal from her looks the very apparent proof
that her charms have some effect on a particular part
of my being, and she refuses to grant me the favour
which would soon afford both relief and calm. I try
to kiss her, and she repulses me, whereupon I lose patience, and in spite of herself she has to witness the last
stage of my excitement. At the sight of this, she pours
out every insulting word she can think of; I endeavour
to prove that she is to blame, but it is all in vain,

However, she is compelled to complete my disguise.

There is no doubt that an honest woman would not have exposed herself to such an adventure, unless she had intended to prove her tender feelings, and that she would not have drawn back at the very moment she saw them shared by her companion; but women like Juliette are often guided by a spirit of contradiction which causes them to act against their own interests. Besides, she felt disappointed when she found out that I was not timid, and my want of restraint appeared to her a want of respect. She would not have objected to my stealing a few light favours which she would have allowed me to take, as being of no importance, but, by doing that, I should have flattered her vanity too highly.

Our disguise being complete, we went together to the dancing-hall, where the enthusiastic applause of the guests soon restored our good temper. Everybody gave me credit for a piece of fortune which I had not enjoyed, but I was not ill-pleased with the rumour, and went on dancing with the false abbé, who was only too charming. Juliette treated me so well during the night that I construed her manners towards me into some sort of repentance, and I almost regretted what had taken place between us; it was a momentary weakness for which I was sorely punished.

At the end of the quadrille all the men thought they had a right to take liberties with the abbé, and I became myself rather free with the young girls, who would have been afraid of exposing themselves to ridicule had they offered any opposition to my caresses.

M. Querini was foolish enough to enquire from me whether I had kept on my breeches, and as I answered that I had been compelled to lend them to Juliette, he looked very unhappy, sat down in a corner of the room, and refused to dance.

Every one of the guests soon remarked that I had on a woman's chemise, and nobody entertained a doubt of the sacrifice having been consummated, with the exception of Nanette and Marton, who could not imagine the possibility of my being unfaithful to them. Juliette perceived that she had been guilty of great imprudence, but it was too late to remedy the evil.

When we returned to my chamber upstairs, thinking that she had repented of her previous behaviour, and feeling some desire to possess her, I thought I would kiss her, and I took hold of her hand, saying I was disposed to give her every satisfaction, but she quickly slapped my face in so violent a manner that, in my indignation, I was very near returning the compliment. I undressed myself rapidly without looking at her, she did the same, and we came downstairs; but, in spite of the cold water I had applied to my cheek, everyone could easily see the stamp of the large hand which had come in contact with my face.

Before leaving the house, Juliette took me apart, and told me, in the most decided and impressive manner, that if I had any fancy for being thrown out of the window, I could enjoy that pleasure whenever I liked to enter her dwelling, and that she would have me murdered if this night's adventure ever became publicly known. I took care not to give her any cause for the execution of either of her threats, but I could not prevent the fact of our having exchanged shirts being rather notorious. As I was not seen at her house, it was generally supposed that she had been compelled by M. Querini to keep me at a distance. The reader will see how, six years later, this extraordinary woman thought proper to feign entire forgetfulness of this adventure.

I passed Lent, partly in the company of my loved ones, partly in the study of experimental physics at the Convent of the Salutation. My evenings were always given to M. de Malipiero's assemblies. At Easter, in order to keep the promise I had made to the Countess of Mont-Réal, and longing to see again my beautiful Lucie, I went to Paséan. I found the guests entirely different to the set I had met the previous autumn. Count Daniel, the eldest of the family, had married a Countess Gozzi, and a young and wealthy government official, who had married a god-daughter of the old countess, was there with his wife and his sister-in-law. I thought the supper very long. The same room had been given to me, and I was burning to see Lucie, whom I did not intend to treat any more like a child. I did not see her before going to bed, but I expected her early the next morning, when lo! instead of her pretty face brightening my eyes, I see standing before me a fat, ugly servant-girl! I enquire after the gate-keeper's family, but her answer is given in the peculiar dialect of the place, and is, of course, unintelligible to me.

I wonder what has become of Lucie; I fancy that our intimacy has been found out, I fancy that she is ill— dead, perhaps. I dress myself with the intention of looking for her. If she has been forbidden to see me, I think to myself, I will be even with them all, for somehow or other I will contrive the means of speaking to her, and out of spite I will do with her that which honour prevented love from accomplishing. As I was revolving such thoughts, the gate-keeper comes in with a sorrowful countenance. I enquire after his wife's health, and after his daughter, but at the name of Lucie his eyes are filled with tears.

"What! is she dead?"

"Would to God she were!"

"What has she done?"

"She has run away with Count Daniel's courier, and we have been unable to trace her anywhere."

His wife comes in at the moment he replies, and at these words, which renewed her grief, the poor woman faints away. The keeper, seeing how sincerely I felt for his misery, tells me that this great misfortune befell them only a week before my arrival.

"I know that man l'Aigle," I say; "he is a scoundrel. Did he ask to marry Lucie?"

"No; he knew well enough that our consent would have been refused."

"I wonder at Lucie acting in such a way."

"He seduced her, and her running away made us suspect the truth, for she had become very stout."

"Had he known her long?"

"About a month after your last visit she saw him for the first time. He must have thrown a spell over her, for our Lucie was as pure as a dove, and you can, I believe, bear testimony to her goodness."

"And no one knows where they are?"

"No one. God alone knows what this villain will do with her."

I grieved as much as the unfortunate parents; I went out and took a long ramble in the woods to give way to my sad feelings. During two hours I cogitated over considerations, some true, some false, which were all prefaced by an *if*. If I had paid this visit, as I might have done, a week sooner, loving Lucie would have confided in me, and I would have prevented that self-mur-

der. If I had acted with her as with Nanette and
Marton, she would not have been left by me in that state
of ardent excitement which must have proved the principal cause of her fault, and she would not have fallen a
prey to that scoundrel. If she had not known me before
meeting the courier, her innocent soul would never have
listened to such a man. I was in despair, for in my conscience I acknowledged myself the primary agent of
this infamous seduction; I had prepared the way for
the villain.

E'l fior che sol potea pormi fra dei,
Quel fior che intatto io me venia serbando
Per non turbar, ohimè, l'animo casto,
Ohimè! il bel fior colui m'ha colto, e gusto!

Had I known where to find Lucie, I would certainly
have gone forth on the instant to seek for her, but no
trace whatever of her whereabouts had been discovered.

Before I had been made acquainted with Lucie's misfortune I felt great pride at having had sufficient power
over myself to respect her innocence; but after hearing
what had happened I was ashamed of my own reserve,
and I promised myself that for the future I would on
that score act more wisely. I felt truly miserable when
my imagination painted the probability of the unfortunate girl being left to poverty and shame, cursing the
remembrance of me, and hating me as the first cause of
her misery. This fatal event caused me to adopt a new
system, which in after years I carried sometimes rather
too far.

I joined the cheerful guests of the countess in the gardens, and received such a welcome that I was soon again
in my usual spirits, and at dinner I delighted everyone.

My sorrow was so great that it was necessary either to drive it away at once or to leave Paséan. But a new life crept into my being as I examined the face and the disposition of the newly-married lady. Her sister was prettier, but I was beginning to feel afraid of a novice; I thought the work too great.

This newly-married lady, who was between nineteen and twenty years of age, drew upon herself everybody's attention by her overstrained and unnatural manners. A great talker, with a memory crammed with maxims and precepts often without sense, but of which she loved to make a show, very devout, and so jealous of her husband that she did not conceal her vexation when he expressed his satisfaction at being seated at table opposite her sister, she laid herself open to much ridicule. Her husband was a giddy young fellow, who perhaps felt very deep affection for his wife, but who imagined that, through good breeding, he ought to appear very indifferent, and whose vanity found pleasure in giving her constant causes for jealousy. She, in her turn, had a great dread of passing for an idiot if she did not shew her appreciation of, and her resentment for, his conduct. She felt uneasy in the midst of good company, precisely because she wished to appear thoroughly at home. If I prattled away with some of my trifling nonsense, she would stare at me, and in her anxiety not to be thought stupid, she would laugh out of season. Her oddity, her awkwardness, and her self-conceit gave me the desire to know her better, and I began to dance attendance upon her.

My attentions, important and unimportant, my constant care, ever my fopperies, let everybody know that I meditated conquest. The husband was duly warned, but, with a great show of intrepidity, he answered with a joke every time he was told that I was a formidable rival. On my side I assumed a modest, and even sometimes a careless appearance, when, to shew his freedom from jealousy, he excited me to make love to his wife, who, on her part, understood but little how to perform the part of fancy free.

I had been paying my address to her for five or six days with great constancy, when, taking a walk with her in the garden, she imprudently confided to me the reason of her anxiety respecting her husband, and how wrong he was to give her any cause for jealousy. I told her, speaking as an old friend, that the best way to punish him would be to take no apparent notice of her husband's preference for her sister, and to feign to be herself in love with me. In order to entice her more easily to follow my advice, I added that I was well aware of my plan being a very difficult one to carry out, and that to play successfully such a character a woman must be particularly witty. I had touched her weak point, and she exclaimed that she would play the part to perfection; but in spite of her self-confidence she acquitted herself so badly that everybody understood that the plan was of my own scheming.

If I happened to be alone with her in the dark paths of the garden, and tried to make her play her part in real earnest, she would take the dangerous step of running away, and rejoining the other guests; the result being that, on my reappearance, I was called a bad sportsman who frightened the bird away. I would not fail at the first opportunity to reproach her for her flight, and to represent the triumph she had thus prepared for her spouse. I praised her mind, but lamented over the shortcomings of her education; I said that the tone, the manners I adopted towards her, were those of good society, and proved the great esteem I entertained for her intelligence, but in the middle of all my fine speeches, towards the eleventh or twelfth day of my courtship, she suddenly put me out of all conceit by telling me that, being a priest, I ought to know that every amorous connection was a deadly sin, that God could see every action of His creatures, and that she would neither damn her soul nor place herself under the necessity of saying to her confessor that she had so far forgotten herself as to commit such a sin with a priest. I objected that I was not yet a priest, but she foiled me by enquiring point-blank whether or not the act I had in view was to be numbered amongst the cardinal sins, for, not feeling the courage to deny it, I felt that I must give up the argument and put an end to the adventure.

A little consideration having considerably calmed my feelings, everybody remarked my new countenance during dinner; and the old count, who was very fond of a joke, expressed loudly his opinion that such quiet demeanour on my part announced the complete success of my campaign. Considering such a remark to be favourable to me, I took care to shew my cruel devotee that such was the way the world would judge, but all this was lost labour. Luck, however, stood me in good stead, and my efforts were crowned with success in the following manner.

On Ascension Day, we all went to pay a visit to Madame Bergali, a celebrated Italian poetess. On my return to Paséan the same evening, my pretty mistress wished to get into a carriage for four persons in which her husband and sister were already seated, while I was alone in a two-wheeled chaise. I exclaimed at this, saying that such a mark of distrust was indeed too pointed, and everybody remonstrated with her, saying that she ought not to insult me so cruelly. She was compelled to come with me, and having told the postillion that I wanted to go by the nearest road, he left the other carriages, and took the way through the forest of Cequini. The sky was clear and cloudless when we left, but in less than half-an-hour we were visited by one of those storms so frequent in the south, which appear likely to overthrow heaven and earth, and which end rapidly, leaving behind them a bright sky and a cool atmosphere, so that they do more good than harm.

"Oh, heavens!" exclaimed my companion, "we shall have a storm."

"Yes," I say, "and although the chaise is covered, the rain will spoil your pretty dress. I am very sorry."

"I do not mind the dress; but the thunder frightens me so!"

"Close your ears."

"And the lightning?"

"Postillion, let us go somewhere for shelter."

"There is not a house, sir, for a league, and before we come to it, the storm will have passed off."

He quietly keeps on his way, and the lightning flashes, the thunder sends forth its mighty voice, and the lady shudders with fright. The rain comes down in torrents, I take off my cloak to shelter us in front, at the same moment we are blinded by a flash of lightning, and the electric fluid strikes the earth within one hundred yards of us. The horses plunge and prance with fear, and my companion falls in spasmodic convulsions. She throws herself upon me, and folds me in her arms. The cloak had gone down, I stoop to place it around us, and improving my opportunity I take up her clothes. She tries to pull them down, but another clap of thunder deprives her of every particle of strength. Covering her with the cloak, I draw her towards me, and the motion of the chaise coming to my assistance, she falls over me in the most favourable position. I lose no time, and under pretence of arranging my watch in my fob, I prepare myself for the assault. On her side, conscious that, unless she stops me at once, all is lost, she makes a great effort; but I hold her tightly, saying that if she does not feign a fainting fit, the post-boy will turn round and see everything; I let her enjoy the pleasure of calling me an infidel, a monster, anything she likes, but my victory is the most complete that ever a champion achieved.

The rain, however, was falling, the wind, which was very high, blew in our faces, and, compelled to stay where she was, she said I would ruin her reputation, as the postillion could see everything.

"I keep my eye upon him," I answered, "he is not thinking of us, and even if he should turn his head, the cloak shelters us from him. Be quiet, and pretend to have fainted, for I will not let you go."

She seems resigned, and asks how I can thus set the storm at defiance.

"The storm, dear one, is my best friend to-day."

She almost seems to believe me, her fear vanishes, and feeling my rapture, she enquires whether I have done. I smile and answer in the negative, stating that I cannot let her go till the storm is over. "Consent to everything, or I let the cloak drop," I say to her.

"Well, you dreadful man, are you satisfied, now that you have insured my misery for the remainder of my life?"

"No, not yet."

"What more do you want?"

"A shower of kisses."

"How unhappy I am! Well! here they are."

"Tell me you forgive me, and confess that you have shared all my pleasure."

"You know I did. Yes, I forgive you."

Then I give her her liberty, and treating her to some very pleasant caresses, I ask her to have the same kindness for me, and she goes to work with a smile on her pretty lips.

"Tell me you love me," I say to her.

"No, I do not, for you are an atheist, and hell awaits you."

The weather was fine again, and the elements calm; I kissed her hands and told her that the postillion had certainly not seen anything, and that I was sure I had cured her of her dread of thunder, but that she was not likely to reveal the secret of my remedy. She answered that one thing at least was certain, namely that no other woman had ever been cured by the same prescription.

"Why," I said, "the same remedy has very likely been applied a million of times within the last thousand years. To tell you the truth, I had somewhat depended upon it, when we entered the chaise together, for I did not know any other way of obtaining the happiness of possessing you. But console yourself with the belief that, placed in the same position, no frightened woman could have resisted."

"I believe you; but for the future I will travel only with my husband."

"You would be wrong, for your husband would not have been clever enough to cure your fright in the way I have done."

"True, again. One learns some curious things in your company; but we shall not travel *tête-à-tête* again."

We reached Paséan an hour before our friends. We

get out of the chaise, and my fair mistress ran off to her chamber, while I was looking for a crown for the postillion. I saw that he was grinning.

"What are you laughing at?"

"Oh! you know."

"Here, take this ducat and keep a quiet tongue in your head."

CHAPTER VI

My Grandmother's Death and Its Consequences—I Lose M. de Malipiero's Friendship—I Have No Longer a Home—La Tintoretta—I Am Sent to a Clerical Seminary—I Am Expelled From It, and Confined in a Fortress

DURING supper the conversation turned altogether upon the storm, and the official, who knew the weakness of his wife, told me that he was quite certain I would never travel with her again. "Nor I with him," his wife remarked, "for, in his fearful impiety, he exorcised the lightning with jokes."

Henceforth she avoided me so skilfully that I never could contrive another interview with her.

When I returned to Venice I found my grandmother ill, and I had to change all my habits, for I loved her too dearly not to surround her with every care and attention; I never left her until she had breathed her last. She was unable to leave me anything, for during her life she had given me all she could, and her death compelled me to adopt an entirely different mode of life.

A month after her death, I received a letter from my mother informing me that, as there was no probability of her return to Venice, she had determined to give up the house, the rent of which she was still paying, that she had communicated her intention to the Abbé Grimani, and that I was to be guided entirely by his advice.

He was instructed to sell the furniture, and to place me, as well as my brothers and my sister, in a good boarding-house. I called upon Grimani to assure him of my perfect disposition to obey his commands.

The rent of the house had been paid until the end of the year; but, as I was aware that the furniture would be sold on the expiration of the term, I placed my wants under no restraint. I had already sold some linen, most of the china, and several tapestries; I now began to dispose of the mirrors, beds, etc. I had no doubt that my conduct would be severely blamed, but I knew likewise that it was my father's inheritance, to which my mother had no claim whatever, and, as to my brothers, there was plenty of time before any explanation could take place between us.

Four months afterwards I had a second letter from my mother, dated from Warsaw, and enclosing another. Here is the translation of my mother's letter:

"My dear son, I have made here the acquaintance of a learned Minim friar, a Calabrian by birth, whose great qualities have made me think of you every time he has honoured me with a visit. A year ago I told him that I had a son who was preparing himself for the Church, but that I had not the means of keeping him during his studies, and he promised that my son would become his own child, if I could obtain for him from the queen a bishopric in his native country, and he added that it would be very easy to succeed if I could induce the sovereign to recommend him to her daughter, the queen of Naples.

"Full of trust in the Almighty, I threw myself at the feet of her majesty, who granted me her gracious protection. She wrote to her daughter, and the worthy friar has been appointed by the Pope to the bishopric of Mon-

terano. Faithful to his promise, the good bishop will
take you with him about the middle of next year, as he
passes through Venice to reach Calabria. He informs
you himself of his intentions in the enclosed letter.
Answer him immediately, my dear son, and forward your
letter to me; I will deliver it to the bishop. He will pave
your way to the highest dignities of the Church, and you
may imagine my consolation if, in some twenty or thirty
years, I had the happiness of seeing you a bishop, at
least! Until his arrival, M. Grimani will take care of
you. I give you my blessing, and I am, my dear child,
etc., etc."

The bishop's letter was written in Latin, and was only
a repetition of my mother's. It was full of unction, and
informed me that he would tarry but three days in
Venice.

I answered according to my mother's wishes, but those
two letters had turned my brain. I looked upon my fortune as made. I longed to enter the road which was to
lead me to it, and I congratulated myself that I could
leave my country without any regret. Farewell, Venice!
I exclaimed; the days for vanity are gone by, and in the
future I will only think of a great, of a substantial
career! M. Grimani congratulated me warmly on my
good luck, and promised all his friendly care to secure a
good boarding-house, to which I would go at the beginning of the year, and where I would wait for the bishop's
arrival.

M. de Malipiero, who in his own way had great wisdom, and who saw that in Venice I was plunging headlong into pleasures and dissipation, and was only
wasting a precious time, was delighted to see me on the
eve of going somewhere else to fulfil my destiny, and
much pleased with my ready acceptance of those new cir-

cumstances in my life. He read me a lesson which I have never forgotten. "The famous precept of the Stoic philosophers," he said to me, *"Sequere Deum,* can be perfectly explained by these words: ' Give yourself up to whatever fate offers to you, provided you do not feel an invincible repugnance to accept it.' " He added that it was the genius of Socrates, *sæpe revocans, raro impellens;* and that it was the origin of the *fata viam inveniunt* of the same philosophers.

M. de Malipiero's science was embodied in that very lesson, for he had obtained his knowledge by the study of only one book—the book of man. However, as if it were to give me the proof that perfection does not exist, and that there is a bad side as well as a good one to everything, a certain adventure happened to me a month afterwards which, although I was following his own maxims, cost me the loss of his friendship, and which certainly did not teach me anything.

The senator fancied that he could trace upon the physiognomy of young people certain signs which marked them out as the special favourites of fortune. When he imagined that he had discovered those signs upon any individual, he would take him in hand and instruct him how to assist fortune by good and wise principles; and he used to say, with a great deal of truth, that a good remedy would turn into poison in the hands of a fool, but that poison is a good remedy when administered by a learned man. He had, in my time, three favourites in whose education he took great pains. They were, besides myself, Thérèse Imer, with whom the reader has a slight acquaintance already, and the third was the daughter of the boatman Gardela, a girl three years younger than I, who had the prettiest and most fascinating countenance. The speculative old man, in order to assist fortune in her particular case, made her learn dancing, for, he would say, the ball cannot reach the pocket unless someone pushes it. This girl made a great reputation at Stuttgard under the name of Augusta. She was the favourite mistress of the Duke of Wurtemburg in 1757. She was a most charming woman. The last time I saw her she was in Venice, and she died two years afterwards. Her husband, Michel de l'Agata, poisoned himself a short time after her death.

One day we had all three dined with him, and after dinner the senator left us, as was his wont, to enjoy his siesta; the little Gardela, having a dancing lesson to take, went away soon after him, and I found myself alone with Thérèse, whom I rather admired, although I had never made love to her. We were sitting down at a table very near each other, with our backs to the door of the room in which we thought our patron fast asleep, and somehow or other we took a fancy to examine into the difference of conformation between a girl and a boy; but at the most interesting part of our study a violent blow on my shoulders from a stick, followed by another, and which would have been itself followed by many more if I had not ran away, compelled us to abandon our interesting investigation unfinished. I got off without hat or cloak, and went home; but in less than a quarter of an hour the old housekeeper of the senator brought my clothes with a letter which contained a command never to present myself again at the mansion of his excellency. I immediately wrote him an answer in the following terms: "You have struck me while you were the slave of your anger; you cannot therefore boast of having given me a lesson, and I have not learned anything. To forgive you I must forget that you are a man of great wisdom, and I can never forget it."

This nobleman was perhaps quite right not to be pleased with the sight we gave him; yet, with all his prudence, he proved himself very unwise, for all the servants were acquainted with the cause of my exile, and, of course, the adventure was soon known through the city, and was received with great merriment. He dared not address any reproaches to Thérèse, as I heard from her soon after, but she could not venture to entreat him to pardon me.

The time to leave my father's house was drawing near, and one fine morning I received the visit of a man about forty years old, with a black wig, a scarlet cloak, and a very swarthy complexion, who handed me a letter from M. Grimani, ordering me to consign to the bearer all the furniture of the house according to the inventory, a copy of which was in my possession. Taking the inventory in my hand, I pointed out every article marked down, except when the said article, having through my instrumentality taken an airing out of the house, happened to be missing, and whenever any article was absent I said that I had not the slightest idea where it might be. But the uncouth fellow, taking a very high tone, said loudly that he must know what I had done with the furniture. His manner being very disagreeable to me, I answered that I had nothing to do with him, and as he still raised his voice I advised him to take himself off as quickly as possible, and I gave him that piece of advice in such a way as to prove to him that, at home, I knew I was the more powerful of the two.

Feeling it my duty to give information to M. Grimani of what had just taken place, I called upon him as soon as he was up, but I found that my man was already there, and that he had given his own account of the affair. The abbé, after a very severe lecture to which I had to listen in silence, ordered me to render an account of all the missing articles. I answered that I had found myself under the necessity of selling them to avoid running into debt. This confession threw him in a violent passion; he called me a rascal, said that those things did not belong to me, that he knew what he had to do, and he commanded me to leave his house on the very instant.

Mad with rage, I ran for a Jew, to whom I wanted to sell what remained of the furniture, but when I returned to my house I found a bailiff waiting at the door, and he handed me a summons. I looked over it and perceived that it was issued at the instance of Antonio Razetta. It was the name of the fellow with the swarthy countenance. The seals were already affixed on all the doors, and I was not even allowed to go to my room, for a keeper had been left there by the bailiff. I lost no time, and called upon M. Rosa, to whom I related all the circumstances. After reading the summons he said,——

"The seals shall be removed to-morrow morning, and in the meantime I shall summon Razetta before the *avogador*. But to-night, my dear friend," he added, "you must beg the hospitality of some one of your acquaintances. It has been a violent proceeding, but you shall be paid handsomely for it; the man is evidently acting under M. Grimani's orders."

"Well, that is their business."

I spent the night with Nanette and Marton, and on the following morning, the seals having been taken off, I took possession of my dwelling. Razetta did not appear before the *avogador*, and M. Rosa summoned him in my name before the criminal court, and obtained against him a writ of *capias* in case he should not obey the second summons. On the third day M. Grimani wrote to me, commanding me to call upon him. I went immediately. As soon as I was in his presence he enquired abruptly what my intentions were.

"I intend to shield myself from your violent proceedings under the protection of the law, and to defend myself against a man with whom I ought never to have had any connection, and who has compelled me to pass the night in a disreputable place."

"In a disreputable place?"

"Of course. Why was I, against all right and justice, prevented from entering my own dwelling?"

"You have possession of it now. But you must go to your lawyer and tell him to suspend all proceedings against Razetta, who has done nothing but under my instructions. I suspected that your intention was to sell the rest of the furniture; I have prevented it. There is a room at your disposal at St. Chrysostom's, in a house of mine, the first floor of which is occupied by La Tintoretta, our first opera dancer. Send all your things there, and come and dine with me every day. Your sister and your brothers have been provided with a comfortable home; therefore, everything is now arranged for the best."

I called at once upon M. Rosa, to whom I explained all that had taken place, and his advice being to give way to M. Grimani's wishes, I determined to follow it. Besides, the arrangement offered the best satisfaction I could obtain, as to be a guest at his dinner table was an honour for me. I was likewise full of curiosity respecting my new lodging under the same roof with La Tintoretta, who was much talked of, owing to a certain Prince of Waldeck who was extravagantly generous with her.

The bishop was expected in the course of the summer;

I had, therefore, only six months more to wait in Venice before taking the road which would lead me, perhaps, to the throne of Saint Peter: everything in the future assumed in my eyes the brightest hue, and my imagination revelled amongst the most radiant beams of sunshine; my castles in the air were indeed most beautiful.

I dined the same day with M. Grimani, and I found myself seated next to Razetta—an unpleasant neighbour, but I took no notice of him. When the meal was over, I paid a last visit to my beautiful house in Saint-Samuel's parish, and sent all I possessed in a gondola to my new lodging.

I did not know Signora Tintoretta, but I was well acquainted with her reputation, character and manners. She was but a poor dancer, neither handsome nor plain, but a woman of wit and intellect. Prince Waldeck spent a great deal for her, and yet he did not prevent her from retaining the titulary protection of a noble Venetian of the Lin family, now extinct, a man about sixty years of age, who was her visitor at every hour of the day. This nobleman, who knew me, came to my room towards the evening, with the compliments of the lady, who, he added, was delighted to have me in her house, and would be pleased to receive me in her intimate circle.

To excuse myself for not having been the first to pay my respects to the signora, I told M. Lin that I did not know she was my neighbour, that M. Grimani had not mentioned the circumstance, otherwise I would have paid my duties to her before taking possession of my lodging. After this apology I followed the ambassador, he presented me to his mistress, and the acquaintance was made.

She received me like a princess, took off her glove

before giving me her hand to kiss, mentioned my name before five or six strangers who were present, and whose names she gave me, and invited me to take a seat near her. As she was a native of Venice, I thought it was absurd for her to speak French to me, and I told her that I was not acquainted with that language, and would feel grateful if she would converse in Italian. She was surprised at my not speaking French, and said I would cut but a poor figure in her drawing-room, as they seldom spoke any other language there, because she received a great many foreigners. I promised to learn French. Prince Waldeck came in during the evening; I was introduced to him, and he gave me a very friendly welcome. He could speak Italian very well, and during the carnival he shewed me great kindness. He presented me with a gold snuff-box as a reward for a very poor sonnet which I had written for his dear Grizellini. This was her family name; she was called Tintoretta because her father had been a dyer.

The Tintoretta had greater claims than Juliette to the admiration of sensible men. She loved poetry, and if it had not been that I was expecting the bishop, I would have fallen in love with her. She was herself smitten with a young physician of great merit, named Righelini, who died in the prime of life, and whom I still regret. I shall have to mention him in another part of my Memoirs.

Towards the end of the carnival, my mother wrote to M. Grimani that it would be a great shame if the bishop found me under the roof of an opera dancer, and he made up his mind to lodge me in a respectable and decent place. He took the Abbé Tosello into consultation, and the two gentlemen thought that the best thing they could do for me would be to send me to a clerical seminary. They arranged everything unknown to me, and the abbé undertook to inform me of their plan and to obtain from me a gracious consent. But when I heard him speak with beautiful flowers of rhetoric for the purpose of gilding the bitter pill, I could not help bursting into a joyous laughter, and I astounded his reverence when I expressed my readiness to go anywhere he might think right to send me.

The plan of the two worthy gentlemen was absurd, for at the age of seventeen, and with a nature like mine, the idea of placing me in a seminary ought never to have been entertained, but ever a faithful disciple of Socrates, feeling no unconquerable reluctance, and the plan, on the contrary, appearing to me rather a good joke, I not only gave a ready consent, but I even longed to enter the seminary. I told M. Grimani I was prepared to accept anything, provided Razetta had nothing to do with it. He gave me his promise, but he did not keep it when I left the seminary. I have never been able to decide whether this Grimani was kind because he was a fool, or whether his stupidity was the result of his kindness, but all his brothers were the same. The worst trick that Dame Fortune can play upon an intelligent young man is to place him under the dependence of a fool. A few days afterwards, having been dressed as a pupil of a clerical seminary by the care of the abbé, I was taken to Saint-Cyprian de Muran and introduced to the rector.

The patriarchal church of Saint-Cyprian is served by an order of the monks, founded by the blessed Jérôme Miani, a nobleman of Venice. The rector received me with tender affection and great kindness. But in his address (which was full of unction) I thought I could perceive a suspicion on his part that my being sent to the seminary was a punishment, or at least a way to put a stop to an irregular life, and, feeling hurt in my dignity, I told him at once, "Reverend father, I do not think that any one has the right of punishing me."

"No, no, my son," he answered, "I only meant that you would be very happy with us."

We were then shewn three halls, in which we found at least one hundred and fifty seminarists, ten or twelve schoolrooms, the refectory, the dormitory, the gardens for play hours, and every pain was taken to make me imagine life in such a place the happiest that could fall to the lot of a young man, and to make me suppose that I would even regret the arrival of the bishop. Yet they all tried to cheer me up by saying that I would only remain there five or six months. Their eloquence amused me greatly.

I entered the seminary at the beginning of March, and prepared myself for my new life by passing the night between my two young friends, Nanette and Marton, who bathed their pillows with tears; they could not understand, and this was likewise the feeling of their aunt and of the good M. Rosa, how a young man like myself could shew such obedience.

The day before going to the seminary, I had taken care to entrust all my papers to Madame Manzoni. They made a large parcel, and I left it in her hands for fifteen years. The worthy old lady is still alive, and with her ninety years she enjoys good health and a cheerful temper. She received me with a smile, and told me that I would not remain one month in the seminary.

"I beg your pardon, madam, but I am very glad to go there, and intend to remain until the arrival of the bishop."

"You do not know your own nature, and you do not know your bishop, with whom you will not remain very long either."

The abbé accompanied me to the seminary in a gondola, but at Saint-Michel he had to stop in consequence of a violent attack of vomiting which seized me suddenly; the apothecary cured me with some mint-water.

I was indebted for this attack to the too frequent sacrifices which I had been offering on the altar of love. Any lover who knows what his feelings were when he found himself with the woman he adored and with the fear that it was for the last time, will easily imagine my feelings during the last hours that I expected ever to spend with my two charming mistresses. I could not be induced to let the last offering be the last, and I went on offering until there was no more incense left.

The priest committed me to the care of the rector, and my luggage was carried to the dormitory, where I went myself to deposit my cloak and my hat. I was not placed amongst the adults, because, notwithstanding my size, I was not old enough. Besides, I would not shave myself, through vanity, because I thought that the down on my face left no doubt of my youth. It was ridiculous, of course; but when does man cease to be so? We get rid of our vices more easily than of our follies. Tyranny has not had sufficient power over me to compel me to shave myself; it is only in that respect that I have found tyranny to be tolerant.

"To which school do you wish to belong?" asked the rector.

"To the dogmatic, reverend father; I wish to study the history of the Church."

"I will introduce you to the father examiner."

"I am doctor in divinity, most reverend father, and do not want to be examined."

"It is necessary, my dear son; come with me."

This necessity appeared to me an insult, and I felt very angry; but a spirit of revenge quickly whispered to me the best way to mystify them, and the idea made me very joyful. I answered so badly all the questions propounded in Latin by the examiner, I made so many solecisms, that he felt it his duty to send me to an inferior class of grammar, in which, to my great delight, I found myself the companion of some twenty young urchins of about ten years, who, hearing that I was doctor in divinity, kept on saying: *Accipiamus pecuniam, et mittamus asinum in patriam suam.*

Our play hours afforded me great amusement; my companions of the dormitory, who were all in the class of philosophy at least, looked down upon me with great contempt, and when they spoke of their own sublime discourses, they laughed if I appeared to be listening attentively to their discussions which, as they thought, must have been perfect enigmas to me. I did not intend to betray myself, but an accident, which I could not avoid, forced me to throw off the mask.

Father Barbarigo, belonging to the Convent of the Salutation at Venice, whose pupil I had been in physics, came to pay a visit to the rector, and seeing me as we were coming from mass paid me his friendly compliments. His first question was to enquire what science I was studying, and he thought I was joking when I answered that I was learning the grammar. The rector having joined us, I left them together, and went to my class. An our later, the rector sent for me.

"Why did you feign such ignorance at the examination?" he asked.

"Why," I answered, "were you unjust enough to compel me to the degradation of an examination?"

He looked annoyed, and escorted me to the dogmatic school, where my comrades of the dormitory received me with great astonishment, and in the afternoon, at play time, they gathered around me and made me very happy with their professions of friendship.

One of them, about fifteen years old, and who at the present time must, if still alive, be a bishop, attracted my notice by his features as much as by his talents. He inspired me with a very warm friendship, and during recess, instead of playing skittles with the others, we always walked together. We conversed upon poetry, and we both delighted in the beautiful odes of Horace. We liked Ariosto better than Tasso, and Petrarch had our whole admiration, while Tassoni and Muratori, who had been his critics, were the special objects of our contempt. We were such fast friends, after four days of acquaintance, that we were actually jealous of each other, and to such an extent that if either of us walked about with any seminarist, the other would be angry and sulk like a disappointed lover.

The dormitory was placed under the supervision of a lay friar, and it was his province to keep us in good order. After supper, accompanied by this lay friar, who had the title of prefect, we all proceeded to the dormitory. There, everyone had to go to his own bed, and to undress quietly after having said his prayers in a low voice. When all the pupils were in bed, the prefect would go to his own. A large lantern lighted up the dormitory, which had the shape of a parallelogram eighty yards by ten. The beds were placed at equal distances, and to each bed there were a fald-stool, a chair, and room for the trunk of the Seminarist. At one end was the washing place, and at the other the bed of the prefect. The bed of my friend was opposite mine, and the lantern was between us.

The principal duty of the prefect was to take care that no pupil should go and sleep with one of his comrades, for such a visit was never supposed an innocent one. It was a cardinal sin, and, bed being accounted the place for sleep and not for conversation, it was admitted that a pupil who slept out of his own bed, did so only for immoral purposes. So long as he stopped in his own bed, he could do what he liked; so much the worse for him if he gave himself up to bad practices. It has been remarked in Germany that it is precisely in those institutions for young men in which the directors have taken most pains to prevent onanism that this vice is most prevalent.

Those who had framed the regulations in our seminary were stupid fools, who had not the slightest knowledge of either morals or human nature. Nature has wants which must be administered to, and Tissot is right only as far as the abuse of nature is concerned, but this abuse would very seldom occur if the directors exercised proper wisdom and prudence, and if they did not make a point of forbidding it in a special and peculiar manner; young people give way to dangerous excesses from a sheer delight in disobedience—a disposition very natural to humankind, since it began with Adam and Eve.

I had been in the seminary for nine or ten days, when one night I felt someone stealing very quietly in my bed; my hand was at once clutched, and my name whispered. I could hardly restrain my laughter. It was my friend, who, having chanced to wake up and finding that the lantern was out, had taken a sudden fancy to pay me a visit. I very soon begged him to go away for fear the prefect should be awake, for in such a case we should have found ourselves in a very unpleasant dilemma, and most likely would have been accused of some abominable offence. As I was giving him that good advice we heard someone moving, and my friend made his escape; but immediately after he had left me I heard the fall of some person, and at the same time the hoarse voice of the prefect exclaiming:

"Ah, villain! wait until to-morrow—until to-morrow!"

After which threat he lighted the lantern and retired to his couch.

The next morning, before the ringing of the bell for rising, the rector, followed by the prefect, entered the dormitory, and said to us:

"Listen to me, all of you. You are aware of what has taken place this last night. Two amongst you must be guilty; but I wish to forgive them, and to save their honour I promise that their names shall not be made public. I expect every one of you to come to me for confession before recess."

He left the dormitory, and we dressed ourselves. In the afternoon, in obedience to his orders, we all went to him and confessed, after which ceremony we repaired to the garden, where my friend told me that, having unfortunately met the prefect after he left me, he had thought that the best way was to knock him down, in order to get time to reach his own bed without being known.

"And now," I said, "you are certain of being forgiven, for, of course, you have wisely confessed your error?"

"You are joking," answered my friend; "why, the good rector would not have known any more than he knows at present, even if my visit to you had been paid with a criminal intent."

"Then you must have made a false confession: you are at all events guilty of disobedience?"

"That may be, but the rector is responsible for the guilt, as he used compulsion."

"My dear friend, you argue in a very forcible way, and the very reverend rector must by this time be satisfied that the inmates of our dormitory are more learned than he is himself."

No more would have been said about the adventure if, a few nights after, I had not in my turn taken a fancy to return the visit paid by my friend. Towards midnight, having had occasion to get out of bed, and hearing the loud snoring of the prefect, I quickly put out the lantern and went to lie beside my friend. He knew me at once, and gladly received me; but we both listened attentively to the snoring of our keeper, and when it ceased, understanding our danger, I got up and reached my own bed without losing a second, but the moment I got to it I had a double surprise. In the first place I felt somebody lying in my bed, and in the second I saw the prefect, with a candle in his hand, coming along slowly and taking a survey of all the beds right and left. I could understand the prefect suddenly lighting a candle, but how could I realize what I saw—namely, one of my comrades sleeping soundly in my bed, with his back turned to me? I immediately made up my mind to feign sleep. After two or three shakings given by the prefect, I pretended to wake up, and my bed-companion woke up in earnest. Astonished at finding himself in my bed, he offered me an apology:

"I have made a mistake," he said, "as I returned from a certain place in the dark, I found your bed empty, and mistook it for mine."

"Very likely," I answered; "I had to get up, too."

"Yes," remarked the prefect; "but how does it happen that you went to bed without making any remark when, on your return, you found your bed already tenanted? And how is it that, being in the dark, you did not suppose that you were mistaken yourself?"

"I could not be mistaken, for I felt the pedestal of this crucifix of mine, and I knew I was right; as to my companion here, I did not feel him."

"It is all very unlikely," answered our Argus; and he went to the lantern, the wick of which he found crushed down.

"The wick has been forced into the oil, gentlemen; it has not gone out of itself; it has been the handiwork of one of you, but it will be seen to in the morning."

My stupid companion went to his own bed, the prefect lighted the lamp and retired to his rest, and after this scene, which had broken the repose of every pupil, I quietly slept until the appearance of the rector, who, at the dawn of day, came in great fury, escorted by his satellite, the prefect.

The rector, after examining the localities and submitting to a lengthy interrogatory first my accomplice, who very naturally was considered as the most guilty, and then myself, whom nothing could convict of the offence, ordered us to get up and go to church to attend mass. As soon as we were dressed, he came back, and addressing us both, he said, kindly:

"You stand both convicted of a scandalous connivance, and it is proved by the fact of the lantern having been wilfully extinguished. I am disposed to believe that the cause of all this disorder is, if not entirely innocent, at least due only to extreme thoughtlessness; but the scandal given to all your comrades, the outrage offered to the discipline and to the established rules of the seminary, call loudly for punishment. Leave the room."

We obeyed; but hardly were we between the double doors of the dormitory than we were seized by four servants, who tied our hands behind us, and led us to the class room, where they compelled us to kneel down before the great crucifix. The rector told them to execute his orders, and, as we were in that position, the wretches administered to each of us seven or eight blows with a stick, or with a rope, which I received, as well as my companion, without a murmur. But the moment my hands were free, I asked the rector whether I could write two lines at the very foot of the cross. He gave orders to bring ink and paper, and I traced the following words:

"I solemnly swear by this God that I have never spoken to the seminarist who was found in my bed. As an innocent person I must protest against this shameful violence. I shall appeal to the justice of his lordship the patriarch."

My comrade in misery signed this protest with me; after which, addressing myself to all the pupils, I read it aloud, calling upon them to speak the truth if any one could say the contrary of what I had written. They, with one voice, immediately declared that we had never been seen conversing together, and that no one knew who had put the lamp out. The rector left the room in the midst of hisses and curses, but he sent us to prison all the same at the top of the house and in separate cells. An hour afterwards, I had my bed, my trunk and all my things, and my meals were brought to me every day. On the fourth day, the Abbé Tosello came for me with instructions to bring me to Venice. I asked him whether he had sifted this unpleasant affair; he told me that he had enquired into it, that he had seen the other semi-

narist, and that he believed we were both innocent; but
the rector would not confess himself in the wrong, and
he did not see what could be done.

I threw off my seminarist's habit, and dressed myself
in the clothes I used to wear in Venice, and, while my
luggage was carried to a boat, I accompanied the abbé
to M. Grimani's gondola in which he had come, and we
took our departure. On our way, the abbé ordered the
boatman to leave my things at the Palace Grimani, adding that he was instructed by M. Grimani to tell me
that, if I had the audacity to present myself at his mansion, his servants had received orders to turn me away.

He landed me near the convent of the Jesuits, without
any money, and with nothing but what I had on my
back.

I went to beg a dinner from Madame Manzoni, who
laughed heartily at the realization of her prediction.
After dinner I called upon M. Rosa to see whether the
law could protect me against the tyranny of my enemies,
and after he had been made acquainted with the circumstances of the case, he promised to bring me the same
evening, at Madame Orio's house, an extra-judicial act.
I repaired to the place of appointment to wait for him,
and to enjoy the pleasure of my two charming friends
at my sudden reappearance. It was indeed very great,
and the recital of my adventures did not astonish them
less than my unexpected presence. M. Rosa came and
made me read the act which he had prepared; he had
not had time to have it engrossed by the notary, but he
undertook to have it ready the next day.

I left Madame Orio to take supper with my brother
François, who resided with a painter called Guardi; he
was, like me, much oppressed by the tyranny of Grimani, and I promised to deliver him. Towards midnight

I returned to the two amiable sisters who were expecting me with their usual loving impatience, but, I am bound to confess it with all humility, my sorrows were prejudicial to love in spite of the fortnight of absence and of abstinence. They were themselves deeply affected to see me so unhappy, and pitied me with all their hearts. I endeavoured to console them, and assured them that all my misery would soon come to an end, and that we would make up for lost time.

In the morning, having no money, and not knowing where to go, I went to St. Mark's Library, where I remained until noon. I left it with the intention of dining with Madame Manzoni, but I was suddenly accosted by a soldier who informed me that someone wanted to speak to me in a gondola to which he pointed. I answered that the person might as well come out, but he quietly remarked that he had a friend at hand to conduct me forcibly to the gondola, if necessary, and without any more hesitation I went towards it. I had a great dislike to noise or to anything like a public exhibition. I might have resisted, for the soldiers were unarmed, and I would not have been taken up, this sort of arrest not being legal in Venice, but I did not think of it. The *sequere deum* was playing its part; I felt no reluctance. Besides, there are moments in which a courageous man has no courage, or disdains to shew it.

I enter the gondola, the curtain is drawn aside, and I see . . . my evil genius, Razetta, with an officer. The two soldiers sit down at the prow; I recognize M. Grimani's own gondola, it leaves the landing and takes the direction of the Lido. No one spoke to me, and I remained silent. After half-an-hour's sailing, the gondola stopped before the small entrance of the Fortress St.-André, at the mouth of the Adriatic, on the very spot where the Bucentaur stands, when, on Ascension Day, the doge comes to espouse the sea.

The sentinel calls the corporal; we alight, the officer who accompanied me introduces me to the major, and presents a letter to him. The major, after reading its contents, gives orders to M. Zen, his adjutant, to consign me to the guard-house. In another quarter of an hour my conductors take their departure, and M. Zen brings me three livres and a half, stating that I would receive the same amount every week. It was exactly the pay of a private.

I did not give way to any burst of passion, but I felt the most intense indignation. Late in the evening I expressed a wish to have some food bought, for I could not starve; then, stretching myself upon a hard camp bed, I passed the night amongst the soldiers without closing my eyes, for these Sclavonians were singing, eating garlic, smoking a bad tobacco which was most noxious, and drinking a wine of their own country, as black as ink, which nobody else could swallow.

Early next morning Major Pelodoro (the governor of the fortress) called me up to his room, and told me that, in compelling me to spend the night in the guard-house, he had only obeyed the orders he had received from Venice from the secretary of war. "Now, reverend sir," he added, "my further orders are only to keep you a prisoner in the fort, and I am responsible for your remaining here. I give you the whole of the fortress for your prison. You shall have a good room in which you will find your bed and all your luggage. Walk anywhere you please; but recollect that, if you should escape, you would cause my ruin. I am sorry that my instructions are to give you only ten sous a day, but if you have any friends in Venice able to send you some money, write to them, and trust to me for the security of your letters. Now you may go to bed, if you need rest."

I was taken to my room; it was large and on the first story, with two windows from which I had a very fine view. I found my bed, and I ascertained with great satisfaction that my trunk, of which I had the keys, had not been forced open. The major had kindly supplied my table with all the implements necessary for writing. A Sclavonian soldier informed me very politely that he would attend upon me, and that I would pay him for his services whenever I could, for everyone knew that I had only ten sous a day. I began by ordering some soup, and, when I had dispatched it, I went to bed and slept for nine hours. When I woke, I received an invitation to supper from the major, and I began to imagine that things, after all, would not be so very bad.

I went to the honest governor, whom I found in numerous company. He presented me to his wife and to every person present. I met there several officers, the chaplain of the fortress, a certain Paoli Vida, one of the singers of St.-Mark's Church, and his wife, a pretty woman, sister-in-law of the major, whom the husband chose to confine in the fort because he was very jealous (jealous men are not comfortable at Venice), together with several other ladies, not very young, but whom I thought very agreeable, owing to their kind welcome.

Cheerful as I was by nature, those pleasant guests easily managed to put me in the best of humours. Everyone expressed a wish to know the reasons which could have induced M. Grimani to send me to the fortress, so I gave a faithful account of all my adventures since my grandmother's death. I spoke for three hours without any bitterness, and even in a pleasant tone, upon things which, said in a different manner, might have displeased my audience; all expressed their satisfaction, and shewed so much sympathy that, as we parted for the night, I received from all an assurance of friendship and the offer of their services. This is a piece of good fortune which has never failed me whenever I have been the victim of oppression, until I reached the age of fifty. Whenever I met with honest persons expressing a curiosity to know the history of the misfortune under which I was labouring, and whenever I satisfied their curiosity, I have inspired them with friendship, and with that sympathy which was necessary to render them favourable and useful to me.

That success was owing to a very simple artifice; it was only to tell my story in a quiet and truthful manner, without even avoiding the facts which told against me. It is simple secret that many men do not know, because the larger portion of humankind is composed of cowards; a man who always tells the truth must be possessed of great moral courage. Experience has taught me that truth is a talisman, the charm of which never fails in its effect, provided it is not wasted upon unworthy people, and I believe that a guilty man, who candidly speaks the truth to his judge, has a better chance of being acquitted, than the innocent man who hesitates and evades true statements. Of course the speaker must be young, or at least in the prime of manhood; for an old man finds the whole of nature combined against him.

The major had his joke respecting the visit paid and returned to the seminarist's bed, but the chaplain and the ladies scolded him. The major advised me to write out my story and send it to the secretary of war, undertaking that he should receive it, and he assured me that he would become my protector. All the ladies tried to induce me to follow the major's advice.

CHAPTER VII

My Short Stay in Fort St.-André—My First Repentance in Love Affairs—I Enjoy the Sweets of Revenge, and Prove a Clever Alibi—Arrest of Count Bonafède—My Release—Arrival of the Bishop—Farewell to Venice

THE fort, in which the Republic usually kept only a garrison of one hundred half-pay Sclavonians, happened to contain at that time two thousand Albanian soldiers, who were called *Cimariotes.*

The secretary of war, who was generally known under the title of *sage à l'écriture,* had summoned these men from the East in consequence of some impending promotion, as he wanted the officers to be on the spot in order to prove their merits before being rewarded. They all came from the part of Epirus called Albania, which belongs to the Republic of Venice, and they had distinguished themselves in the last war against the Turks. It was for me a new and extraordinary sight to examine some eighteen or twenty officers, all of an advanced age, yet strong and healthy, shewing the scars which covered their face and their chest, the last naked and entirely exposed through military pride. The lieutenant-colonel was particularly conspicuous by his wounds, for, without exaggeration, he had lost one-fourth of his head. He had but one eye, but one ear, and no jaw to speak of. Yet he could eat very well, speak without difficulty, and was very cheerful. He had with him all his family, composed of two pretty daughters, who looked all the prettier in their national costume, and of seven sons, every one of them a soldier. This lieutenant-colonel stood six feet high, and his figure was magnificent, but his scars so completely deformed his features that his face was truly horrid to look at. Yet I found so much attraction in him that I liked him the moment I saw him, and I would have been much pleased to converse with him if his breath had not sent forth such a strong smell of garlic. All the Albanians had their pockets full of it, and they enjoyed a piece of garlic with as much relish as we do a sugar-plum. After this none can maintain it to be a poison, though the only medicinal virtue it possesses is to excite the appetite, because it acts like a tonic upon a weak stomach.

The lieutenant-colonel could not read, but he was not ashamed of his ignorance, because not one amongst his men, except the priest and the surgeon, could boast greater learning. Every man, officer or private, had his purse full of gold; half of them, at least, were married, and we had in the fortress a colony of five or six hundred women, with God knows how many children! I felt greatly interested in them all. Happy idleness! I often regret thee because thou hast often offered me new sights, and for the same reason I hate old age which never offers but what I know already, unless I should take up a gazette, but I cared nothing for them in my young days.

Alone in my room I made an inventory of my trunk, and having put aside everything of an ecclesiastical character, I sent for a Jew, and sold the whole parcel unmercifully. Then I wrote to M. Rosa, enclosing all the tickets of the articles I had pledged, requesting him to have them sold without any exception, and to forward me the surplus raised by the sale. Thanks to that double operation, I was enabled to give my Sclavonian servant the ten sous allowed to me every day. Another soldier, who had been a hair-dresser, took care of my hair which I had been compelled to neglect, in consequence of the rules of the seminary. I spent my time in walking about the fort and through the barracks, and my two places of resort were the major's apartment for some intellectual enjoyment, and the rooms of the Albanian lieutenant-colonel for a sprinkling of love. The Albanian feeling certain that his colonel would be appointed brigadier, solicited the command of the regiment, but he had a rival and he feared his success. I wrote him a petition, short, but so well composed that the secretary of war, having enquired the name of the author, gave the Albanian his colonelcy. On his return to the fort, the brave fellow, overjoyed at his success, hugged me in his arms, saying that he owed it all to me; he invited me to a family dinner, in which my very soul was parched by his garlic, and he presented me with twelve botargoes and two pounds of excellent Turkish tobacco.

The result of my petition made all the other officers think that they could not succeed without the assistance of my pen, and I willingly gave it to everybody; this entailed many quarrels upon me, for I served all interests, but, finding myself the lucky possessor of some forty sequins, I was no longer in dread of poverty, and laughed at everything. However, I met with an accident which made me pass six weeks in a very unpleasant condition.

On the 2nd of April, the fatal anniversary of my first appearance in this world, as I was getting up in the morning, I received in my room the visit of a very handsome Greek woman, who told me that her husband, then

ensign in the regiment, had every right to claim the rank
of lieutenant, and that he would certainly be appointed,
if it were not for the opposition of his captain who was
against him, because she had refused him certain favours
which she could bestow only upon her husband. She
handed me some certificates, and begged me to write a
petition which she would present herself to the secretary
of war, adding that she could only offer me her heart in
payment. I answered that her heart ought not to go
alone; I acted as I had spoken, and I met with no other
resistance than the objection which a pretty woman is
always sure to feign for the sake of appearance. After
that, I told her to come back at noon, and that the
petition would be ready. She was exact to the appointment, and very kindly rewarded me a second time; and
in the evening, under pretence of some alterations to be
made in the petition, she afforded an excellent opportunity of reaping a third recompense.

But, alas! the path of pleasure is not strewn only
with roses! On the third day, I found out, much to my
dismay, that a serpent had been hid under the flowers.
Six weeks of care and of rigid diet re-established my
health.

When I met the handsome Greek again, I was foolish
enough to reproach her for the present she had bestowed
upon me, but she baffled me by laughing, and saying that
she had only offered me what she possessed, and that it
was my own fault if I had not been sufficiently careful.
The reader cannot imagine how much this first misfortune grieved me, and what deep shame I felt. I looked
upon myself as a dishonoured man, and while I am on
that subject I may as well relate an incident which will
give some idea of my thoughtlessness.

Madame Vida, the major's sister-in-law, being alone

with me one morning, confided in me in a moment of un-
reserved confidence what she had to suffer from the jealous disposition of her husband, and his cruelty in having
allowed her to sleep alone for the last four years, when
she was in the very flower of her age.

"I trust to God," she added, "that my husband will
not find out that you have spent an hour alone with me,
for I should never hear the end of it."

Feeling deeply for her grief, and confidence begetting
confidence, I was stupid enough to tell her the sad state
to which I had been reduced by the cruel Greek woman,
assuring her that I felt my misery all the more deeply,
because I should have been delighted to console her,
and to give her the opportunity of a revenge for her
jealous husband's coldness. At this speech, in which my
simplicity and good faith could easily be traced, she
rose from her chair, and upbraided me with every insult
which an outraged honest woman might hurl at the head
of a bold libertine who has presumed too far. Astounded, but understanding perfectly well the nature of
my crime, I bowed myself out of her room; but as I
was leaving it she told me in the same angry tone that
my visits would not be welcome for the future, as I was
a conceited puppy, unworthy of the society of good and
respectable women. I took care to answer that a respectable woman would have been rather more reserved
than she had been in her confidences. On reflection I
felt pretty sure that, if I had been in good health, or
had said nothing about my mishap, she would have been
but too happy to receive my consolations.

A few days after that incident I had a much greater
cause to regret my acquaintance with the Greek woman.
On Ascension Day, as the ceremony of the Bucentaur
was celebrated near the fort, M. Rosa brought Madame

Orio and her two nieces to witness it, and I had the
pleasure of treating them all to a good dinner in my
room. I found myself, during the day, alone with my
young friends in one of the casemetes, and they both
loaded me with the most loving caresses and kisses. I
felt that they expected some substantial proof of my
love; but, to conceal the real state of things, I pretended
to be afraid of being surprised, and they had to be satisfied with my shallow excuse.

I had informed my mother by letter of all I had suffered from Grimani's treatment; she answered that she
had written to him on the subject, that she had no doubt
he would immediately set me at liberty, and that an
arrangement had been entered into by which M. Grimani
would devote the money raised by Razetta from the sale
of the furniture to the settlement of a small patrimony
on my youngest brother. But in this matter Grimani
did not act honestly, for the patrimony was only settled
thirteen years afterwards, and even then only in a fictitious manner. I shall have an opportunity later on of
mentioning this unfortunate brother, who died very
poor in Rome twenty years ago.

Towards the middle of June the Cimariotes were sent
back to the East, and after their departure the garrison
of the fort was reduced to its usual number. I began to
feel weary in this comparative solitude, and I gave way
to terrible fits of passion.

The heat was intense, and so disagreeable to me that
I wrote to M. Grimani, asking for two summer suits of
clothes, and telling him where they would be found, if
Razetta had not sold them. A week afterwards I was
in the major's apartment when I saw the wretch Razetta
come in, accompanied by a man whom he introduced as
Petrillo, the celebrated favourite of the Empress of

Russia, just arrived from St. Petersburg. He ought to have said *infamous* instead of celebrated, and *clown* instead of favourite.

The major invited them to take a seat, and Razetta, receiving a parcel from Grimani's gondolier, handed it to me, saying,——

"I have brought you your rags; take them."

I answered:

"Some day I will bring you a *rigano.*"

At these words the scoundrel dared to raise his cane, but the indignant major compelled him to lower his tone by asking him whether he had any wish to pass the night in the guard-house. Petrillo, who had not yet opened his lips, told me then that he was sorry not to have found me in Venice, as I might have shewn him round certain places which must be well known to me.

"Very likely we should have met your wife in such places," I answered.

"I am a good judge of faces," he said, "and I can see that you are a true gallows-bird."

I was trembling with rage, and the major, who shared my utter disgust, told them that he had business to transact, and they took their leave. The major assured me that on the following day he would go to the war office to complain of Razetta, and that he would have him punished for his insolence.

I remained alone, a prey to feelings of the deepest indignation, and to a most ardent thirst for revenge.

The fortress was entirely surrounded by water, and my windows were not overlooked by any of the sentinels. A boat coming under my windows could therefore easily take me to Venice during the night and bring me back to the fortress before day-break. All that was necessary was to find a boatman who, for a certain amount, would risk the galleys in case of discovery. Amongst several who brought provisions to the fort, I chose a boatman whose countenance pleased me, and I offered him one sequin; he promised to let me know his decision on the following day. He was true to his time, and declared himself ready to take me. He informed me that, before deciding to serve me, he had wished to know whether I was kept in the fort for any great crime, but as the wife of the major had told him that my imprisonment had been caused by very trifling frolics, I could rely upon him. We arranged that he should be under my window at the beginning of the night, and that his boat should be provided with a mast long enough to enable me to slide along it from the window to the boat.

The appointed hour came, and everything being ready I got safely into the boat, landed at the Sclavonian quay, ordered the boatman to wait for me, and wrapped up in a mariner's cloak I took my way straight to the gate of Saint-Sauveur, and engaged the waiter of a coffee-room to take me to Razetta's house.

Being quite certain that he would not be at home at that time, I rang the bell, and I heard my sister's voice telling me that if I wanted to see him I must call in the morning. Satisfied with this, I went to the foot of the bridge and sat down, waiting there to see which way he would come, and a few minutes before midnight I saw him advancing from the square of Saint-Paul. It was all I wanted to know; I went back to my boat and returned to the fort without any difficulty. At five o'clock in the morning everyone in the garrison could see me enjoying my walk on the platform.

Taking all the time necessary to mature my plans, I made the following arrangements to secure my revenge with perfect safety, and to prove an *alibi* in case I should kill my rascally enemy, as it was my intention to do. The day preceding the night fixed for my expedition, I walked about with the son of the Adjutant Zen, who was only twelve years old, but who amused me much by his shrewdness. The reader will meet him again in the year 1771. As I was walking with him, I jumped down from one of the bastions, and feigned to sprain my ankle. Two soldiers carried me to my room, and the surgeon of the fort, thinking that I was suffering from a luxation, ordered me to keep to bed, and wrapped up the ankle in towels saturated with camphorated spirits of wine. Everybody came to see me, and I requested the soldier who served me to remain and to sleep in my room. I knew that a glass of brandy was enough to stupefy the man, and to make him sleep soundly. As soon as I saw him fast asleep, I begged the surgeon and the chaplain, who had his room over mine, to leave me, and at half-past ten I lowered myself in the boat.

As soon as I reached Venice, I bought a stout cudgel, and I sat myself down on a door-step, at the corner of the street near Saint-Paul's Square. A narrow canal at the end of the street, was, I thought, the very place to throw my enemy in. That canal has now disappeared.

At a quarter before twelve I see Razetta walking along leisurely. I come out of the street with rapid strides, keeping near the wall to compel him to make room for me, and I strike a first blow on the head, and a second on his arm; the third blow sends him tumbling in the canal, howling and screaming my name. At the same instant a Forlan, or citizen of Forli, comes out of a house on my left side with a lantern in his hand. A blow from my cudgel knocks the lantern out of his grasp, and the man, frightened out of his wits, takes to his heels. I throw away my stick, I run at full speed through the

square and over the bridge, and while people are hasten-
ing towards the spot where the disturbance had taken
place, I jump into the boat, and, thanks to a strong
breeze swelling our sail, I get back to the fortress.
Twelve o'clock was striking as I re-entered my room
through the window. I quickly undress myself, and the
moment I am in my bed I wake up the soldier by my
loud screams, telling him to go for the surgeon, as I am
dying of the colic.

The chaplain, roused by my screaming, comes down
and finds me in convulsions. In the hope that some
diascordium would relieve me, the good old man runs to
his room and brings it, but while he has gone for some
water I hide the medicine. After half an hour of wry
faces, I say that I feel much better, and thanking all my
friends, I beg them to retire, which everyone does, wishing me a quiet sleep.

The next morning I could not get up in consequence
of my sprained ankle, although I had slept very well; the
major was kind enough to call upon me before going to
Venice, and he said that very likely my colic had been
caused by the melon I had eaten for my dinner the day
before.

The major returned at one o'clock in the afternoon.
"I have good news to give you," he said to me, with a
joyful laugh. "Razetta was soundly cudgelled last night
and thrown into a canal."

"Has he been killed?"

"No; but I am glad of it for your sake, for his death
would make your position much more serious. You are
accused of having done it."

"I am very glad people think me guilty; it is something of a revenge, but it will be rather difficult to bring
it home to me."

"Very difficult! All the same, Razetta swears he recognized you, and the same declaration is made by the Forlan who says that you struck his hand to make him drop his lantern. Razetta's nose is broken, three of his teeth are gone, and his right arm is severely hurt. You have been accused before the *avogador,* and M. Grimani has written to the war office to complain of your release from the fortress without his knowledge. I arrived at the office just in time. The secretary was reading Grimani's letter, and I assured his excellency that it was a false report, for I left you in bed this morning, suffering from a sprained ankle. I told him likewise that at twelve o'clock last night you were very near death from a severe attack of colic."

"Was it at midnight that Razetta was so well treated?"

"So says the official report. The war secretary wrote at once to M. Grimani and informed him that you have not left the fort, and that you are even now detained in it, and that the plaintiff is at liberty, if he chooses, to send commissaries to ascertain the fact. Therefore, my dear abbé, you must prepare yourself for an interrogatory."

"I expect it, and I will answer that I am very sorry to be innocent."

Three days afterwards, a commissary came to the fort with a clerk of the court, and the proceedings were soon over. Everybody knew that I had sprained my ankle; the chaplain, the surgeon, my body-servant, and several others swore that at midnight I was in bed suffering from colic. My *alibi* being thoroughly proved, the *avogador* sentenced Razetta and the Forlan to pay all expenses without prejudice to my rights of action.

After this judgment, the major advised me to address

to the secretary of war a petition which he undertook to deliver himself, and to claim my release from the fort. I gave notice of my proceedings to M. Grimani, and a week afterwards the major told me that I was free, and that he would himself take me to the abbé. It was at dinner-time, and in the middle of some amusing conversation, that he imparted that piece of information. Not supposing him to be in earnest, and in order to keep up the joke, I told him very politely that I preferred his house to Venice, and that, to prove it, I would be happy to remain a week longer, if he would grant me permission to do so. I was taken at my word, and everybody seemed very pleased. But when, two hours later, the news was confirmed, and I could no longer doubt the truth of my release, I repented the week which I had so foolishly thrown away as a present to the major; yet I had not the courage to break my word, for everybody, and particularly his wife, had shown such unaffected pleasure, it would have been contemptible of me to change my mind. The good woman knew that I owed her every kindness which I had enjoyed, and she might have thought me ungrateful.

But I met in the fort with a last adventure, which I must not forget to relate.

On the following day, an officer dressed in the national uniform called upon the major, accompanied by an elderly man of about sixty years of age, wearing a sword, and, presenting to the major a dispatch with the seal of the war office, he waited for an answer, and went away as soon as he had received one from the governor.

After the officer had taken leave, the major, addressing himself to the elderly gentleman, to whom he gave the title of count, told him that his orders were to keep him a prisoner, and that he gave him the whole of the fort for his prison. The count offered him his sword, but the major nobly refused to take it, and escorted him to the room he was to occupy. Soon after, a servant in livery brought a bed and a trunk, and the next morning the same servant, knocking at my door, told me that his master begged the honour of my company to breakfast. I accepted the invitation, and he received me with these words:

"Dear sir, there has been so much talk in Venice about the skill with which you proved your incredible *alibi*, that I could not help asking for the honour of your acquaintance."

"But, count, the *alibi* being a true one, there can be no skill required to prove it. Allow me to say that those who doubt its truth are paying me a very poor compliment, for——"

"Never mind; do not let us talk any more of that, and forgive me. But as we happen to be companions in misfortune, I trust you will not refuse me your friendship. Now for breakfast."

After our meal, the count, who had heard from me some portion of my history, thought that my confidence called for a return on his part, and he began: "I am the Count de Bonafède. In my early days I served under Prince Eugène, but I gave up the army, and entered on a civil career in Austria. I had to fly from Austria and take refuge in Bavaria in consequence of an unfortunate duel. In Munich I made the acquaintance of a young lady belonging to a noble family; I eloped with her and brought her to Venice, where we were married. I have now been twenty years in Venice. I have six children, and everybody knows me. About a week ago I sent my servant to the postoffice for my letters, but they were refused him because he had not any money to pay the postage. I went myself, but the clerk would not deliver me my letters, although I assured him that I would pay for them the next time. This made me angry, and I called upon the Baron de Taxis, the post-master, and complained of the clerk, but he answered very rudely that the clerk had simply obeyed his orders, and that my letters would only be delivered on payment of the postage. I felt very indignant, but as I was in his house I controlled my anger, went home, and wrote a note to him asking him to give me satisfaction for his rudeness, telling him that I would never go out without my sword, and that I would force him to fight whenever and wherever I should meet him. I never came across him, but yesterday I was accosted by the secretary of the inquisitors, who told me that I must forget the baron's rude conduct, and go under the guidance of an officer whom he pointed out to me, to imprison myself for a week in this fortress. I shall thus have the pleasure of spending that time with you."

I told him that I had been free for the last twenty-four hours, but that to shew my gratitude for his friendly confidence I would feel honoured if he would allow me to keep him company. As I had already engaged myself with the major, this was only a polite falsehood.

In the afternoon I happened to be with him on the tower of the fort, and pointed out a gondola advancing towards the lower gate; he took his spy-glass and told me that it was his wife and daughter coming to see him. We went to meet the ladies, one of whom might once have been worth the trouble of an elopement; the other, a young person between fourteen and sixteen, struck me as a beauty of a new style. Her hair was of a beautiful light auburn, her eyes were blue and very fine, her nose a Roman, and her pretty mouth, half-open and laughing, exposed a set of teeth as white as her complexion, although a beautiful rosy tint somewhat veiled the whiteness of the last. Her figure was so slight that it seemed out of nature, but her perfectly-formed breast appeared an altar on which the god of love would have delighted to breathe the sweetest incense. This splendid chest was, however, not yet well furnished, but in my imagination I gave her all the *embonpoint* which might have been desired, and I was so pleased that I could not take my looks from her. I met her eyes, and her laughing countenance seemed to say to me: "Only wait for two years, at the utmost, and all that your imagination is now creating will then exist in reality."

She was elegantly dressed in the prevalent fashion, with large hoops, and like the daughters of the nobility who have not yet attained the age of puberty, although the young countess was marriageable. I had never dared to stare so openly at the bosom of a young lady of quality, but I thought there was no harm in fixing my eyes on a spot where there was nothing yet but in expectation.

The count, after having exchanged a few words in German with his wife, presented me in the most flattering manner, and I was received with great politeness. The major joined us, deeming it his duty to escort the countess all over the fortress, and I improved the excellent opportunity thrown in my way by the inferiority of my position; I offered my arm to the young lady, and the count left us to go to his room.

I was still an adept in the old Venetian fashion of attending upon ladies, and the young countess thought me rather awkward, though I believed myself very fashionable when I placed my hand under her arm, but she drew it back in high merriment. Her mother turned round to enquire what she was laughing at, and I was terribly confused when I heard her answer that I had tickled her.

"This is the way to offer your arm to a lady," she said, and she passed her hand through my arm, which I rounded in the most clumsy manner, feeling it a very difficult task to resume a dignified countenance. Thinking me a novice of the most innocent species, she very likely determined to make sport of me. She began by remarking that by rounding my arm as I had done I placed it too far from her waist, and that I was consequently out of drawing. I told her I did not know how to draw, and inquired whether it was one of her accomplishments.

"I am learning," she answered, "and when you call upon us I will shew you Adam and Eve, after the Chevalier Liberi; I have made a copy which has been found very fine by some professors, although they did not know it was my work."

"Why did you not tell them?"

"Because those two figures are too naked."

"I am not curious to see your Adam, but I will look at your Eve with pleasure, and keep your secret."

This answer made her laugh again, and again her mother turned round. I put on the look of a simpleton, for, seeing the advantage I could derive from her opinion of me, I had formed my plan at the very moment she tried to teach me how to offer my arm to a lady.

She was so convinced of my simplicity that she ventured to say that she considered her Adam by far more beautiful than her Eve, because in her drawing of the man she had omitted nothing, every muscle being visible, while there was none conspicuous in Eve. "It is," she added, "a figure with nothing in it."

"Yet it is the one which I shall like best."

"No; believe me, Adam will please you most."

This conversation had greatly excited me. I had on a pair of linen breeches, the weather being very warm. . . . I was afraid of the major and the countess, who were a few yards in front of us, turning round. . . . I was on thorns. To make matters worse, the young lady stumbled, one of her shoes slipped off, and presenting me her pretty foot she asked me to put the shoe right. I knelt on the ground, and, very likely without thinking, she lifted up her skirt . . . she had very wide hoops and no petticoat . . . what I saw was enough to strike me dead on the spot. . . . When I rose, she asked if anything was the matter with me.

A moment after, coming out of one of the casemates, her head-dress got slightly out of order, and she begged that I would remedy the accident, but, having to bend her head down, the state in which I was could no longer remain a secret for her. In order to avoid greater confusion to both of us, she enquired who had made my watch ribbon; I told her it was a present from my sister, and she desired to examine it, but when I answered her that it was fastened to the fob-pocket, and found that she disbelieved me, I added that she could see for herself. She put her hand to it, and a natural but involuntary excitement caused me to be very indiscreet. She must have felt vexed, for she saw that she had made a mistake in her estimate of my character; she became more timid, she would not laugh any more, and we joined her mother and the major who was shewing her, in a sentry-box, the body of Marshal de Schulenburg which had been deposited there until the mausoleum erected for him was completed. As for myself, I felt deeply ashamed. I thought myself the first man who had alarmed her innocence, and I felt ready to do anything to atone for the insult.

Such was my delicacy of feeling in those days. I used to credit people with exalted sentiments, which often existed only in my imagination. I must confess that time has entirely destroyed that delicacy; yet I do not believe myself worse than other men, my equals in age and in experience.

We returned to the count's apartment, and the day passed off rather gloomily. Towards evening the ladies went away, but the countess gave me a pressing invitation to call upon them in Venice.

The young lady, whom I thought I had insulted, had made such a deep impression upon me that the seven following days seemed very long; yet I was impatient to see her again only that I might entreat her forgiveness, and convince her of my repentance.

The following day the count was visited by his son; he was plain-featured, but a thorough gentleman, and modest withal. Twenty-five years afterwards I met him in Spain, a cadet in the king's body-guard. He had served as a private twenty years before obtaining this poor promotion. The reader will hear of him in good time; I will only mention here that when I met him in Spain, he stood me out that I had never known him; his self-love prompted this very contemptible lie.

Early on the eighth day the count left the fortress, and I took my departure the same evening, having made an appointment at a coffee-house in St.-Mark's Square with the major who was to accompany me to M. Grimani's house. I took leave of his wife, whose memory will always be dear to me, and she said, "I thank you for your skill in proving your *alibi,* but you have also to thank me for having understood you so well. My husband never heard anything about it until it was all over."

As soon as I reached Venice, I went to pay a visit to Madame Orio, where I was made welcome. I remained to supper, and my two charming sweethearts who were praying for the death of the bishop, gave me the most delightful hospitality for the night.

At noon the next day I met the major according to our appointment, and we called upon the Abbé Grimani. He received me with the air of a guilty man begging for mercy, and I was astounded at his stupidity when he entreated me to forgive Razetta and his companion. He told me that the bishop was expected very soon, and that he had ordered a room to be ready for me, and that I could take my meals with him. Then he introduced me to M. Valavero, a man of talent, who had just left the ministry of war, his term of office having lasted the usual six months. I paid my duty to him, and we kept up a kind of desultory conversation until the departure of the major. When he had left us M. Valavero entreated me to confess that I had been the guilty party in the attack upon Razetta. I candidly told him that the thrashing had been my handiwork, and I gave him all the particulars, which amused him immensely. He remarked that, as I had perpetrated the affair before midnight, the fools had made a mistake in their accusation; but that, after all, the mistake had not materially helped me in proving the *alibi,* because my sprained ankle, which everybody had supposed a real accident, would of itself have been sufficient.

But I trust that my kind reader has not forgotten that I had a very heavy weight upon my conscience, of

which I longed to get rid. I had to see the goddess of
my fancy, to obtain my pardon, or die at her feet.

I found the house without difficulty; the count was
not at home. The countess received me very kindly,
but her appearance caused me so great a surprise that I
did not know what to say to her. I had fancied that I
was going to visit an angel, that I would find her in a
lovely paradise, and I found myself in a large sitting-
room furnished with four rickety chairs and a dirty old
table. There was hardly any light in the room because
the shutters were nearly closed. It might have been a
precaution against the heat, but I judged that it was
more probably for the purpose of concealing the windows, the glass of which was all broken. But this visible
darkness did not prevent me from remarking that the
countess was wrapped up in an old tattered gown, and
that her chemise did not shine by its cleanliness. Seeing
that I was ill at ease, she left the room, saying that she
would send her daughter, who, a few minutes afterwards,
came in with an easy and noble appearance, and told me
that she had expected me with great impatience, but
that I had surprised her at a time at which she was not
in the habit of receiving any visits.

I did not know what to answer, for she did not
seem to me to be the same person. Her miserable dishabille made her look almost ugly, and I wondered at the
impression she had produced upon me at the fortress.
She saw my surprise, and partly guessed my thoughts,
for she put on a look, not of vexation, but of sorrow
which called forth all my pity. If she had been a philosopher she might have rightly despised me as a man
whose sympathy was enlisted only by her fine dress, her
nobility, or her apparent wealth; but she endeavoured
to bring me round by her sincerity. She felt that if she

could call a little sentiment into play, it would certainly plead in her favour.

"I see that you are astonished, reverend sir, and I know the reason of your surprise. You expected to see great splendour here, and you find only misery. The government allows my father but a small salary, and there are nine of us. As we must attend church on Sundays and holidays in a style proper to our condition, we are often compelled to go without our dinner, in order to get out of pledge the clothes which urgent need too often obliges us to part with, and which we pledge anew on the following day. If we did not attend mass, the curate would strike our names off the list of those who share the alms of the Confraternity of the Poor, and those alms alone keep us afloat."

What a sad tale! She had guessed rightly. I was touched, but rather with shame than true emotion. I was not rich myself, and, as I was no longer in love, I only heaved a deep sigh, and remained as cold as ice. Nevertheless, her position was painful, and I answered politely, speaking with kindness and assuring her of my sympathy. "Were I wealthy," I said, "I would soon shew you that your tale of woe has not fallen on unfeeling ears; but I am poor, and, being at the eve of my departure from Venice, even my friendship would be useless to you." Then, after some desultory talk, I expressed a hope that her beauty would yet win happiness for her. She seemed to consider for a few minutes, and said, "That may happen some day, provided that the man who feels the power of my charms understands that they can be bestowed only with my heart, and is willing to render me the justice I deserve; I am only looking for a lawful marriage, without dreaming of rank or fortune; I no longer believe in the first, and I know how to

live without the second; for I have been accustomed to
poverty, and even to abject need; but you cannot realize
that. Come and see my drawings."

"You are very good, mademoiselle."

Alas! I was not thinking of her drawings, and I could
no longer feel interested in her Eve, but I followed her.

We came to a chamber in which I saw a table, a
chair, a small toilet-glass and a bed with the straw pal-
liasse turned over, very likely for the purpose of allowing
the looker-on to suppose that there were sheets under-
neath, but I was particularly disgusted by a certain
smell, the cause of which was recent; I was thunderstruck, and if I had been still in love, this antidote
would have been sufficiently powerful to cure me instanter. I wished for nothing but to make my escape,
never to return, and I regretted that I could not throw
on the table a handful of ducats, which I should have
considered the price of my ransom.

The poor girl shewed me her drawings; they were fine,
and I praised them, without alluding particularly to Eve,
and without venturing a joke upon Adam. I asked her,
for the sake of saying something, why she did not try
to render her talent remunerative by learning pastel
drawing.

"I wish I could," she answered, "but the box of chalks
alone costs two sequins."

"Will you forgive me if I am bold enough to offer
you six?"

"Alas! I accept them gratefully, and to be indebted to
you for such a service makes me truly happy."

Unable to keep back her tears, she turned her head
round to conceal them from me, and I took that opportunity of laying the money on the table, and out of
politeness, wishing to spare her every unnecessary hu-

miliation, I saluted her lips with a kiss which she was at liberty to consider a loving one, as I wanted her to ascribe my reserve to the respect I felt for her. I then left her with a promise to call another day to see her father. I never kept my promise. The reader will see how I met her again after ten years.

How many thoughts crowded upon my mind as I left that house! What a lesson! I compared reality with the imagination, and I had to give the preference to the last, as reality is always dependent on it. I then began to forsee a truth which has been clearly proved to me in my after life, namely, that love is only a feeling of curiosity more or less intense, grafted upon the inclination placed in us by nature that the species may be preserved. And truly, woman is like a book, which, good or bad, must at first please us by the frontispiece. If this is not interesting, we do not feel any wish to read the book, and our wish is in direct proportion to the interest we feel. The frontispiece of woman runs from top to bottom like that of a book, and her feet, which are most important to every man who shares my taste, offer the same interest as the edition of the work. If it is true that most amateurs bestow little or no attention upon the feet of a woman, it is likewise a fact that most readers care little or nothing whether a book is of the first edition or the tenth. At all events, women are quite right to take the greatest care of their face, of their dress, of their general appearance; for it is only by that part of the frontispiece that they can call forth a wish to read them in those men who have not been endowed by nature with the privilege of blindness. And just in the same manner that men, who have read a great many books, are certain to feel at last a desire for perusing new works even if they are bad, a man who

has known many women, and all handsome women, feels
at last a curiosity for ugly specimens when he meets
with entirely new ones. It is all very well for his eye to
discover the paint which conceals the reality, but his
passion has become a vice, and suggests some argument
in favour of the lying frontispiece. It is possible, at
least he thinks so, that the work may prove better than
the title-page, and the reality more acceptable than the
paint which hides it. He then tries to peruse the book,
but the leaves have not been opened; he meets with some
resistance, the living book must be read according to
established rules, and the book-worm falls a victim to
coquetry, the monster which persecutes all those who
make a business of love.

As for thee, intelligent man, who hast read the few
preceding lines, let me tell thee that, if they do not assist
in opening thy eyes, thou art lost; I mean that thou art
certain of being a victim to the fair sex to the very last
moment of thy life. If my candour does not displease
thee, accept my congratulations.

In the evening I called upon Madame Orio, as I
wanted to inform her charming nieces that, being an
inmate of Grimani's house, I could not sleep out for the
first night. I found there the faithful Rosa, who told
me that the affair of the *alibi* was in every mouth, and
that, as such celebrity was evidently caused by a very
decided belief in the untruth of the *alibi* itself, I ought
to fear a retaliation of the same sort on the part of
Razetta, and to keep on my guard, particularly at night.
I felt all the importance of this advice, and I took care
never to go out in the evening otherwise than in a gondola, or accompanied by some friends. Madame Manzoni told me that I was acting wisely, because, although
the judges could not do otherwise than acquit me, every-

body knew the real truth of the matter, and Razetta could not fail to be my deadly foe.

Three or four days afterwards M. Grimani announced the arrival of the bishop, who had put up at the convent of his order, at Saint-François de Paul. He presented me himself to the prelate as a jewel highly prized by himself, and as if he had been the only person worthy of descanting upon its beauty.

I saw a fine monk wearing his pectoral cross. He would have reminded me of Father Mancia if he had not looked stouter and less reserved. He was about thirty-four, and had been made a bishop by the grace of God, the Holy See, and my mother. After pronouncing over me a blessing, which I received kneeling, and giving me his hand to kiss, he embraced me warmly, calling me his dear son in the Latin language, in which he continued to address me. I thought that, being a Calabrian, he might feel ashamed of his Italian, but he undeceived me by speaking in that language to M. Grimani. He told me that, as he could not take me with him from Venice, I should have to proceed to Rome, where Grimani would take care to send me, and that I would procure his address at Ancona from one of his friends, called Lazari, a Minim monk, who would likewise supply me with the means of continuing my journey.

"When we meet in Rome," he added, "we can go together to Martorano by way of Naples. Call upon me to-morrow morning, and have your breakfast with me. I intend to leave the day after."

As we were on our way back to his house, M. Grimani treated me to a long lecture on morals, which nearly caused me to burst into loud laughter. Amongst other things, he informed me that I ought not to study too hard, because the air in Calabria was very heavy, and

I might become consumptive from too close application
to my books.

The next morning at day-break I went to the bishop.
After saying his mass, we took some chocolate, and for
three hours he laid me under examination. I saw clearly
that he was not pleased with me, but I was well enough
pleased with him. He seemed to me a worthy man, and
as he was to lead me along the great highway of the
Church, I felt attracted towards him, for, at the time,
although I entertained a good opinion of my personal
appearance, I had no confidence whatever in my talents.

After the departure of the good bishop, M. Grimani
gave me a letter left by him, which I was to deliver to
Father Lazari, at the Convent of the Minims, in Ancona.
M. Grimani informed me that he would send me to that
city with the ambassador from Venice, who was on the
point of sailing. I had therefore to keep myself in readiness, and, as I was anxious to be out of his hands, I approved all his arrangements. As soon as I had notice
of the day on which the suite of the ambassador would
embark, I went to pay my last farewell to all my acquaintances. I left my brother François in the school
of M. Joli, a celebrated decorative painter. As the
peotta in which I was to sail would not leave before day-
break, I spent the short night in the arms of the two
sisters, who, this time, entertained no hope of ever seeing me again. On my side I could not forsee what would
happen, for I was abandoning myself to fate, and I
thought it would be useless to think of the future. The
night was therefore spent between joy and sadness, between pleasures and tears. As I bade them adieu, I
returned the key which had opened so often for me the
road to happiness.

This, my first love affair, did not give me any experience of the world, for our intercourse was always a happy one, and was never disturbed by any quarrel or stained by any interested motive. We often felt, all three of us, as if we must raise our souls towards the eternal Providence of God, to thank Him for having, by His particular protection, kept from us all the accidents which might have disturbed the sweet peace we were enjoying.

I left in the hands of Madame Manzoni all my papers, and all the forbidden books I possessed. The good woman, who was twenty years older than I, and who, believing in an immutable destiny, took pleasure in turning the leaves of the great book of fate, told me that she was certain of restoring to me all I left with her, before the end of the following year, at the latest. Her prediction caused me both surprise and pleasure, and feeling deep reverence for her, I thought myself bound to assist the realization of her foresight. After all, if she predicted the future, it was not through superstition, or in consequence of some vain foreboding which reason must condemn, but through her knowledge of the world, and of the nature of the person she was addressing. She used to laugh because she never made a mistake.

I embarked from St.-Mark's landing. M. Grimani had given me ten sequins, which he thought would keep me during my stay in the lazzaretto of Ancona for the necessary quarantine, after which it was not to be supposed that I could want any money. I shared Grimani's certainty on the subject, and with my natural thoughtlessness I cared nothing about it. Yet I must say that, unknown to everybody, I had in my purse forty bright sequins, which powerfully contributed to increase my cheerfulness, and I left Venice full of joy and without one regret.

CHAPTER VIII

My Misfortunes in Chiozza—Father Stephano—The Lazzaretto at Ancona—The Greek Slave—My Pilgrimage to Our Lady of Loretto—I Go to Rome on Foot, and From Rome to Naples to Meet the Bishop—I Cannot Join Him—Good Luck Offers Me the Means of Reaching Martorano, Which Place I Very Quickly Leave to Return to Naples

THE retinue of the ambassador, which was styled "grand," appeared to me very small. It was composed of a Milanese steward, named Carcinelli, of a priest who fulfilled the duties of secretary because he could not write, of an old woman acting as housekeeper, of a man cook with his ugly wife, and eight or ten servants.

We reached Chiozza about noon. Immediately after landing, I politely asked the steward where I should put up, and his answer was:

"Wherever you please, provided you let this man know where it is, so that he can give you notice when the peotta is ready to sail. My duty," he added, "is to leave you at the lazzaretto of Ancona free of expense from the moment we leave this place. Until then enjoy yourself as well as you can."

The man to whom I was to give my address was the captain of the peotta. I asked him to recommend me a lodging.

"You can come to my house," he said, "if you have no objection to share a large bed with the cook, whose wife remains on board."

Unable to devise any better plan, I accepted the offer, and a sailor, carrying my trunk, accompanied me to the dwelling of the honest captain. My trunk had to be placed under the bed which filled up the room. I was amused at this, for I was not in a position to be over-fastidious, and, after partaking of some dinner at the inn, I went about the town. Chiozza is a peninsula, a sea-port belonging to Venice, with a population of ten thousand inhabitants, seamen, fishermen, merchants, lawyers, and government clerks.

I entered a coffee-room, and I had scarcely taken a seat when a young doctor-at-law, with whom I had studied in Padua, came up to me, and introduced me to a druggist whose shop was near by, saying that his house was the rendezvous of all the literary men of the place. A few minutes afterwards, a tall Jacobin friar, blind of one eye, called Corsini, whom I had known in Venice, came in and paid me many compliments. He told me that I had arrived just in time to go to a picnic got up by the Macaronic academicians for the next day, after a sitting of the academy in which every member was to recite something of his composition. He invited me to join them, and to gratify the meeting with the delivery of one of my productions. I accepted the invitation, and, after the reading of ten stanzas which I had written for the occasion, I was unanimously elected a member. My success at the picnic was still greater, for I disposed of such a quantity of macaroni that I was found worthy of the title of prince of the academy.

The young doctor, himself one of the academicians, introduced me to his family. His parents, who were in

easy circumstances, received me very kindly. One of
his sisters was very amiable, but the other, a professed
nun, appeared to me a prodigy of beauty. I might have
enjoyed myself in a very agreeable way in the midst of
that charming family during my stay in Chiozza, but
I suppose that it was my destiny to meet in that place
with nothing but sorrows. The young doctor forewarned
me that the monk Corsini was a very worthless fellow,
despised by everybody, and advised me to avoid him.
I thanked him for the information, but my thoughtlessness prevented me from profiting by it. Of a very easy
disposition, and too giddy to fear any snares, I was foolish enough to believe that the monk would, on the contrary, be the very man to throw plenty of amusement
in my way.

On the third day the worthless dog took me to a house
of ill-fame, where I might have gone without his introduction, and, in order to shew my mettle, I obliged a
low creature whose ugliness ought to have been a sufficient antidote against any fleshly desire. On leaving
the place, he brought me for supper to an inn where we
met four scoundrels of his own stamp. After supper one
of them began a bank of faro, and I was invited to join
in the game. I gave way to that feeling of false pride
which so often causes the ruin of young men, and after
losing four sequins I expressed a wish to retire, but my
honest friend, the Jacobin contrived to make me risk
four more sequins in partnership with him. He held the
bank, and it was broken. I did not wish to play any
more, but Corsini, feigning to pity me and to feel great
sorrow at being the cause of my loss, induced me to try
myself a bank of twenty-five sequins; my bank was likewise broken. The hope of winning back my money made
me keep up the game, and I lost everything I had.

Deeply grieved, I went away and laid myself down near the cook, who woke up and said I was a libertine.

"You are right," was all I could answer.

I was worn out with fatigue and sorrow, and I slept soundly. My vile tormentor, the monk, woke me at noon, and informed me with a triumphant joy that a very rich young man had been invited by his friends to supper, that he would be sure to play and to lose, and that it would be a good opportunity for me to retrieve my losses.

"I have lost all my money. Lend me twenty sequins."

"When I lend money I am sure to lose; you may call it superstition, but I have tried it too often. Try to find money somewhere else, and come. Farewell."

I felt ashamed to confess my position to my friend, and sending for a money-lender I emptied my trunk before him. We made an inventory of my clothes, and the honest broker gave me thirty sequins, with the understanding that if I did not redeem them within three days all my things would become his property. I am bound to call him an honest man, for he advised me to keep three shirts, a few pairs of stockings, and a few handkerchiefs; I was disposed to let him take everything, having a presentiment that I would win back all I had lost; a very common error. A few years later I took my revenge by writing a diatribe against presentiments. I am of opinion that the only foreboding in which man can have any sort of faith is the one which forbodes evil, because it comes from the mind, while a presentiment of happiness has its origin in the heart, and the heart is a fool worthy of reckoning foolishly upon fickle fortune.

I did not lose any time in joining the honest company, which was alarmed at the thought of not seeing me. Supper went off without any allusion to gambling, but my

admirable qualities were highly praised, and it was decided that a brilliant fortune awaited me in Rome. After
supper there was no talk of play, but giving way to my
evil genius I loudly asked for my revenge. I was told
that if I would take the bank everyone would punt. I
took the bank, lost every sequin I had, and retired, begging the monk to pay what I owed to the landlord, which
he promised to do.

I was in despair, and to crown my misery I found out
as I was going home that I had met the day before with
another living specimen of the Greek woman, less beautiful but as perfidious. I went to bed stunned by my
grief, and I believe that I must have fainted into a heavy
sleep, which lasted eleven hours; my awaking was that
of a miserable being, hating the light of heaven, of which
he felt himself unworthy, and I closed my eyes again,
trying to sleep for a little while longer. I dreaded to
rouse myself up entirely, knowing that I would then
have to take some decision; but I never once thought
of returning to Venice, which would have been the very
best thing to do, and I would have destroyed myself
rather than confide my sad position to the young doctor.
I was weary of my existence, and I entertained vaguely
some hope of starving where I was, without leaving my
bed. It is certain that I should not have got up if M.
Alban, the master of the peotta, had not roused me by
calling upon me and informing me that the boat was
ready to sail.

The man who is delivered from great perplexity, no
matter by what means, feels himself relieved. It seemed
to me that Captain Alban had come to point out the
only thing I could possibly do; I dressed myself in haste,
and tying all my wordly possessions in a handkerchief
I went on board. Soon afterwards we left the shore, and

in the morning we cast anchor in Orsara, a seaport of Istria. We all landed to visit the city, which would more properly be called a village. It belongs to the Pope, the Republic of Venice having abandoned it to the Holy See.

A young monk of the order of the Recollects who called himself Friar Stephano of Belun, and had obtained a free passage from the devout Captain Alban, joined me as we landed and enquired whether I felt sick.

"Reverend father, I am unhappy."

"You will forget all your sorrow, if you will come and dine with me at the house of one of our devout friends."

I had not broken my fast for thirty-six hours, and having suffered much from sea-sickness during the night, my stomach was quite empty. My erotic inconvenience made me very uncomfortable, my mind felt deeply the consciousness of my degradation, and I did not possess a groat! I was in such a miserable state that I had no strength to accept or to refuse anything. I was thoroughly torpid, and I followed the monk mechanically.

He presented me to a lady, saying that he was accompanying me to Rome, where I intend to become a Franciscan. This untruth disgusted me, and under any other circumstances I would not have let it pass without protest, but in my actual position it struck me as rather comical. The good lady gave us a good dinner of fish cooked in oil, which in Orsara is delicious, and we drank some exquisite refosco. During our meal, a priest happened to drop in, and, after a short conversation, he told me that I ought not to pass the night on board the tartan, and pressed me to accept a bed in his house and a good dinner for the next day in case the wind should not allow us to sail; I accepted without hesitation. I offered my most sincere thanks to the good old lady, and the priest took me all over the town. In the evening, he brought me to his house where we partook of an excellent supper prepared by his housekeeper, who sat down to the table with us, and with whom I was much pleased. The refosco, still better than that which I had drunk at dinner, scattered all my misery to the wind, and I conversed gaily with the priest. He offered to read to me a poem of his own composition, but, feeling that my eyes would not keep open, I begged he would excuse me and postpone the reading until the following day.

I went to bed, and in the morning, after ten hours of the most profound sleep, the housekeeper, who had been watching for my awakening, brought me some coffee. I thought her a charming woman, but, alas! I was not in a fit state to prove to her the high estimation in which I held her beauty.

Entertaining feelings of gratitude for my kind host, and disposed to listen attentively to his poem, I dismissed all sadness, and I paid his poetry such compliments that he was delighted, and, finding me much more talented than he had judged me to be at first, he insisted upon treating me to the reading of his idylls, and I had to swallow them, bearing the infliction cheerfully. The day passed off very agreeably; the housekeeper surrounded me with the kindest attentions—a proof that she was smitten with me; and, giving way to that pleasing idea, I felt that, by a very natural system of reciprocity, she had made my conquest. The good priest thought that the day had passed like lightning, thanks to all the beauties I had discovered in his poetry, which, to speak the truth, was below mediocrity, but time seemed to me to drag along very slowly, because the friendly glances of the housekeeper made me long for bedtime, in spite of the miserable condition in which I felt myself morally and physically. But such was my nature; I abandoned myself to joy and happiness, when, had I been more reasonable, I ought to have sunk under my grief and sadness.

But the golden time came at last. I found the pretty housekeeper full of compliance, but only up to a certain point, and as she offered some resistance when I shewed myself disposed to pay a full homage to her charms, I quietly gave up the undertaking, very well pleased for both of us that it had not been carried any further, and I sought my couch in peace. But I had not seen the end of the adventure, for the next morning, when she brought my coffee, her pretty, enticing manners allured me to bestow a few loving caresses upon her, and if she did not abandon herself entirely, it was only, as she said, because she was afraid of some surprise. The day passed off very pleasantly with the good priest, and at night, the housekeeper no longer fearing detection, and I having on my side taken every precaution necessary in the state in which I was, we passed two most delicious hours. I left Orsara the next morning.

Friar Stephano amused me all day with his talk, which plainly showed me his ignorance combined with knavery under the veil of simplicity. He made me look at the alms he had received in Orsara—bread, wine, cheese, sausages, preserves, and chocolate; every nook and cranny of his holy garment was full of provisions.

"Have you received money likewise?" I enquired.

"God forbid! In the first place, our glorious order does not permit me to touch money, and, in the second place, were I to be foolish enough to receive any when I am begging, people would think themselves quit of me with one or two sous, whilst they give me ten times as

much in eatables. Believe me, Saint-Francis was a very
judicious man."

I bethought myself that what this monk called wealth
would be poverty to me. He offered to share with me,
and seemed very proud at my consenting to honour him
so far.

The tartan touched at the harbour of Pola, called Veruda, and we landed. After a walk up hill of nearly a
quarter of an hour, we entered the city, and I devoted
a couple of hours to visiting the Roman antiquities,
which are numerous, the town having been the metropolis
of the empire. Yet I saw no other trace of grand buildings except the ruins of the arena. We returned to
Veruda, and went again to sea. On the following day we
sighted Ancona, but the wind being against us we were
compelled to tack about, and we did not reach the port
till the second day. The harbour of Ancona, although
considered one of the great works of Trajan, would be
very unsafe if it were not for a causeway which has
cost a great deal of money, and which makes it somewhat better. I observed a fact worthy of notice, namely,
that, in the Adriatic, the northern coast has many harbours, while the opposite coast can only boast of one
or two. It is evident that the sea is retiring by degrees
towards the east, and that in three or four more centuries Venice must be joined to the land.

We landed at the old lazzaretto, where we received the
pleasant information that we would go through a quarantine of twenty-eight days, because Venice had admitted,
after a quarantine of three months, the crew of two
ships from Messina, where the plague had recently been
raging. I requested a room for myself and for Brother
Stephano, who thanked me very heartily. I hired from
a Jew a bed, a table and a few chairs, promising to pay

for the hire at the expiration of our quarantine. The monk would have nothing but straw. If he had guessed that without him I might have starved, he would most likely not have felt so much vanity at sharing my room. A sailor, expecting to find in me a generous customer, came to enquire where my trunk was, and, hearing from me that I did not know, he, as well as Captain Alban, went to a great deal of trouble to find it, and I could hardly keep down my merriment when the captain called, begging to be excused for having left it behind, and assuring me that he would take care to forward it to me in less than three weeks.

The friar, who had to remain with me four weeks, expected to live at my expense, while, on the contrary, he had been sent by Providence to keep me. He had provisions enough for one week, but it was necessary to think of the future.

After supper, I drew a most affecting picture of my position, shewing that I should be in need of everything until my arrival at Rome, where I was going, I said, to fill the post of secretary of memorials, and my astonishment may be imagined when I saw the blockhead delighted at the recital of my misfortunes.

"I undertake to take care of you until we reach Rome; only tell me whether you can write."

"What a question! Are you joking?"

"Why should I? Look at me; I cannot write anything but my name. True, I can write it with either hand; and what else do I want to know?"

"You astonish me greatly, for I thought you were a priest."

"I am a monk; I say the mass, and, as a matter of course, I must know how to read. Saint-Francis, whose unworthy son I am, could not read, and that is the reason why he never said a mass. But as you can write, you will to-morrow pen a letter in my name to the persons whose names I will give you, and I warrant you we shall have enough sent here to live like fighting cocks all through our quarantine."

The next day he made me write eight letters, because, in the oral tradition of his order, it is said that, when a monk has knocked at seven doors and has met with a refusal at every one of them, he must apply to the eighth with perfect confidence, because there he is certain of receiving alms. As he had already performed the pilgrimage to Rome, he knew every person in Ancona devoted to the cult of Saint-Francis, and was acquainted with the superiors of all the rich convents. I had to write to every person he named, and to set down all the lies he dictated to me. He likewise made me sign the letters for him, saying, that, if he signed himself, his correspondents would see that the letters had not been written by him, which would injure him, for, he added, in this age of corruption, people will esteem only learned men. He compelled me to fill the letters with Latin passages and quotations, even those addressed to ladies, and I remonstrated in vain, for, when I raised any objection, he threatened to leave me without anything to eat. I made up my mind to do exactly as he wished. He desired me to write to the superior of the Jesuits that he would not apply to the Capuchins, because they were no better than atheists, and that that was the reason of the great dislike of Saint-Francis for them. It was in vain that I reminded him of the fact that, in the time of Saint-Francis, there were neither Capuchins nor Recollets. His answer was that I had proved myself an ignoramus. I firmly believed that he would be thought a madman, and that we should not receive anything, but I was mistaken, for such a quantity of provisions came pouring in that I was amazed. Wine was sent from three or four different quarters, more than enough for us during all our stay, and yet I drank nothing but water, so great was my wish to recover my health. As for eatables, enough was sent in every day for six persons; we gave all our surplus to our keeper, who had a large family. But the monk felt no gratitude for the kind souls who bestowed their charity upon him; all his thanks were reserved for Saint-Francis.

He undertook to have my linen washed by the keeper; I would not have dared to give it myself, and he said that he had nothing to fear, as everybody was well aware that the monks of his order never wear any kind of linen.

I kept myself in bed nearly all day, and thus avoided shewing myself to visitors. The persons who did not come wrote letters full of incongruities cleverly worded, which I took good care not to point out to him. It was with great difficulty that I tried to persuade him that those letters did not require any answer.

A fortnight of repose and severe diet brought me round towards complete recovery, and I began to walk in the yard of the lazzaretto from morning till night; but the arrival of a Turk from Thessalonia with his family compelled me to suspend my walks, the ground-floor having been given to him. The only pleasure left me was to spend my time on the balcony overlooking the yard. I soon saw a Greek slave, a girl of dazzling beauty, for whom I felt the deepest interest. She was in the habit of spending the whole day sitting near the door with a book or some embroidery in her hand. If she happened to raise her eyes and to meet mine, she modestly bent her head down, and sometimes she rose and went in slowly, as if she meant to say, "I did not know that somebody was looking at me." Her figure was tall and slender, her features proclaimed her to be very young; she had a very fair complexion, with beautiful black hair and eyes. She wore the Greek costume, which gave her person a certain air of very exciting voluptuousness.

I was perfectly idle, and with the temperament which nature and habit had given me, was it likely that I could feast my eyes constantly upon such a charming object without falling desperately in love? I had heard her conversing in Lingua Franca with her master, a fine old man, who, like her, felt very weary of the quarantine, and used to come out but seldom, smoking his pipe, and remaining in the yard only a short time. I felt a great temptation to address a few words to the beautiful girl, but I was afraid she might run away and never come out again; however, unable to control myself any longer, I determined to write to her; I had no difficulty in conveying the letter, as I had only to let it fall from my balcony. But she might have refused to pick it up, and this is the plan I adopted in order not to risk any unpleasant result.

Availing myself of a moment during which she was alone in the yard, I dropped from my balcony a small piece of paper folded like a letter, but I had taken care not to write anything on it, and held the true letter in my hand. As soon as I saw her stooping down to pick up the first, I quickly let the second drop at her feet, and she put both into her pocket. A few minutes afterwards she left the yard. My letter was somewhat to this effect:

"Beautiful angel from the East, I worship you. I

will remain all night on this balcony in the hope that you will come to me for a quarter of an hour, and listen to my voice through the hole under my feet. We can speak softly, and in order to hear me you can climb up to the top of the bale of goods which lies beneath the same hole."

I begged from my keeper not to lock me in as he did every night, and he consented on condition that he would watch me, for if I had jumped down in the yard his life might have been the penalty, and he promised not to disturb me on the balcony.

At midnight, as I was beginning to give her up, she came forward. I then laid myself flat on the floor of the balcony, and I placed my head against the hole, about six inches square. I saw her jump on the bale, and her head reached within a foot from the balcony. She was compelled to steady herself with one hand against the wall for fear of falling, and in that position we talked of love, of ardent desires, of obstacles, of impossibilities, and of cunning artifices. I told her the reason for which I dared not jump down in the yard, and she observed that, even without that reason, it would bring ruin upon us, as it would be impossible to come up again, and that, besides, God alone knew what her master would do if he were to find us together. Then, promising to visit me in this way every night, she passed her hand through the hole. Alas! I could not leave off kissing it, for I thought that I had never in my life toughed so soft, so delicate a hand. But what bliss when she begged for mine! I quickly thrust my arm through the hole, so that she could fasten her lips to the bend of the elbow. How many sweet liberties my hand ventured to take! But we were at last compelled by prudence to separate, and when I returned to my room I saw with great pleasure that the keeper was fast asleep.

Although I was delighted at having obtained every favour I could possibly wish for in the uncomfortable position we had been in, I racked my brain to contrive the means of securing more complete enjoyment for the following night, but I found during the afternoon that the feminine cunning of my beautiful Greek was more fertile than mine.

Being alone in the yard with her master, she said a few words to him in Turkish, to which he seemed to give his approval, and soon after a servant, assisted by the keeper, brought under the balcony a large basket of goods. She overlooked the arrangement, and in order to secure the basket better, she made the servant place a bale of cotton across two others. Guessing at her purpose, I fairly leaped for joy, for she had found the way of raising herself two feet higher; but I thought that she would then find herself in the most inconvenient position, and that, forced to bend double, she would not be able to resist the fatigue. The hole was not wide enough for her head to pass through, otherwise she might have stood erect and been comfortable. It was necessary at all events to guard against that difficulty; the only way was to tear out one of the planks of the floor of the balcony, but it was not an easy undertaking. Yet I decided upon attempting it, regardless of consequences; and I went to my room to provide myself with a large pair of pincers. Luckily the keeper was absent, and availing myself of the opportunity, I succeeded in dragging out carefully the four large nails which fastened the plank. Finding that I could lift it at my will, I replaced the pincers, and waited for the night with amorous impatience.

The darling girl came exactly at midnight, noticing the difficulty she experienced in climbing up, and in getting a footing upon the third bale of cotton, I lifted the plank, and, extending my arm as far as I could, I offered her a steady point of support. She stood straight, and found herself agreeably surprised, for she could pass her head and her arms through the hole. We wasted no time in empty compliments; we only congratulated each other upon having both worked for the same purpose.

If, the night before, I had found myself master of her person more than she was of mine, this time the position was entirely reversed. Her hand roamed freely over every part of my body, but I had to stop half-way down hers. She cursed the man who had packed the bale for not having made it half a foot bigger, so as to get nearer to me. Very likely even that would not have satisfied us, but she would have felt happier.

Our pleasures were barren, yet we kept up our enjoyment until the first streak of light. I put back the plank carefully, and I lay down in my bed in great need of recruiting my strength.

My dear mistress had informed me that the Turkish Bairam began that very morning, and would last three days during which it would be impossible for her to see me.

The night after Bairam, she did not fail to make her appearance, and, saying that she could not be happy without me, she told me that, as she was a Christian woman, I could buy her, if I waited for her after leaving the lazzaretto. I was compelled to tell her that I did not possess the means of doing so, and my confession made her sigh. On the following night, she informed me that her master would sell her for two thousand piasters, that she would give me the amount, that she was yet a virgin, and that I would be pleased with my bargain. She added that she would give me a casket full of diamonds, one of which was alone worth two thousand piasters, and that the sale of the others would place us beyond the reach of poverty for the remainder of our life. She assured me that her master would not notice the loss of the casket, and that, if he did, he would never think of accusing her.

I was in love with this girl; and her proposal made me uncomfortable, but when I woke in the morning I did not hesitate any longer. She brought the casket in the evening, but I told her that I never could make up my mind to be accessory to a robbery; she was very unhappy, and said that my love was not as deep as her own, but that she could not help admiring me for being so good a Christian.

This was the last night; probably we should never meet again. The flame of passion consumed us. She proposed that I should lift her up to the balcony through the open space. Where is the lover who would have objected to so attractive a proposal? I rose, and without being a Milo, I placed my hands under her arms, I drew her up towards me, and my desires are on the point of being fulfilled. Suddenly I feel two hands upon my shoulders, and the voice of the keeper exclaims, "What are you about?" I let my precious burden drop; she regains her chamber, and I, giving vent to my rage, throw myself flat on the floor of the balcony, and remain there without a movement, in spite of the shaking of the keeper whom I was sorely tempted to strangle. At last I rose from the floor and went to bed without uttering one word, and not even caring to replace the plank.

In the morning, the governor informed us that we were free. As I left the lazzaretto, with a breaking heart, I caught a glimpse of the Greek slave drowned in tears.

I agreed to meet Friar Stephano at the exchange, and I took the Jew from whom I had hired the furniture, to the convent of the Minims, where I received from Father Lazari ten sequins and the address of the bishop, who, after performing quarantine on the frontiers of Tuscany, had proceeded to Rome, where he would expect me to meet him.

I paid the Jew, and made a poor dinner at an inn. As I was leaving it to join the monk, I was so unlucky as to meet Captain Alban, who reproached me bitterly for having led him to believe that my trunk had been left behind. I contrived to appease his anger by telling him all my misfortunes, and I signed a paper in which I declared that I had no claim whatever upon him. I then purchased a pair of shoes and an overcoat, and met Stephano, whom I informed of my decision to make a pilgrimage to Our Lady of Loretto. I said I would await there for him, and that we would afterwards travel together as far as Rome. He answered that he did not wish to go through Loretto, and that I would repent of my contempt for the grace of Saint-Francis. I did not alter my mind, and I left for Loretto the next day in the enjoyment of perfect health.

I reached the Holy City, tired almost to death, for it was the first time in my life that I had walked fifteen miles, drinking nothing but water, although the weather was very warm, because the dry wine used in that part of the country parched me too much. I must observe that, in spite of my poverty, I did not look like a beggar.

As I was entering the city, I saw coming towards me an elderly priest of very respectable appearance, and, as he was evidently taking notice of me, as soon as he drew near, I saluted him, and enquired where I could find a comfortable inn. "I cannot doubt," he said, "that a person like you, travelling on foot, must come here from devout motives; come with me." He turned back, I followed him, and he took me to a fine-looking house. After whispering a few words to a man who appeared to be a steward, he left me saying, very affably, "You shall be well attended to."

My first impression was that I had been mistaken for some other person, but I said nothing.

I was led to a suite of three rooms; the chamber was decorated with damask hangings, the bedstead had a canopy, and the table was supplied with all materials necessary for writing. A servant brought me a light dressing-gown, and another came in with linen and a large tub full of water, which he placed before me; my shoes and stockings were taken off, and my feet washed. A very decent-looking woman, followed by a servant girl, came in a few minutes after, and curtsying very low, she proceeded to make my bed. At that moment the Angelus bell was heard; everyone knelt down, and I followed their example. After the prayer, a small table was neatly laid out, I was asked what sort of wine I wished to drink, and I was provided with newspapers and two silver candlesticks. An hour afterwards I had a delicious fish supper, and, before I retired to bed, a servant came to enquire whether I would take chocolate in the morning before or after mass.

As soon as I was in bed, the servant brought me a night-lamp with a dial, and I remained alone. Except in France I have never had such a good bed as I had that night. It would have cured the most chronic insomnia, but I was not labouring under such a disease, and I slept for ten hours.

This sort of treatment easily led me to believe that I was not in any kind of hostelry; but where was I? How was I to suppose that I was in a hospital?

When I had taken my chocolate, a hair-dresser—quite a fashionable, dapper fellow—made his appearance, dying to give vent to his chattering propensities. Guessing that I did not wish to be shaved, he offered to clip my soft down with the scissors, saying that I would look younger.

"Why do you suppose that I want to conceal my age?"

"It is very natural, because, if your lordship did not wish to do so, your lordship would have shaved long ago. Countess Marcolini is here; does your lordship know her? I must go to her at noon to dress her hair."

I did not feel interested in the Countess Marcolini, and, seeing it, the gossip changed the subject.

"Is this your lordship's first visit to this house? It is the finest hospital throughout the papal states."

"I quite agree with you, and I shall compliment His Holiness on the establishment."

"Oh! His Holiness knows all about it, he resided here before he became pope. If Monsignor Caraffa had not been well acquainted with you, he would not have introduced you here."

Such is the use of barbers throughout Europe; but you must not put any questions to them, for, if you do, they are sure to threat you to an impudent mixture of truth and falsehood, and instead of you pumping them, they will worm everything out of you.

Thinking that it was my duty to present my respectful compliments to Monsignor Caraffa, I desired to be taken to his apartment. He gave me a pleasant welcome, shewed me his library, and entrusted me to the care of one of his abbés, a man of parts, who acted as my cicerone every where. Twenty years afterwards, this same abbé was of great service to me in Rome, and, if still alive, he is a canon of St.-John Lateran.

On the following day, I took the communion in the Santa-Casa. The third day was entirely employed in examining the exterior of this truly wonderful sanctuary, and early the next day I resumed my journey, having spent nothing except three paoli for the barber. Halfway to Macerata, I overtook Brother Stephano walking on at a very slow rate. He was delighted to see me again, and told me that he had left Ancona two hours after me, but that he never walked more than three miles a day, being quite satisfied to take two months for a journey which, even on foot, can easily be accomplished in a week. "I want," he said, "to reach Rome without fatigue and in good health. I am in no hurry, and if you feel disposed to travel with me and in the same quiet way, Saint-Francis will not find it difficult to keep us both during the journey."

This lazy fellow was a man about thirty, red-haired, very strong and healthy; a true peasant who had turned himself into a monk only for the sake of living in idle comfort. I answered that, as I was in a hurry to reach Rome, I could not be his travelling companion.

"I undertake to walk six miles, instead of three, to-day," he said, "if you will carry my cloak, which I find very heavy."

The proposal struck me as a rather funny one; I put on his cloak, and he took my great-coat, but, after the exchange, we cut such a comical figure that every peasant we met laughed at us. His cloak would truly have proved a load for a mule. There were twelve pockets quite full, without taken into account a pocket behind, which he called *il batticulo,* and which contained alone twice as much as all the others. Bread, wine, fresh and salt meat, fowls, eggs, cheese, ham, sausages—everything was to be found in those pockets, which contained provisions enough for a fortnight.

I told him how well I had been treated in Loretto, and he assured me that I might have asked Monsignor Caraffa to give me letters for all the hospitals on my road to Rome, and that everywhere I would have met with the same reception. "The hospitals," he added, "are all under the curse of Saint-Francis, because the mendicant friars are not admitted in them; but we do not mind their gates being shut against us, because they are too far apart from each other. We prefer the homes of the persons attached to our order; these we find everywhere."

"Why do you not ask hospitality in the convents of your order?"

"I am not so foolish. In the first place, I should not be admitted, because, being a fugitive, I have not the written obedience which must be shown at every convent, and I should even run the risk of being thrown into prison; your monks are a cursed bad lot. In the second place, I should not be half so comfortable in the convents as I am with our devout benefactors."

"Why and how are you a fugitive?"

He answered my question by the narrative of his imprisonment and flight, the whole story being a tissue of absurdities and lies. The fugitive Recollet friar was a fool, with something of the wit of harlequin, and he thought that every man listening to him was a greater fool than himself. Yet with all his folly he was not deficient in a certain species of cunning. His religious principles were singular. As he did not wish to be taken for a bigoted man he was scandalous, and for the sake of making people laugh he would often make use of the most disgusting expressions. He had no taste whatever for women, and no inclination towards the pleasures of the flesh; but this was only owing to a deficiency in his natural temperament, and yet he claimed for himself the virtue of continence. On that score, everything appeared to him food for merriment, and when he had drunk rather too much, he would ask questions of such an indecent character that they would bring blushes on everybody's countenance. Yet the brute would only laugh.

As we were getting within one hundred yards from the house of the devout friend whom he intended to honour with his visit, he took back his heavy cloak. On entering the house he gave his blessing to everybody, and everyone in the family came to kiss his hand. The mistress of the house requested him to say mass for them, and the compliant monk asked to be taken to the vestry, but when I whispered in his ear,——

"Have you forgotten that we have already broken our fast to-day?" he answered, dryly,——

"Mind your own business."

I dared not make any further remark, but during the mass I was indeed surprised, for I saw that he did not understand what he was doing. I could not help being amused at his awkwardness, but I had not yet seen the best part of the comedy. As soon as he had somehow or other finished his mass he went to the confessional, and after hearing in confession every member of the family he took it into his head to refuse absolution to the daughter of his hostess, a girl of twelve or thirteen, pretty and quite charming. He gave his refusal publicly, scolding her and threatening her with the torments of hell. The poor girl, overwhelmed with shame, left the church crying bitterly, and I, feeling real sympathy for her, could not help saying aloud to Stephano that he was a madman. I ran after the girl to offer her my consolations, but she had disappeared, and could not be induced to join us at dinner. This piece of extravagance on the part of the monk exasperated me to such an extent that I felt a very strong inclination to thrash him. In the presence of all the family I told him that he was an impostor, and the infamous destroyer of the poor child's honour; I challenged him to explain his reasons for refusing to give her absolution, but he closed my lips by answering very coolly that he could not betray the secrets of the confessional. I could eat nothing, and was fully determined to leave the scoundrel. As we left the house I was compelled to accept one paolo as the price of the mock mass he had said. I had to fulfil the sorry duty of his treasurer.

The moment we were on the road, I told him that I was going to part company, because I was afraid of being sent as a felon to the galleys if I continued my journey with him. We exchanged high words; I called him an ignorant scoundrel, he styled me beggar. I struck him a violent slap on the face, which he returned with a blow from his stick, but I quickly snatched it from him, and, leaving him, I hastened towards Macerata. A carrier who was going to Tolentino took me with him for two paoli, and for six more I might have reached Foligno in a waggon, but unfortunately a wish for economy made me refuse the offer. I felt well, and I thought I could easily walk as far as Valcimare, but I arrived there only after five hours of hard walking, and thoroughly beaten with fatigue. I was strong and healthy, but a walk of five hours was more than I could bear, because in my infancy I had never gone a league on foot. Young people cannot practise too much the art of walking.

The next day, refreshed by a good night's rest, and ready to resume my journey, I wanted to pay the inn-keeper, but, alas! a new misfortune was in store for me! Let the reader imagine my sad position! I recollected that I had forgotten my purse, containing seven sequins, on the table of the inn at Tolentino. What a thunder-bolt! I was in despair, but I gave up the idea of going back, as it was very doubtful whether I would find my money. Yet it contained all I possessed, save a few copper coins I had in my pocket. I paid my small bill, and, deeply grieved at my loss, continued my journey towards Seraval. I was within three miles of that place when, in jumping over a ditch, I sprained my ankle, and was compelled to sit down on one side of the road, and to wait until someone should come to my assistance.

In the course of an hour a peasant happened to pass with his donkey, and he agreed to carry me to Seraval for one paolo. As I wanted to spend as little as possible, the peasant took me to an ill-looking fellow who, for two paoli paid in advance, consented to give me a lodging. I asked him to send for a surgeon, but I did not obtain one until the following morning. I had a wretched supper, after which I lay down in a filthy bed. I was in hope that sleep would bring me some relief, but my evil genius was preparing for me a night of torments.

Three men, armed with guns and looking like ban-

ditti, came in shortly after I had gone to bed, speaking
a kind of slang which I could not make out, swearing,
raging, and paying no attention to me. They drank and
sang until midnight, after which they threw themselves
down on bundles of straw brought for them, and my host,
who was drunk, came, greatly to my dismay, to lie down
near me. Disgusted at the idea of having such a fellow
for my bed companion, I refused to let him come, but
he answered, with fearful blasphemies, that all the devils
in hell could not prevent him from taking possession of
his own bed. I was forced to make room for him, and
exclaimed "Heavens, where am I?" He told me that
I was in the house of the most honest constable in all
the papal states.

Could I possibly have supposed that the peasant would
have brought me amongst those accursed enemies of
humankind!

He laid himself down near me, but the filthy scoundrel soon compelled me to give him, for certain reasons,
such a blow in his chest that he rolled out of bed. He
picked himself up, and renewed his beastly attempt.
Being well aware that I could not master him without
great danger, I got out of bed, thinking myself lucky
that he did not oppose my wish, and crawling along as
well as I could, I found a chair on which I passed the
night. At day-break, my tormentor, called up by his
honest comrades, joined them in drinking and shouting,
and the three strangers, taking their guns, departed. Left
alone by the departure of the vile rabble, I passed another unpleasant hour, calling in vain for someone. At
last a young boy came in, I gave him some money and
he went for a surgeon. The doctor examined my foot,
and assured me that three or four days would set me
to rights. He advised me to be removed to an inn, and

I most willingly followed his counsel. As soon as I was brought to the inn, I went to bed, and was well cared for, but my position was such that I dreaded the moment of my recovery. I feared that I should be compelled to sell my coat to pay the inn-keeper, and the very thought made me feel ashamed. I began to consider that if I had controlled my sympathy for the young girl so ill-treated by Stephano, I should not have fallen into this sad predicament, and I felt conscious that my sympathy had been a mistake. If I had put up with the faults of the friar, if this and if that, and every other if was conjured up to torment my restless and wretched brain. Yet I must confess that the thoughts which have their origin in misfortune are not without some advantage to a young man, for they give him the habit of thinking, and the man who does not think never does anything right.

The morning of the fourth day came, and I was able to walk, as the surgeon had predicted; I made up my mind, although reluctantly, to beg the worthy man to sell my great coat for me—a most unpleasant necessity, for rain had begun to fall. I owed fifteen paoli to the inn-keeper and four to the surgeon. Just as I was going to proffer my painful request, Brother Stephano made his appearance in my room, and burst into loud laughter enquiring whether I had forgotten the blow from his stick!

I was struck with amazement! I begged the surgeon to leave me with the monk, and he immediately complied.

I must ask my readers whether it is possible, in the face of such extraordinary circumstances, not to feel superstitious! What is truly miraculous in this case is the precise minute at which the event took place, for the friar entered the room as the word was hanging on

my lips. What surprised me most was the force of
Providence, of fortune, of chance, whatever name is
given to it, of that very necessary combination which
compelled me to find no hope but in that fatal monk,
who had begun to be my protective genius in Chiozza at
the moment my distress had likewise commenced. And
yet, a singular guardian angel, this Stephano! I felt
that the mysterious force which threw me in his hands
was a punishment rather than a favour.

Nevertheless he was welcome, because I had no doubt
of his relieving me from my difficulties, and whatever
might be the power that sent him to me, I felt that I
could not do better than to submit to its influence; the
destiny of that monk was to escort me to Rome.

"Chi va piano va sano," said the friar as soon as we
were alone. He had taken five days to traverse the road
over which I had travelled in one day, but he was in
good health, and he had met with no misfortune. He
told me that, as he was passing, he heard that an abbé,
secretary to the Venetian ambassador at Rome, was
lying ill at the inn, after having been robbed in Val-
cimara. "I came to see you," he added, "and as I find
you recovered from your illness, we can start again together; I agree to walk six miles every day to please
you. Come, let us forget the past, and let us be at once
on our way."

"I cannot go; I have lost my purse, and I owe twenty
paoli."

"I will go and find the amount in the name of Saint-
Francis."

He returned within an hour, but he was accompanied
by the infamous constable who told me that, if I had
let him know who I was, he would have been happy to
keep me in his house. "I will give you," he continued,

"forty paoli, if you will promise me the protection of your ambassador; but if you do not succeed in obtaining it for me in Rome, you will undertake to repay me. Therefore you must give me an acknowledgement of the debt."

"I have no objection." Every arrangement was speedily completed; I received the money, paid my debts, and left Seraval with Stephano.

About one o'clock in the afternoon, we saw a wretched-looking house at a short distance from the road, and the friar said, "It is a good distance from here to Collefiorito; we had better put up there for the night." It was in vain that I objected, remonstrating that we were certain of having very poor accommodation! I had to submit to his will. We found a decrepit old man lying on a pallet, two ugly women of thirty or forty, three children entirely naked, a cow, and a cursed dog which barked continually. It was a picture of squalid misery; but the niggardly monk, instead of giving alms to the poor people, asked them to entertain us to supper in the name of Saint-Francis.

"You must boil the hen," said the dying man to the females, "and bring out of the cellar the bottle of wine which I have kept now for twenty years." As he uttered those few words, he was seized with such a fit of coughing that I thought he would die. The friar went near him, and promised him that, by the grace of Saint-Francis, he would get young and well. Moved by the sight of so much misery, I wanted to continue my journey as far as Collefiorito, and to wait there for Stephano, but the women would not let me go, and I remained. After boiling for four hours the hen set the strongest teeth at defiance, and the bottle which I uncorked proved to be nothing but sour vinegar. Losing patience, I got hold of the monk's *batticulo*, and took out of it enough for a plentiful supper, and I saw the two women opening their eyes very wide at the sight of our provisions.

We all ate with good appetite, and, after our supper the women made for us two large beds of fresh straw, and we lay down in the dark, as the last bit of candle to be found in the miserable dwelling was burnt out. We had not been lying on the straw five minutes, when Stephano called out to me that one of the women had just placed herself near him, and at the same instant the other one takes me in her arms and kisses me. I push her away, and the monk defends himself against the other; but mine, nothing daunted, insists upon laying herself near me; I get up, the dog springs at my neck, and fear compels me to remain quiet on my straw bed; the monk screams, swears, struggles, the dog barks furiously, the old man coughs; all is noise and confusion. At last Stephano, protected by his heavy garments, shakes off the too loving shrew, and, braving the dog, manages to find his stick. Then he lays about to right and left, striking in every direction; one of the women exclaims, "Oh, God!" the friar answers, "She has her quietus." Calm reigns again in the house, the dog, most likely dead, is silent; the old man, who perhaps has received his death-blow, coughs no more; the children sleep, and the women, afraid of the singular caresses of the monk, sheer off into a corner; the remainder of the night passed off quietly.

At day-break I rose; Stephano was likewise soon up. I looked all round, and my surprise was great when I found that the women had gone out, and seeing that the old man gave no sign of life, and had a bruise on his forehead, I shewed it to Stephano, remarking that very likely he had killed him.

"It is possible," he answered, "but I have not done it intentionally."

Then taking up his *batticulo* and finding it empty he flew into a violent passion; but I was much pleased, for I had been afraid that the women had gone out to get assistance and to have us arrested, and the robbery of our provisions reassured me, as I felt certain that the poor wretches had gone out of the way so as to secure impunity for their theft. But I laid great stress upon the danger we should run by remaining any longer, and I succeeded in frightening the friar out of the house. We soon met a waggoner going to Folligno; I persuaded Stephano to take the opportunity of putting a good distance between us and the scene of our last adventures; and, as we were eating our breakfast at Folligno, we saw another waggon, quite empty, got a lift in it for a trifle, and thus rode to Pisignano, where a devout person gave us a charitable welcome, and I slept soundly through the night without the dread of being arrested.

Early the next day we reached Spoleti, where Brother Stephano had two benefactors, and, careful not to give either of them a cause of jealousy, he favoured both; we dined with the first, who entertained us like princes, and we had supper and lodging in the house of the second, a wealthy wine merchant, and the father of a large and delightful family. He gave us a delicious supper, and everything would have gone on pleasantly had not the friar, already excited by his good dinner, made himself quite drunk. In that state, thinking to please his new host, he began to abuse the other, greatly to my annoyance; he said the wine he had given us to drink was adulterated, and that the man was a thief. I gave him the lie to his face, and called him a scoundrel. The host and his wife pacified me, saying that they were well acquainted with their neighbour, and knew what to think of him; but the monk threw his napkin at my face, and the host took him very quietly by the arm and put him to bed in a room in which he locked him up. I slept in another room.

In the morning I rose early, and was considering whether it would not be better to go alone, when the friar, who had slept himself sober, made his appearance and told me that we ought for the future to live together like good friends, and not give way to angry feelings; I followed my destiny once more. We resumed our journey, and at Soma, the inn-keeper, a woman of rare beauty, gave us a good dinner, and some excellent Cyprus wine which the Venetian couriers exchanged with her against delicious truffles found in the vicinity of Soma, which sold for a good price in Venice. I did not leave the handsome inn-keeper without losing a part of my heart.

It would be difficult to draw a picture of the indignation which overpowered me when, as we were about two miles from Terni, the infamous friar shewed me a small bag full of truffles which the scoundrel had stolen from the amiable woman by way of thanks for her generous hospitality. The truffles were worth two sequins at least. In my indignation I snatched the bag from him, saying that I would certainly return it to its lawful owner. But, as he had not committed the robbery to give himself the pleasure of making restitution, he threw himself upon me, and we came to a regular fight. But victory did not remain long in abeyance; I forced his stick out of his hands, knocked him into a ditch, and went off. On reaching Terni, I wrote a letter of apology to our beautiful hostess of Soma, and sent back the truffles.

From Terni I went on foot to Otricoli, where I only stayed long enough to examine the fine old bridge, and from there I paid four paoli to a waggoner who carried me to Castel-Nuovo, from which place I walked to Rome. I reached the celebrated city on the 1st of September, at nine in the morning.

I must not forget to mention here a rather peculiar circumstance, which, however ridiculous it may be in reality, will please many of my readers.

An hour after I had left Castel-Nuovo, the atmosphere being calm and the sky clear, I perceived on my right, and within ten paces of me, a pyramidal flame about two feet long and four or five feet above the ground. This apparition surprised me, because it seemed to accompany me. Anxious to examine it, I endeavoured to get nearer to it, but the more I advanced towards it the further it went from me. It would stop when I stood still, and when the road along which I was travelling happened to be lined with trees, I no longer saw it, but it was sure to reappear as soon as I reached a portion of the road without trees. I several times retraced my steps purposely, but, every time I did so, the flame disappeared, and would not shew itself again until I proceeded towards Rome. This extraordinary beacon left me when daylight chased darkness from the sky.

What a splendid field for ignorant superstition, if there had been any witnesses to that phenomenon, and if I had chanced to make a great name in Rome! History is full of such trifles, and the world is full of people who attach great importance to them in spite of the so-called light of science. I must candidly confess that, although somewhat versed in physics, the sight of that small meteor gave me singular ideas. But I was prudent enough not to mention the circumstance to any one.

When I reached the ancient capital of the world, I possessed only seven paoli, and consequently I did not loiter about. I paid no attention to the splendid entrance through the gate of the *poplar trees,* which is by mistake pompously called of *the people,* or to the beautiful square of the same name, or to the portals of the magnificent churches, or to all the stately buildings which generally strike the traveller as he enters the city. I went straight towards Monte-Magnanopoli, where, according to the address given to me, I was to find the bishop. There I was informed that he had left Rome ten days before, leaving instructions to send me to Naples free of expense. A coach was to start for Naples the next day; not caring to see Rome, I went to bed until the time for the departure of the coach. I travelled with three low fellows to whom I did not address one word through the whole of the journey. I entered Naples on the 6th day of September.

I went immediately to the address which had been given to me in Rome; the bishop was not there. I called at the Convent of the Minims, and I found that he had left Naples to proceed to Martorano. I enquired whether he had left any instructions for me, but all in vain, no one could give me any information. And there I was, alone in a large city, without a friend, with eight carlini in my pocket, and not knowing what to do! But never mind; fate calls me to Martorano, and to Martorano I must go. The distance, after all, is only two hundred miles.

I found several drivers starting for Cosenza, but when they heard that I had no luggage, they refused to take me, unless I paid in advance. They were quite right, but their prudence placed me under the necessity of going on foot. Yet I felt I must reach Martorano, and I made up my mind to walk the distance, begging food and lodging like the very reverend Brother Stephano.

First of all I made a light meal for one fourth of my money, and, having been informed that I had to follow the Salerno road, I went towards Portici where I arrived in an hour and a half. I already felt rather fatigued; my legs, if not my head, took me to an inn, where I ordered a room and some supper. I was served in good style, my appetite was excellent, and I passed a quiet night in a comfortable bed. In the morning I told the inn-keeper that I would return for my dinner, and I went out to visit the royal palace. As I passed through the gate, I was met by a man of prepossessing appearance, dressed in the eastern fashion, who offered to shew me all over the palace, saying that I would thus save my money. I was in a position to accept any offer; I thanked him for his kindness.

Happening during the conversation to state that I was a Venetian, he told me that he was my subject, since he came from Zante. I acknowledged his polite compliment with a reverence.

"I have," he said, "some very excellent muscatel wine grown in the East, which I could sell you cheap."

"I might buy some, but I warn you I am a good judge."

"So much the better. Which do you prefer?"

"The Cerigo wine."

"You are right. I have some rare Cerigo muscatel, and we can taste it if you have no objection to dine with me."

"None whatever."

"I can likewise give you the wines of Samos and Cephalonia. I have also a quantity of minerals, plenty of vitriol, cinnabar, antimony, and one hundred quintals of mercury."

"Are all these goods here?"

"No, they are in Naples. Here I have only the muscatel wine and the mercury."

It is quite naturally and without any intention to deceive, that a young man accustomed to poverty, and ashamed of it when he speaks to a rich stranger, boasts of his means—of his fortune. As I was talking with my new acquaintance, I recollected an amalgam of mercury with lead and bismuth, by which the mercury increases one-fourth in weight. I said nothing, but I bethought myself that if the mystery should be unknown to the Greek I might profit by it. I felt that some cunning was necessary, and that he would not care for my secret if I proposed to sell it to him without preparing the way. The best plan was to astonish my man with the miracle of the augmentation of the mercury, treat it as a jest, and see what his intentions would be. Cheating is a crime, but honest cunning may be considered as a species of prudence. True, it is a quality which is near akin to roguery; but that cannot be helped, and the man who, in time of need, does not know how to exercise his cunning nobly is a fool. The Greeks call this sort of wisdom *Cerdaleophron* from the word *cerdo*, fox, and it might be translated by *foxdom* if there were such a word in English.

After we had visited the palace we returned to the inn, and the Greek took me to his room, in which he ordered the table to be laid for two. In the next room I saw several large vessels of muscatel wine and four flagons of mercury, each containing about ten pounds.

My plans were laid, and I asked him to let me have one of the flagons of mercury at the current price, and took it to my room. The Greek went out to attend to his business, reminding me that he expected me to dinner. I went out likewise, and bought two pounds and a half of lead and an equal quantity of bismuth; the druggist had no more. I came back to the inn, asked for some large empty bottles, and made the amalgam.

We dined very pleasantly, and the Greek was delighted because I pronounced his Cerigo excellent. In the course of conversation he inquired laughingly why I had bought one of his flagons of mercury.

"You can find out if you come to my room," I said.

After dinner we repaired to my room, and he found his mercury divided in two vessels. I asked for a piece of chamois, strained the liquid through it, filled his own flagon, and the Greek stood astonished at the sight of the fine mercury, about one-fourth of a flagon, which remained over, with an equal quantity of a powder unknown to him; it was the bismuth. My merry laugh kept company with his astonishment, and calling one of the servants of the inn I sent him to the druggist to sell the mercury that was left. He returned in a few minutes and handed me fifteen carlini.

The Greek, whose surprise was complete, asked me to give him back his own flagon, which was there quite full, and worth sixty carlini. I handed it to him with a smile, thanking him for the opportunity he had afforded me of earning fifteen carlini, and took care to add that I should leave for Salerno early the next morning.

"Then we must have supper together this evening," he said.

During the afternoon we took a walk towards Mount Vesuvius. Our conversation went from one subject to another, but no allusion was made to the mercury, though I could see that the Greek had something on his mind. At supper he told me, jestingly, that I ought to stop in Portici the next day to make forty-five carlini out of the three other flagons of mercury. I answered gravely that I did not want the money, and that I had augmented the first flagon only for the sake of procuring him an agreeable surprise.

"But," said he, "you must be very wealthy."

"No, I am not, because I am in search of the secret of the augmentation of gold, and it is a very expensive study for us."

"How many are there in your company?"

"Only my uncle and myself."

"What do you want to augment gold for? The augmentation of mercury ought to be enough for you. Pray, tell me whether the mercury augmented by you to-day is again susceptible of a similar increase."

"No, if it were so, it would be an immense source of wealth for us."

"I am much pleased with your sincerity."

Supper over I paid my bill, and asked the landlord to get me a carriage and pair of horses to take me to Salerno early the next morning. I thanked the Greek for his delicious muscatel wine, and, requesting his address in Naples, I assured him that he would see me within a fortnight, as I was determined to secure a cask of his Cerigo.

We embraced each other, and I retired to bed well pleased with my day's work, and in no way astonished at the Greek's not offering to purchase my secret, for I was certain that he would not sleep for anxiety, and that I should see him early in the morning. At all events, I had enough money to reach the Tour-du-Grec, and there Providence would take care of me. Yet it seemed to me very difficult to travel as far as Martorano, begging like a mendicant-friar, because my outward appearance did not excite pity; people would feel interested in me only from a convcition that I needed nothing—a very unfortunate conviction, when the object of it is truly poor.

As I had forseen, the Greek was in my room at daybreak. I received him in a friendly way, saying that we could take coffee together.

"Willingly; but tell me, reverend abbé, whether you would feel disposed to sell me your secret?"

"Why not? When we meet in Naples——"

"But why not now?"

"I am expected in Salerno; besides, I would only sell the secret for a large sum of money, and I am not acquainted with you."

"That does not matter, as I am sufficiently known here to pay you in cash. How much would you want?"

"Two thousand ounces."

"I agree to pay you that sum provided that I succeed in making the augmentation myself with such matter as you name to me, which I will purchase."

"It is impossible, because the necessary ingredients cannot be got here; but they are common enough in Naples."

"If it is any sort of metal, we can get it at the Tour-du-Grec. We could go there together. Can you tell me what is the expense of the augmentation?"

"One and a half per cent.: but are you likewise known at the Tour-du-Grec, for I should not like to lose my time?"

"Your doubts grieve me."

Saying which, he took a pen, wrote a few words, and handed to me this order:

"At sight, pay to bearer the sum of fifty gold ounces, on account of Panagiotti."

He told me that the banker resided within two hundred yards of the inn, and he pressed me to go there myself. I did not stand upon ceremony, but went to the banker who paid me the amount. I returned to my room in which he was waiting for me, and placed the gold on the table, saying that we could now proceed together to the Tour-du-Grec, where we would complete our arrangements after the signature of a deed of agreement. The Greek had his own carriage and horses; he gave orders for them to be got ready, and we left the inn; but he had nobly insisted upon my taking possession of the fifty ounces.

When we arrived at the Tour-du-Grec, he signed a document by which he promised to pay me two thousand ounces as soon as I should have discovered to him the process of augmenting mercury by one-fourth without injuring its quality, the amalgam to be equal to the mercury which I had sold in his presence at Portici.

He then gave me a bill of exchange payable at sight in eight days on M. Genaro de Carlo. I told him that the ingredients were lead and bismuth; the first, combining with mercury, and the second giving to the whole the perfect fluidity necessary to strain it through the chamois leather. The Greek went out to try the amalgam—I do not know where, and I dined alone, but toward evening he came back, looking very disconsolate, as I had expected.

"I have made the amalgam," he said, "but the mercury is not perfect."

"It is equal to that which I have sold in Portici, and that is the very letter of your engagement."

"But my engagement says likewise *without injury to the quality*. You must agree that the quality is injured, because it is no longer susceptible of further augmentation."

"You knew that to be the case; the point is its equality with the mercury I sold in Portici. But we shall have to go to law, and you will lose. I am sorry the secret should become public. Congratulate yourself, sir, for, if you should gain the lawsuit, you will have obtained my secret for nothing. I would never have believed you capable of deceiving me in such a manner."

"Reverend sir, I can assure you that I would not willingly deceive any one."

"Do you know the secret, or do you not? Do you suppose I would have given it to you without the agreement we entered into? Well, there will be some fun over this affair in Naples, and the lawyers will make money out of it. But I am much grieved at this turn of affairs, and I am very sorry that I allowed myself to be so easily deceived by your fine talk. In the mean time, here are your fifty ounces."

As I was taking the money out of my pocket, frightened to death lest he should accept it, he left the room, saying that he would not have it. He soon returned; we had supper in the same room, but at separate tables; war had been openly declared, but I felt certain that a treaty of peace would soon be signed. We did not exchange one word during the evening, but in the morning he came to me as I was getting ready to go. I again offered to return the money I received, but he told me to keep it, and proposed to give me fifty ounces more if I would give him back his bill of exchange for two thousand. We began to argue the matter quietly, and after two hours of discussion I gave in. I received fifty ounces more, we dined together like old friends, and embraced each other cordially. As I was bidding him adieu, he gave me an order on his house at Naples for a barrel of muscatel wine, and he presented me with a splendid box containing twelve razors with silver handles, manufactured in the Tour-du-Grec. We parted the best friends in the world and well pleased with each other.

I remained two days in Salerno to provide myself with linen and other necessaries. Possessing about one hundred sequins, and enjoying good health, I was very proud of my success, in which I could not see any cause of reproach to myself, for the cunning I had brought into play to insure the sale of my secret could not be found fault with except by the most intolerant of moralists, and such men have no authority to speak on matters of business. At all events, free, rich, and certain of presenting myself before the bishop with a respectable appearance, and not like a beggar, I soon recovered my natural spirits, and congratulated myself upon having bought sufficient experience to insure me against falling a second time an easy prey to a Father Corsini, to thieving gamblers, to mercenary women, and particularly to the impudent scoundrels who barefacedly praise so well those they intend to dupe—a species of knaves very common in the world, even amongst people who form what is called good society.

I left Salerno with two priests who were going to Cosenza on business, and we traversed the distance of one hundred and forty-two miles in twenty-two hours. The day after my arrival in the capital of Calabria, I took a small carriage and drove to Martorano. During the journey, fixing my eyes upon the famous *mare Auso-*

nium, I felt delighted at finding myself in the middle
of Magna Grecia, rendered so celebrated for twenty-
four centuries by its connection with Pythagoras. I
looked with astonishment upon a country renowned for
its fertility, and in which, in spite of nature's prodigality,
my eyes met everywhere the aspect of terrible misery,
the complete absence of that pleasant superfluity which
helps man to enjoy life, and the degradation of the inhabitants sparsely scattered on a soil where they ought
to be so numerous; I felt ashamed to acknowledge them
as originating from the same stock as myself. Such is,
however the *Terra di Lavoro* where labour seems to be
execrated, where everything is cheap, where the miserable inhabitants consider that they have made a good
bargain when they have found anyone disposed to take
care of the fruit which the ground supplies almost spon-
taneously in too great abundance, and for which there
is no market. I felt compelled to admit the justice of
the Romans who had called them *Brutes* instead of *Bru-
tians.* The good priests with whom I had been travelling laughed at my dread of the tarantula and of the
crasydra, for the disease brought on by the bite of those
insects appeared to me more fearful even than a certain
disease with which I was already too well acquainted.
They assured me that all the stories relating to those
creatures were fables; they laughed at the lines which
Virgil has devoted to them in the Georgics as well as
at all those I quoted to justify my fears.

I found Bishop Bernard de Bernardis occupying a hard
chair near an old table on which he was writing. I fell
on my knees, as it is customary to do before a prelate,
but, instead of giving me his blessing, he raised me up
from the floor, and, folding me in his arms, embraced me
tenderly. He expressed his deep sorrow when I told

him that in Naples I had not been able to find any instructions to enable me to join him, but his face lighted up again when I added that I was indebted to no one for money, and that I was in good health. He bade me take a seat, and with a heavy sigh he began to talk of his poverty, and ordered a servant to lay the cloth for three persons. Besides this servant, his lordship's suite consisted of a most devout-looking housekeeper, and of a priest whom I judged to be very ignorant from the few words he uttered during our meal. The house inhabited by his lordship was large, but badly built and poorly kept. The furniture was so miserable that, in order to make up a bed for me in the room adjoining his chamber, the poor bishop had to give up one of his two mattresses! His dinner, not to say any more about it, frightened me, for he was very strict in keeping the rules of his order, and this being a fast day, he did not eat any meat, and the oil was very bad. Nevertheless, monsignor was an intelligent man, and, what is still better, an honest man. He told me, much to my surprise, that his bishopric, although not one of little importance, brought him in only five hundred ducat-di-regno yearly, and that, unfortunately, he had contracted debts to the amount of six hundred. He added, with a sigh, that his only happiness was to feel himself out of the clutches of the monks, who had persecuted him, and made his life a perfect purgatory for fifteen years. All these confidences caused me sorrow and mortification, because they proved to me, not only that I was not in the promised land where a mitre could be picked up, but also that I would be a heavy charge for him. I felt that he was grieved himself at the sorry present his patronage seemed likely to prove.

I enquired whether he had a good library, whether

there were any literary men, or any good society in which one could spend a few agreeable hours. He smiled and answered that throughout his diocese there was not one man who could boast of writing decently, and still less of any taste or knowledge in literature; that there was not a single bookseller, nor any person caring even for the newspapers. But he promised me that we would follow our literary tastes together, as soon as he received the books he had ordered from Naples.

That was all very well, but was this the place for a young man of eighteen to live in, without a good library, without good society, without emulation and literary intercourse? The good bishop, seeing me full of sad thoughts, and almost astounded at the prospect of the miserable life I should have to lead with him, tried to give me courage by promising to do everything in his power to secure my happiness.

The next day, the bishop having to officiate in his pontifical robes, I had an opportunity of seeing all the clergy, and all the faithful of the diocese, men and women, of whom the cathedral was full; the sight made me resolve at once to leave Martorano. I thought I was gazing upon a troop of brutes for whom my external appearance was a cause of scandal. How ugly were the women! What a look of stupidity and coarseness in the men! When I returned to the bishop's house I told the prelate that I did not feel in me the vocation to die within a few months a martyr in this miserable city.

"Give me your blessing," I added, "and let me go; or, rather, come with me. I promise you that we shall make a fortune somewhere else."

The proposal made him laugh repeatedly during the day. Had he agreed to it he would not have died two years afterwards in the prime of manhood. The worthy

man, feeling how natural was my repugnance, begged me
to forgive him for having summoned me to him, and,
considering it his duty to send me back to Venice, having no money himself and not being aware that I had
any, he told me that he would give me an introduction
to a worthy citizen of Naples who would lend me sixty
ducati-di-regno to enable me to reach my native city.
I accepted his offer with gratitude, and going to my room
I took out of my trunk the case of fine razors which
the Greek had given me, and I begged his acceptance
of it as a souvenir of me. I had great difficulty in forc-
ing it upon him, for it was worth the sixty ducats, and
to conquer his resistance I had to threaten to remain
with him if he refused my present. He gave me a very
flattering letter of recommendation for the Archbishop
of Cosenza, in which he requested him to forward me as
far as Naples without any expense to myself. It was
thus I left Martorano sixty hours after my arrival, pitying the bishop whom I was leaving behind, and who
wept as he was pouring heartfelt blessings upon me.

The Archbishop of Cosenza, a man of wealth and of
intelligence, offered me a room in his palace. During
the dinner I made, with an overflowing heart, the eulogy
of the Bishop of Martorano; but I railed mercilessly at
his diocese and at the whole of Calabria in so cutting a
manner that I greatly amused the archbishop and all his
guests, amongst whom were two ladies, his relatives, who
did the honours of the dinner-table. The youngest, however, objected to the satirical style in which I had depicted her country, and declared war against me; but
I contrived to obtain peace again by telling her that
Calabria would be a delightful country if one-fourth only
of its inhabitants were like her. Perhaps it was with
the idea of proving to me that I had been wrong in my

opinion that the archbishop gave on the following day a splendid supper.

Cosenza is a city in which a gentleman can find plenty of amusement; the nobility are wealthy, the women are pretty, and men generally well-informed, because they have been educated in Naples or in Rome.

I left Cosenza on the third day with a letter from the archbishop for the far-famed Genovesi.

I had five travelling companions, whom I judged, from their appearance, to be either pirates or banditti, and I took very good care not to let them see or guess that I had a well-filled purse. I likewise thought it prudent to go to bed without undressing during the whole journey—an excellent measure of prudence for a young man travelling in that part of the country.

I reached Naples on the 16th of September, 1743, and I lost no time in presenting the letter of the Bishop of Martorano. It was addressed to a M. Gennaro Polo at St.-Anné's. This excellent man, whose duty was only to give me the sum of sixty ducats, insisted, after perusing the bishop's letter, upon receiving me in his house, because he wished me to make the acquaintance of his son, who was a poet like myself. The bishop had represented my poetry as sublime. After the usual ceremonies, I accepted his kind invitation, my trunk was sent for, and I was a guest in the house of M. Gennaro Polo.

CHAPTER IX

My Stay in Naples; It Is Short but Happy—Don Antonio Casanova—Don Lelio Caraffa—I Go to Rome in Very Agreeable Company, and Enter the Service of Cardinal Acquaviva—Barbara—Testaccio—Frascati

I HAD no difficulty in answering the various questions which Doctor Gennaro addressed to me, but I was surprised, and even displeased, at the constant peals of laughter with which he received my answers. The piteous description of miserable Calabria, and the picture of the sad situation of the Bishop of Martorano, appeared to me more likely to call forth tears than to excite hilarity, and, suspecting that some mystification was being played upon me, I was very near getting angry when, becoming more composed, he told me with feeling that I must kindly excuse him; that his laughter was a disease which seemed to be endemic in his family, for one of his uncles died of it.

"What!" I exclaimed, "died of laughing!"

"Yes. This disease, which was not known to Hippocrates, is called *li flati.*"

"What do you mean? Does an hypochondriac affection, which causes sadness and lowness in all those who suffer from it, render you cheerful?"

"Yes, because, most likely, my *flati,* instead of influencing the hypochondrium, affects my spleen, which my

physician asserts to be the organ of laughter. It is quite
a discovery."

"You are mistaken; it is a very ancient notion, and it
is the only function which is ascribed to the spleen in
our animal organization."

"Well, we must discuss the matter at length, for I hope
you will remain with us a few weeks."

"I wish I could, but I must leave Naples to-morrow
or the day after."

"Have you got any money?"

"I rely upon the sixty ducats you have to give me."

At these words, his peals of laughter began again, and
as he could see that I was annoyed, he said, "I am
amused at the idea that I can keep you here as long as
I like. But be good enough to see my son; he writes
pretty verses enough."

And truly his son, although only fourteen, was already
a great poet.

A servant took me to the apartment of the young man
whom I found possessed of a pleasing countenance and
engaging manners. He gave me a polite welcome, and
begged to be excused if he could not attend to me altogether for the present, as he had to finish a song which
he was composing for a relative of the Duchess de Ro-
vino, who was taking the veil at the Convent of St.-
Claire, and the printer was waiting for the manuscript.
I told him that his excuse was a very good one, and I
offered to assist him. He then read his song, and I found
it so full of enthusiasm, and so truly in the style of
Guidi, that I advised him to call it an ode; but as I
had praised all the truly beautiful passages, I thought
I could venture to point out the weak ones, and I replaced them by verses of my own composition. He was
delighted, and thanked me warmly, inquiring whether I

was Apollo. As he was writing his ode, I composed a sonnet on the same subject, and, expressing his admiration for it he begged me to sign it, and to allow him to send it with his poetry.

While I was correcting and recopying my manuscript, he went to his father to find out who I was, which made the old man laugh until supper-time. In the evening, I had the pleasure of seeing that my bed had been prepared in the young man's chamber.

Doctor Gennaro's family was composed of this son and of a daughter unfortunately very plain, of his wife and of two elderly, devout sisters. Amongst the guests at the supper-table I met several literary men, and the Marquis Galiani, who was at that time annotating Vitruvius. He had a brother, an abbé whose acquaintance I made twenty years after, in Paris, when he was secretary of embassy to Count Cantillana. The next day, at supper, I was presented to the celebrated Genovesi; I had already sent him the letter of the Archbishop of Cosenza. He spoke to me of Apostolo Zeno and of the Abbé Conti. He remarked that it was considered a very venial sin for a regular priest to say two masses in one day for the sake of earning two carlini more, but that for the same sin a secular priest would deserve to be burnt at the stake.

The nun took the veil on the following day, and Gennaro's ode and my sonnet had the greatest success. A Neapolitan gentleman, whose name was the same as mine, expressed a wish to know me, and, hearing that I resided at the doctor's, he called to congratulate him on the occasion of his feast-day, which happened to fall on the day following the ceremony at Sainte-Claire.

Don Antonio Casanova, informing me of his name, enquired whether my family was originally from Venice.

"I am, sir," I answered modestly, "the great-grandson of the unfortunate Marco Antonio Casanova, secretary to Cardinal Pompeo Colonna, who died of the plague in Rome, in the year 1528, under the pontificate of Clement VII." The words were scarcely out of my lips when he embraced me, calling me his cousin, but we all thought that Doctor Gennaro would actually die with laughter, for it seemed impossible to laugh so immoderately without risk of life. Madame Gennaro was very angry and told my newly-found cousin that he might have avoided enacting such a scene before her husband, knowing his disease, but he answered that he never thought the circumstance likely to provoke mirth. I said nothing, for, in reality, I felt that the recognition was very comic. Our poor laugher having recovered his composure, Casanova, who had remained very serious, invited me to dinner for the next day with my young friend Paul Gennaro, who had already become my *alter ego.*

When we called at his house, my worthy cousin showed me his family tree, beginning with a Don Francisco, brother of Don Juan. In my pedigree, which I knew by heart, Don Juan, my direct ancestor, was a posthumous child. It was possible that there might have been a brother of Marco Antonio's; but when he heard that my genealogy began with Don Francisco, from Aragon, who had lived in the fourteenth century, and that consequently all the pedigree of the illustrious house of the Casanovas of Saragossa belonged to him, his joy knew no bounds; he did not know what to do to convince me that the same blood was flowing in his veins and in mine.

He expressed some curiosity to know what lucky accident had brought me to Naples; I told him that, hav-

ing embraced the ecclesiastical profession, I was going
to Rome to seek my fortune. He then presented me to
his family, and I thought that I could read on the countenance of my cousin, his dearly-beloved wife, that she
was not much pleased with the newly-found relation-
ship, but his pretty daughter, and a still prettier niece
of his, might very easily have given me faith in the doctrine that blood is thicker than water, however fabulous
it may be.

After dinner, Don Antonio informed me that the
Duchess de Bovino had expressed a wish to know the
Abbé Casanova who had written the sonnet in honour
of her relative, and that he would be very happy to introduce me to her as his own cousin. As we were alone
at that moment, I begged he would not insist on presenting me, as I was only provided with travelling suits,
and had to be careful of my purse so as not to arrive
in Rome without money. Delighted at my confidence,
and approving my economy, he said, "I am rich, and you
must not scruple to come with me to my tailor;" and
he accompanied his offer with an assurance that the
circumstance would not be known to anyone, and that he
would feel deeply mortified if I denied him the pleasure
of serving me. I shook him warmly by the hand, and answered that I was ready to do anything he pleased. We
went to a tailor who took my measure, and who brought
me on the following day everything necessary to the
toilet of the most elegant abbé. Don Antonio called on
me, and remained to dine with Don Gennaro, after
which he took me and my friend Paul to the duchess.
This lady, according to the Neapolitan fashion, called
me *thou* in her very first compliment of welcome. Her
daughter, then only ten or twelve years old, was very
handsome, and a few years later became Duchess de Ma-

talona. The duchess presented me with a snuff-box in pale tortoise-shell with arabesque incrustations in gold, and she invited us to dine with her on the morrow, promising to take us after dinner to the Convent of St.-Claire to pay a visit to the new nun.

As we came out of the palace of the duchess, I left my friends and went alone to Panagiotti's to claim the barrel of muscatel wine. The manager was kind enough to have the barrel divided into two smaller casks of equal capacity, and I sent one to Don Antonio, and the other to Don Gennaro. As I was leaving the shop I met the worthy Panagiotti, who was glad to see me. Was I to blush at the sight of the good man I had at first deceived? No, for in his opinion I had acted very nobly towards him.

Don Gennaro, as I returned home, managed to thank me for my handsome present without laughing, and the next day Don Antonio, to make up for the muscatel wine I had sent him, offered me a gold-headed cane, worth at least fifteen ounces, and his tailor brought me a travelling suit and a blue great coat, with the button-holes in gold lace. I therefore found myself splendidly equipped.

At the Duchess de Bovino's dinner I made the acquaintance of the wisest and most learned man in Naples, the illustrious Don Lelio Caraffa, who belonged to the ducal family of Matalona, and whom King Carlos honoured with the title of friend.

I spent two delightful hours in the convent parlour, coping successfully with the curiosity of all the nuns who were pressing against the grating. Had destiny allowed me to remain in Naples my fortune would have been made; but, although I had no fixed plan, the voice of fate summoned me to Rome, and therefore I resisted all the entreaties of my cousin Antonio to accept the honourable position of tutor in several houses of the highest order.

Don Antonio gave a splendid dinner in my honour, but he was annoyed and angry because he saw that his wife looked daggers at her new cousin. I thought that, more than once, she cast a glance at my new costume, and then whispered to the guest next to her. Very likely she knew what had taken place. There are some positions in life to which I could never be reconciled. If, in the most brilliant circle, there is one person who affects to stare at me I lose all presence of mind. Self-dignity feels outraged, my wit dies away, and I play the part of a dolt. It is a weakness on my part, but a weakness I cannot overcome.

Don Lelio Caraffa offered me a very liberal salary if I would undertake the education of his nephew, the Duke de Matalona, then ten years of age. I expressed my gratitude, and begged him to be my true benefactor in a different manner—namely, by giving me a few good letters of introduction for Rome, a favour which he granted at once. He gave me one for Cardinal Acquaviva, and another for Father Georgi.

I found out that the interest felt towards me by my friends had induced them to obtain for me the honour of kissing the hand of Her Majesty the Queen, and I hastened my preparations to leave Naples, for the queen would certainly have asked me some questions, and I could not have avoided telling her that I had just left Martorano and the poor bishop whom she had sent there. The queen likewise knew my mother; she would very likely have alluded to my mother's profession in Dresden; it would have mortified Don Antonio, and my pedigree would have been covered with ridicule. I knew the force of prejudice! I should have been ruined, and I felt I should do well to withdraw in good time. As I took leave of him, Don Antonio presented me with a fine gold watch and gave me a letter for Don Gaspar Vidaldi, whom he called his best friend. Don Gennaro paid me the sixty ducats, and his son, swearing eternal friendship, asked me to write to him. They all accompanied me to the coach, blending their tears with mine, and loading me with good wishes and blessings.

From my landing in Chiozza up to my arrival in Naples, fortune had seemed bent upon frowning on me; in Naples it began to shew itself less adverse, and on my return to that city it entirely smiled upon me. Naples has always been a fortunate place for me, as the reader of my memoirs will discover. My readers must not forget that in Portici I was on the point of disgracing myself, and there is no remedy against the degradation of the mind, for nothing can restore it to its former standard. It is a case of disheartening atony for which there is no possible cure.

I was not ungrateful to the good Bishop of Martorano, for, if he had unwittingly injured me by summoning me to his diocese, I felt that to his letter for M. Gennaro I was indebted for all the good fortune which had just befallen me. I wrote to him from Rome.

I was wholly engaged in drying my tears as we were driving through the beautiful street of Toledo, and it was only after we had left Naples that I could find time to examine the countenance of my travelling companions. Next to me, I saw a man of from forty to fifty, with a pleasing face and a lively air, but, opposite to me, two charming faces delighted my eyes. They belonged to two ladies, young and pretty, very well dressed, with a look of candour and modesty. This discovery was most agreeable, but I felt sad and I wanted calm and silence. We reached Avessa without one word being exchanged, and as the *vetturino* stopped there only to water his mules, we did not get out of the coach. From Avessa to Capua my companions conversed almost without interruption, and, wonderful to relate! I did not open my lips once. I was amused by the Neapolitan jargon of the gentleman, and by the pretty accent of the ladies, who were evidently Romans. It was a most wonderful feat for me to remain five hours before two charming women without addressing one word to them, without paying them one compliment.

At Capua, where we were to spend the night, we put up at an inn, and were shown into a room with two beds—a very usual thing in Italy. The Neapolitan, addressing himself to me, said,

"Am I to have the honour of sleeping with the reverend gentleman?"

I answerd in a very serious tone that it was for him to choose or to arrange it otherwise, if he liked. The answer made the two ladies smile, particularly the one whom I preferred, and it seemed to me a good omen.

We were five at supper, for it is usual for the *vetturino* to supply his travellers with their meals, unless some private agreement is made otherwise, and to sit down at table with them. In the desultory talk which went on during the supper, I found in my travelling companions decorum, propriety, wit, and the manners of persons accustomed to good society. I became curious to know who they were, and going down with the driver after supper, I asked him.

"The gentleman," he told me, "is an advocate, and one of the ladies is his wife, but I do not know which of the two."

I went back to our room, and I was polite enough to
go to bed first, in order to make it easier for the ladies
to undress themselves with freedom; I likewise got up
first in the morning, left the room, and only returned
when I was called for breakfast. The coffee was delicious. I praised it highly, and the lady, the one who
was my favourite, promised that I should have the same
every morning during our journey. The barber came in
after breakfast; the advocate was shaved, and the barber
offered me his services, which I declined, but the rogue
declared that it was slovenly to wear one's beard.

When we had resumed our seats in the coach, the advocate made some remark upon the impudence of barbers
in general.

"But we ought to decide first," said the lady, "whether
or not it is slovenly to go bearded."

"Of course it is," said the advocate. "Beard is nothing but a dirty excrescence."

"You may think so," I answered, "but everybody does
not share your opinion. Do we consider as a dirty
excrescence the hair of which we take so much care, and
which is of the same nature as the beard? Far from
it; we admire the length and the beauty of the hair."

"Then," remarked the lady, "the barber is a fool."

"But after all," I asked, "have I any beard?"

"I thought you had," she answered.

"In that case, I will begin to shave as soon as I reach
Rome, for this is the first time that I have been convicted
of having a beard."

"My dear wife," exclaimed the advocate, "you should
have held your tongue; perhaps the reverend abbé is
going to Rome with the intention of becoming a Capuchin friar."

The pleasantry made me laugh, but, unwilling that he

should have the last word, I answered that he had guessed rightly, that such had been my intention, but that I had entirely altered my mind since I had seen his wife.

"Oh! you are wrong," said the joyous Neapolitan, "for my wife is very fond of Capuchins, and if you wish to please her, you had better follow your original vocation." Our conversation continued in the same tone of pleasantry, and the day passed off in an agreeable manner; in the evening we had a very poor supper at Garillan, but we made up for it by cheerfulness and witty conversation. My dawning inclination for the advocate's wife borrowed strength from the affectionate manner she displayed towards me.

The next day she asked me, after we had resumed our journey, whether I intended to make a long stay in Rome before returning to Venice. I answered that, having no acquaintances in Rome, I was afraid my life there would be very dull.

"Strangers are liked in Rome," she said, "I feel certain that you will be pleased with your residence in that city."

"May I hope, madam, that you will allow me to pay you my respects?"

"We shall be honoured by your calling on us," said the advocate.

My eyes were fixed upon his charming wife. She blushed, but I did not appear to notice it. I kept up the conversation, and the day passed as pleasantly as the previous one. We stopped at Terracina, where they gave us a room with three beds, two single beds and a large one between the two others. It was natural that the two sisters should take the large bed; they did so, and undressed themselves while the advocate and I went on talking at the table, with our backs turned to them.

As soon as they had gone to rest, the advocate took the bed on which he found his nightcap, and I the other, which was only about one foot distant from the large bed. I remarked that the lady by whom I was captivated was on the side nearest my couch, and, without much vanity, I could suppose that it was not owing only to chance.

I put the light out and laid down, revolving in my mind a project which I could not abandon, and yet durst not execute. In vain did I court sleep. A very faint light enabled me to perceive the bed in which the pretty woman was lying, and my eyes would, in spite of myself, remain open. It would be difficult to guess what I might have done at last (I had already fought a hard battle with myself for more than an hour), when I saw her rise, get out of her bed, and go and lay herself down near her husband, who, most likely, did not wake up, and continued to sleep in peace, for I did not hear any noise.

Vexed, disgusted . . . I tried to compose myself to sleep, and I woke only at day-break. Seeing the beautiful wandering star in her own bed, I got up, dressed myself in haste, and went out, leaving all my companions fast asleep. I returned to the inn only at the time fixed for our departure, and I found the advocate and the two ladies already in the coach, waiting for me.

The lady complained, in a very obliging manner, of my not having cared for her coffee; I pleaded as an excuse a desire for an early walk, and I took care not to honour her even with a look; I feigned to be suffering from the toothache, and remained in my corner dull and silent. At Piperno she managed to whisper to me that my toothache was all sham; I was pleased with the re-

proach, because it heralded an explanation which I
craved for, in spite of my vexation.

During the afternoon I continued my policy of the
morning. I was morose and silent until we reached
Sermonetta, where we were to pass the night. We arrived early, and the weather being fine, the lady said
that she could enjoy a walk, and asked me politely to
offer her my arm. I did so, for it would have been rude
to refuse; besides I had had enough of my sulking fit.
An explanation could alone bring matters back to their
original standing, but I did not know how to force it
upon the lady. Her husband followed us at some distance with the sister.

When we were far enough in advance, I ventured to
ask her why she had supposed my toothache to have
been feigned.

"I am very candid," she said; "it is because the difference in your manner was so marked, and because
you were so careful to avoid looking at me through the
whole day. A toothache would not have prevented you
from being polite, and therefore I thought it had been
feigned for some purpose. But I am certain that not
one of us can possibly have given you any grounds for
such a rapid change in your manner."

"Yet something must have caused the change, and
you, madam, are only half sincere."

"You are mistaken, sir, I am entirely sincere; and if
I have given you any motive for anger, I am, and must
remain, ignorant of it. Be good enough to tell me what
I have done."

"Nothing, for I have no right to complain."

"Yes, you have; you have a right, the same that I
have myself; the right which good society grants to

every one of its members. Speak, and shew yourself as
sincere as I am."

"You are certainly bound not to know, or to pretend
not to know the real cause, but you must acknowledge
that my duty is to remain silent."

"Very well; now it is all over; but if your duty bids
you to conceal the cause of your bad humour, it also bids
you not to shew it. Delicacy sometimes enforces upon a
polite gentleman the necessity of concealing certain feelings which might implicate either himself or others; it is
a restraint for the mind, I confess, but it has some advantage when its effect is to render more amiable the
man who forces himself to accept that restraint."

Her close argument made me blush for shame, and
carrying her beautiful hand to my lips, I confessed myself in the wrong.

"You would see me at your feet," I exclaimed, "in
token of my repentance, were I not afraid of injuring
you——"

"Do not let us allude to the matter any more," she
answered.

And, pleased with my repentance, she gave me a look
so expressive of forgiveness that, without being afraid
of augmenting my guilt, I took my lips off her hand and
raised them to her half-open, smiling mouth.

Intoxicated with rapture, I passed so rapidly from a
state of sadness to one of overwhelming cheerfulness that
during our supper the advocate enjoyed a thousand jokes
upon my toothache, so quickly cured by the simple
remedy of a walk.

On the following day we dined at Velletri and slept
in Marino, where, although the town was full of troops,
we had two small rooms and a good supper.

I could not have been on better terms with my charming Roman; for, although I had received but a rapid proof of her regard, it had been such a true one—such a tender one! In the coach our eyes could not say much; but I was opposite to her, and our feet spoke a very eloquent language.

The advocate had told me that he was going to Rome on some ecclesiastical business, and that he intended to reside in the house of his mother-in-law, whom his wife had not seen since her marriage, two years ago, and her sister hoped to remain in Rome, where she expected to marry a clerk at the Spirito Santo Bank. He gave me their address, with a pressing invitation to call upon them, and I promised to devote all my spare time to them.

We were enjoying our dessert, when my beautiful lady-love, admiring my snuff-box, told her husband that she wished she had one like it.

"I will buy you one, dear."

"Then buy mine," I said; "I will let you have it for twenty ounces, and you can give me a note of hand payable to bearer in payment. I owe that amount to an Englishman, and I will give it him to redeem my debt."

"Your snuff-box, my dear abbé, is worth twenty ounces, but I cannot buy it unless you agree to receive payment in cash; I should be delighted to see it in my wife's possession, and she would keep it as a remembrance of you."

His wife, thinking that I would not accept his offer, said that she had no objection to give me the note of hand.

"But," exclaimed the advocate, "can you not guess the Englishman exists only in our friend's imagination? He would never enter an appearance, and we would have the snuff-box for nothing. Do not trust the abbé, my dear, he is a great cheat."

"I had no idea," answered his wife, looking at me, "that the world contained rogues of this species."

I affected a melancholy air, and said that I only wished myself rich enough to be often guilty of such cheating.

When a man is in love, very little is enough to throw him into despair, and as little to enhance his joy to the utmost. There was but one bed in the room where supper had been served, and another in a small closet leading out of the room, but without a door. The ladies chose the closet, and the advocate retired to rest before me. I bid the ladies good night as soon as they had gone to bed; I looked at my dear mistress, and after undressing myself I went to bed, intending not to sleep through the night. But the reader may imagine my rage when I found, as I got into the bed, that it creaked loud enough to wake the dead. I waited, however, quite motionless, until my companion should be fast asleep, and as soon as his snoring told me that he was entirely under the influence of Morpheus, I tried to slip out of the bed; but the infernal creaking which took place whenever I moved, woke my companion, who felt about with his hand, and, finding me near him, went to sleep again. Half an hour after, I tried a second time, but with the same result. I had to give it up in despair.

Love is the most cunning of gods; in the midst of obstacles he seems to be in his own element, but as his very existence depends upon the enjoyment of those who ardently worship him, the shrewd, all-seeing, little blind god contrives to bring success out of the most desperate case.

I had given up all hope for the night, and had nearly

gone to sleep, when suddenly we hear a dreadful noise. Guns are fired in the street, people, screaming and howling, are running up and down the stairs; at last there is a loud knocking at our door. The advocate, frightened out of his slumbers, asks me what it can all mean; I pretend to be very indifferent, and beg to be allowed to sleep. But the ladies are trembling with fear, and loudly calling for a light. I remain very quiet, the advocate jumps out of bed, and runs out of the room to obtain a candle; I rise at once, I follow him to shut the door, but I slam it rather too hard, the double spring of the lock gives way, and the door cannot be reopened without the key.

I approach the ladies in order to calm their anxiety, telling them that the advocate would soon return with a light, and that we should then know the cause of the tumult, but I am not losing my time, and am at work while I am speaking. I meet with very little opposition, but, leaning rather too heavily upon my fair lady, I break through the bottom of the bedstead, and we suddenly find ourselves, the two ladies and myself, all together in a heap on the floor. The advocate comes back and knocks at the door; the sister gets up, I obey the prayers of my charming friend, and, feeling my way, reach the door, and tell the advocate that I cannot open it, and that he must get the key. The two sisters are behind me. I extend my hand; but I am abruptly repulsed, and judge that I have addressed myself to the wrong quarter; I go to the other side, and there I am better received. But the husband returns, the noise of the key in the lock announces that the door is going to be opened, and we return to our respective beds.

The advocate hurries to the bed of the two frightened ladies, thinking of relieving their anxiety, but, when he sees them buried in their broken-down bedstead, he bursts into a loud laugh. He tells me to come and have a look at them, but I am very modest, and decline the invitation. He then tells us that the alarm has been caused by a German detachment attacking suddenly the Spanish troops in the city, and that the Spaniards are running away. In a quarter of an hour the noise has ceased, and quiet is entirely re-established.

The advocate complimented me upon my coolness, got into bed again, and was soon asleep. As for me, I was careful not to close my eyes, and as soon as I saw daylight I got up in order to perform certain ablutions and to change my shirt; it was an absolute necessity.

I returned for breakfast, and while we were drinking the delicious coffee which Donna Lucrezia had made, as I thought, better than ever, I remarked that her sister frowned on me. But how little I cared for her anger when I saw the cheerful, happy countenance, and the approving looks of my adored Lucrezia! I felt a delightful sensation run through the whole of my body.

We reached Rome very early. We had taken breakfast at the Tour, and the advocate being in a very gay mood I assumed the same tone, loading him with compliments, and predicting that a son would be born to him, I compelled his wife to promise it should be so. I did not forget the sister of my charming Lucrezia, and to make her change her hostile attitude towards me I addressed to her so many pretty compliments, and behaved in such a friendly manner, that she was compelled to forgive the fall of the bed. As I took leave of them, I promised to give them a call on the following day.

I was in Rome! with a good wardrobe, pretty well supplied with money and jewellery, not wanting in experience, and with excellent letters of introduction. I was free, my own master, and just reaching the age in which a man can have faith in his own fortune, provided he is not deficient in courage, and is blessed with a face likely to attract the sympathy of those he mixes with. I was not handsome, but I had something better than beauty—a striking expression which almost compelled a kind interest in my favour, and I felt myself ready for anything. I knew that Rome is the one city in which a man can begin from the lowest rung, and reach the very top of the social ladder. This knowledge increased my courage, and I must confess that a most inveterate feeling of self-esteem which, on account of my inexperience, I could not distrust, enhanced wonderfully my confidence in myself.

The man who intends to make his fortune in this ancient capital of the world must be a chameleon susceptible of reflecting all the colours of the atmosphere that surrounds him—a Proteus apt to assume every form, every shape. He must be supple, flexible, insinuating, close, inscrutable, often base, sometimes sincere, sometimes perfidious, always concealing a part of his knowledge, indulging but in one tone of voice, patient, a perfect master of his own countenance, as cold as ice when any other man would be all fire; and if unfortunately he is not religious at heart—a very common occurrence for a soul possessing the above requisites—he must have religion in his mind, that is to say, on his face, on his lips, in his manners; he must suffer quietly, if he be an honest man, the necessity of knowing himself an arrant hypocrite. The man whose soul would loathe such a life should leave Rome and seek his fortune elsewhere. I do not know whether I am praising or excusing myself, but of all those qualities I possessed but one—namely, flexibility; for the rest, I was only an interesting, heedless young fellow, a pretty good blood horse, but not broken, or rather badly broken; and that is much worse.

I began by delivering the letter I had received from Don Lelio for Father Georgi. The learned monk enjoyed the esteem of everyone in Rome, and the Pope himself had a great consideration for him, because he disliked the Jesuits, and did not put a mask on to tear the mask from their faces, although they deemed themselves powerful enough to despise him.

He read the letter with great attention, and expressed himself disposed to be my adviser; and that consequently I might make him responsible for any evil which might befall me, as misfortune is not to be feared by a man who acts rightly. He asked me what I intended to do in Rome, and I answered that I wished him to tell me what to do.

"Perhaps I may; but in that case you must come and see me often, and never conceal from me anything, you understand, not anything, of what interests you, or of what happens to you."

"Don Lelio has likewise given me a letter for the Cardinal Acquaviva."

"I congratulate you; the cardinal's influence in Rome is greater even than that of the Pope."

"Must I deliver the letter at once?"

"No; I will see him this evening, and prepare him for your visit. Call on me to-morrow morning, and I will then tell you where and when you are to deliver your letter to the cardinal. Have you any money?"

"Enough for all my wants during one year."

"That is well. Have you any acquaintances?"

"Not one."

"Do not make any without first consulting me, and,

above all, avoid coffee-houses and ordinaries, but if you should happen to frequent such places, listen and never speak. Be careful to form your judgment upon those who ask any questions from you, and if common civility obliges you to give an answer, give only an evasive one, if any other is likely to commit you. Do you speak French?"

"Not one word."

"I am sorry for that; you must learn French. Have you been a student?"

"A poor one, but I have a sufficient smattering to converse with ordinary company."

"That is enough; but be very prudent, for Rome is the city in which smatterers unmask each other, and are always at war amongst themselves. I hope you will take your letter to the cardinal, dressed like a modest abbé, and not in this elegant costume which is not likely to conjure fortune. Adieu, let me see you to-morrow."

Highly pleased with the welcome I had received at his hands, and with all he had said to me, I left his house and proceeded towards Campo-di-Fiore to deliver the letter of my cousin Antonio to Don Gaspar Vivaldi, who received me in his library, where I met two respectable-looking priests. He gave me the most friendly welcome, asked for my address, and invited me to dinner for the next day. He praised Father Georgi most highly, and, accompanying me as far as the stairs, he told me that he would give me on the morrow the amount his friend Don Antonio requested him to hand me.

More money which my generous cousin was bestowing on me! It is easy enough to give away when one possesses sufficient means to do it, but it is not every man who knows how to give. I found the proceeding of Don Antonio more delicate even than generous; I could not refuse his present; it was my duty to prove my gratitude by accepting it.

Just after I had left M. Vivaldi's house I found myself face to face with Stephano, and this extraordinary original loaded me with friendly caresses. I inwardly despised him, yet I could not feel hatred for him; I looked upon him as the instrument which Providence had been pleased to employ in order to save me from ruin. After telling me that he had obtained from the Pope all he wished, he advised me to avoid meeting the fatal constable who had advanced me two sequins in Seraval, because he had found out that I had deceived him, and had sworn revenge against me. I asked Stephano to induce the man to leave my acknowledgement of the debt in the hands of a certain merchant whom we both knew, and that I would call there to discharge the amount. This was done, and it ended the affair.

That evening I dined at the ordinary, which was frequented by Romans and foreigners; but I carefully followed the advice of Father Georgi. I heard a great deal of harsh language used against the Pope and against the Cardinal Minister, who had caused the Papal States to be inundated by eighty thousand men, Germans as well as Spaniards. But I was much surprised when I saw that everybody was eating meat, although it was Saturday. But a stranger during the first few days after his arrival in Rome is surrounded with many things which at first cause surprise, and to which he soon gets accustomed. There is not a Catholic city in the world in which a man is half so free on religious matters as in Rome. The inhabitants of Rome are like the men employed at the Government tobacco works, who are allowed to take gratis as much tobacco as they want for their own use. One can live in Rome with the most complete freedom, except that the *ordini santissimi* are as much to be dreaded as the famous *lettres-de-cachet* before the Revolution came and destroyed them, and shewed the whole world the general character of the French nation.

The next day, the 1st of October, 1743, I made up my mind to be shaved. The down on my chin had become a beard, and I judged that it was time to renounce some of the privileges enjoyed by adolescence. I dressed myself completely in the Roman fashion, and Father Georgi was highly pleased when he saw me in that costume, which had been made by the tailor of my dear cousin, Don Antonio.

Father Georgi invited me to take a cup of chocolate with him, and informed me that the cardinal had been apprised of my arrival by a letter from Don Lelio, and that his eminence would receive me at noon at the Villa Negroni, where he would be taking a walk. I told Father Georgi that I had been invited to dinner by M. Vivaldi, and he advised me to cultivate his acquaintance.

I proceeded to the Villa Negroni; the moment he saw me the cardinal stopped to receive my letter, allowing two persons who accompanied him to walk forward. He put the letter in his pocket without reading it, examined me for one or two minutes, and enquired whether I felt any taste for politics. I answered that, until now, I had not felt in me any but frivolous tastes, but that I would make bold to answer for my readiness to execute all the orders which his eminence might be pleased to lay upon me, if he should judge me worthy of entering his service.

"Come to my office to-morrow morning," said the cardinal, "and ask for the Abbé Gama, to whom I will give my instructions. You must apply yourself diligently to the study of the French language; it is indispensable."

He then enquired after Don Leilo's health, and after kissing his hand I took my leave.

I hastened to the house of M. Gaspar Vivaldi, where I dined amongst a well-chosen party of guests. M. Vivaldi was not married; literature was his only passion. He loved Latin poetry even better than Italian, and Horace, whom I knew by heart, was his favourite poet. After dinner, we repaired to his study, and he handed me one hundred Roman crowns, and Don Antonio's present, and assured me that I would be most welcome whenever I would call to take a cup of chocolate with him.

After I had taken leave of Don Gaspar, I proceeded towards the Minerva, for I longed to enjoy the surprise of my dear Lucrezia and of her sister; I inquired for Donna Cecilia Monti, their mother, and I saw, to my great astonishment, a young widow who looked like the sister of her two charming daughters. There was no need for me to give her my name; I had been announced, and she expected me. Her daughters soon came in, and their greeting caused me some amusement, for I did not appear to them to be the same individual. Donna Lucrezia presented me to her youngest sister, only eleven years of age, and to her brother, an abbé of fifteen, of charming appearance. I took care to behave so as to please the mother; I was modest, respectful, and shewed a deep interest in everything I saw. The good advocate arrived, and was surprised at the change in my appearance. He launched out in his usual jokes, and I followed him on that ground, yet I was careful not to give to my conversation the tone of levity which used to cause so much mirth in our travelling coach; so that, to pay me a compliment, he told me that, if I had had the sign of manhood shaved from my face, I had certainly transferred it to my mind. Donna Lucrezia did not know what to think of the change in my manners.

Towards evening I saw, coming in rapid succession, five or six ordinary-looking ladies, and as many abbés, who appeared to me some of the volumes with which I was to begin my Roman education. They all listened attentively to the most insignificant word I uttered, and I was very careful to let them enjoy their conjectures about me. Donna Cecilia told the advocate that he was but a poor painter, and that his portraits were not like the originals; he answered that she could not judge, because the original was shewing under a mask, and I pretended to be mortified by his answer. Donna Lucrezia said that she found me exactly the same, and her sister was of opinion that the air of Rome gave strangers a peculiar appearance. Everybody applauded, and Angélique turned red with satisfaction. After a visit of four hours I bowed myself out, and the advocate, following me, told me that his mother-in-law begged me to consider myself as a friend of the family, and to be certain of a welcome at any hour I liked to call. I thanked him gratefully and took my leave, trusting that I had pleased this amiable society as much as it had pleased me.

The next day I presented myself to the Abbé Gama. He was a Portuguese, about forty years old, handsome, and with a countenance full of candour, wit, and good temper. His affability claimed and obtained confidence. His manners and accent were quite Roman. He informed me, in the blandest manner, that his eminence had himself given his instructions about me to his major-domo, that I would have a lodging in the cardinal's palace, that I would have my meals at the secretaries' table, and that, until I learned French, I would have nothing to do but make extracts from letters that he would supply me with. He then gave me the address of the French teacher to whom he had already spoken in my behalf. He was a Roman advocate, Dalacqua by name, residing precisely opposite the palace.

After this short explanation, and an assurance that I could at all times rely upon his friendship, he had me taken to the major-domo, who made me sign my name at the bottom of a page in a large book, already filled with other names, and counted out sixty Roman crowns which he paid me for three months salary in advance. After this he accompanied me, followed by a *staffiere* to my apartment on the third floor, which I found very comfortably furnished. The servant handed me the key, saying that he would come every morning to attend upon me, and the major-domo accompanied me to the gate to make me known to the gate-keeper. I immediately repaired to my inn, sent my luggage to the palace, and found myself established in a place in which a great fortune awaited me, if I had only been able to lead a wise and prudent life, but unfortunately it was not in my nature. *Volentem ducit, nolentem trahit.*

I naturally felt it my duty to call upon my mentor, Father Georgi, to whom I gave all my good news. He said I was on the right road, and that my fortune was in my hands.

"Recollect," added the good father, "that to lead a blameless life you must curb your passions, and that whatever misfortune may befall you it cannot be ascribed by any one to a want of good luck, or attributed to fate; those words are devoid of sense, and all the fault will rightly fall on your own head."

"I foresee, reverend father, that my youth and my want of experience will often make it necessary for me to disturb you. I am afraid of proving myself too heavy a charge for you, but you will find me docile and obedient."

" I suppose you will often think me rather too severe; but you are not likely to confide everything to me."

"Everything, without any exception."

"Allow me to feel somewhat doubtful; you have not told me where you spent four hours yesterday."

"Because I did not think it was worth mentioning. I made the acquaintance of those persons during my journey; I believe them to be worthy and respectable, and the right sort of people for me to visit, unless you should be of a different opinion."

"God forbid! It is a very respectable house, frequented by honest people. They are delighted at having made your acquaintance; you are much liked by everybody, and they hope to retain you as a friend; I have heard all about it this morning; but you must not go there too often and as a regular guest."

"Must I cease my visits at once, and without cause?"

"No, it would be a want of politeness on your part. You may go there once or twice every week, but do not be a constant visitor. You are sighing, my son?"

"No, I assure you not. I will obey you."

"I hope it may not be only a matter of obedience, and I trust your heart will not feel it a hardship, but, if necessary, your heart must be conquered. Recollect that the heart is the greatest enemy of reason."

"Yet they can be made to agree."

"We often imagine so; but distrust the *animum* of your dear Horace. You know that there is no middle course with it: *nisi paret, imperat.*"

"I know it, but in the family of which we were speaking there is no danger for my heart."

"I am glad of it, because in that case it will be all the

easier for you to abstain from frequent visits. Remember that I shall trust you."

"And I, reverend father, will listen to and follow your good advice. I will visit Donna Cecilia only now and then." Feeling most unhappy, I took his hand to press it against my lips, but he folded me in his arms as a father might have done, and turned himself round so as not to let me see that he was weeping.

I dined at the cardinal's palace and sat near the Abbé Gama; the table was laid for twelve persons, who all wore the costume of priests, for in Rome everyone is a priest or wishes to be thought a priest, and as there is no law to forbid anyone to dress like an ecclesiastic, that dress is adopted by all those who wish to be respected (noblemen excepted) even if they are not in the ecclesiastical profession.

I felt very miserable, and did not utter a word during the dinner; my silence was construed into a proof of my sagacity. As we rose from the table, the Abbé Gama invited me to spend the day with him, but I declined under pretence of letters to be written, and I truly did so for seven hours. I wrote to Don Lelio, to Don Antonio, to my young friend Paul, and to the worthy Bishop of Martorano, who answered that he heartily wished himself in my place.

Deeply enamoured of Lucrezia and happy in my love, to give her up appeared to me a shameful action. In order to insure the happiness of my future life, I was beginning to be the executioner of my present felicity, and the tormentor of my heart. I revolted against such a necessity which I judged fictitious, and which I could not admit unless I stood guilty of vileness before the tribunal of my own reason. I thought that Father Georgi, if he wished to forbid my visiting that family, ought not to have said that it was worthy of respect; my sorrow would not have been so intense. The day and the whole of the night were spent in painful thoughts.

In the morning the Abbé Gama brought me a great book filled with ministerial letters from which I was to compile for my amusement. After a short time devoted to that occupation, I went out to take my first French lesson, after which I walked towards the Strada-Condotta. I intended to take a long walk, when I heard myself called by my name. I saw the Abbé Gama in front of a coffee-house. I whispered to him that Minerva had forbidden me the coffee-rooms of Rome. "Minerva," he answered, "desires you to form some idea of such places. Sit down by me."

I heard a young abbé telling aloud, but without bitterness, a story, which attacked in a most direct manner the justice of His Holiness. Everybody was laughing and echoing the story. Another, being asked why he had left the services of Cardinal B., answered that it was because his eminence did not think himself called upon to pay him apart for certain private services, and everybody laughed outright. Another came to the Abbé Gama, and told him that, if he felt any inclination to spend the afternoon at the Villa Medicis, he would find him there with two young Roman girls who were satisfied with a *quartino,* a gold coin worth one-fourth of a sequin. Another abbé read an incendiary sonnet against the government, and several took a copy of it. Another read a satire of his own composition, in which he tore to pieces the honour of a family. In the middle of all that confusion, I saw a priest with a very attractive countenance come in. The size of his hips made me take him for a woman dressed in men's clothes, and I said so to Gama, who told me that he was the celebrated *castrato,*

Bepino della Mamana. The abbé called him to us, and told him with a laugh that I had taken him for a girl. The impudent fellow looked me full in the face, and said that, if I liked, he would shew me whether I had been right or wrong.

At the dinner-table everyone spoke to me, and I fancied I had given proper answers to all, but, when the repast was over, the Abbé Gama invited me to take coffee in his own apartment. The moment we were alone, he told me that all the guests I had met were worthy and honest men, and he asked me whether I believed that I had succeeded in pleasing the company.

"I flatter myself I have," I answered.

"You are wrong," said the abbé, "you are flattering yourself. You have so conspicuously avoided the questions put to you that everybody in the room noticed your extreme reserve. In the future no one will ask you any questions."

"I should be sorry if it should turn out so, but was I to expose my own concerns?"

"No, but there is a medium in all things."

"Yes, the medium of Horace, but it is often a matter of great difficulty to hit it exactly."

"A man ought to know how to obtain affection and esteem at the same time."

"That is the very wish nearest to my heart."

"To-day you have tried for the esteem much more than for the affection of your fellow-creatures. It may be a noble aspiration, but you must prepare yourself to fight jealousy and her daughter, calumny; if those two monsters do not succeed in destroying you, the victory must be yours. Now, for instance, you thoroughly refuted Salicetti to-day. Well, he is a physician, and what is more a Corsican; he must feel badly towards you."

"Could I grant that the longings of women during their pregnancy have no influence whatever on the skin of the fœtus, when I know the reverse to be the case? Are you not of my opinion?"

"I am for neither party; I have seen many children with some such marks, but I have no means of knowing with certainty whether those marks have their origin in some longing experienced by the mother while she was pregnant."

"But I can swear it is so."

"All the better for you if your conviction is based upon such evidence, and all the worse for Salicetti if he denies the possibility of the thing without certain authority. But let him remain in error; it is better thus than to prove him to be in the wrong, and to make a bitter enemy of him."

In the evening I called upon Lucrezia. The family knew my success, and warmly congratulated me. Lucrezia told me that I looked sad, and I answered that I was assisting at the funeral of my liberty, for I was no longer my own master. Her husband, always fond of a joke, told her that I was in love with her, and his mother-in-law advised him not to show so much intrepidity. I only remained an hour with those charming persons, and then took leave of them, but the very air around me was heated by the flame within my breast. When I reached my room I began to write, and spent the night in composing an ode which I sent the next day to the advocate. I was certain that he would shew it to his wife, who loved poetry, and who did not yet know that I was a poet. I abstained from seeing her again for three or four days. I was learning French, and making extracts from ministerial letters.

His eminence was in the habit of receiving every eve-

ning, and his rooms were thronged with the highest
nobility of Rome; I had never attended these receptions.
The Abbé Gama told me that I ought to do so as well as
he did, without any pretension. I followed his advice
and went; nobody spoke to me, but as I was unknown
everyone looked at me and enquired who I was. The
Abbé Gama asked me which was the lady who appeared
to me the most amiable, and I shewed one to him; but I
regretted having done so, for the courtier went to her,
and of course informed her of what I had said. Soon
afterwards I saw her look at me through her eye-glass
and smile kindly upon me. She was the Marchioness
G——, whose *cicisbeo* was Cardinal S—— C——.

On the very day I had fixed to spend the evening with
Donna Lucrezia the worthy advocate called upon me.
He told me that if I thought I was going to prove I was
not in love with his wife by staying away I was very
much mistaken, and he invited me to accompany all the
family to Testaccio, where they intended to have lunch-
eon on the following Thursday. He added that his wife
knew my ode by heart, and that she had read it to the
intended husband of Angélique, who had a great wish to
make my acquaintance. That gentleman was likewise a
poet, and would be one of the party to Testaccio. I
promised the advocate I would come to his house on the
Thursday with a carriage for two.

At that time every Thursday in the month of October
was a festival day in Rome. I went to see Donna Cecilia
in the evening, and we talked about the excursion the
whole time. I felt certain that Donna Lucrezia looked
forward to it with as much pleasure as I did myself.
We had no fixed plan, we could not have any, but we
trusted to the god of love, and tacitly placed our confidence in his protection.

I took care that Father Georgi should not hear of that excursion before I mentioned it to him myself, and I hastened to him in order to obtain his permission to go. I confess that, to obtain his leave, I professed the most complete indifference about it, and the consequence was that the good man insisted upon my going, saying that it was a family party, and that it was quite right for me to visit the environs of Rome and to enjoy myself in a respectable way.

I went to Donna Cecilia's in a carriage which I hired from a certain Roland, a native of Avignon, and if I insist here upon his name it is because my readers will meet him again in eighteen years, his acquaintance with me having had very important results. The charming widow introduced me to Don Francisco, her intended son-in-law, whom she represented as a great friend of literary men, and very deeply learned himself. I accepted it as gospel, and behaved accordingly; yet I thought he looked rather heavy and not sufficiently elated for a young man on the point of marrying such a pretty girl as Angélique. But he had plenty of good-nature and plenty of money, and these are better than learning and gallantry.

As we were ready to get into the carriages, the advocate told me that he would ride with me in my carriage, and that the three ladies would go with Don Francisco in the other. I answered at once that he ought to keep Don Francisco company, and that I claimed the privilege of taking care of Donna Cecilia, adding that I should feel dishonoured if things were arranged differently. Thereupon I offered my arm to the handsome widow, who thought the arrangement according to the rules of etiquette and good breeding, and an approving look of my Lucrezia gave me the most agreeable sensation. Yet

the proposal of the advocate struck me somewhat unpleasantly, because it was in contradiction with his
former behaviour, and especially with what he had said
to me in my room a few days before. "Has he become
jealous?" I said to myself; that would have made me
almost angry, but the hope of bringing him round during
our stay at Testaccio cleared away the dark cloud on
my mind, and I was very amiable to Donna Cecilia.
What with lunching and walking we contrived to pass
the afternoon very pleasantly; I was very gay, and my
love for Lucrezia was not once mentioned; I was all attention to her mother. I occasionally addressed myself
to Lucrezia, but not once to the advocate, feeling this the
best way to shew him that he had insulted me.

As we prepared to return, the advocate carried off
Donna Cecilia and went with her to the carriage in
which were already seated Angélique and Don Francisco.
Scarcely able to control my delight, I offered my arm to
Donna Lucrezia, paying her some absurd compliment,
while the advocate laughed outright, and seemed to enjoy
the trick he imagined he had played me.

How many things we might have said to each other
before giving ourselves up to the material enjoyment of
our love, had not the instants been so precious! But,
aware that we had only half an hour before us, we were
sparing of the minutes. We were absorbed in voluptuous pleasure when suddenly Lucrezia exclaims,——

"Oh! dear, how unhappy we are!"

She pushes me back, composes herself, the carriage
stops, and the servant opens the door.

"What is the matter?" I enquire.

"We are at home."

Whenever I recollect the circumstance, it seems to me
fabulous, for it is not possible to annihilate time, and

the horses were regular old screws. But we were lucky all through. The night was dark, and my beloved angel happened to be on the right side to get out of the carriage first, so that, although the advocate was at the door of the brougham as soon as the footman, everything went right, owing to the slow manner in which Lucrezia alighted. I remained at Donna Cecilia's until midnight.

When I got home again, I went to bed; but how could I sleep? I felt burning in me the flame which I had not been able to restore to its original source in the too short distance from Testaccio to Rome. It was consuming me. Oh! unhappy are those who believe that the pleasures of Cythera are worth having, unless they are enjoyed in the most perfect accord by two hearts overflowing with love!

I only rose in time for my French lesson. My teacher had a pretty daughter, named Barbara, who was always present during my lessons, and who sometimes taught me herself with even more exactitude than her father. A good-looking young man, who likewise took lessons, was courting her, and I soon perceived that she loved him. This young man called often upon me, and I liked him, especially on account of his reserve, for, although I made him confess his love for Barbara, he always changed the subject, if I mentioned it in our conversation.

I had made up my mind to respect his reserve, and had not alluded to his affection for several days. But all at once I remarked that he had ceased his visits both to me and to his teacher, and at the same time I observed that the young girl was no longer present at my lessons; I felt some curiosity to know what had happened, although it was not, after all, any concern of mine.

A few days after, as I was returning from church, I

met the young man, and reproached him for keeping away from us all. He told me that great sorrow had befallen him, which had fairly turned his brain, and that he was a prey to the most intense despair. His eyes were wet with tears. As I was leaving him, he held me back, and I told him that I would no longer be his friend unless he opened his heart to me. He took me to one of the cloisters, and he spoke thus:

"I have loved Barbara for the last six months, and for three months she has given me indisputable proofs of her affection. Five days ago, we were betrayed by the servant, and the father caught us in a rather delicate position. He left the room without saying one word, and I followed him, thinking of throwing myself at his feet; but, as I appeared before him, he took hold of me by the arm, pushed me roughly to the door, and forbade me ever to present myself again at his house. I cannot claim her hand in marriage, because one of my brothers is married, and my father is not rich; I have no profession, and my mistress has nothing. Alas, now that I have confessed all to you, tell me, I entreat you, how she is. I am certain that she is as miserable as I am myself. I cannot manage to get a letter delivered to her, for she does not leave the house, even to attend church. Unhappy wretch! What shall I do?"

I could but pity him, for, as a man of honour, it was impossible for me to interfere in such a business. I told him that I had not seen Barbara for five days, and, not knowing what to say, I gave him the advice which is tendered by all fools under similar circumstances; I advised him to forget his mistress.

We had then reached the quay of Ripetta, and, observing that he was casting dark looks towards the Tiber, I feared his despair might lead him to commit some foolish attempt against his own life, and, in order to calm his excited feelings, I promised to make some enquiries from the father about his mistress, and to inform him of all I heard. He felt quieted by my promise, and entreated me not to forget him.

In spite of the fire which had been raging through my veins ever since the excursion to Testaccio, I had not seen my Lucrezia for four days. I dreaded Father Georgi's suave manner, and I was still more afraid of finding he had made up his mind to give me no more advice. But, unable to resist my desires, I called upon Lucrezia after my French lesson, and found her alone, sad and dispirited.

"Ah!" she exclaimed, as soon as I was by her side, "I think you might find time to come and see me!"

"My beloved one, it is not that I cannot find time, but I am so jealous of my love that I would rather die than let it be known publicly. I have been thinking of inviting you all to dine with me at Frascati. I will send you a phaeton, and I trust that some lucky accident will smile upon our love."

"Oh! yes, do, dearest! I am sure your invitation will be accepted."

In a quarter of an hour the rest of the family came in, and I proffered my invitation for the following Sunday, which happened to be the Festival of St.-Ursula, patroness of Lucrezia's youngest sister. I begged Donna Cecilia to bring her as well as her son. My proposal being readily accepted, I gave notice that the phaeton would be at Donna Cecilia's door at seven o'clock, and that I would come myself with a carriage for two persons.

The next day I went to M. Dalacqua, and, after my lesson, I saw Barbara who, passing from one room to another, dropped a paper and earnestly looked at me. I felt bound to pick it up, because a servant, who was at hand, might have seen it and taken it. It was a letter, enclosing another addressed to her lover. The note for me ran thus: "If you think it to be a sin to deliver the enclosed to your friend, burn it. Have pity on an unfortunate girl, and be discreet."

The enclosed letter which was unsealed, ran as follows: "If you love me as deeply as I love you, you cannot hope to be happy without me; we cannot correspond in any other way than the one I am bold enough to adopt. I am ready to do anything to unite our lives until death. Consider and decide."

The cruel situation of the poor girl moved me almost to tears; yet I determined to return her letter the next day, and I enclosed it in a note in which I begged her to excuse me if I could not render her the service she required at my hands. I put it in my pocket ready for delivery. The next day I went for my lesson as usual, but, not seeing Barbara, I had no opportunity of returning her letter, and postponed its delivery to the following day. Unfortunately, just after I had returned to my room, the unhappy lover made his appearance. His eyes were red from weeping, his voice hoarse; he drew such a vivid picture of his misery, that, dreading some mad action counselled by despair, I could not withhold from him the consolation which I knew it was in my power to give. This was my first error in this fatal business; I was the victim of my own kindness.

The poor fellow read the letter over and over; he kissed it with transports of joy; he wept, hugged me, and thanked me for saving his life, and finally entreated me to take charge of his answer, as his beloved mistress must be longing for consolation as much as he had been himself, assuring me that his letter could not in any way implicate me, and that I was at liberty to read it.

And truly, although very long, his letter contained nothing but the assurance of everlasting love, and hopes which could not be realized. Yet I was wrong to accept the character of Mercury to the two young lovers. To refuse, I had only to recollect that Father Georgi would certainly have disapproved of my easy compliance.

The next day I found M. Dalacqua ill in bed; his daughter gave me my lesson in his room, and I thought that perhaps she had obtained her pardon. I contrived to give her her lover's letter, which she dextrously conveyed to her pocket, but her blushes would have easily betrayed her if her father had been looking that way. After the lesson I gave M. Dalacqua notice that I would not come on the morrow, as it was the Festival of St.-Ursula, one of the eleven thousand princesses and martyr-virgins.

In the evening, at the reception of his eminence, which I attended regularly, although persons of distinction seldom spoke to me, the cardinal beckoned to me. He was speaking to the beautiful Marchioness G——, to whom Gama had indiscreetly confided that I thought her the handsomest woman amongst his eminence's guests.

"Her grace," said the Cardinal, "wishes to know whether you are making rapid progress in the French language, which she speaks admirably."

I answered in Italian that I had learned a great deal, but that I was not yet bold enough to speak.

"You should be bold," said the marchioness, "but without showing any pretension. It is the best way to disarm criticism."

My mind having almost unwittingly lent to the words "You should be bold" a meaning which had very likely been far from the idea of the marchioness, I turned very red, and the handsome speaker, observing it, changed the conversation and dismissed me.

The next morning, at seven o'clock, I was at Donna Cecilia's door. The phaeton was there as well as the carriage for two persons, which this time was an elegant *vis-à-vis,* so light and well-hung that Donna Cecilia praised it highly when she took her seat.

"I shall have my turn as we return to Rome," said Lucrezia; and I bowed to her as if in acceptance of her promise.

Lucrezia thus set suspicion at defiance in order to prevent suspicion arising. My happiness was assured, and I gave way to my natural flow of spirits. I ordered a splendid dinner, and we all set out towards the Villa Ludovisi. As we might have missed each other during our ramblings, we agreed to meet again at the inn at one o'clock. The discreet widow took the arm of her son-in-law, Angélique remained with her sister, and Lucrezia was my delightful share; Ursula and her brother were running about together, and in less than a quarter of an hour I had Lucrezia entirely to myself.

"Did you remark," she said, "with what candour I secured for us two hours of delightful *tête-à-tête,* and a *tête-à-tête* in a *vis-à-vis,* too! How clever Love is!"

"Yes, darling, Love has made but one of our two souls. I adore you, and if I have the courage to pass so many days without seeing you it is in order to be rewarded by the freedom of one single day like this."

"I did not think it possible. But you have managed it all very well. You know too much for your age, dearest."

"A month ago, my beloved, I was but an ignorant child, and you are the first woman who has initiated me

into the mysteries of love. Your departure will kill me,
for I could not find another woman like you in all Italy."
"What! am I your first love? Alas! you will never be
cured of it. Oh! why am I not entirely your own? You
are also the first true love of my heart, and you will be
the last. How great will be the happiness of my suc-
cessor! I should not be jealous of her, but what suffering would be mine if I thought that her heart was not
like mine!"

Lucrezia, seeing my eyes wet with tears, began to give
way to her own, and, seating ourselves on the grass, our
lips drank our tears amidst the sweetest kisses. How
sweet is the nectar of the tears shed by love, when that
nectar is relished amidst the raptures of mutual ardour!
I have often tasted them—those delicious tears, and I can
say knowingly that the ancient physicians were right,
and that the modern are wrong!

In a moment of calm, seeing the disorder in which we
both were, I told her that we might be surprised.

"Do not fear, my best beloved," she said, "we are
under the guardianship of our good angels."

We were resting and reviving our strength by gazing
into one another's eyes, when suddenly Lucrezia, casting
a glance to the right, exclaimed,

"Look there! idol of my heart, have I not told you
so? Yes, the angels are watching over us! Ah! how he
stares at us! He seems to try to give us confidence.
Look at that little demon; admire him! He must certainly be your guardian spirit or mine."

I thought she was delirious.

"What are you saying, dearest? I do not understand
you. What am I to admire?"

"Do you not see that beautiful serpent with the blazing skin, which lifts its head and seems to worship us?"

I looked in the direction she indicated, and saw a serpent with changeable colours about three feet in length, which did seem to be looking at us. I was not particularly pleased at the sight, but I could not show myself less courageous than she was.

"What!" said I, "are you not afraid?"

"I tell you, again, that the sight is delightful to me, and I feel certain that it is a spirit with nothing but the shape, or rather the appearance, of a serpent."

"And if the spirit came gliding along the grass and hissed at you?"

"I would hold you tighter against my bosom, and set him at defiance. In your arms Lucrezia is safe. Look! the spirit is going away. Quick, quick! He is warning us of the approach of some profane person, and tells us to seek some other retreat to renew our pleasures. Let us go."

We rose and slowly advanced towards Donna Cecilia and the advocate, who were just emerging from a neighbouring alley. Without avoiding them, and without hurrying, just as if to meet one another was a very natural occurrence, I enquired of Donna Cecilia whether her daughter had any fear of serpents.

"In spite of all her strength of mind," she answered, "she is dreadfully afraid of thunder, and she will scream with terror at the sight of the smallest snake. There are some here, but she need not be frightened, for they are not venomous."

I was speechless with astonishment, for I discovered that I had just witnessed a wonderful love miracle. At that moment the children came up, and, without ceremony, we again parted company.

"Tell me, wonderful being, bewitching woman, what would you have done if, instead of your pretty serpent, you had seen your husband and your mother?"

"Nothing. Do you not know that, in moments of such rapture, lovers see and feel nothing but love? Do you doubt having possessed me wholly, entirely?"

Lucrezia, in speaking thus, was not composing a poetical ode; she was not feigning fictitious sentiments; her looks, the sound of her voice, were truth itself!

"Are you certain," I enquired, "that we are not suspected?"

"My husband does not believe us to be in love with each other, or else he does not mind such trifling pleasures as youth is generally wont to indulge in. My mother is a clever woman, and perhaps she suspects the truth, but she is aware that it is no longer any concern of hers. As to my sister, she must know everything, for she cannot have forgotten the broken-down bed; but she is prudent, and besides, she has taken it into her head to pity me. She has no conception of the nature of my feelings towards you. If I had not met you, my beloved, I should probably have gone through life without realizing such feelings myself; for what I feel for my husband . . . well, I have for him the obedience which my position as a wife imposes upon me."

"And yet he is most happy, and I envy him! He can clasp in his arms all your lovely person whenever he likes! There is no hateful veil to hide any of your charms from his gaze."

"Oh! where art thou, my dear serpent? Come to us, come and protect us against the surprise of the uninitiated, and this very instant I fulfil all the wishes of him I adore!"

We passed the morning in repeating that we loved each other, and in exchanging over and over again substantial proofs of our mutual passion.

We had a delicious dinner, during which I was all attention for the amiable Donna Cecilia. My pretty tortoise-shell box, filled with excellent snuff, went more than once round the table. As it happened to be in the hands of Lucrezia who was sitting on my left, her husband told her that, if I had no objection, she might give me her ring and keep the snuff-box in exchange. Thinking that the ring was not of as much value as my box, I immediately accepted, but I found the ring of greater value. Lucrezia would not, however, listen to anything on that subject. She put the box in her pocket, and thus compelled me to keep her ring.

Dessert was nearly over, the conversation was very animated, when suddenly the intended husband of Angélique claimed our attention for the reading of a sonnet which he had composed and dedicated to me. I thanked him, and placing the sonnet in my pocket promised to write one for him. This was not, however, what he wished; he expected that, stimulated by emulation, I would call for paper and pen, and sacrifice to Apollo hours which it was much more to my taste to employ in worshipping another god whom his cold nature knew only by name. We drank coffee, I paid the bill, and we went about rambling through the labyrinthine alleys of the Villa Aldobrandini.

What sweet recollections that villa has left in my memory! It seemed as if I saw my divine Lucrezia for the first time. Our looks were full of ardent love, our hearts were beating in concert with the most tender impatience, and a natural instinct was leading us towards a solitary asylum which the hand of Love seemed to have prepared on purpose for the mysteries of its secret worship. There, in the middle of a long avenue, and under a canopy of thick foliage, we found a wide sofa made of grass, and sheltered by a deep thicket; from that place our eyes could range over an immense plain, and

view the avenue to such a distance right and left that
we were perfectly secure against any surprise. We did
not require to exchange one word at the sight of this
beautiful temple so favourable to our love; our hearts
spoke the same language.

Without a word being spoken, our ready hands soon
managed to get rid of all obstacles, and to expose in a
state of nature all the beauties which are generally veiled
by troublesome wearing apparel. Two whole hours were
devoted to the most delightful, loving ecstasies. At last
we exclaimed together in mutual ecstasy, "O Love, we
thank thee!"

We slowly retraced our steps towards the carriages,
revelling in our intense happiness. Lucrezia informed
me that Angélique's suitor was wealthy, that he owned
a splendid villa at Tivoli, and that most likely he would
invite us all to dine and pass the night there. "I pray
the god of love," she added, "to grant us a night as
beautiful as this day has been." Then, looking sad, she
said, "But alas! the ecclesiastical lawsuit which has
brought my husband to Rome is progressing so favourably that I am mortally afraid he will obtain judgment
all too soon."

The journey back to the city lasted two hours; we
were alone in my *vis-à-vis* and we overtaxed nature, ex-
acting more than it can possibly give. As we were getting near Rome we were compelled to let the curtain
fall before the *dénouement* of the drama which we had
performed to the complete satisfaction of the actors.

I returned home rather fatigued, but the sound sleep
which was so natural at my age restored my full vigour,
and in the morning I took my French lesson at the usual
hour.

CHAPTER X

*Benedict XIV—Excursion to Tivoli—Departure of Lu-
crezia—The Marchioness G.—Barbara Dalacqua—My
Misfortunes—I Leave Rome*

M. DALACQUA being very ill, his daughter Barbara gave me my lesson. When it was over, she seized an opportunity of slipping a letter into my pocket, and immediately disappeared, so that I had no chance of refusing. The letter was addressed to me, and expressed feelings of the warmest gratitude. She only desired me to inform her lover that her father had spoken to her again, and that most likely he would engage a new servant as soon as he had recovered from his illness, and she concluded her letter by assuring me that she never would implicate me in this business.

Her father was compelled to keep his bed for a fortnight, and Barbara continued to give me my lesson every day. I felt for her an interest which, from me towards a young and pretty girl, was, indeed, quite a new sentiment. It was a feeling of pity, and I was proud of being able to help and comfort her. Her eyes never rested upon mine, her hand never met mine, I never saw in her toilet the slightest wish to please me. She was very pretty, and I knew she had a tender, loving nature; but nothing interfered with the respect and the regard which I was bound in honour and in good faith to feel towards her, and I was proud to remark that she never thought me capable of taking advantage of her weakness or of her position.

When the father had recovered he dismissed his servant and engaged another. Barbara entreated me to inform her friend of the circumstance, and likewise of her hope to gain the new servant to their interests, at least sufficiently to secure the possibility of carrying on some correspondence. I promised to do so, and as a mark of her gratitude she took my hand to carry it to her lips, but quickly withdrawing it I tried to kiss her; she turned her face away, blushing deeply. I was much pleased with her modesty.

Barbara having succeeded in gaining the new servant over, I had nothing more to do with the intrigue, and I was very glad of it, for I knew my interference might have brought evil on my own head. Unfortunately, it was already too late.

I seldom visited Don Gaspar; the study of the French language took up all my mornings, and it was only in the morning that I could see him; but I called every evening upon Father Georgi, and, although I went to him only as one of his *protégés*, it gave me some reputation. I seldom spoke before his guests, yet I never felt weary, for in his circle his friends would criticise without slandering, discuss politics without stubbornness, literature without passion, and I profited by all. After my visit to the sagacious monk, I used to attend the assembly of the cardinal, my master, as a matter of duty. Almost every evening, when she happened to see me at her card-table, the beautiful marchioness would address to me a few gracious words in French, and I always answered in Italian, not caring to make her laugh before so many persons. My feelings for her were of a singular kind. I must leave them to the analysis of the reader. I

thought that woman charming, yet I avoided her; it was
not because I was afraid of falling in love with her; I
loved Lucrezia, and I firmly believed that such an affection was a shield against any other attachment, but
it was because I feared that she might love me or have
a passing fancy for me. Was it self-conceit or modesty,
vice or virtue? Perhaps neither one nor the other.

One evening she desired the Abbé Gama to call me
to her; she was standing near the cardinal, my patron,
and the moment I approached her she caused me a
strange feeling of surprise by asking me in Italian a
question which I was far from anticipating:

"How did you like Frascati?"

"Very much, madam; I have never seen such a beautiful place."

"But your company was still more beautiful, and your
vis-à-vis was very smart."

I only bowed low to the marchioness, and a moment
after Cardinal Acquaviva said to me, kindly,—

"You are astonished at your adventure being known?"

"No, my lord; but I am surprised that people should
talk of it. I could not have believed Rome to be so much
like a small village."

"The longer you live in Rome," said his eminence,
"the more you will find it so. You have not yet presented yourself to kiss the foot of our Holy Father?"

"Not yet, my lord."

"Then you must do so."

I bowed in compliance to his wishes.

The Abbé Gama told me to present myself to the Pope
on the morrow, and he added,—

"Of course you have already shewn yourself in the
Marchioness G.'s palace?"

"No, I have never been there."

"You astonish me; but she often speaks to you!"

"I have no objection to go with you."

"I never visit at her palace."

"Yet she speaks to you likewise."

"Yes, but . . . You do not know Rome; go alone; believe me, you ought to go."

"Will she receive me?"

"You are joking, I suppose. Of course it is out of the question for you to be announced. You will call when the doors are wide open to everybody. You will meet there all those who pay homage to her."

"Will she see me?"

"No doubt of it."

On the following day I proceeded to Monte-Cavallo, and I was at once led into the room where the Pope was alone. I threw myself on my knees and kissed the holy cross on his most holy slipper. The Pope enquiring who I was, I told him, and he answered that he knew me, congratulating me upon my being in the service of so eminent a cardinal. He asked me how I had succeeded in gaining the cardinal's favour; I answered with a faithful recital of my adventures from my arrival at Martorano. He laughed heartily at all I said respecting the poor and worthy bishop, and remarked that, instead of trying to address him in Tuscan, I could speak in the Venetian dialect, as he was himself speaking to me in the dialect of Bologna. I felt quite at my ease with him, and I told him so much news and amused him so well that the Holy Father kindly said that he would be glad to see me whenever I presented myself at Monte-Cavallo. I begged his permission to read all forbidden books, and he granted it with his blessing, saying that I should have the permisison in writing, but he forgot it.

Benedict XIV, was a learned man, very amiable, and

fond of a joke. I saw him for the second time at the Villa Medicis. He called me to him, and continued his walk, speaking of trifling things. He was then accompanied by Cardinal Albani and the ambassador from Venice. A man of modest appearance approached His Holiness, who asked what he required; the man said a few words in a low voice, and, after listening to him, the Pope answered, "You are right, place your trust in God;" and he gave him his blessing. The poor fellow went away very dejected, and the Holy Father continued his walk.

"This man," I said, "most Holy Father, has not been pleased with the answer of Your Holiness."

"Why?"

"Because most likely he had already addressed himself to God before he ventured to apply to you; and when Your Holiness sends him to God again, he finds himself sent back, as the proverb says, from Herod to Pilate."

The Pope, as well as his two companions, laughed heartily; but I kept a serious countenance.

"I cannot," continued the Pope, "do any good without God's assistance."

"Very true, Holy Father; but the man is aware that you are God's prime minister, and it is easy to imagine his trouble now that the minister sends him again to the master. His only resource is to give money to the beggars of Rome, who for one *bajocco* will pray for him. They boast of their influence before the throne of the Almighty, but as I have faith only in your credit, I entreat Your Holiness to deliver me of the heat which inflames my eyes by granting me permission to eat meat."

"Eat meat, my son."

"Holy Father, give me your blessing."

He blessed me, adding that I was not dispensed from fasting.

That very evening, at the cardinal's assembly, I found that the news of my dialogue with the Pope was already known. Everybody was anxious to speak to me. I felt flattered, but I was much more delighted at the joy which Cardinal Acquaviva tried in vain to conceal.

As I wished not to neglect Gama's advice, I presented myself at the mansion of the beautiful marchioness at the hour at which everyone had free access to her ladyship. I saw her, I saw the cardinal and a great many abbés; but I might have supposed myself invisible, for no one honoured me with a look, and no one spoke to me. I left after having performed for half an hour the character of a mute. Five or six days afterwards, the marchioness told me graciously that she had caught a sight of me in her reception-rooms.

"I was there, it is true, madam; but I had no idea that I had had the honour to be seen by your ladyship."

"Oh! I see everybody. They tell me that you have wit."

"If it is not a mistake on the part of your informants, your ladyship gives me very good news."

"Oh! they are excellent judges."

"Then, madam, those persons must have honoured me with their conversation; otherwise, it is not likely that they would have been able to express such an opinion."

"No doubt; but let me see you often at my receptions."

Our conversation had been overheard by those who were around; his excellency the cardinal told me that, when the marchioness addressed herself particularly to me in French, my duty was to answer her in the same language, good or bad. The cunning politician Gama took me apart, and remarked that my repartees were too smart, too cutting, and that, after a time, I would be sure to displease. I had made considerable progress in French; I had given up my lessons, and practice was all I required. I was then in the habit of calling sometimes upon Lucrezia in the morning, and of visiting in the evening Father Georgi, who was acquainted with the excursion to Frascati, and had not expressed any dissatisfaction.

Two days after the sort of command laid upon me by the marchioness, I presented myself at her reception. As soon as she saw me, she favoured me with a smile which I acknowledged by a deep reverence; that was all. In a quarter of an hour afterwards I left the mansion. The marchioness was beautiful, but she was powerful, and I could not make up my mind to crawl at the feet of power, and, on that head, I felt disgusted with the manners of the Romans.

One morning towards the end of November the advocate, accompanied by Angélique's intended, called on me. The latter gave me a pressing invitation to spend twenty-four hours at Tivoli with the friends I had entertained at Frascati. I accepted with great pleasure, for I had found no opportunity of being alone with Lucrezia since the Festival of St. Ursula. I promised to be at Donna Cecilia's house at day-break with the same vis-à-vis.. It was necessary to start very early, because Tivoli is sixteen miles from Rome, and has so many objects of interest that it requires many hours to see them all. As I had to sleep out that night, I craved permission to do so from the cardinal himself, who, hearing with whom I was going, told me that I was quite right not to lose such an opportunity of visiting that splendid place in such good society.

The first dawn of day found me with my *vis-à-vis* and four at the door of Donna Cecilia, who came with me as before. The charming widow, notwithstanding her strict morality, was delighted at my love for her daughter. The family rode in a large phaeton hired by Don Francisco, which gave room for six persons.

At half-past seven in the morning we made a halt at a small place where had been prepared, by Don Franciso's orders, an excellent breakfast, which was intended to replace the dinner, and we all made a hearty meal, as we were not likely to find time for anything but supper at Tivoli. I wore on my finger the beautiful ring which Lucrezia had given me. At the back of the ring I had had a piece of enamel placed, on it was delineated a saduceus, with one serpent between the letters Alpha and Omega. This ring was the subject of conversation during breakfast, and Don Francisco, as well as the advocate, exerted himself in vain to guess the meaning of the hieroglyphs; much to the amusement of Lucrezia, who understood the mysterious secret so well. We continued our road, and reached Tivoli at ten o'clock.

We began by visiting Don Francisco's villa. It was a beautiful little house, and we spent the following six hours in examining together the antiquities of Tivoli. Lucrezia having occasion to whisper a few words to Don Francisco, I seized the opportunity of telling Angélique that after her marriage I should be happy to spend a few days of the fine season with her.

"Sir," she answered, "I give you fair notice that the moment I become mistress in this house you will be the very first person to be excluded."

"I feel greatly obliged to you, signora, for your timely notice."

But the most amusing part of the affair was that I

construed Angélique's wanton insult into a declaration
of love. I was astounded. Lucrezia, remarking the
state I was in, touched my arm, enquiring what ailed
me. I told her, and she said at once,—

"My darling, my happiness cannot last long; the cruel
moment of our separation is drawing near. When I have
gone, pray undertake the task of compelling her to acknowledge her error. Angélique pities me, be sure to
avenge me."

I have forgotten to mention that at Don Francisco's
villa I happened to praise a very pretty room opening
upon the orange-house, and the amiable host, having
heard me, came obligingly to me, and said that it should
be my room that night. Lucrezia feigned not to hear,
but it was to her Ariadne's clue, for, as we were to remain altogether during our visit to the beauties of Tivoli,
we had no chance of a *tête-à-tête* through the day.

I have said that we devoted six hours to an examination of the antiquities of Tivoli, but I am bound to
confess here that I saw, for my part, very little of them,
and it was only twenty-eight years later that I made a
thorough acquaintance with the beautiful spot.

We returned to the villa towards evening, fatigued
and very hungry, but an hour's rest before supper—a
repast which lasted two hours, the most delicious dishes,
the most exquisite wines, and particularly the excellent
wine of Tivoli—restored us so well that everybody
wanted nothing more than a good bed and the freedom
to enjoy the bed according to his own taste.

As everybody objected to sleep alone, Lucrezia said
that she would sleep with Angélique in one of the rooms
leading to the orange-house, and proposed that her husband should share a room with the young abbé, his

brother-in-law, and that Donna Cecilia should take her youngest daughter with her.

The arrangement met with general approbation, and Don Francisco, taking a candle, escorted me to my pretty little room adjoining the one in which the two sisters were to sleep, and, after shewing me how I could lock myself in, he wished me good night and left me alone.

Angélique had no idea that I was her near neighbour, but Lucrezia and I, without exchanging a single word on the subject, had perfectly understood each other.

I watched through the key-hole and saw the two sisters come into their room, preceded by the polite Don Francisco, who carried a taper, and, after lighting a night-lamp, bade them good night and retired. Then my two beauties, their door once locked, sat down on the sofa and completed their night toilet, which, in that fortunate climate, is similar to the costume of our first mother. Lucrezia, knowing that I was waiting to come in, told her sister to lie down on the side towards the window, and the virgin, having no idea that she was exposing her most secret beauties to my profane eyes, crossed the room in a state of complete nakedness. Lucrezia put out the lamp and lay down near her innocent sister.

Happy moments which I can no longer enjoy, but the sweet remembrance of which death alone can make me lose! I believe I never undressed myself as quickly as I did that evening.

I open the door and fall into the arms of my Lucrezia, who says to her sister, "It is my angel, my love; never mind him, and go to sleep."

What a delightful picture I could offer to my readers if it were possible for me to paint voluptuousnes in its most enchanting colours! What ecstasies of love from the very onset! What delicious raptures succeed each other until the sweetest fatigue made us give way to the soothing influence of Morpheus!

The first rays of the sun, piercing through the crevices of the shutters, wake us out of our refreshing slumbers, and like two valorous knights who have ceased fighting only to renew the contest with increased ardour, we lose no time in giving ourselves up to all the intensity of the flame which consumes us.

"Oh, my beloved Lucrezia! how supremely happy I am! But, my darling, mind your sister; she might turn round and see us."

"Fear nothing, my life; my sister is kind, she loves me, she pities me; do you not love me, my dear Angélique? Oh! turn round, see how happy your sister is, and know what felicity awaits you when you own the sway of love."

Angélique, a young maiden of seventeen summers, who must have suffered the torments of Tantalus during the night, and who only wishes for a pretext to shew that she has forgiven her sister, turns round, and covering her sister with kisses, confesses that she has not closed her eyes through the night.

"Then forgive likewise, darling Angélique, forgive him who loves me, and whom I adore," says Lucrezia.

Unfathomable power of the god who conquers all human beings!

"Angélique hates me," I say, "I dare not . . ."

"No, I do not hate you!" answers the charming girl.

"Kiss her, dearest," says Lucrezia, pushing me towards her sister, and pleased to see her in my arms motionless and languid.

But sentiment, still more than love, forbids me to deprive Lucrezia of the proof of my gratitude, and I turn to her with all the rapture of a beginner, feeling that my ardour is increased by Angélique's ecstasy, as for the first time she witnesses the amorous contest. Lucrezia, dying of enjoyment, entreats me to stop, but, as I do not listen to her prayer, she tricks me, and the sweet Angélique makes her first sacrifice to the mother of love. It is thus, very likely, that when the gods inhabited this earth, the voluptuous Arcadia, in love with the soft and pleasing breath of Zephyrus, one day opened her arms, and was fecundated.

Lucrezia was astonished and delighted, and covered us both with kisses. Angélique, as happy as her sister, expired deliciously in my arms for the third time, and she seconded me with so much loving ardour, that it seemed to me I was tasting happiness for the first time.

Phœbus had left the nuptial couch, and his rays were already diffusing light over the universe; and that light, reaching us through the closed shutters, gave me warning to quit the place; we exchanged the most loving adieus, I left my two divinities and retired to my own room. A few minutes afterwards, the cheerful voice of the advocate was heard in the chamber of the sisters; he was reproaching them for sleeping too long! Then he knocked at my door, threatening to bring the ladies to me, and went away, saying that he would send me the hair-dresser.

After many ablutions and a careful toilet, I thought I could shew my face, and I presented myself coolly in the drawing-room. The two sisters were there with the other members of our society, and I was delighted with their rosy cheeks. Lucrezia was frank and gay, and beamed with happiness; Angélique, as fresh as the morning dew, was more radiant than usual, but fidgety, and carefully avoided looking me in the face. I saw that my useless attempts to catch her eyes made her smile, and I remarked to her mother, rather mischievously, that it was a pity Angélique used paint for her face. She was duped by this stratagem, and compelled me to pass a handkerchief over her face, and was then obliged to look at me. I offered her my apologies, and Don Francisco appeared highly pleased that the complexion of his intended had met with such triumph.

After breakfast we took a walk through the garden, and, finding myself alone with Lucrezia, I expostulated tenderly with her for having almost thrown her sister in my arms.

"Do not reproach me," she said, "when I deserve praise. I have brought light into the darkness of my charming sister's soul; I have initiated her in the sweetest of mysteries, and now, instead of pitying me, she must envy me. Far from having hatred for you, she must love you dearly, and as I am so unhappy as to have to part from you very soon, my beloved, I leave her to you; she will replace me."

"Ah, Lucrezia! how can I love her?"

"Is she not a charming girl?"

"No doubt of it; but my adoration for you is a shield against any other love. Besides Don Francisco must, of course, entirely monopolize her, and I do not wish to cause coolness between them, or to ruin the peace of their home. I am certain your sister is not like you, and I would bet that, even now, she upbraids herself for having given way to the ardour of her temperament."

"Most likely; but, dearest, I am sorry to say my husband expects to obtain judgment in the course of this week, and then the short instants of happiness will for ever be lost to me."

This was sad news indeed, and to cause a diversion at the breakfast-table I took much notice of the generous Don Francisco, and promised to compose a nuptial song for his wedding-day, which had been fixed for the early part of January.

We returned to Rome, and for the three hours that she was with me in my *vis-à-vis*, Lucrezia had no reason to think that my ardour was at all abated. But when we reached the city I was rather fatigued, and proceeded at once to the palace.

Lucrezia had guessed rightly; her husband obtained his judgment three or four days afterwards, and called upon me to announce their departure for the day after the morrow; he expressed his warm friendship for me, and by his invitation I spent the two last evenings with Lucrezia, but we were always surrounded by the family. The day of her departure, wishing to cause her an agreeable surprise, I left Rome before them and waited for them at the place where I thought they would put up for the night, but the advocate, having been detained by several engagements, was detained in Rome, and they only reached the place next day for dinner. We dined together, we exchanged a sad, painful farewell, and they continued their journey while I returned to Rome.

After the departure of this charming woman, I found myself in sort of solitude very natural to a young man whose heart is not full of hope.

I passed whole days in my room, making extracts from the French letters written by the cardinal, and his eminence was kind enough to tell me that my extracts were judiciously made, but that he insisted upon my not working so hard. The beautiful marchioness was present when he paid me that compliment.

Since my second visit to her, I had not presented myself at her house; she was consequently rather cool to me, and, glad of an opportunity of making me feel her displeasure, she remarked to his eminence that very likely work was a consolation to me in the great void caused by the departure of Donna Lucrezia.

"I candidly confess, madam, that I have felt her loss deeply. She was kind and generous; above all, she was indulgent when I did not call often upon her. My friendship for her was innocent."

"I have no doubt of it, although your ode was the work of a poet deeply in love."

"Oh!" said the kindly cardinal, "a poet cannot possibly write without professing to be in love."

"But," replied the marchioness, "if the poet is really in love, he has no need of professing a feeling which he possesses."

As she was speaking, the marchioness drew out of her pocket a paper which she offered to his eminence.

"This is the ode," she said, "it does great honour to the poet, for it is admitted to be a masterpiece by all the *literati* in Rome, and Donna Lucrezia knows it by heart."

The cardinal read it over and returned it, smiling, and remarking that, as he had no taste for Italian poetry, she must give herself the pleasure of translating it into French rhyme if she wished him to admire it.

"I only write French prose," answered the marchioness, "and a prose translation destroys half the beauty of poetry. I am satisfied with writing occasionally a little Italian poetry without any pretension to poetical fame."

Those words were accompanied by a very significant glance in my direction.

"I should consider myself fortunate, madam, if I

could obtain the happiness of admiring some of your poetry."

"Here is a sonnet of her ladyship's," said Cardinal S. C.

I took it respectfully, and I prepared to read it, but the amiable marchioness told me to put it in my pocket and return it to the cardinal the next day, although she did not think the sonnet worth so much trouble. "If you should happen to go out in the morning," said Cardinal S. C., "you could bring it back, and dine with me." Cardinal Aquaviva immediately answered for me: "He will be sure to go out purposely."

With a deep reverence, which expressed my thanks, I left the room quietly and returned to my apartment, very impatient to read the sonnet. Yet, before satisfying my wish, I could not help making some reflections on the situation. I began to think myself somebody since the gigantic stride I had made this evening at the cardinal's assembly. The Marchioness de G. had shewn in the most open way the interest she felt in me, and, under cover of her grandeur, had not hesitated to compromise herself publicly by the most flattering advances. But who would have thought of disapproving? A young abbé like me, without any importance whatever, who could scarcely pretend to her high protection! True, but she was precisely the woman to grant it to those who, feeling themselves unworthy of it, dared not shew any pretensions to her patronage. On that head, my modesty must be evident to everyone, and the marchioness would certainly have insulted me had she supposed me capable of sufficient vanity to fancy that she felt the slightest inclination for me. No, such a piece of self-conceit was not in accordance with my nature. Her cardinal himself had invited me to dinner. Would he have done so if he had admitted the possibility of the beautiful marchioness feeling anything for me? Of course not, and he gave me an invitation to dine with him only because he had understood, from the very words of the lady, that I was just the sort of person with whom they could converse for a few hours without any risk; to be sure, without any risk whatever. Oh, Master Casanova! do you really think so?

Well, why should I put on a mask before my readers? They may think me conceited if they please, but the fact of the matter is that I felt sure of having made a conquest of the marchioness. I congratulated myself because she had taken the first, most difficult, and most important step. Had she not done so, I should never have dared to lay siege to her even in the most approved fashion; I should never have even ventured to dream of winning her. It was only this evening that I thought she might replace Lucrezia. She was beautiful, young, full of wit and talent; she was fond of literary pursuits, and very powerful in Rome; what more was necessary? Yet I thought it would be good policy to appear ignorant of her inclination for me, and to let her suppose from the very next day that I was in love with her, but that my love appeared to me hopeless. I knew that such a plan was infallible, because it saved her dignity. It seemed to me that Father Georgi himself would be compelled to approve such an undertaking, and I had remarked with great satisfaction that Cardinal Acquaviva had expressed his delight at Cardinal S. C.'s invitation—an honour which he had never yet bestowed on me himself. This affair might have very important results for me.

I read the marchioness's sonnet, and found it easy, flowing, and well written. It was composed in praise of the King of Prussia, who had just conquered Silesia by a masterly stroke. As I was copying it, the idea struck me to personify Silesia, and to make her, in answer to the sonnet, bewail that Love (supposed to be the author of the sonnet of the marchioness) could applaud the man who had conquered her, when that conqueror was the sworn enemy of Love.

It is impossible for a man accustomed to write poetry to abstain when a happy subject smiles upon his delighted imagination. If he attempted to smother the poetical flame running through his veins it would consume him. I composed my sonnet, keeping the same rhymes as in the original, and, well pleased with my muse, I went to bed.

The next morning the Abbé Gama came in just as I had finished recopying my sonnet, and said he would breakfast with me. He complimented me upon the honour conferred on me by the invitation of Cardinal S. C.

"But be prudent," he added, "for his eminence has the reputation of being jealous."

I thanked him for his friendly advice, taking care to assure him that I had nothing to fear, because I did not feel the slightest inclination for the handsome marchioness.

Cardinal S. C. received me with great kindness mingled with dignity, to make me realize the importance of the favour he was bestowing upon me.

"What do you think," he enquired, "of the sonnet?"

"Monsignor, it is perfectly written, and, what is more, it is a charming composition. Allow me to return it to you with my thanks."

"She has much talent. I wish to shew you ten stanzas of her composition, my dear abbé, but you must promise to be very discreet about it."

"Your eminence may rely on me."

He opened his bureau and brought forth the stanzas of which he was the subject. I read them, found them well written, but devoid of enthusiasm; they were the work of a poet, and expressed love in the words of passion, but were not pervaded by that peculiar feeling by which true love is so easily discovered. The worthy cardinal was doubtless guilty of a very great indiscretion, but self-love is the cause of so many injudicious steps! I asked his eminence whether he had answered the stanzas.

"No," he replied, "I have not; but would you feel disposed to lend me your poetical pen, always under the seal of secrecy?"

"As to secrecy, monsignor, I promise it faithfully; but I am afraid the marchioness will remark the difference between your style and mine."

"She has nothing of my composition," said the cardinal; "I do not think she supposes me a fine poet, and for that reason your stanzas must be written in such a manner that she will not esteem them above my abilities."

"I will write them with pleasure, monsignor, and your eminence can form an opinion; if they do not seem good enough to be worthy of you, they need not be given to the marchioness."

"That is well said. Will you write them at once?"

"What! now, monsignor? It is not like prose."

"Well, well! try to let me have them to-morrow."

We dined alone, and his eminence complimented me upon my excellent appetite, which he remarked was as good as his own; but I was beginning to understand my eccentric host, and, to flatter him, I answered that he praised me more than I deserved, and that my appetite was inferior to his. The singular compliment delighted him, and I saw all the use I could make of his eminence.

Towards the end of the dinner, as we were conversing, the marchioness made her appearance, and, as a matter of course, without being announced. Her looks threw me into raptures; I thought her a perfect beauty. She did not give the cardinal time to meet her, but sat down near him, while I remained standing, according to etiquette.

Without appearing to notice me, the marchioness ran wittily over various topics until coffee was brought in. Then, addressing herself to me, she told me to sit down, just as if she was bestowing charity upon me.

"By-the-by, abbé," she said, a minute after, "have you read my sonnet?"

"Yes, madam, and I have had the honour to return it to his eminence. I have found it so perfect that I am certain it must have cost you a great deal of time."

"Time?" exclaimed the cardinal; "Oh! you do not know the marchioness."

"Monsignor," I replied, "nothing can be done well without time, and that is why I have not dared to shew to your eminence an answer to the sonnet which I have written in half an hour."

"Let us see it, abbé," said the marchioness; "I want to read it."

"*Answer of Silesia to Love.*" This title brought the most fascinating blushes on her countenance. "But Love is not mentioned in the sonnet," exclaimed the cardinal. "Wait," said the marchioness, "we must respect the idea of the poet."

She read the sonnet over and over, and thought that the reproaches addressed by Silesia to Love were very just. She explained my idea to the cardinal, making him understand why Silesia was offended at having been conquered by the King of Prussia.

"Ah, I see, I see!" exclaimed the cardinal, full of joy; "Silesia is a woman . . . . and the King of Prussia . . . . Oh! oh! that is really a fine idea!" And the good cardinal laughed heartily for more than a quarter of an hour. "I must copy that sonnet," he added, "indeed I must have it."

"The abbé," said the obliging marchioness, "will save you the trouble: I will dictate it to him."

I prepared to write, but his eminence suddenly exclaimed, "My dear marchioness, this is wonderful; he has kept the same rhymes as in your own sonnet: did you observe it?"

The beautiful marchioness gave me then a look of such expression that she completed her conquest. I understood that she wanted me to know the cardinal as well as she knew him; it was a kind of partnership in which I was quite ready to play my part.

As soon as I had written the sonnet under the charming woman's dictation, I took my leave, but not before the cardinal had told me that he expected me to dinner the next day.

I had plenty of work before me, for the ten stanzas I had to compose were of the most singular character, and I lost no time in shutting myself up in my room to think of them. I had to keep my balance between two points of equal difficulty, and I felt that great care was indispensable. I had to place the marchioness in such a position that she could pretend to believe the cardinal the author of the stanzas, and, at the same time, compel her to find out that I had written them, and that I was aware of her knowing it. It was necessary to speak so carefully that not one expression should breathe even the faintest hope on my part, and yet to make my stanzas blaze with the ardent fire of my love under the thin veil of poetry. As for the cardinal, I knew well enough that the better the stanzas were written, the more disposed he would be to sign them. All I wanted was clearness, so difficult to obtain in poetry, while a little doubtful darkness would have been accounted sublime by my new Midas. But, although I wanted to please him, the cardinal was only a secondary consideration, and the handsome marchioness the principal object.

As the marchioness in her verses had made a pompous enumeration of every physical and moral quality of his eminence, it was of course natural that he should return the compliment, and here my task was easy. At last having mastered my subject well, I began my work, and giving full career to my imagination and to my feelings I composed the ten stanzas, and gave the finishing stroke with these two beautiful lines from Ariosto:

Le angelicche bellezze nate al cielo
Non si ponno celar sotto alcum velo.

Rather pleased with my production, I presented it the next day to the cardinal, modestly saying that I doubted whether he would accept the authorship of so ordinary a composition. He read the stanzas twice over without taste or expression, and said at last that they were indeed not much, but exactly what he wanted. He thanked me particularly for the two lines from Ariosto, saying that they would assist in throwing the authorship upon himself, as they would prove to the lady for whom they were intended that he had not been able to write them without borrowing. And, as to offer me some consolation, he told me that, in recopying the lines, he would take care to make a few mistakes in the rhythm to complete the illusion.

We dined earlier than the day before, and I withdrew immediately after dinner so as to give him leisure to make a copy of the stanzas before the arrival of the lady.

The next evening I met the marchioness at the entrance of the palace, and offered her my arm to come out of her carriage. The instant she alighted, she said to me,——

"If ever your stanzas and mine become known in Rome, you may be sure of my enmity."

"Madam, I do not understand what you mean."

"I expected you to answer me in this manner," replied the marchioness, "but recollect what I have said."

I left her at the door of the reception-room, and thinking that she was really angry with me, I went away in despair. "My stanzas," I said to myself, "are too fiery; they compromise her dignity, and her pride is offended at my knowing the secret of her intrigue with Cardinal S. C. Yet, I feel certain that the dread she expresses of my want of discretion is only feigned, it is but a pretext to turn me out of her favour. She has not understood my reserve! What would she have done, if I had painted her in the simple apparel of the golden age, without any of those veils which modesty imposes upon her sex!" I was sorry I had not done so. I undressed and went to bed. My head was scarcely on the pillow when the Abbé Gama knocked at my door. I pulled the door-string, and coming in, he said,——

"My dear sir, the cardinal wishes to see you, and I am sent by the beautiful marchioness and Cardinal S. C., who desire you to come down."

"I am very sorry, but I cannot go; tell them the truth; I am ill in bed."

As the abbé did not return, I judged that he had faithfully acquitted himself of the commission, and I spent a quiet night. I was not yet dressed in the morning, when I received a note from Cardinal S. C. inviting me to dinner, saying that he had just been bled, and that he wanted to speak to me: he concluded by entreating me to come to him early, even if I did not feel well.

The invitation was pressing; I could not guess what had caused it, but the tone of the letter did not forebode anything unpleasant. I went to church, where I was sure that Cardinal Acquaviva would see me, and he did. After mass, his eminence beckoned to me.

"Are you truly ill?" he enquired.

"No, monsignor, I was only sleepy."

"I am very glad to hear it; but you are wrong, for you are loved. Cardinal S. C. has been bled this morning."

"I know it, monsignor. The cardinal tells me so in this note, in which he invites me to dine with him, with your excellency's permission."

"Certainly. But this is amusing! I did not know that he wanted a third person."

"Will there be a third person?"

"I do not know, and I have no curiosity about it."

The cardinal left me, and everybody imagined that his eminence had spoken to me of state affairs.

I went to my new Mæcenas, whom I found in bed.

"I am compelled to observe strict diet," he said to me; "I shall have to let you dine alone, but you will not lose by it as my cook does not know it. What I wanted to tell you is that your stanzas are, I am afraid, too pretty, for the marchioness adores them. If you had read them to me in the same way that she does, I could never have made up my mind to offer them."

"But she believes them to be written by your eminence?"

"Of course."

"That is the essential point, monsignor."

"Yes; but what should I do if she took it into her head to compose some new stanzas for me?"

"You would answer through the same pen, for you can dispose of me night and day, and rely upon the utmost secrecy."

"I beg of you to accept this small present; it is some negrillo snuff from Habana, which Cardinal Acquaviva has given me."

The snuff was excellent, but the object which contained it was still better. It was a splendid gold-enamelled box. I received it with respect, and with the expression of the deepest gratitude.

If his eminence did not know how to write poetry, at least he knew how to be generous, and in a delicate manner, and that science is, at least in my estimation, superior to the other for a great nobleman.

At noon, and much to my surprise, the beautiful marchioness made her appearance in the most elegant morning toilet.

"If I had known you were in good company," she said to the cardinal, "I would not have come."

"I am sure, dear marchioness, you will not find our dear abbé in the way."

"No, for I believe him to be honest and true."

I kept at a respectful distance, ready to go away with my splendid snuff-box at the first jest she might hurl at me.

The cardinal asked her if she intended to remain to dinner.

"Yes," she answered; "but I shall not enjoy my dinner, for I hate to eat alone."

"If you would honour him so far, the abbé would keep you company."

She gave me a gracious look, but without uttering one word.

This was the first time I had anything to do with a woman of quality, and that air of patronage, whatever kindness might accompany it, always put me out of temper, for I thought it made love out of the question. However, as we were in the presence of the cardinal, I fancied that she might be right in treating me in that fashion.

The table was laid out near the cardinal's bed, and the marchioness, who ate hardly anything, encouraged me in my good appetite.

"I have told you that the abbé is equal to me in that respect," said S. C.

"I truly believe," answered the marchioness, "that he does not remain far behind you; but," added she with flattery, "you are more dainty in your tastes."

"Would her ladyship be so good as to tell me in what I have appeared to her to be a mere glutton? For in all things I like only dainty and exquisite morsels."

"Explain what you mean by saying *in all things*," said the cardinal. Taking the liberty of laughing, I composed a few impromptu verses in which I named all I thought dainty and exquisite. The marchioness applauded, saying that she admired my courage.

"My courage, madam, is due to you, for I am as timid as a hare when I am not encouraged; you are the author of my impromptu."

"I admire you. As for myself, were I encouraged by

Apollo himself, I could not compose four lines without paper and ink."

"Only give way boldly to your genius, madam, and you will produce poetry worthy of heaven."

"That is my opinion, too," said the cardinal. "I entreat you to give me permission to shew your ten stanzas to the abbé."

"They are not very good, but I have no objection provided it remains between us."

The cardinal gave me, then, the stanzas composed by the marchioness, and I read them aloud with all the expression, all the feeling necessary to such reading.

"How well you have read those stanzas!" said the marchioness; "I can hardly believe them to be my own composition; I thank you very much. But have the goodness to give the benefit of your reading to the stanzas which his eminence has written in answer to mine. They surpass them much."

"Do not believe it, my dear abbé," said the cardinal, handing them to me. "Yet try not to let them lose anything through your reading."

There was certainly no need of his eminence enforcing upon me such a recommendation; it was my own poetry. I could not have read it otherwise than in my best style, especially when I had before me the beautiful woman who had inspired them, and when, besides, Bacchus was in me giving courage to Apollo as much as the beautiful eyes of the marchioness were fanning into an ardent blaze the fire already burning through my whole being.

I read the stanzas with so much expression that the cardinal was enraptured, but I brought a deep carnation tint upon the cheeks of the lovely marchioness when I came to the description of those beauties which the imagination of the poet is allowed to guess at, but which I could not, of course, have gazed upon. She snatched the paper from my hands with passion, saying that I was adding verses of my own; it was true, but I did not confess it. I was all aflame, and the fire was scorching her as well as me.

The cardinal having fallen asleep, she rose and went to take a seat on the balcony; I followed her. She had a rather high seat; I stood opposite to her, so that her knee touched the fob-pocket in which was my watch. What a position! Taking hold gently of one of her hands, I told her that she had ignited in my soul a devouring flame, that I adored her, and that, unless some hope was left to me of finding her sensible to my sufferings, I was determined to fly away from her for ever.

"Yes, beautiful marchioness, pronounce my sentence."

"I fear you are a libertine and an unfaithful lover."

"I am neither one nor the other."

With these words I folded her in my arms, and I pressed upon her lovely lips, as pure as a rose, an ardent kiss which she received with the best possible grace. This kiss, the forerunner of the most delicious pleasures, had imparted to my hands the greatest boldness; I was on the point of . . . . but the marchioness, changing her position, entreated me so sweetly to respect her, that, enjoying new voluptuousness through my very obedience, I not only abandoned an easy victory, but I even begged her pardon, which I soon read in the most loving look.

She spoke of Lucrezia, and was pleased with my discretion. She then alluded to the cardinal, doing her best to make me believe that there was nothing between them but a feeling of innocent friendship. Of course I had my opinion on that subject, but it was my interest to appear to believe every word she uttered. We recited together lines from our best poets, and all the time she was still sitting down and I standing before her, with my looks rapt in the contemplation of the most lovely charms, to which I remained insensible in appearance, for I had made up my mind not to press her that evening for greater favours than those I had already received.

The cardinal, waking from his long and peaceful siesta, got up and joined us in his night-cap, and good-naturedly enquired whether we had not felt impatient at his protracted sleep. I remained until dark and went home highly pleased with my day's work, but determined to keep my ardent desires in check until the opportunity for complete victory offered itself.

From that day, the charming marchioness never ceased to give me the marks of her particular esteem, without the slightest constraint; I was reckoning upon the carnival, which was close at hand, feeling certain that the more I should spare her delicacy, the more she would endeavour to find the opportunity of rewarding my loyalty, and of crowning with happiness my loving constancy. But fate ordained otherwise; Dame Fortune turned her back upon me at the very moment when the Pope and Cardinal Acquaviva were thinking of giving me a really good position.

The Holy Father had congratulated me upon the beautiful snuff-box presented to me by Cardinal S. C., but he had been careful never to name the marchioness. Cardinal Acquaviva expressed openly his delight at his brother-cardinal having given me a taste of his negrillo snuff in so splendid an envelope; the abbé Gama, finding me so forward on the road to success, did not venture to counsel me any more, and the virtuous Father Georgi gave me but one piece of advice—namely, to cling to the lovely marchioness and not to make any other acquaintances.

Such was my position—truly a brilliant one, when, on Christmas Day, the lover of Barbara Dalacqua entered my room, locked the door, and threw himself on the sofa, exclaiming that I saw him for the last time.

"I only come to beg of you some good advice."

"On what subject can I advise you?"

"Take this and read it; it will explain everything."

It was a letter from his mistress; the contents were these:

"I am pregnant of a child, the pledge of our mutual love; I can no longer have any doubt of it, my beloved, and I forewarn you that I have made up my mind to quit Rome alone, and to go away to die where it may please God, if you refuse to take care of me and save me. I would suffer anything, do anything, rather than let my father discover the truth."

"If you are a man of honour," I said, "you cannot abandon the poor girl. Marry her in spite of your father, in spite of her own, and live together honestly. The eternal Providence of God will watch over you and help you in your difficulties."

My advice seemed to bring calm to his mind, and he left me more composed.

At the beginning of January, 1744, he called again, looking very cheerful. "I have hired," he said, "the top floor of the house next to Barbara's dwelling; she knows it, and to-night I will gain her apartment through one of the windows of the garret, and we will make all our arrangements to enable me to carry her off. I have

made up my mind; I have decided upon taking her to
Naples, and I will take with us the servant who, sleeping
in the garret, had to be made a confidante of."

"God speed you, my friend!"

A week afterwards, towards eleven o'clock at night, he
entered my room accompanied by an abbé.

"What do you want so late?"

"I wish to introduce you to this handsome abbé."

I looked up, and to my consternation I recognized
Barbara.

"Has anyone seen you enter the house?" I enquired.

"No; and if we had been seen, what of it? It is only
an abbé. We now pass every night together."

"I congratulate you."

"The servant is our friend; she has consented to follow us, and all our arrangements are completed."

"I wish you every happiness. Adieu. I beg you to
leave me."

Three or four days after that visit, as I was walking
with the Abbé Gama towards the Villa Medicis, he told
me deliberately that there would be an execution during
the night in the Piazza di Spagna.

"What kind of execution?"

"The *bargello* or his lieutenant will come to execute
some *ordine santissimo,* or to visit some suspicious dwelling in order to arrest and carry off some person who does
not expect anything of the sort."

"How do you know it?"

"His eminence has to know it, for the Pope would not
venture to encroach upon his jurisdiction without asking his permission."

"And his eminence has given it?"

"Yes, one of the Holy Father's auditors came for that
purpose this morning."

"But the cardinal might have refused?"

"Of course; but such a permission is never denied."

"And if the person to be arrested happened to be under the protection of the cardinal—what then?"

"His eminence would give timely warning to that person."

We changed the conversation, but the news had disturbed me. I fancied that the execution threatened Barbara and her lover, for her father's house was under the Spanish jurisdiction. I tried to see the young man but I could not succeed in meeting him, and I was afraid lest a visit at his home or at M. Dalacqua's dwelling might implicate me. Yet it is certain that this last consideration would not have stopped me if I had been positively sure that they were threatened; had I felt satisfied of their danger, I would have braved everything.

About midnight, as I was ready to go to bed, and just as I was opening my door to take the key from outside, an abbé rushed panting into my room and threw himself on a chair. It was Barbara; I guessed what had taken place, and, foreseeing all the evil consequences her visit might have for me, deeply annoyed and very anxious, I upbraided her for having taken refuge in my room, and entreated her to go away.

Fool that I was! Knowing that I was only ruining myself without any chance of saving her, I ought to have compelled her to leave my room, I ought to have called for the servants if she had refused to withdraw. But I had not courage enough, or rather I voluntarily obeyed the decrees of destiny.

When she heard my order to go away, she threw herself on her knees, and melting into tears, she begged, she entreated my pity!

Where is the heart of steel which is not softened by the tears, by the prayers of a pretty and unfortunate woman? I gave way, but I told her that it was ruin for both of us.

"No one," she replied, "has seen me, I am certain, when I entered the mansion and came up to your room, and I consider my visit here a week ago as most fortunate; otherwise, I never could have known which was your room."

"Alas! how much better if you had never come! But what has become of your lover?"

"The *sbirri* have carried him off, as well as the servant. I will tell you all about it. My lover had informed me that a carriage would wait to-night at the foot of the flight of steps before the Church of Trinita del Monte, and that he would be there himself. I entered his room through the garret window an hour ago. There I put on this disguise, and, accompanied by the servant, proceeded to meet him. The servant walked a few yards before me, and carried a parcel of my things. At the corner of the street, one of the buckles of my shoes being unfastened, I stopped an instant, and the servant went on, thinking that I was following her. She reached the carriage, got into it, and, as I was getting nearer, the light from a lantern disclosed to me some thirty *sbirri;* at the same instant, one of them got on the driver's box and drove off at full speed, carrying off the servant, whom they must have mistaken for me, and my lover who was in the coach awaiting me. What could I do at such a fearful moment? I could not go back to my father's house, and I followed my first impulse which brought me here. And here I am! You tell me that my presence will cause your ruin; if it is so, tell me what to do; I feel I am dying; but find some expedient.

and I am ready to do anything, even to lay my life down, rather than be the cause of your ruin."

But she wept more bitterly than ever.

Her position was so sad that I thought it worse even than mine, although I could almost fancy I saw ruin before me despite my innocence.

"Let me," I said, "conduct you to your father; I feel sure of obtaining your pardon."

But my proposal only enhanced her fears.

"I am lost," she exclaimed; "I know my father. Ah! reverend sir, turn me out into the street, and abandon me to my miserable fate."

No doubt I ought to have done so, and I would have done it if the consciousness of what was due to my own interest had been stronger than my feeling of pity. But her tears! I have often said it, and those amongst my readers who have experienced it, must be of the same opinion; there is nothing on earth more irresistible than two beautiful eyes shedding tears, when the owner of those eyes is handsome, honest, and unhappy. I found myself physically unable to send her away.

"My poor girl," I said at last, "when daylight comes, and that will not be long, for it is past midnight, what do you intend to do?"

"I must leave the palace," she replied, sobbing. "In this disguise no one can recognize me; I will leave Rome, and I will walk straight before me until I fall on the ground, dying with grief and fatigue."

With these words she fell on the floor. She was choking; I could see her face turn blue; I was in the greatest distress.

I took off her neck-band, unlaced her stays under the abbé's dress, I threw cold water in her face, and I finally succeeded in bringing her back to consciousness.

The night was extremely cold, and there was no fire in my room. I advised her to get into my bed, promising to respect her.

"Alas! reverend sir, pity is the only feeling with which I can now inspire anyone."

And, to speak the truth I was too deeply moved, and, at the same time, too full of anxiety, to leave room in me for any desire. Having induced her to go to bed, and her extreme weakness preventing her from doing anything for herself, I undressed her and put her to bed, thus proving once more that compassion will silence the most imperious requirements of nature, in spite of all the charms which would, under other circumstances, excite to the highest degree the senses of a man. I lay down near her in my clothes, and woke her at day-break. Her strength was somewhat restored, she dressed herself alone, and I left my room, telling her to keep quiet until my return. I intended to proceed to her father's house, and to solicit her pardon, but, having perceived some suspicious-looking men loitering about the palace, I thought it wise to alter my mind, and went to a coffee-house.

I soon ascertanied that a spy was watching my movements at a distance; but I did not appear to notice him, and having taken some chocolate and stored a few biscuits in my pocket, I returned towards the palace, apparently without any anxiety or hurry, always followed by the same individual. I judged that the *bargello,* having failed in his project, was now reduced to guess-work, and I was strengthened in that view of the case when the gate-keeper of the palace told me, without my asking any question, as I came in, that an arrest had been attempted during the night, and had not succeeded. While he was speaking, one of the auditors of the Vicar-

General called to enquire when he could see the Abbé Gama. I saw that no time was to be lost, and went up to my room to decide upon what was to be done.

I began by making the poor girl eat a couple of biscuits soaked in some Canary wine, and I took her afterwards to the top story of the palace, where, leaving her in a not very decent closet which was not used by anyone, I told her to wait for me.

My servant came soon after, and I ordered him to lock the door of my room as soon as he finished cleaning it, and to bring me the key at the Abbé Gama's apartment, where I was going. I found Gama in conversation with the auditor sent by the Vicar-General. As soon as he had dismissed him, he came to me, and ordered his servant to serve the chocolate. When we were left alone he gave me an account of his interview with the auditor, who had come to entreat his eminence to give orders to turn out of his palace a person who was supposed to have taken refuge in it about midnight. "We must wait," said the abbé, "until the cardinal is visible, but I am quite certain that, if anyone has taken refuge here unknown to him, his eminence will compel that person to leave the palace." We then spoke of the weather and other trifles until my servant brought my key. Judging that I had at least an hour to spare, I bethought myself of a plan which alone could save Barbara from shame and misery.

Feeling certain that I was unobserved, I went up to my poor prisoner and made her write the following words in French:

"I am an honest girl, monsignor, though I am disguised in the dress of an abbé. I entreat your eminence to allow me to give my name only to you and in person. I hope that, prompted by the great goodness of your soul, your eminence will save me from dishonour."

I gave her the necessary instructions, as to sending the note to the cardinal, assuring her that he would have her brought to him as soon as he read it.

"When you are in his presence," I added, "throw yourself on your knees, tell him everything without any concealment, except as regards your having passed the night in my room. You must be sure not to mention that circumstance, for the cardinal must remain in complete ignorance of my knowing anything whatever of this intrigue. Tell him that, seeing your lover carried off, you rushed to his palace and ran upstairs as far as you could go, and that after a most painful night Heaven inspired you with the idea of writing to him to entreat his pity. I feel certain that, one way or the other, his eminence will save you from dishonour, and it certainly is the only chance you have of being united to the man you love so dearly."

She promised to follow my instructions faithfully, and, coming down, I had my hair dressed and went to church, where the cardinal saw me. I then went out and returned only for dinner, during which the only subject of conversation was the adventure of the night. Gama alone said nothing, and I followed his example, but I understood from all the talk going on round the table that the cardinal had taken my poor Barbara under his protection. That was all I wanted, and thinking that I had nothing more to fear I congratulated myself, *in petto*, upon my stratagem, which had, I thought, proved a master-stroke. After dinner, finding myself alone with Gama, I asked him what was the meaning of it all, and this is what he told me:

"A father, whose name I do not know yet, had requested the assistance of the Vicar-General to prevent his son from carrying off a young girl, with whom he intended to leave the States of the Church; the pair had arranged to meet at midnight in this very square, and the Vicar, having previously obtained the consent of our cardinal, as I told you yesterday, gave orders to the *bargello* to dispose his men in such a way as to catch the young people in the very act of running away, and to arrest them. The orders were executed, but the *sbirri* found out, when they returned to the *bargello*, that they had met with only a half success, the woman who got out of the carriage with the young man not belonging to that species likely to be carried off. Soon afterwards a spy informed the *bargello* that, at the very moment the arrest was executed, he had seen a young abbé run away very rapidly and take refuge in this palace, and the suspicion immediately arose that it might be the missing young lady in the disguise of an ecclesiastic. The *bargello* reported to the Vicar-General the failure of his men, as well as the account given by the spy, and the Prelate, sharing the suspicion of the police, sent to his eminence, our master, requesting him to have the person in question, man or woman, turned out of the palace, unless such persons should happen to be known to his excellency, and therefore above suspicion. Cardinal Acquaviva was made acquainted with these circumstances at nine this morning through the auditor you met in my room, and he promised to have the person sent away unless she belonged to his household.

"According to his promise, the cardinal ordered the palace to be searched, but, in less than a quarter of an hour, the major-domo received orders to stop, and the only reason for these new instructions must be this:

"I am told by the major-domo that at nine o'clock exactly a very handsome, young abbé, whom he imme-

diately judged to be a girl in disguise, asked him to deliver a note to his eminence, and that the cardinal, after
reading it, had desired the said abbé be brought to his
apartment, which he has not left since. As the order to
stop searching the palace was given immediately after
the introduction of the abbé to the cardinal, it is easy
enough to suppose that this ecclesiastic is no other than
the young girl missed by the police, who took refuge in
the palace in which she must have passed the whole
night."

"I suppose," said I, "that his eminence will give her
up to-day, if not to the *bargello,* at least to the Vicar-
General."

"No, not even to the Pope himself," answered Gama.
"You have not yet a right idea of the protection of our
cardinal, and that protection is evidently granted to
her, since the young person is not only in the palace of
his eminence, but also in his own apartment and under
his own guardianship."

The whole affair being in itself very interesting, my
attention could not appear extraordinary to Gama, however suspicious he might be naturally, and I was certain
that he would not have told me anything if he had
guessed the share I had taken in the adventure, and the
interest I must have felt in it.

The next day, Gama came to my room with a radiant
countenance, and informed me that the Cardinal-Vicar
was aware of the ravisher being my friend, and supposed
that I was likewise the friend of the girl, as she was the
daughter of my French teacher. "Everybody," he added,
"is satisfied that you knew the whole affair, and it is
natural to suspect that the poor girl spent the night in
your room. I admire your prudent reserve during our
conversation of yesterday. You kept so well on your

guard that I would have sworn you knew nothing whatever of the affair."

"And it is the truth," I answered, very seriously; "I have only learned all the circumstances from you this moment. I know the girl, but I have not seen her for six weeks, since I gave up my French lessons; I am much better acquainted with the young man, but he never confided his project to me. However, people may believe whatever they please. You say that it is natural for the girl to have passed the night in my room, but you will not mind my laughing in the face of those who accept their own suppositions as realities."

"That, my dear friend," said the abbé, "is one of the vices of the Romans; happy those who can afford to laugh at it; but this slander may do you harm, even in the mind of our cardinal."

As there was no performance at the Opera that night, I went to the cardinal's reception; I found no difference towards me either in the cardinal's manners, or in those of any other person, and the marchioness was even more gracious than usual.

After dinner, on the following day, Gama informed me that the cardinal had sent the young girl to a convent in which she would be well treated at his eminence's expense, and that he was certain that she would leave it only to become the wife of the young doctor.

"I should be very happy if it should turn out so," I replied; "for they are both most estimable people."

Two days afterwards, I called upon Father Georgi, and he told me, with an air of sorrow, that the great news of the day in Rome was the failure of the attempt to carry off Dalacqua's daughter, and that all the honour of the intrigue was given to me, which displeased him much. I told him what I had already told Gama, and he appeared to believe me, but he added that in Rome people did not want to know things as they truly were, but only as they wished them to be.

"It is known, that you have been in the habit of going every morning to Dalacqua's house; it is known that the young man often called on you; that is quite enough. People do not care to know the circumstances which might counteract the slander, but only those likely to give it new force, for slander is vastly relished in the Holy City. Your innocence will not prevent the whole adventure being booked to your account, if, in forty years time you were proposed as pope in the conclave."

During the following days the fatal adventure began to cause me more annoyance than I could express, for everyone mentioned it to me, and I could see clearly that people pretended to believe what I said only because they did not dare to do otherwise. The marchioness told me jeeringly that the Signora Dalacqua had contracted peculiar obligations towards me, but my sorrow was very great when, during the last days of the carnival, I remarked that Cardinal Acquaviva's manner had become constrained, although I was the only person who observed the change.

The noise made by the affair was, however, beginning to subside, when, in the first days of Lent, the cardinal desired me to come to his private room, and spoke as follows:

"The affair of the girl Dalacqua is now over; it is no longer spoken of, but the verdict of the public is that you and I have profited by the clumsiness of the young man who intended to carry her off. In reality I care little for such a verdict, for, under similar circumstances, I should always act in a similar manner, and I do not wish to know that which no one can compel you to confess, and which, as a man of honour, you must not admit. If you had no previous knowledge of the intrigue, and had actually turned the girl out of your room (supposing she did come to you), you would have been guilty of a wrong and cowardly action, because you would have sealed her misery for the remainder of her days, and it would not have caused you to escape the suspicion of being an accomplice, while at the same time it would have attached to you the odium of dastardly treachery. Notwithstanding all I have just said, you can easily imagine that, in spite of my utter contempt for all gossiping fools, I cannot openly defy them. I therefore feel myself compelled to ask you not only to quit my service, but even to leave Rome. I undertake to supply you with an honourable pretext for your departure, so as to insure you the continuation of the respect which you may have secured through the marks of esteem I have bestowed upon you. I promise you to whisper in the ear of any person you may choose, and even to inform everybody, that you are going on an important mission which I have entrusted to you. You have only to name the country where you want to go; I have friends everywhere, and can recommend you to such purpose that you will be sure to find employment. My letters of recommendation will be in my own handwriting, and nobody need know where you are going. Meet me to-morrow at the Villa Negroni, and let me know where my letters are to be addressed. You must be ready to start within a week. Believe me, I am sorry to lose you; but the sacrifice is forced upon me by the most absurd prejudice. Go now, and do not let me witness your grief."

He spoke the last words because he saw my eyes

filling with tears, and he did not give me time to answer. Before leaving his room, I had the strength of
mind to compose myself, and I put on such an air of
cheerfulness that the Abbé Gama, who took me to his
room to drink some coffee, complimented me upon my
happy looks.

"I am sure," he said, "that they are caused by the
conversation you have had with his eminence."

"You are right; but you do not know the sorrow
at my heart which I try not to shew outwardly."

"What sorrow?"

"I am afraid of failing in a difficult mission which the
cardinal has entrusted me with this morning. I am compelled to conceal how little confidence I feel in myself
in order not to lessen the good opinion his eminence is
pleased to entertain of me."

"If my advice can be of any service to you, pray
dispose of me; but you are quite right to shew yourself calm and cheerful. Is it any business to transact
in Rome?"

"No; it is a journey I shall have to undertake in a
week or ten days."

"Which way?"

"Towards the west."

"Oh! I am not curious to know."

I went out alone and took a walk in the Villa Borg-
hese, where I spent two hours wrapped in dark despair.
I liked Rome, I was on the high road to fortune, and
suddenly I found myself in the abyss, without knowing
where to go, and with all my hopes scattered to the
winds. I examined my conduct, I judged myself severely, I could not find myself guilty of any crime save
of too much kindness, but I perceived how right the
good Father Georgi had been. My duty was not only

to take no part in the intrigue of the two lovers, but
also to change my French teacher the moment I heard
of it; but this was like calling in a doctor after death
has struck the patient. Besides, young as I was, having
no experience yet of misfortune, and still less of the
wickedness of society, it was very difficult for me to have
that prudence which a man gains only by long intercourse with the world.

"Where shall I go?" This was the question which
seemed to me impossible of solution. I thought of it
all through the night, and through the morning, but I
thought in vain; after Rome, I was indifferent where
I went to!

In the evening, not caring for any supper, I had gone
to my room; the Abbé Gama came to me with a request
from the cardinal not to accept any invitation to dinner
for the next day, as he wanted to speak to me. I therefore waited upon his eminence the next day at the Villa
Negroni; he was walking with his secretary, whom he
dismissed the moment he saw me. As soon as we were
alone, I gave him all the particulars of the intrigue
of the two lovers, and I expressed in the most vivid
manner the sorrow I felt at leaving his service.

"I have no hope of success," I added, "for I am certain that Fortune will smile upon me only as long as
I am near your eminence."

For nearly an hour I told him all the grief with which
my heart was bursting, weeping bitterly; yet I could
not move him from his decision. Kindly, but firmly
he pressed me to tell him to what part of Europe I
wanted to go, and despair as much as vexation made
me name Constantinople.

"Constantinople!" he exclaimed, moving back a step
or two.

"Yes, monsignor, Constantinople," I repeated, wiping away my tears.

The prelate, a man of great wit, but a Spaniard to the very back-bone, after remaining silent a few minutes, said, with a smile,—

"I am glad you have not chosen Ispahan, as I should have felt rather embarrassed. When do you wish to go?"

"This day week, as your eminence has ordered me."

"Do you intend to sail from Naples or from Venice?"

"From Venice."

"I will give you such a passport as will be needed, for you will find two armies in winter-quarters in the Romagna. It strikes me that you may tell everybody that I sent you to Constantinople, for nobody will believe you."

This diplomatic suggestion nearly made me smile. The cardinal told me that I should dine with him, and he left me to join his secretary.

When I returned to the palace, thinking of the choice I had made, I said to myself, "Either I am mad, or I am obeying the impulse of a mysterious genius which sends me to Constantinople to work out my fate." I was only astonished that the cardinal had so readily accepted my choice. "Without any doubt," I thought, "he did not wish me to believe that he had boasted of more than he could achieve, in telling me that he had friends everywhere. But to whom can he recommend me in Constantinople? I have not the slightest idea, but to Constantinople I must go."

I dined alone with his eminence; he made a great show of peculiar kindness and I of great satisfaction, for my self-pride, stronger even than my sorrow, forbade me to let anyone guess that I was in disgrace. My deepest grief was, however, to leave the marchioness, with whom I was in love, and from whom I had not obtained any important favour.

Two days afterwards, the cardinal gave me a passport for Venice, and a sealed letter addressed to Osman Bonneval, Pacha of Caramania, in Constantinople. There was no need of my saying anything to anyone, but, as the cardinal had not forbidden me to do it, I shewed the address on the letter to all my acquaintances.

The Chevalier de Lezze, the Venetian Ambassador, gave me a letter for a wealthy Turk, a very worthy man who had been his friend; Don Gaspar and Father Georgi asked me to write to them, but the Abbé Gama laughed, and said he was quite sure I was not going to Constantinople.

I went to take my farewell of Donna Cecilia, who had just received a letter from Lucrezia, imparting the news that she would soon be a mother. I also called upon Angélique and Don Francisco, who had lately been married and had not invited me to the wedding.

When I called to take Cardinal Acquaviva's final instructions he gave me a purse containing one hundred ounces, worth seven hundred sequins. I had three hundred more, so that my fortune amounted to one thousand sequins; I kept two hundred, and for the rest I took a letter of exchange upon a Ragusan who was established in Ancona. I left Rome in the coach with a lady going to Our Lady of Loretto, to fulfil a vow made during a severe illness of her daughter, who accompanied her. The young lady was ugly; my journey was a rather tedious one.

CHAPTER XI

My Short But Rather Too Gay Visit To Ancona—
Cecilia, Marina, Bellino—the Greek Slave of the Laz-
zaretto—Bellino Discovers Himself

I ARRIVED in Ancona on the 25th of February,
1744, and put up at the best inn. Pleased with my
room, I told mine host to prepare for me a good meat
dinner; but he answered that during Lent all good Cath-
olics eat nothing but fish.

"The Holy Father has granted me permission to eat
meat."

"Let me see your permission."

"He gave it to me by word of mouth."

"Reverend sir, I am not obliged to believe you."

"You are a fool."

"I am master in my own house, and I beg you will
go to some other inn."

Such an answer, coupled to a most unexpected notice
to quit, threw me into a violent passion. I was swearing, raving, screaming, when suddenly a grave-looking
individual made his appearance in my room, and said
to me:

"Sir, you are wrong in calling for meat, when in Ancona fish is much better; you are wrong in expecting
the landlord to believe you on your bare word; and
if you have obtained the permission from the Pope,

you have been wrong in soliciting it at your age; you have been wrong in not asking for such permission in writing; you are wrong in calling the host a fool, because it is a compliment that no man is likely to accept in his own house; and, finally, you are wrong in making such an uproar."

Far from increasing my bad temper, this individual, who had entered my room only to treat me to a sermon, made me laugh.

"I willingly plead guilty, sir," I answered, "to all the counts which you allege against me; but it is raining, it is getting late, I am tired and hungry, and therefore you will easily understand that I do not feel disposed to change my quarters. Will you give me some supper, as the landlord refuses to do so?"

"No," he replied, with great composure, "because I am a good Catholic and fast. But I will undertake to make it all right for you with the landlord, who will give you a good supper."

Thereupon he went downstairs, and I, comparing my hastiness to his calm, acknowledged the man worthy of teaching me some lessons. He soon came up again, informed me that peace was signed, and that I would be served immediately.

"Will you not take supper with me?"

"No, but I will keep you company."

I accepted his offer, and to learn who he was, I told him my name, giving myself the title of secretary to Cardinal Acquaviva.

"My name is Sancio Pico," he said; "I am a Castilian, and the *proveditore* of the army of H. C. M., which is commanded by Count de Gages under the orders of the generalissimo, the Duke of Modena."

My excellent appetite astonished him, and he en-

quired whether I had dined. "No," said I; and I saw
his countenance assume an air of satisfaction.

"Are you not afraid such a supper will hurt you?"
he said.

"On the contrary, I hope it will do me a great deal
of good."

"Then you have deceived the Pope?"

"No, for I did not tell him that I had no appetite,
but only that I liked meat better than fish."

"If you feel disposed to hear some good music," he
said a moment after, "follow me to the next room; the
prima donna of Ancona lives there."

The words prima donna interested me at once, and I
followed him. I saw, sitting before a table, a woman
already somewhat advanced in age, with two young
girls and two boys, but I looked in vain for the actress,
whom Don Sancio Pico at last presented to me in the
shape of one of the two boys, who was remarkably
handsome and might have been seventeen. I thought
he was a *castrato* who, as is the custom in Rome, performed all the parts of a prima donna. The mother
presented to me her other son, likewise very good-looking, but more manly than the *castrato*, although younger.
His name was Petronio, and, keeping up the transforma-
tions of the family, he was the first female dancer at
the opera. The eldest girl, who was also introduced to
me, was named Cecilia, and studied music; she was
twelve years old; the youngest, called Marina, was only
eleven, and like her brother Petronio was consecrated to
the worship of Terpsichore. Both the girls were very
pretty.

The family came from Bologna and lived upon the
talent of its members; cheerfulness and amiability replaced wealth with them.

Bellino, such was the name of the *castrato*, yielding to the entreaties of Don Sancio, rose from the table, went to the harpiscord, and sang with the voice of an angel and with delightful grace. The Castilian listened with his eyes closed in an ecstasy of enjoyment, but I, far from closing my eyes, gazed into Bellino's, which seemed to dart amorous lightnings upon me. I could discover in him some of the features of Lucrezia and the graceful manner of the marchioness, and everything betrayed a beautiful woman, for his dress concealed but imperfectly the most splendid bosom. The consequence was that, in spite of his having been introduced as a man, I fancied that the so-called Bellino was a disguised beauty, and, my imagination taking at once the highest flight, I became thoroughly enamoured.

We spent two very pleasant hours, and I returned to my room accompanied by the Castilian. "I intend to leave very early to-morrow morning," he said, "for Sinigaglia, with the Abbé Vilmarcati, but I expect to return for supper the day after to-morrow." I wished him a happy journey, saying that we would most likely meet on the road, as I should probably leave Ancona myself on the same day, after paying a visit to my banker.

I went to bed thinking of Bellino and of the impression he had made upon me; I was sorry to go away without having proved to him that I was not the dupe of his disguise. Accordingly, I was well pleased to see him enter my room in the morning as soon as I had opened my door. He came to offer me the services of his young brother Petronio during my stay in Ancona, instead of my engaging a *valet de place*. I willingly agreed to the proposal, and sent Petronio to get coffee for all the family.

I asked Bellino to sit on my bed with the intention of making love to him, and of treating him
like a girl, but the two young sisters ran into my room
and disturbed my plans. Yet the trio formed before me
a very pleasing sight; they represented natural beauty
and artless cheerfulness of three different kinds; un-
obtrusive familiarity, theatrical wit, pleasing playfulness, and pretty Bolognese manners which I witnessed
for the first time; all this would have sufficed to cheer
me if I had been downcast. Cecilia and Marina were
two sweet rosebuds, which, to bloom in all their beauty,
required only the inspiration of love, and they would
certainly have had the preference over Bellino if I had
seen in him only the miserable outcast of mankind, or
rather the pitiful victim of sacerdotal cruelty, for, in
spite of their youth, the two amiable girls offered on
their dawning bosom the precious image of womanhood.

Petronio came with the coffee which he poured out,
and I sent some to the mother, who never left her room.
Petronio was a true male harlot by taste and by profession. The species is not scare in Italy, where the
offence is not regarded with the wild and ferocious in-
tolerance of England and Spain. I had given him one
sequin to pay for the coffee, and told him to keep the
change, and, to shew me his gratitude, he gave me a
voluptuous kiss with half-open lips, supposing in me a
taste which I was very far from entertaining. I dis-
abused him, but he did not seem the least ashamed.
I told him to order dinner for six persons, but he remarked that he would order it only for four, as he had
to keep his dear mother company; she always took her
dinner in bed. Everyone to his taste, I thought, and
I let him do as he pleased.

Two minutes after he had gone, the landlord came

to my room and said, "Reverend sir, the persons you
have invited here have each the appetite of two men at
least; I give you notice of it, because I must charge accordingly." "All right," I replied, "but let us have a
good dinner."

When I was dressed, I thought I ought to pay my
compliments to the compliant mother. I went to her
room, and congratulated her upon her children. She
thanked me for the present I had given to Petronio, and
began to make me the confidant of her distress. "The
manager of the theatre," she said, "is a miser who has
given us only fifty Roman crowns for the whole carnival.
We have spent them for our living, and, to return to
Bologna, we shall have to walk and beg our way." Her
confidence moved my pity, so I took a gold quadruple
from my purse and offered it to her; she wept for joy
and gratitude.

"I promise you another gold quadruple, madam," I
said, "if you will confide in me entirely. Confess that
Bellino is a pretty woman in disguise."

"I can assure you it is not so, although he has the
appearance of a woman."

"Not only the appearance, madam, but the tone, the
manners; I am a good judge."

"Nevertheless, he is a boy, for he has had to be examined before he could sing on the stage here."

"And who examined him?"

"My lord bishop's chaplain."

"A chaplain?"

"Yes, and you may satisfy yourself by enquiring from
him."

"The only way to clear my doubts would be to examine him myself."

"You may, if he has no objection, but truly I cannot

interfere, as I do not know what your intentions are."

"They are quite natural."

I returned to my room and sent Petronio for a bottle of Cyprus wine. He brought the wine and seven sequins, the change for the doubloon I had given him. I divided them between Bellino, Cecilia and Marina, and begged the two young girls to leave me alone with their brother.

"Bellino, I am certain that your natural conformation is different from mine; my dear, you are a girl."

"I am a man, but a *castrato;* I have been examined."

"Allow me to examine you likewise, and I will give you a doubloon."

"I cannot, for it is evident that you love me, and such love is condemned by religion."

"You did not raise these objections with the bishop's chaplain."

"He was an elderly priest, and besides, he only just glanced at me."

"I will know the truth," said I, extending my hand boldly.

But he repulsed me and rose from his chair. His obstinacy vexed me, for I had already spent fifteen or sixteen sequins to satisfy my curiosity.

I began my dinner with a very bad humour, but the excellent appetite of my pretty guests brought me round, and I soon thought that, after all, cheerfulness was better than sulking, and I resolved to make up for my disappointment with the two charming sisters, who seemed well disposed to enjoy a frolic.

I began by distributing a few innocent kisses right and left, as I sat between them near a good fire, eating chestnuts which we wetted with Cyprus wine. But very soon my greedy hands touched every part which my lips could not kiss, and Cecilia, as well as Marina, delighted in the game. Seeing that Bellino was smiling, I kissed him likewise, and his half-open ruffle attracting my hand, I ventured and went in without resistance. The chisel of Praxiteles had never carved a finer bosom!

"Oh! this is enough," I exclaimed; "I can no longer doubt that you are a beautifully-formed woman!"

"It is," he replied, "the defect of all *castrati*."

"No, it is the perfection of all handsome women. Bellino, believe me, I am enough of a good judge to distinguish between the deformed breast of a *castrato*, and that of a beautiful woman; and your alabaster bosom belongs to a young beauty of seventeen summers."

Who does not know that love, inflamed by all that can excite it, never stops in young people until it is satisfied, and that one favour granted kindles the wish for a greater one? I had begun well, I tried to go further and to smother with burning kisses that which my hand was pressing so ardently, but the false Bellino, as if he had only just been aware of the illicit pleasure I was enjoying, rose and ran away. Anger increased in me the ardour of love, and feeling the necessity of calming myself either by satisfying my ardent desires or by evaporating them, I begged Cecilia, Bellino's pupil, to sing a few Neapolitan airs.

I then went out to call upon the banker, from whom I took a letter of exchange at sight upon Bologna for the amount I had to receive from him, and on my return, after a light supper with the two young sisters, I prepared to go to bed, having previously instructed Petronio to order a carriage for the morning.

I was just locking my door when Cecilia, half undressed, came in to say that Bellino begged me to take him to Rimini, where he was engaged to sing in an opera to be performed after Easter.

"Go and tell him, my dear little seraph, that I am ready to do what he wishes, if he will only grant me in your presence what I desire; I want to know for a certainty whether he is a man or a woman."

She left me and returned soon, saying that Bellino had gone to bed, but that if I would postpone my departure for one day only he promised to satisfy me on the morrow.

"Tell me the truth, Cecilia, and I will give you six sequins."

"I cannot earn them, for I have never seen him naked, and I cannot swear to his being a girl. But he must be a man, otherwise he would not have been allowed to perform here."

"Well, I will remain until the day after to-morrow, provided you keep me company tonight."

"Do you love me very much?"

"Very much indeed, if you shew yourself very kind."

"I will be very kind, for I love you dearly likewise. I will go and tell my mother."

"Of course you have a lover?"

"I never had one."

She left my room, and in a short time came back full of joy, saying that her mother believed me an honest man; she of course meant a generous one. Cecilia locked the door, and throwing herself in my arms covered me with kisses. She was pretty, charming, but I was not in love with her, and I was not able to say to her as to Lucrezia: "You have made me so happy!" But she said it herself, and I did not feel much flattered, although I pretended to believe her. When I woke up in the morning I gave her a tender salutation, and presenting her with three doubloons, which must have particularly delighted the mother, I sent her away without losing my time in promising everlasting constancy—a promise as absurd as it is trifling, and which the most virtuous man ought never to make even to the most beautiful of women.

After breakfast I sent for mine host and ordered an excellent supper for five persons, feeling certain that Don Sancio, whom I expected in the evening, would not refuse to honour me by accepting my invitation, and with that idea I made up my mind to go without my dinner. The Bolognese family did not require to imitate my diet to insure a good appetite for the evening.

I then summoned Bellino to my room, and claimed the performance of his promise but he laughed, remarked that the day was not passed yet, and said that he was certain of traveling with me.

"I fairly warn you that you cannot accompany me unless I am fully satisfied."

"Well, I will satisfy you."

"Shall we go and take a walk together?"

"Willingly; I will dress myself."

While I was waiting for him, Marina came in with a dejected countenance, enquiring how she had deserved my contempt.

"Cecilia has passed the night with you, Bellino will go with you to-morrow, I am the most unfortunate of us all."

"Do you want money?"

"No, for I love you."

"But, Marinetta, you are too young."

"I am much stronger than my sister."

"Perhaps you have a lover."

"Oh! no."

"Very well, we can try this evening."

"Good! Then I will tell mother to prepare clean

sheets for to-morrow morning; otherwise everybody here would know that I slept with you."

I could not help admiring the fruits of a theatrical education, and was much amused.

Bellino came back, we went out together, and we took our walk towards the harbour. There were several vessels at anchor, and amongst them a Venetian ship and a Turkish tartan. We went on board the first which we visited with interest, but not seeing anyone of my acquaintance, we rowed towards the Turkish tartan, where the most romantic surprise awaited me. The first person I met on board was the beautiful Greek woman I had left in Ancona, seven months before, when I went away from the lazzaretto. She was seated near the old captain, of whom I enquired, without appearing to notice his handsome slave, whether he had any fine goods to sell. He took us to his cabin, but as I cast a glance towards the charming Greek, she expressed by her looks all her delight at such an unexpected meeting.

I pretended not to be pleased with the goods shewn by the Turk, and under the impulse of inspiration I told him that I would willingly buy something pretty which would take the fancy of his better-half. He smiled, and the Greek slave having whispered a few words to him, he left the cabin. The moment he was out of sight, this new Aspasia threw herself in my arms, saying, "Now is your time!" I would not be found wanting in courage, and taking the most convenient position in such a place, I did to her in one instant that which her old master had not done in five years. I had not yet reached the goal of my wishes, when the unfortunate girl, hearing her master, tore herself from my arms with a deep sigh, and placing herself cunningly in front of me, gave me time to repair the disorder of my dress, which might have cost me my life, or at least all I possessed to compromise the affair. In that curious situation, I was highly amused at the surprise of Bellino, who stood there trembling like an aspen leaf.

The trifles chosen by the handsome slave cost me only thirty sequins. *Spolaitis,* she said to me in her own language, and the Turk telling her that she ought to kiss me, she covered her face with her hands, and ran away. I left the ship more sad than pleased, for I regretted that, in spite of her courage, she should have enjoyed only an incomplete pleasure. As soon as we were in our row boat, Bellino, who had recovered from his fright, told me that I had just made him acquainted with a phenomenon, the reality of which he could not admit, and which gave him a very strange idea of my nature; that, as far as the Greek girl was concerned, he could not make her out, unless I should assure him that every woman in her country was like her. "How unhappy they must be!" he added.

"Do you think," I asked, " that coquettes are happier?"

"No, but I think that when a woman yields to love, she should not be conquered before she has fought with her own desires; she should not give way to the first impulse of a lustful desire and abandon herself to the first man who takes her fancy, like an animal—the slave of sense. You must confess that the Greek woman has given you an evident proof that you had taken her fancy, but that she has at the same time given you a proof not less certain of her beastly lust, and of an effrontery which exposed her to the shame of being repulsed, for she could not possibly know whether you would feel as well disposed for her as she felt for you. She is very handsome, and it all turned out well, but the adventure has thrown me into a whirlpool of agitation which I cannot yet control."

I might easily have put a stop to Bellino's perplexity, and rectified the mistake he was labouring under; but such a confession would not have ministered to my self-love, and I held my peace, for, if Bellino happened to be a girl, as I suspected, I wanted her to be convinced that I attached, after all, but very little importance to the great affair, and that it was not worth while employing cunning expedients to obtain it.

We returned to the inn, and, towards evening, hearing Don Sancio's travelling carriage roll into the yard, I hastened to meet him, and told him that I hoped he would excuse me if I had felt certain that he would not refuse me the honour of his company to supper with Bellino. He thanked me politely for the pleasure I was so delicately offering him, and accepted my invitation.

The most exquisite dishes, the most delicious wines of Spain, and, more than everything else, the cheerfulness and the charming voices of Bellino and of Cecilia, gave the Castilian five delightful hours. He left me at midnight, saying that he could not declare himself thoroughly pleased unless I promised to sup with him the next evening with the same guests. It would compel me to postpone my departure for another day, but I accepted.

As soon as Don Sancio had gone, I called upon Bellino to fulfil his promise, but he answered that Marinetta was waiting for me, and that, as I was not going away the next day, he would find an opportunity of satisfying my doubts; and wishing me a good night, he left the room.

Marinetta, as cheerful as a lark, ran to lock the door and came back to me, her eyes beaming with ardour. She was more formed than Cecilia, although one year younger, and seemed anxious to convince me of her superiority, but, thinking that the fatigue of the preceding night might have exhausted my strength, she unfolded all the armorous ideas of her mind, explained at length all she knew of the great mystery she was going to enact with me, and of all the contrivances she had had recourse to in order to acquire her imperfect knowledge, the whole interlarded with the foolish talk natural to her age. I made out that she was afraid of my not finding her a maiden, and of my reproaching her about it. Her anxiety pleased me, and I gave her a new confidence by telling her that nature had refused to many young girls what is called maidenhood, and that only a fool could be angry with a girl for such a reason.

My science gave her courage and confidence, and I was compelled to acknowledge that she was very superior to her sister.

"I am delighted you find me so," she said; "we must not sleep at all throughout the night."

"Sleep, my darling, will prove our friend, and our strength renewed by repose will reward you in the morning for what you may suppose lost time."

And truly, after a quiet sleep, the morning was for her a succession of fresh triumphs, and I crowned her happiness by sending her away with three doubloons, which she took to her mother, and which gave the good woman an insatiable desire to contract new obligations towards Providence.

I went out to get some money from the banker, as I did not know what might happen during my journey. I had enjoyed myself, but I had spent too much: yet there was Bellino who, if a girl, was not to find me less generous than I had been with the two young sisters. It was to be decided during the day, and I fancied that I was sure of the result.

There are some persons who pretend that life is only a succession of misfortunes, which is as much as to say that life itself is a misfortune; but if life is a misfortune, death must be exactly the reverse and therefore death must be happiness, since death is the very reverse of life. That deduction may appear too finely drawn. But those who say that life is a succession of misfortunes are certainly either ill or poor; for, if they enjoyed good health, if they had cheerfulness in their heart and money in their purse, if they had for their enjoyment a Cecilia, a Marinetta, and even a more lovely beauty in perspective, they would soon entertain a very different opinion of life! I hold them to be a race of pessimists, recruited amongst beggarly philosophers and knavish, atrabilious theologians. If pleasure does exist, and if life is necessary to enjoy pleasure, then life is happiness. There are misfortunes, as I know by experience; but the very existence of such misfortunes proves that the sum-total of happiness is greater. Because a few thorns are to be found in a basket full of roses, is the existence of those beautiful flowers to be denied? No; it is a slander to deny that life is happiness. When I am in a dark room, it pleases me greatly to see through a window an immense horizon before me.

As supper-time was drawing near, I went to Don Sancio, whom I found in magnificently-furnished apartments. The table was loaded with silver plate, and his servants were in livery. He was alone, but all his guests arrived soon after me—Cecilia, Marina, and Bellino, who, either by caprice or from taste, was dressed as a woman. The two young sisters, prettily arranged, looked charming, but Bellino, in his female costume, so completely threw them into the shade, that my last doubt vanished.

"Are you satisfied," I said to Don Sancio, "that Bellino is a woman?"

"Woman or man, what do I care! I think he is a very pretty *castrato,* and I have seen many as good-looking as he is."

"But are you sure he is a *castrato?*"

"*Valgame Dios!*" answered the grave Castilian, "I have not the slightest wish to ascertain the truth."

Oh, how widely different our thoughts were! I admired in him the wisdom of which I was so much in need, and did not venture upon any more indiscreet questions. During the supper, however, my greedy eyes could not leave that charming being; my vicious nature caused me to feel intense voluptuousness in believing him to be of that sex to which I wanted him to belong.

Don Sancio's supper was excellent, and, as a matter of course, superior to mine; otherwise the pride of the Castilian would have felt humbled. As a general rule, men are not satisfied with what is *good;* they want the *best,* or, to speak more to the point, *the most.* He gave us white truffles, several sorts of shell-fish, the best fish of the Adriatic, dry champagne, peralta, sherry and pedroximenes wines.

After that supper worthy of Lucullus, Bellino sang with a voice of such beauty that it deprived us of the small amount of reason left in us by the excellent wine. His movements, the expression of his looks, his gait, his walk, his countenance, his voice, and, above all, my own instinct, which told me that I could not possibly feel for a *castrato* what I felt for Bellino, confirmed me in my hopes; yet it was necessary that my eyes should ascertain the truth.

After many compliments and a thousand thanks, we took leave of the grand Spaniard, and went to my room, where the mystery was at last to be unravelled. I called upon Bellino to keep his word, or I threatened to leave him alone the next morning at day-break.

I took him by the hand, and we seated ourselves near the fire. I dismissed Cecilia and Marina, and I said to him,—

"Bellino, everything must have an end; you have promised: it will soon be over. If you are what you represent yourself to be, I will let you go back to your own room; if you are what I believe you to be, and if you consent to remain with me to-night, I will give you one hundred sequins, and we will start together to-morrow morning."

"You must go alone, and forgive me if I cannot fulfil my promise. I am what I told you, and I can neither reconcile myself to the idea of exposing my shame before you, nor lay myself open to the terrible consequences that might follow the solution of your doubts."

"There can be no consequences, since there will be an end to it at the moment I have assured myself that you are unfortunate enough to be what you say, and without ever mentioning the circumstances again, I promise to take you with me to-morrow and to leave you at Rimini."

"No, my mind is made up; I cannot satisfy your curiosity."

Driven to madness by his words, I was very near using violence, but subduing my angry feelings, I endeavored to succeed by gentle means and by going straight to the spot where the mystery could be solved. I was very near it, when his hand opposed a very strong resistance. I repeated my efforts, but Bellino, rising suddenly, repulsed me, and I found myself undone. After a few moments of calm, thinking I should take him by surprise, I extended my hand, but I drew back terrified, for I fancied that I had recognized in him a man, and a degraded man, contemptible less on account of his degradation than for the want of feeling I thought I could read on his countenance. Disgusted, confused, and almost blushing for myself, I sent him away.

His sisters came to my room, but I dismissed them, sending word to their brother that he might go with me, without any fear of further indiscretion on my part. Yet, in spite of the conviction I thought I had acquired, Bellino, even such as I believe him to be, filled my thoughts; I could not make it out.

Early the next morning I left Ancona with him, distracted by the tears of the two charming sisters and loaded with the blessings of the mother who, with beads in hand, mumbled her *paternoster*, and repeated her constant theme: *Dio provederà*.

The trust placed in Providence by most of those persons who earn their living by some profession forbidden by religion is neither absurd, nor false, nor deceitful; it is real and even godly, for it flows from an excellent source. Whatever may be the ways of Providence, human beings must always acknowledge it in its action, and those who call upon Providence independently of all external consideration must, at the bottom, be worthy, although guilty of transgressing its laws.

Pulchra Laverna,
Da mihi fallere; da justo sanctoque videri;
Noctem peccatis, et fraudibus objice nubem.

Such was the way in which, in the days of Horace, robbers addressed their goddess, and I recollect a Jesuit who told me once that Horace would not have known his own language, if he had said *justo sanctoque:* but there were ignorant men even amongst the Jesuits, and robbers most likely have but little respect for the rules of grammar.

The next morning I started with Bellino, who, believing me to be undeceived, could suppose that I would not shew any more curiosity about him, but we had not been a quarter of an hour together when he found out his mistake, for I could not let my looks fall upon his splendid eyes without feeling in me a fire which the sight of a man could not have ignited. I told him that all his features were those of a woman, and that I wanted the testimony of my eyes before I could feel perfectly satisfied, because the protuberance I had felt in a certain place might be only a freak of nature. "Should it be the case," I added, "I should have no difficulty in passing over a deformity which, in reality, is only laughable. Bellino, the impression you produce upon me, this sort of magnetism, your bosom worthy of Venus herself, which you have once abandoned to my eager hand, the sound of your voice, every movement of yours, assure me that you do not belong to my sex. Let me see for myself, and, if my conjectures are right, depend upon my faithful love; if, on the contrary, I find that I have been mistaken, you can rely upon my friendship. If you refuse me, I shall be compelled to believe that you are cruelly enjoying my misery, and that you have learned in the most accursed school that the best way of preventing a young man from curing himself of an amorous passion is to excite it constantly; but you must agree with me that, to put such tyranny in practice, it is necessary to hate the person it is practised upon, and, if that be so, I ought to call upon my reason to give me the strength necessary to hate you likewise."

I went on speaking for a long time; Bellino did not answer, but he seemed deeply moved. At last I told him that, in the fearful state to which I was reduced by his resistance, I should be compelled to treat him without any regard for his feelings, and find out the truth by force. He answered with much warmth and dignity: "Recollect that you are not my master, that I am in your hands, because I had faith in your promise, and that, if you use violence, you will be guilty of murder. Order the postillion to stop, I will get out of the carriage, and you may rely upon my not complaining of your treatment."

Those few words were followed by a torrent of tears, a sight which I never could resist. I felt myself moved in the inmost recesses of my soul, and I almost thought that I had been wrong. I say *almost*, because, had I been convinced of it, I would have thrown myself at his feet entreating pardon; but, not feeling myself competent to stand in judgment in my own cause, I satisfied myself by remaining dull and silent, and I never uttered one word until we were only half a mile from Sinigaglia, where I intended to take supper and to remain for the night. Having fought long enough with my own feelings, I said to him,—

"We might have spent a little time in Rimini like good friends, if you had felt any friendship for me, for, with a little kind compliance, you could have easily cured me of my passion."

"It would not cure you," answered Bellino, courgeously, but with a sweetness of tone which surprised me; "no, you would not be cured, whether you found me to be man or woman, for you are in love with me independently of my sex, and the certainty you would acquire would make you furious. In such a state, should you find me inexorable, you would very likely give way to excesses which would afterwards cause you deep sorrow."

"You expect to make me admit that you are right, but you are completely mistaken, for I feel that I should remain perfectly calm, and that by complying with my wishes you would gain my friendship."

"I tell you again that you would become furious."

"Bellino, that which has made me furious is the sight of your charms, either too real or too completely deceiving, the power of which you cannot affect to ignore. You have not been afraid to ignite my amorous fury, how can you expect me to believe you now, when you pretend to fear it, and when I am only asking you to let me touch a thing, which, if it be as you say, will only disgust me?"

"Ah! disgust you; I am quite certain of the contrary. Listen to me. Were I a girl, I feel I could not resist loving you, but, being a man, it is my duty not to grant what you desire, for your passion, now very natural, would then become monstrous. Your ardent nature would be stronger than your reason, and your reason itself would easily come to the assistance of your senses and of your nature. That violent clearing-up of the mystery, were you to obtain it, would leave you deprived of all control over yourself. Disappointed in not finding what you had expected, you would satisfy your passion upon that which you would find, and the result would, of course, be an abomination. How can you, intelligent as you are, flatter yourself that, finding me to be a man, you could all at once cease to love me? Would the charms which you now see in me cease to exist then? Perhaps their power would, on the contrary, be enhanced, and your passion, becoming brutal, would lead you to take any means your imagination suggested to gratify it. You would persuade yourself that you might change me into a woman, or, what is worse, that you might change yourself into one. Your passion would invent a thousand sophisms to justify your love, decorated with the fine appellation of friendship, and you would not fail to allege hundreds of similarly disgusting cases in order to excuse your conduct. You would certainly never find me compliant; and how am I to know that you would not threaten me with death?"

"Nothing of the sort would happen, Bellino," I answered, rather tired of the length of his argument, "positively nothing, and I am sure you are exaggerating your fears. Yet I am bound to tell you that, even if all you say should happen, it seems to me that to allow what can strictly be considered only as a temporary fit of insanity, would prove a less evil than to render incurable a disease of the mind which reason would soon cut short."

Thus does a poor philosopher reason when he takes it into his head to argue at those periods during which a passion raging in his soul makes all its faculties wander. To reason well, we must be under the sway neither of love nor of anger, for those two passions have one thing in common which is that, in their excess, they lower us to the condition of brutes acting only under the influence of their predominating instinct, and, unfortunately, we are never more disposed to argue than when we feel ourselves under the influence of either of those two powerful human passions.

We arrived at Sinigaglia late at night, and I went to

the best inn, and, after choosing a comfortable room, ordered supper. As there was but one bed in the room, I asked Bellino, in as calm a tone as I could assume, whether he would have a fire lighted in another chamber, and my surprise may be imagined when he answered quietly that he had no objection to sleep in the same bed with me. Such an answer, however, unexpected, was necessary to dispel the angry feelings under which I was labouring. I guessed that I was near the *dénouement* of the romance, but I was very far from congratulating myself, for I did not know whether the *dénouement* would prove agreeable or not. I felt, however, a real satisfaction at having conquered, and was sure of my self-control, in case the senses, my natural instinct, led me astray. But if I found myself in the right, I thought I could expect the most precious favours.

We sat down to supper opposite each other, and during the meal, his words, his countenance, the expression of his beautiful eyes, his sweet and voluptuous smile, everything seemed to announce that he had had enough of playing a part which must have proved as painful to him as to me.

A weight was lifted off my mind, and I managed to shorten the supper as much as possible. As soon as we had left the table, my amiable companion called for a night-lamp, undressed himself, and went to bed. I was not long in following him, and the reader will soon know the nature of a *dénouement* so long and so ardently desired; in the mean time I beg to wish him as happy a night as the one which was then awaiting me.

CHAPTER XII

Bellino's History—I Am Put Under Arrest—I Run Away Against My Will—My Return To Rimini, and My Arrival In Bologna

DEAR reader, I said enough at the end of the last chapter to make you guess what happened, but no language would be powerful enough to make you realize all the voluptuousness which that charming being had in store for me. *She* came close to me the moment I was in bed. Without uttering one word our lips met, and I found myself in the ecstasy of enjoyment before I had had time to seek for it. After so complete a victory, what would my eyes and my fingers have gained from investigations which could not give me more certainty than I had already obtained? I could not take my gaze off that beautiful face, which was all aflame with the ardour of love.

After a moment of quiet rapture, a spark lighted up in our veins a fresh conflagration which we drowned in a sea of new delights. Bellino felt bound to make me forget my sufferings, and to reward me by an ardour equal to the fire kindled by her charms.

The happiness I gave her increased mine twofold, for it has always been my weakness to compose the four-fifths of my enjoyment from the sum-total of the happiness which I gave the charming being from whom I derived it. But such a feeling must necessarily cause

hatred for old age which can still receive pleasure, but
can no longer give enjoyment to another. And ycuth
runs away from old age, because it is its most cruel
enemy.

An interval of repose became necessary, in consequence
of the activity of our enjoyment. Our senses were not
tired out, but they required the rest which renews theit
sensitiveness and restores the buoyancy necessary to
active service.

Bellino was the first to break our silence.

"Dearest," she said, "are you satisfied now? Have
you found me truly loving?"

"Truly loving? Ah! traitress that you are! Do you,
then, confess that I was not mistaken when I guessed
that you were a charming woman? And if you truly
loved me, tell me how you could contrive to defer your
happiness and mine so long? But is it quite certain
that I did not make a mistake?"

"I am yours all over; see for yourself."

Oh, what delightful survey! what charming beauties! what an ocean of enjoyment! But I could not
find any trace of the protuberance which had so much
terrified and disgusted me.

"What has become," I said, "of that dreadful mon-
strosity?"

"Listen to me," she replied, "and I will tell you everything.

"My name is Thérèse. My father, a poor clerk in
the Institute of Bologna, had let an apartment in his
house to the celebrated Salimberi, a *castrato,* and a delightful musician. He was young and handsome, he
became attached to me, and I felt flattered by his affection and by the praise he lavished upon me. I was
only twelve years of age; he proposed to teach me music,

and finding that I had a fine voice, he cultivated it carefully, and in less than a year I could accompany myself on the harpsichord. His reward was that which his love for me induced him to ask, and I granted the reward without feeling any humiliation, for I worshipped him. Of course, men like yourself are much above men of his species, but Salimberi was an exception. His beauty, his manners, his talent, and the rare qualities of his soul, made him superior in my eyes to all the men I had seen until then. He was modest and reserved, rich and generous, and I doubt whether he could have found a woman able to resist him; yet I never heard him boast of having seduced any. The mutilation practised upon his body had made him a monster, but he was an angel by his rare qualities and endowments.

"Salimberi was at that time educating a boy of the same age as myself, who was in Rimini with a music teacher. The father of the boy, who was poor and had a large family, seeing himself near death, had thought of having his unfortunate son maimed so that he should become the support of his brothers with his voice. The name of the boy was Bellino; the good woman whom you have just seen in Ancona was his mother, and everybody believes that she is mine.

"I had belonged to Salimberi for about a year, when he announced to me one day, weeping bitterly, that he was compelled to leave me to go to Rome, but he promised to see me again. The news threw me into despair. He had arranged everything for the continuation of my musical education, but, as he was preparing himself for his departure, my father died very suddenly, after a short illness, and I was left an orphan.

"Salimberi had not courage enough to resist my tears and my entreaties; he made up his mind to take me to Rimini, and to place me in the same house where his young *protégé* was educated. We reached Rimini, and put up at an inn; after a short rest, Salimberi left me to call upon the teacher of music, and to make all necessary arrangements respecting me with him; but he soon returned, looking sad and unhappy; Bellino had died the day before.

"As he was thinking of the grief which the loss of the young man would cause his mother, he was struck with the idea of bringing me back to Bologna under the name of Bellino, where he could arrange for my board with the mother of the deceased Bellino, who, being very poor, would find it to her advantage to keep the secret. 'I will give her,' he said, 'everything necessary for the completion of your musical education, and in four years, I will take you to Dresden (he was in the service of the Elector of Saxony, King of Poland), not as a girl, but as a *castrato*. There we will live together without giving anyone cause for scandal, and you will remain with me and minister to my happiness until I die. All we have to do is to represent you as Bellino, and it is very easy, as nobody knows you in Bologna. Bellino's mother will alone know the secret; her other children have seen their brother only when he was very young, and can have no suspicion. But if you love me you must renounce your sex, lose even the remembrance of it, and leave immediately for Bologna, dressed as a boy, and under the name of Bellino. You must be very careful lest anyone should find out that you are a girl; you must sleep alone, dress yourself in private, and when your bosom is formed, as it will be in a year or two, it will only be thought a deformity not uncommon amongst *castrati*. Besides, before leaving you, I will give you a small instrument, and teach how to fix it in such manner that, if you had at any time to submit to an examination, you would easily be mistaken for a man. If you accept my plan, I feel certain that we can live together in Dresden without losing the good graces of the queen, who is very religious. Tell me, now, whether you will accept my proposal?'

"He could not entertain any doubt of my consent, for I adored him. As soon as he had made a boy of me we left Rimini for Bologna, where we arrived late in the evening. A little gold made everything right with Bellino's mother; I gave her the name of mother, and she kissed me, calling me her dear son. Salimberi left us, and returned a short time afterwards with the instrument which would complete my transformation. He taught me, in the presence of my new mother, how to fix it with some tragacanth gum, and I found myself exactly like my friend. I would have laughed at it, had not my heart been deeply grieved at the departure of my beloved Salimberi, for he bade me farewell as soon as the curious operation was completed. People laugh at forebodings; I do not believe in them myself, but the foreboding of evil, which almost broke my heart as he gave me his farewell kiss, did not deceive me. I felt the cold shivering of death run through me; I felt I was looking at him for the last time, and I fainted away. Alas! my fears proved only too prophetic. Salimberi died a year ago in the Tyrol in the prime of life, with the calmness of a true philosopher. His death compelled me to earn my living with the assistance of my musical talent. My mother advised me to continue to give myself out as a *castrato,* in the hope of being able to take me to Rome. I agreed to do so, for I did not feel sufficient energy to decide upon any other plan. In the meantime she accepted an offer for the Ancona Theatre, and Petronio took the part of first female dancer; in this way we played the comedy of 'The World Turned Upside Down.'

"After Salimberi, you are the only man I have known, and, if you like, you can restore me to my original state, and make me give up the name of Bellino, which I hate since the death of my protector, and which begins to inconvenience me. I have only appeared at two theatres, and each time I have been compelled to submit to the scandalous, degrading examination, because everywhere I am thought to have too much the appearance of a girl, and I am admitted only after the shameful test has brought conviction. Until now, fortunately, I have had to deal only with old priests who, in their good faith, have been satisfied with a very slight examination, and have made a favourable report to the bishop; but I might fall into the hands of some young abbé, and the test would then become a more severe one. Besides, I find myself exposed to the daily persecutions of two sorts of beings: those who, like you, cannot and will not believe me to be a man, and those who, for the satisfaction of their disgusting propensities, are delighted at my being so, or find it advantageous to suppose me so. The last particularly annoy me! Their tastes are so infamous, their habits so low, that I fear I shall murder one of them some day, when I can no longer control the rage in which their obscene language throws me. Out of pity, my beloved angel, be generous; and, if you love me, oh! free me from this state of shame and degradation! Take me with you. I do not ask to become your wife, that would be too much happiness; I will only be your friend, your mistress, as I would have been Salimberi's; my heart is pure and innocent; I feel that I can remain faithful to my lover through my whole life. Do not abandon me. The love I have for you is sincere; my affection for Salimberi was innocent; it was born of my inexperience and of my gratitude, and it is only with you that I have felt myself truly a woman."

Her emotion, an inexpressible charm which seemed to flow from her lips and to enforce conviction, made me shed tears of love and sympathy. I blended my tears with those falling from her beautiful eyes, and deeply moved, I promised not to abandon her and to make her the sharer of my fate. Interested in the history, as singular as extraordinary, that she had just narrated, and having seen nothing in it that did not bear the stamp of truth, I felt really disposed to make her happy but I could not believe that I had inspired her with a very deep passion during my short stay in Ancona, many circumstances of which might, on the contrary, have had an opposite effect upon her heart.

"If you loved me truly," I said, "how could you let me sleep with your sisters, out of spite at your resistance?"

"Alas, dearest! think of our great poverty, and how difficult it was for me to discover myself. I loved you; but was it not natural that I should suppose your inclination for me only a passing caprice? When I saw you go so easily from Cecilia to Marinetta, I thought that you would treat me in the same manner as soon as your desires were satisfied; I was likewise confirmed in my opinion of your want of constancy and of the little importance you attached to the delicacy of the sentiment of love, when I witnessed what you did on board the Turkish vessel without being hindered by my presence; had you loved me, I thought my being present would have made you uncomfortable. I feared to be soon despised, and God knows how much I suffered! You have insulted me, darling, in many different ways, but my heart pleaded in your favour, because I knew you were excited, angry, and thirsting for revenge. Did you not threaten me this very day in your carriage? I confess you greatly frightened me, but do not fancy that I gave myself to you out of fear. No, I had made up my mind to be yours from the moment you sent me word by Cecilia that you would take me to Rimini, and your control over your own feelings during a part of our journey confirmed me in my resolution, for I thought I could trust myself to your honour, to your delicacy."

"Throw up," I said, "the engagement you have in Rimini; let us proceed on our journey, and, after remaining a couple of days in Bologna, you will go with me to Venice; dressed as a woman, and with another name, I would challenge the manager here to find you out."

"I accept. Your will shall always be my law. I am my own mistress, and I give myself to you without any reserve or restriction; my heart belongs to you, and I trust to keep yours."

Man has in himself a moral force of action which always makes him overstep the line on which he is standing. I had obtained everything, I wanted more. "Shew me," I said, "how you were when I mistook you for a man." She got out of bed, opened her trunk, took out the instrument and fixed it with the gum: I was compelled to admire the ingenuity of the contrivance. My curiosity was satisfied, and I passed a most delightful night in her arms.

When I woke up in the morning, I admired her lovely face while she was sleeping: all I knew of her came

back to my mind; the words which had been spoken
by her bewitching mouth, her rare talent, her candour,
her feelings so full of delicacy, and her misfortunes, the
heaviest of which must have been the false character
she had been compelled to assume, and which exposed
her to humiliation and shame, everything strengthened
my resolution to make her the companion of my destiny,
whatever it might be, or to follow her fate, for our
positions were very nearly the same; and wishing truly
to attach myself seriously to that interesting being, I
determined to give to our union the sanction of religion
and of law, and to take her legally for my wife. Such
a step, as I then thought, could but strengthen our love,
increase our mutual esteem, and insure the approbation
of society which could not accept our union unless it
was sanctioned in the usual manner.

The talents of Thérèse precluded the fear of our being
ever in want of the necessaries of life, and, although I
did not know in what way my own talents might be
made available, I had faith in myself. Our love might
have been lessened, she would have enjoyed too great
advantages over me, and my self-dignity would have
too deeply suffered if I had allowed myself to be supported by her earnings only. It might, after a time,
have altered the nature of our feelings; my wife, no
longer thinking herself under any obligation to me,
might have fancied herself the protecting, instead of
the protected party, and I felt that my love would soon
have turned into utter contempt, if it had been my
misfortune to find her harbouring such thoughts. Although I trusted it would not be so, I wanted, before
taking the important step of marriage, to probe her
heart, and I resolved to try an experiment which would
at once enable me to judge the real feelings of her in-

most soul. As soon as she was awake, I spoke to her thus:

"Dearest Thérèse, all you have told me leaves me no doubt of your love for me, and the consciousness you feel of being the mistress of my heart enhances my love for you to such a degree, that I am ready to do every-thing to convince you that you were not mistaken in thinking that you had entirely conquered me. I wish to prove to you that I am worthy of the noble confi-dence you have reposed in me by trusting you with equal sincerity.

"Our hearts must be on a footing of perfect equality. I know you, my dearest Thérèse, but you do not know me yet. I can read in your eyes that you do not mind it, and it proves our great love, but that feeling places me too much below you, and I do not wish you to have so great an advantage over me. I feel certain that my confidence is not necessary to your love; that you only care to be mine, that your only wish is to possess my heart, and I admire you, my Thérèse; but I should feel humiliated if I found myself either too much above or too much below you. You have entrusted your secrets to me, now listen to mine; but before I begin, promise me that, when you know everything that concerns me, you will tell me candidly if any change has taken place either in your feelings or in your hopes."

"I promise it faithfully; I promise not to conceal any-thing from you; but be upright enough not to tell me anything that is not perfectly true, for I warn you that it would be useless. If you tried any artifice in order to find me less worthy of you than I am in reality, you would only succeed in lowering yourself in my estima-tion. I should be very sorry to see you guilty of any cunning towards me. Have no more suspicion of me than I have of you; tell me the whole truth."

"Here it is. You suppose me wealthy, and I am not so; as soon as what there is now in my purse is spent I shall have nothing left. You may fancy that I was born a patrician, but my social condition is really inferior to your own. I have no lucrative talents, no profession, nothing to give me the assurance that I am able to earn my living. I have neither relatives nor friends, nor claims upon anyone, and I have no serious plan or purpose before me. All I possess is youth, health, courage, some intelligence, honour, honesty, and some tincture of letters. My greatest treasure consists in being my own master, perfectly independent, and not afraid of misfortune. With all that, I am naturally inclined to extravagance. Lovely Thérèse, you have my portrait. What is your answer?"

"In the first place, dearest, let me assure you that I believe every word you have just uttered, as I would believe in the Gospel; in the second, allow me to tell you that several times in Ancona I have judged you such as you have just described yourself, but far from being displeased at such a knowledge of your nature, I was only afraid of some illusion on my part, for I could hope to win you if you were what I thought you to be. In one word, dear one, if it is true that you are poor and a very bad hand at economy, allow me to tell you that I feel delighted, because, if you love me, you will not refuse a present from me, or despise me for offering it. The present consists of myself, such as I am, and with all my faculties. I give myself to you without any condition, with no restriction; I am yours, I will take care of you. For the future think only of your love for me, but love me exclusively. From this moment I am no longer Bellino. Let us go to Venice, where my talent will keep us both comfortably; if you wish to go anywhere else, let us go where you please."

"I must go to Constantinople."

"Then let us proceed to Constantinople. If you are afraid to lose me through want of constancy, marry me, and your right over me will be strengthened by law. I should not love you better than I do now, but I should be happy to be your wife."

"It is my intention to marry you, and I am delighted that we agree in that respect. The day after to-morrow, in Bologna, you shall be made my legal wife before the altar of God; I swear it to you here in the presence of Love. I want you to be mine, I want to be yours, I want us to be united by the most holy ties."

"I am the happiest of women! We have nothing to do in Rimini; suppose we do not get up; we can have our dinner in bed, and go away to-morrow well rested after our fatigues."

We left Rimini the next day, and stayed for breakfast at Pesaro. As we were getting into the carriage to leave that place, an officer, accompanied by two soldiers, presented himself, enquired for our names, and demanded our passports. Bellino had one and gave it, but I looked in vain for mine; I could not find it.

The officer, a corporal, orders the postillion to wait and goes to make his report. Half an hour afterwards, he returns, gives Bellino his passport, saying that he can continue his journey, but tells me that his orders are to escort me to the commanding officer, and I follow him.

"What have you done with your passport?" enquires that officer.

"I have lost it."

"A passport is not so easily lost."

"Well, I have lost mine."

"You cannot proceed any further."

"I come from Rome, and I am going to Constantinople, bearing a letter from Cardinal Acquaviva. Here is the letter stamped with his seal."

"All I can do for you is to send you to M. de Gages."

I found the famous general standing, surrounded by his staff. I told him all I had already explained to the officer, and begged him to let me continue my journey.

"The only favour I can grant you is to put you under arrest till you receive another passport from Rome delivered under the same name as the one you have given here. To lose a passport is a misfortune which befalls only a thoughtless, giddy man, and the cardinal will for the future know better than to put his confidence in a giddy fellow like you."

With these words, he gave orders to take me to the guard-house at St.-Mary's Gate, outside the city, as soon as I should have written to the cardinal for a new passport. His orders were executed. I was brought back to the inn, where I wrote my letter, and I sent it by express to his eminence, entreating him to forward the document, without loss of time, direct to the war office. Then I embraced Thérèse who was weeping, and, telling her to go to Rimini and to wait there for my return, I made her take one hundred sequins. She wished to remain in Pesaro, but I would not hear of it; I had my trunk brought out, I saw Thérèse go away from the inn, and was taken to the place appointed by the general.

It is undoubtedly under such circumstances that the most determined optimist finds himself at a loss; but

an easy stoicism can blunt the too sharp edge of misfortune.

My greatest sorrow was the heart-grief of Thérèse
who, seeing me torn from her arms at the very moment
of our union, was suffocated by the tears which she tried
to repress. She would not have left me if I had not
made her understand that she could not remain in
Pesaro, and if I had not promised to join her within
ten days, never to be parted again. But fate had decided otherwise.

When we reached the gate, the officer confined me
immediately in the guard-house, and I sat down on my
trunk. The officer was a taciturn Spaniard who did
not even condescend to honour me with an answer, when
I told him that I had money and would like to have
someone to wait on me. I had to pass the night on a
little straw, and without food, in the midst of the Spanish soldiers. It was the second night of the sort that
my destiny had condemned me to, immediately after
two delightful nights. My good angel doubtless found
some pleasure in bringing such conjunctions before my
mind for the benefit of my instruction. At all events,
teachings of that description have an infallible effect
upon natures of a peculiar stamp.

If you should wish to close the lips of a logician calling himself a philosopher, who dares to argue that in
this life grief overbalances pleasure, ask him whether
he would accept a life entirely without sorrow and happiness. Be certain that he will not answer you, or he
will shuffle, because, if he says no, he proves that he
likes life such as it is, and if he likes it, he must find
it agreeable, which is an utter impossibility, if life is
painful; should he, on the contrary, answer in the affirmative, he would declare himself a fool, for it would

be as much as to say that he can conceive pleasure arising from indifference, which is absurd nonsense.

Suffering is inherent in human nature; but we never suffer without entertaining the hope of recovery, or, at least, very seldom without such hope, and hope itself is a pleasure. If it happens sometimes that man suffers without any expectation of a cure, he necessarily finds pleasure in the complete certainty of the end of his life; for the worst, in all cases, must be either a sleep arising from extreme dejection, during which we have the consolation of happy dreams or the loss of all sensitiveness. But when we are happy, our happiness is never disturbed by the thought that it will be followed by grief. Therefore pleasure, during its active period, is always complete, without alloy; grief is always soothed by hope.

I suppose you, dear reader, at the age of twenty, and devoting yourself to the task of making a man of yourself by furnishing your mind with all the knowledge necessary to render you a useful being through the activity of your brain. Someone comes in and tells you, "I bring you thirty years of existence; it is the immutable decree of fate; fifteen consecutive years must be happy, and fifteen years unhappy. You are at liberty to choose the half by which you wish to begin."

Confess it candidly, dear reader, you will not require much more consideration to decide, and you will certainly begin by the unhappy series of years, because you will feel that the expectation of fifteen delightful years cannot fail to brace you up with the courage necessary to bear the unfortunate years you have to go through, and we can even surmise, with every probability of being right, that the certainty of future happiness will soothe to a considerable extent the misery of the first period.

You have already guessed, I have no doubt, the purpose of this lengthy argument. The sagacious man, believe me, can never be utterly miserable, and I most willingly agree with my friend Horace, who says that, on the contrary, such a man is always happy.

Nisi quum pituita molesta est.

But, pray where is the man who is always suffering from a rheum?

The fact is that the fearful night I passed in the guardhouse of St.-Mary resulted for me in a slight loss and in a great gain. The small loss was to be away from my dear Thérèse, but, being certain of seeing her within ten days, the misfortune was not very great: as to the gain, it was in experience the true school for a man. I gained a complete system against thoughtlessness, a system of foresight. You may safely bet a hundred to one that a young man who has once lost his purse or his passport, will not lose either a second time. Each of those misfortunes has befallen me once only, and I might have been very often the victim of them, if experience had not taught me how much they were to be dreaded. A thoughtless fellow is a man who has not yet found the word *dread* in the dictionary of his life.

The officer who relieved my cross-grained Castilian on the following day seemed of a different nature altogether; his prepossessing countenance pleased me much. He was a Frenchman, and I must say that I have always liked the French, and never the Spaniards; there is in the manners of the first something so engaging, so obliging, that you feel attracted towards them as towards a friend, whilst an air of unbecoming haughtiness gives to the second a dark, forbidding countenance which certainly does not prepossess in their favour. Yet I have often been duped by Frenchmen, and never by Spaniards —a proof that we ought to mistrust our tastes.

The new officer, approaching me very politely, said to me,—

"To what chance, reverend sir, am I indebted for the honour of having you in my custody?"

Ah! here was a way of speaking which restored to my lungs all their elasticity! I gave him all the particulars of my misfortune, and he found the mishap very amusing. But a man disposed to laugh at my disappointment could not be disagreeable to me, for it proved that the turn of his mind had more than one point of resemblance with mine. He gave me at once a soldier to serve me, and I had very quickly a bed, a table, and a few chairs. He was kind enough to have my bed placed in his own room, and I felt very grateful to him for that delicate attention.

He gave me an invitation to share his dinner, and proposed a game of piquet afterwards, but from the very beginning he saw that I was no match for him; he told me so, and he warned me that the officer who would relieve him the next day was a better player even than he was himself; I lost three or four ducats. He advised me to abstain from playing on the following day, and I followed his advice. He told me also that he would have company to supper, that there would be a game of faro, but that the banker being a *Greek* and a crafty player, I ought not to play. I thought his advice very considerate, particularly when I saw that all the punters lost, and that the Greek, very calm in the midst of the insulting treatment of those he had duped, was pocketing his money, after handing a share to the officer who had taken an interest in the bank.

The name of the banker was Don Pépé il Cadetto, and by his accent I knew he was a Neapolitan. I communicated my discovery to the officer, asking him why he had told me that the man was a Greek. He explained to me the meaning of the word *greek* applied to a gambler, and the lesson which followed his explanation proved very useful to me in after years.

During the five following days, my life was uniform and rather dull, but on the sixth day the same French officer was on guard, and I was very glad to see him. He told me, with a hearty laugh, that he was delighted to find me still in the guard-house, and I accepted the compliment for what it was worth. In the evening, we had the same bank at faro, with the same result as the first time, except a violent blow from the stick of one of the punters upon the back of the banker, of which the Greek stoically feigned to take no notice. I saw the same man again nine years afterwards in Vienna, captain in the service of Maria Theresa; he then called himself d'Afflisso. Ten years later, I found him a colonel, and some time after worth a million; but the last time I saw him, some thirteen or fourteen years ago, he was a galley slave. He was handsome, but (rather a singular thing) in spite of his beauty, he had a gallows look. I have seen others with the same stamp —Cagliostro, for instance, and another who has not yet been sent to the galleys, but who cannot fail to pay them a visit. Should the reader feel any curiosity about it, I can whisper the name in his ear.

Towards the ninth or tenth day everyone in the army knew and liked me, and I was expecting the passport, which could not be delayed much longer. I was almost free, and I would often walk about even out of sight

of the sentinel. They were quite right not to fear my
running away, and I should have been wrong if I had
thought of escaping, but the most singular adventure
of my life happened to me then, and most unex-
pectedly.

It was about six in the morning. I was taking a
walk within one hundred yards of the sentinel, when
an officer arrived and alighted from his horse, threw
the bridle on the neck of his steed, and walked off.
Admiring the docility of the horse, standing there like
a faithful servant to whom his master has given orders
to wait for him I got up to him, and without any purpose I get hold of the bridle, put my foot in the stirrup,
and find myself in the saddle. I was on horseback for
the first time in my life. I do not know whether I
touched the horse with my cane or with my heels, but
suddenly the animal starts at full speed. My right
foot having slipped out of the stirrup, I press against
the horse with my heels, and, feeling the pressure, it
gallops faster and faster, for I did not know how to
check it. At the last advanced post the sentinels call
out to me to stop; but I cannot obey the order, and
the horse carrying me away faster than ever, I hear the
whizzing of a few musket balls, the natural consequence
of my involuntary disobedience. At last, when I reach
the first advanced picket of the Austrians, the horse is
stopped, and I get off his back thanking God.

An officer of Hussars asks where I am running so
fast, and my tongue, quicker than my thought, answers
without any privity on my part, that I can render no
account but to Prince Lobkowitz, commander-in-chief
of the army, whose headquarters were at Rimini. Hearing my answer, the officer gave orders for two Hussars
to get on horseback, a fresh one is given me, and I am

taken at full gallop to Rimini, where the officer on guard has me escorted at once to the prince.

I find his highness alone, and I tell him candidly what has just happened to me. My story makes him laugh, although he observes that it is hardly credible.

"I ought," he says, "to put you under arrest, but I am willing to save you that unpleasantness." With that he called one of his officers and ordered him to escort me through the Cesena Gate. "Then you can go wherever you please," he added, turning round to me; "but take care not to again enter the lines of my army without a passport, or you might fare badly."

I asked him to let me have the horse again, but he answered that the animal did not belong to me. I forgot to ask him to send me back to the place I had come from, and I regretted it; but after all perhaps I did for the best.

The officer who accompanied me asked me, as we were passing a coffee-house, whether I would like to take some chocolate, and we went in. At that moment I saw Petronio going by, and availing myself of a moment when the officer was talking to someone, I told him not to appear to be acquainted with me, but to tell me where he lived. When we had taken our chocolate the officer paid and we went out. Along the road we kept up the conversation; he told me his name, I gave him mine, and I explained how I found myself in Rimini. He asked me whether I had not remained some time in Ancona; I answered in the affirmative, and he smiled and said I could get a passport in Bologna, return to Rimini and to Pesaro without any fear, and recover my trunk by paying the officer for the horse he had lost. We reached the gate, he wished me a pleasant journey, and we parted company.

I found myself free, with gold and jewels, but without my trunk. Thérèse was in Rimini, and I could not enter that city. I made up my mind to go to Bologna as quickly as possible in order to get a passport, and to return to Pesaro, where I should find my passport from Rome, for I could not make up my mind to lose my trunk, and I did not want to be separated from Thérèse until the end of her engagement with the manager of the Rimini Theatre.

It was raining; I had silk stockings on, and I longed for a carriage. I took shelter under the portal of a church, and turned my fine overcoat inside out, so as not to look like an abbé. At that moment a peasant happened to come along, and I asked him if a carriage could be had to drive me to Cesena. "I have one, sir," he said, "but I live half a league from here."

"Go and get it, I will wait for you here."

While I was waiting for the return of the peasant with his vehicle, some forty mules laden with provisions came along the road towards Rimini. It was still raining fast, and the mules passing close by me, I placed my hand mechanically upon the neck of one of them, and following the slow pace of the animals I re-entered Rimini without the slightest notice being taken of me, even by the drivers of the mules. I gave some money to the first street urchin I met, and he took me to Thérèse's house.

With my hair fastened under a night-cap, my hat pulled down over my face, and my fine cane concealed under my coat, I did not look a very elegant figure. I enquired for Bellino's mother, and the mistress of the house took me to a room where I found all the family, and Thérèse in a woman's dress. I had reckoned upon surprising them, but Petronio had told them of our meeting, and they were expecting me. I gave a full account of my adventures, but Thérèse, frightened at the danger that threatened me, and in spite of her love, told me that it was absolutely necessary for me to go to Bologna, as I had been advised by M. Vais, the officer.

"I know him," she said, "and he is a worthy man, but he comes here every evening, and you must conceal yourself."

It was only eight o'clock in the morning; we had the whole day before us, and everyone promised to be discreet. I allayed Thérèse's anxiety by telling her that I could easily contrive to leave the city without being observed.

Thérèse took me to her own room, where she told me that she had met the manager of the theatre on her arrival in Rimini, and that he had taken her at once to the apartments engaged for the family. She had informed him that she was a woman, and that she had made up her mind not to appear as a *castrato* any more; he had expressed himself delighted at such news, because women could appear on the stage at Rimini, which was not under the same legate as Ancona. She added that her engagement would be at an end by the 1st of May, and that she would meet me wherever it would be agreeable to me to wait for her.

"As soon as I can get a passport," I said, "there is nothing to hinder me from remaining near you until the end of your engagement. But as M. Vais calls upon you, tell me whether you have informed him of my having spent a few days in Ancona?"

"I did, and I even told him that you had been arrested because you had lost your passport."

I understood why the officer had smiled as he was talking with me. After my conversation with Thérèse, I received the compliments of the mother and of the young sisters who appeared to me less cheerful and less free than they had been in Ancona. They felt that Bellino, transformed into Thérèse, was too formidable a rival. I listened patiently to all the complaints of the mother who maintained that, in giving up the character of *castrato,* Thérèse had bidden adieu to fortune, because she might have earned a thousand sequins a year in Rome.

"In Rome, my good woman," I said, "the false Bellino would have been found out, and Thérèse would have been consigned to a miserable convent for which she was never made."

Notwithstanding the danger of my position, I spent the whole of the day alone with my beloved mistress, and it seemed that every moment gave her fresh beauties and increased my love. At eight o'clock in the evening, hearing someone coming in, she left me, and I remained in the dark, but in such a position that I could see everything and hear every word. The Baron Vais came in, and Thérèse gave him her hand with the grace of a pretty woman and the dignity of a princess. The first thing he told her was the news about me; she appeared to be pleased, and listened with well-feigned indifference, when he said that he had advised me to return with a passport. He spent an hour with her, and I was thoroughly well pleased with her manners and behaviour, which had been such as to leave me no room for the slightest feeling of jealousy. Marina lighted him out and Thérèse returned to me. We had a joyous supper together, and, as we were getting ready

to go to bed, Petronio came to inform me that ten muleteers would start for Cesena two hours before day-break,
and that he was sure I could leave the city with them
if I would go and meet them a quarter of an hour before
their departure, and treat them to something to drink.
I was of the same opinion, and made up my mind to
make the attempt. I asked Petronio to sit up and to
wake me in good time. It proved an unnecessary precaution, for I was ready before the time, and left Thérèse
satisfied with my love, without any doubt of my constancy, but rather anxious as to my success in attempting to leave Rimini. She had sixty sequins which she
wanted to force back upon me, but I asked her what
opinion she would have of me if I accepted them, and
we said no more about it.

I went to the stable, and having treated one of the
muleteers to some drink I told him that I would willingly
ride one of his mules as far as Sarignan.

"You are welcome to the ride," said the good fellow,
"but I would advise you not to get on the mule till we
are outside the city, and to pass through the gate on
foot as if you were one of the drivers."

It was exactly what I wanted. Petronio accompanied
me as far as the gate, where I gave him a substantial
proof of my gratitude. I got out of the city without the
slightest difficulty, and left the muleteers at Sarignan,
whence I posted to Bologna.

I found out that I could not obtain a passport, for the
simple reason that the authorities of the city persisted
that it was not necessary; but I knew better, and it was
not for me to tell them why. I resolved to write to the
French officer who had treated me so well at the guard-
house. I begged him to enquire at the war office whether
my passport had arrived from Rome, and, if so, to for-

ward it to me. I also asked him to find out the owner of
the horse who had run away with me, offering to pay
for it. I made up my mind to wait for Thérèse in
Bologna, and I informed her of my decision, entreating
her to write very often. The reader will soon know the
new resolution I took on the very same day.

CHAPTER XIII

I Renounce the Clerical Profession, and Enter the Military Service—Thérèse Leaves for Naples, and I Go to Venice—I Am Appointed Ensign in the Army of My Native Country—I Embark for Corfu, and Land at Orsera to Take a Walk

I HAD been careful, on my arrival in Bologna, to take up my quarters at a small inn, so as not to attract any notice, and as soon as I had dispatched my letters to Thérèse and the French officer, I thought of purchasing some linen, as it was at least doubtful whether I should ever get my trunk. I deemed it expedient to order some clothes likewise. I was thus ruminating, when it suddenly struck me that I was not likely now to succeed in the Church, but feeling great uncertainty as to the profession I ought to adopt, I took a fancy to transform myself into an officer, as it was evident that I had not to account to anyone for my actions. It was a very natural fancy at my age, for I had just passed through two armies in which I had seen no respect paid to any garb but to the military uniform, and I did not see why I should not cause myself to be respected likewise. Besides, I was thinking of returning to Venice, and felt great delight at the idea of shewing myself there in the garb of honour, for I had been rather ill-treated in that of religion.

I enquired for a good tailor: death was brought to me,

for the tailor sent to me was named *Morte*. I explained to him how I wanted my uniform made, I chose the cloth, he took my measure, and the next day I was transformed into a follower of Mars. I procured a long sword, and with my fine cane in hand, with a well-brushed hat ornamented with a black cockade, and wearing a long false pigtail, I sallied forth and walked all over the city.

I bethought myself that the importance of my new calling required a better and more showy lodging than the one I had secured on my arrival, and I moved to the best inn. I like even now to recollect the pleasing impression I felt when I was able to admire myself full length in a large mirror. I was highly pleased with my own person! I thought myself made by nature to wear and to honour the military costume, which I had adopted through the most fortunate impulse. Certain that nobody knew me, I enjoyed by anticipation all the conjectures which people would indulge in respecting me, when I made my first appearance in the most fashionable café of the town.

My uniform was white, the vest blue, a gold and silver shoulder-knot, and a sword-knot of the same material. Very well pleased with my grand appearance, I went to the coffee-room, and, taking some chocolate, began to read the newspapers, quite at my ease, and delighted to see that everybody was puzzled. A bold individual, in the hope of getting me into conversation, came to me and addressed me; I answered him with a monosyllable, and I observed that everyone was at a loss what to make of me. When I had sufficiently enjoyed public admiration in the coffee-room, I promenaded in the busiest thoroughfares of the city, and returned to the inn, where I had dinner by myself.

I had just concluded my repast when my landlord
presented himself with the travellers' book, in which he
wanted to register my name.

"Casanova."

"Your profession, if you please, sir?"

"Officer."

"In which service?"

"None."

"Your native place?"

"Venice."

"Where do you come from?"

"That is no business of yours."

This answer, which I thought was in keeping with my
external appearance, had the desired effect: the landlord
bowed himself out, and I felt highly pleased with myself,
for I knew that I should enjoy perfect freedom in Bologna, and I was certain that mine host had visited me
at the instance of some curious person eager to know
who I was.

The next day I called on M. Orsi, the banker, to cash
my bill of exchange, and took another for six hundred
sequins on Venice, and one hundred sequins in gold:
after which I again exhibited myself in the public places.
Two days afterwards, whilst I was taking my coffee after
dinner, the banker Orsi was announced. I desired him
to be shewn in, and he made his appearance accompanied
my Monsignor Cornaro, whom I feigned not to know.
M. Orsi remarked that he had called to offer me his
services for my letters of exchange, and introduced the
prelate. I rose and expressed my gratification at making
his acquaintance. "But we have met before," he replied,
"at Venice and Rome." Assuming an air of blank surprise, I told him he must certainly be mistaken. The
prelate, thinking he could guess the reason of my re-

serve, did not insist, and apologized. I offered him a cup of coffee, which he accepted, and, on leaving me, he begged the honour of my company to breakfast the next day.

I made up my mind to persist in my denials, and called upon the prelate, who gave me a polite welcome. He was then apostolic prothonotary in Bologna. Breakfast was served, and as we were sipping our chocolate, he told me that I had most likely some good reasons to warrant my reserve, but that I was wrong not to trust him, the more so that the affair in question did me great honour. "I do not know," said I, "what affair you are alluding to." He then handed me a newspaper, telling me to read a paragraph which he pointed out. My astonishment may be imagined when I read the following correspondence from Pesaro: "M. de Casanova, an officer in the service of the queen, has deserted after having killed his captain in a duel; the circumstances of the duel are not known; all that has been ascertained is that M. de Casanova has taken the road to Rimini, riding the horse belonging to the captain, who was killed on the spot."

In spite of my surprise, and of the difficulty I had in keeping my gravity at the reading of the paragraph, in which so much untruth was blended with so little that was real, I managed to keep a serious countenance, and I told the prelate that the Casanova spoken of in the newspaper must be another man.

"That may be, but you are certainly the Casanova I knew a month ago at Cardinal Acquaviva's, and two years ago at the house of my sister, Madame Lovedan, in Venice. Besides the Ancona banker speaks of you as an ecclesiastic in his letter of advice to M. Orsi."

"Very well, monsignor; your excellency compels me to

agree to my being the same Casanova, but I entreat you
not to ask me any more questions as I am bound in
honour to observe the strictest reserve."

"That is enough for me, and I am satisfied. Let us
talk of something else."

I was amused at the false reports which were being
circulated about me, and, I became from that moment
a thorough sceptic on the subject of historical truth. I
enjoyed, however, very great pleasure in thinking that
my reserve had fed the belief of my being the Casanova
mentioned in the newspaper. I felt certain that the prelate would write the whole affair to Venice, where it
would do me great honour, at least until the truth should
be known, and in that case my reserve would be justified,
besides, I should then most likely be far away. I made
up my mind to go to Venice as soon as I heard from
Thérèse, as I thought that I could wait for her there
more comfortably than in Bologna, and in my native
place there was nothing to hinder me from marrying her
openly. In the mean time the fable from Pesaro amused
me a good deal, and I expected every day to see it denied
in some newspaper. The real officer Casanova must have
laughed at the accusation brought against him of having
run away with the horse, as much as I laughed at the
caprice which had metamorphosed me into an officer
in Bologna, just as if I had done it for the very purpose
of giving to the affair every appearance of truth.

On the fourth day of my stay in Bologna, I received
by express a long letter from Thérèse. She informed me
that, on the day after my escape from Rimini, Baron
Vais had presented to her the Duke de Castropignano,
who, having heard her sing, had offered her one thousand
ounces a year, and all travelling expenses paid, if she
would accept an engagement as prima-donna at the San-

Carlo Theatre, at Naples, where she would have to go immediately after her Rimini engagement. She had requested and obtained a week to come to a decision. She enclosed two documents, the first was the written memorandum of the duke's proposals, which she sent in order that I should peruse it, as she did not wish to sign it without my consent; the second was a formal engagement, written by herself, to remain all her life devoted to me and at my service. She added in her letter that, if I wished to accompany her to Naples, she would meet me anywhere I might appoint, but that, if I had any objection to return to that city, she would immediately refuse the brilliant offer, for her only happiness was to please me in all things.

For the first time in my life I found myself in need of thoughtful consideration before I could make up my mind. Thérèse's letter had entirely upset all my ideas, and, feeling that I could not answer it at once, I told the messenger to call the next day.

Two motives of equal weight kept the balance wavering; self-love and love for Thérèse. I felt that I ought not to require Thérèse to give up such prospects of fortune; but I could not take upon myself either to let her go to Naples without me, or to accompany her there. On one side, I shuddered at the idea that my love might ruin Thérèse's prospects; on the other side, the idea of the blow inflicted on my self-love, on my pride, if I went to Naples with her, sickened me.

How could I make up my mind to reappear in that city, in the guise of a cowardly fellow living at the expense of his mistress or his wife? What would my cousin Antonio, Don Polo and his dear son, Don Lelio Caraffa, and all the patricians who knew me, have said? The thought of Lucrezia and of her husband sent a cold shiver through me. I considered that, in spite of my love for Thérèse, I should become very miserable if everyone despised me. Linked to her destiny as a lover or as a husband, I would be a degraded, humbled, and mean sycophant. Then came the thought, Is this to be the end of all my hopes? The die was cast, my head had conquered my heart. I fancied that I had hit upon an excellent expedient, which at all events made me gain time, and I resolved to act upon it. I wrote to Thérèse, advising her to accept the engagement for Naples, where she might expect me to join her in the month of July, or after my return from Constantinople. I cautioned her to engage an honest-looking waiting-woman, so as to appear respectably in the world, and to lead such a life as would permit me to make her my wife, on my return, without being ashamed of myself. I foresaw that her success would be insured by her beauty even more than by her talent, and, with my nature, I knew that I could never assume the character of an easy-going lover or of a compliant husband.

Had I received Thérèse's letter one week sooner, it is certain that she would not have gone to Naples, for my love would then have proved stronger than my reason; but in matters of love, as well as in all others, Time is a great teacher.

I told Thérèse to direct her answer to Bologna, and, three days after, I received from her a letter loving, and at the same time sad, in which she informed me that she had signed the engagement. She had secured the services of a woman whom she could present as her mother; she would reach Naples towards the middle of May, and she would wait for me there till she heard from me that I no longer wanted her.

Four days after the receipt of that letter, the last but

one that Thérèse wrote me, I left Bologna for Venice. Before my departure I had received an answer form the French officer, advising me that my passport had reached Pesaro, and that he was ready to forward it to me with my trunk, if I would pay M. Marcello Birna, the *proveditore* of the Spanish army, whose address he enclosed, the sum of fifty doubloons for the horse which I had run away with, or which had run away with me. I repaired at once to the house of the *proveditore,* well pleased to settle that affair, and I received my trunk and my passport a few hours before leaving Bologna. But as my paying for the horse was known all over the town, Monsignor Cornaro was confirmed in his belief that I had killed my captain in a duel.

To go to Venice, it was necessary to submit to a quarantine, which had been adhered to only because the two governments had fallen out. The Venetians wanted the Pope to be the first in giving free passage through his frontiers, and the Pope insisted that the Venetians should take the initiative. The result of this trifling pique between the two governments was great hindrance to commerce, but very often that which bears only upon the private interest of the people is lightly treated by the rulers. I did not wish to be quarantined, and determined on evading it. It was rather a delicate undertaking, for in Venice the sanitary laws are very strict, but in those days I delighted in doing, if not everything that was forbidden, at least everything which offered real difficulties.

I knew that between the state of Mantua and that of Venice the passage was free, and I knew likewise that there was no restriction in the communication between Mantua and Modena; if I could therefore penetrate into the state of Mantua by stating that I was coming from

Modena, my success would be certain, because I could then cross the Po and go straight to Venice. I got a carrier to drive me to Revero, a city situated on the river Po, and belonging to the state of Mantua.

The driver told me that, if he took the crossroads, he could go to Revero, and say that we came from Mantua, and that the only difficulty would be in the absence of the sanitary certificate which is delivered in Mantua, and which was certain to be asked for in Revero. I suggested that the best way to manage would be for him to say that he had lost it, and a little money removed every objection on his part.

When we reached the gates of Revero, I represented myself as a Spanish officer going to Venice to meet the Duke of Modena (whom I knew to be there) on business of the greatest importance. The sanitary certificate was not even demanded, military honours were duly paid to me, and I was most civilly treated. A certificate was immediately delivered to me, setting forth that I was travelling from Revero, and with it I crossed the Po, without any difficulty, at Ostiglia, from which place I proceeded to Legnago. There I left my carrier as much pleased with my generosity as with the good luck which had attended our journey, and, taking post-horses, I reached Venice in the evening. I remarked that it was the 2nd of April, 1744, the anniversary of my birth, which, ten times during my life, has been marked by some important event.

The very next morning I went to the exchange in order to procure a passage to Constantinople, but I could not find any passenger ship sailing before two or three months, and I engaged a berth in a Venetian ship called, *Our Lady of the Rosary*, Commander Zane, which was to sail for Corfu in the course of the month.

Having thus prepared myself to obey my destiny, which, according to my superstitious feelings, called me imperiously to Constantinople, I went to St.-Mark's Square in order to see and to be seen, enjoying by anticipation the surprise of my acquaintances at not finding me any longer an abbé. I must not forget to state that at Revero I had decorated my hat with a red cockade.

I thought that my first visit was, by right, due to the Abbé Grimani. The moment he saw me he raised a perfect shriek of astonishment, for he thought I was still with Cardinal Acquaviva, on the road to a political career, and he saw standing before him a son of Mars. He had just left the dinner-table as I entered, and he had company. I observed amongst the guests an officer wearing the Spanish uniform, but I was not put out of countenance. I told the Abbé Grimani that I was only passing through Venice, and that I had felt it a duty and a pleasure to pay my respects to him.

"I did not expect to see you in such a costume."

"I have resolved to throw off the garb which could not procure me a fortune likely to satisfy my ambition."

"Where are you going?"

"To Constantinople; and I hope to find a quick passage to Corfu, as I have dispatches from Cardinal Acquaviva."

"Where do you come from now?"

"From the Spanish army, which I left ten days ago."

These words were hardly spoken, when I heard the voice of a young nobleman exclaiming,—

"That is not true."

"The profession to which I belong," I said to him with great animation, "does not permit me to let anyone give me the lie."

And upon that, bowing all round, I went away, without taking any notice of those who were calling me back.

I wore an uniform; it seemed to me that I was right in showing that sensitive and haughty pride which forms one of the characteristics of military men. I was no longer a priest: I could not bear being given the lie, especially when it had been given to me in so public a manner.

I called upon Madame Manzoni, whom I was longing to see. She was very happy to see me, and did not fail to remind me of her prediction. I told her my history, which amused her much; but she said that if I went to Constantinople I should most likely never see her again.

After my visit to Madame Manzoni I went to the house of Madame Orio, where I found worthy M. Rosa, Nanette, and Marton. They were all greatly surprised, indeed petrified at seeing me. The two lovely sisters looked more beautiful than ever, but I did not think it necessary to tell them the history of my nine months absence, for it would not have edified the aunt or pleased the nieces. I satisfied myself with telling them as much as I thought fit, and amused them for three hours. Seeing that the good old lady was carried away by her enthusiasm, I told her that I should be very happy to pass under her roof the four or five weeks of my stay in Venice, if she could give me a room and supper, but on condition that I should not prove a burden to her or to her charming nieces.

"I should be only too happy," she answered, "to have you so long, but I have no room to offer you."

"Yes, you have one, my dear," exclaimed M. Rosa, "and I undertake to put it to rights within two hours."

It was the room adjoining the chamber of the two sisters. Nanette said immediately that she would come downstairs with her sister, but Madame Orio answered that it was unnecessary, as they could lock themselves in their room.

"There would be no need for them to do that, madam," I said, with a serious and modest air; "and if I am likely to occasion the slightest disturbance, I can remain at the inn."

"There will be no disturbance whatever; but forgive my nieces, they are young prudes, and have a very high opinion of themselves."

Everything being satisfactorily arranged, I forced upon Madame Orio a payment of fifteen sequins in advance, assuring her that I was rich, and that I had made a very good bargain, as I should spend a great deal more if I kept my room at the inn. I added that I would send my luggage, and take up my quarters in her house on the following day. During the whole of the conversation, I could see the eyes of my two dear little wives sparkling with pleasure, and they reconquered all their influence over my heart in spite of my love for Thérèse, whose image was, all the same, brilliant in my soul: this was a passing infidelity, but not inconstancy.

On the following day I called at the war office, but, to avoid every chance of unpleasantness, I took care to remove my cockade. I found in the office Major Pelodoro, who could not control his joy when he saw me in a military uniform, and hugged me with delight. As soon as I had explained to him that I wanted to go to Constantinople, and that, although in uniform, I was free, he advised me earnestly to seek the favour of going to Turkey with the *bailo,* who intended to leave within two months, and even to try to obtain service in the Venetian army.

His advice suited me exactly, and the secretary of

war, who had known me the year before, happening to see me, summoned me to him. He told me that he had received letters from Bologna which had informed him of a certain adventure entirely to my honour, adding that he knew that I would not acknowledge it. He then asked me if I had received my discharge before leaving the Spanish army.

"I could not receive my discharge, as I was never in the service."

"And how did you manage to come to Venice without performing quarantine?"

"Persons coming from Mantua are not subject to it."

"True; but I advise you to enter the Venetian service like Major Pelodoro."

As I was leaving the ducal palace, I met the Abbé Grimani who told me that the abrupt manner in which I had left his house had displeased everybody.

"Even the Spanish officer?"

"No, for he remarked that, if you had truly been with the army, you could not act differently, and he has himself assured me that you were there, and to prove what he asserted he made me read an article in the newspaper, in which it is stated that you killed your captain in a duel. Of course it is only a fable?"

"How do you know that it is not a fact?"

"Is it true, then?"

"I do not say so, but it may be true, quite as true as my having been with the Spanish army ten days ago."

"But that is impossible, unless you have broken through the quarantine."

"I have broken nothing. I have openly crossed the Po at Revero, and here I am. I am sorry not to be able to present myself at your excellency's palace, but I cannot do so until I have received the most complete satisfaction from the person who has given me the lie. I could put up with an insult when I wore the livery of humility, but I cannot bear one now that I wear the garb of honour."

"You are wrong to take it in such a high tone. The person who attacked your veracity is M. Valmarana, the *proveditore* of the sanitary department, and he contends that, as nobody can pass through the cordon, it would be impossible for you to be here. Satisfaction, indeed! Have you forgotten who you are?"

"No, I know who I am; and I know likewise that, if I was taken for a coward before leaving Venice, now that I have returned no one shall insult me without repenting it."

"Come and dine with me."

"No, because the Spanish officer would know it."

"He would even see you, for he dines with me every day."

"Very well, then I will go, and I will let him be the judge of my quarrel with M. Valmarana."

I dined that day with Major Pelodoro and several other officers, who agreed in advising me to enter the service of the Republic, and I resolved to do so. "I am acquainted," said the major, "with a young lieutenant whose health is not sufficiently strong to allow him to go to the East, and who would be glad to sell his commission, for which he wants one hundred sequins. But it would be necessary to obtain the consent of the secretary of war." "Mention the matter to him," I replied, "the one hundred sequins are ready." The major undertook the commission.

In the evening I went to Madame Orio, and I found myself very comfortably lodged. After supper, the aunt told her nieces to shew me to my room, and, as may well be supposed, we spent a most delightful night. After that they took the agreeable duty by turns, and in order to avoid any surprise in case the aunt should take it into her head to pay them a visit, we skilfully displaced a part of the partition, which allowed them to come in and out of my room without opening the door. But the good lady believed us three living specimens of virtue, and never thought of putting us to the test.

Two or three days afterwards, M. Grimani contrived an interview between me and M. Valmarana, who told me that, if he had been aware that the sanitary line could be eluded, he would never have impugned my veracity, and thanked me for the information I had given him. The affair was thus agreeably arranged, and until my departure I honoured M. Grimani's excellent dinner with my presence every day.

Towards the end of the month I entered the service of the Republic in the capacity of ensign in the Bala regiment, then at Corfu; the young man who had left the regiment through the magical virtue of my one hundred sequins was lieutenant, but the secretary of war objected to my having that rank for reasons to which I had to submit, if I wished to enter the army; but he promised me that, at the end of the year, I would be promoted to the grade of lieutenant, and he granted me a furlough to go to Constantinople. I accepted, for I was determined to serve in the army.

M. Pierre Vendramin, an illustrious senator, obtained me the favour of a passage to Constantinople with the Chevalier Vénier, who was proceeding to that city in the quality of *bailo*, but as he would arrive in Corfu a month after me, the chevalier very kindly promised to take me as he called at Corfu.

A few days before my departure, I received a letter

from Thérèse, who informed me that the Duke de Castropignano escorted her everywhere. "The duke is old," she wrote, "but even if he were young, you would have no cause for uneasiness on my account. Should you ever want any money, draw upon me from any place where you may happen to be, and be quite certain that your letters of exchange will be paid, even if I had to sell everything I possess to honour your signature."

There was to be another passenger on board the ship of the line on which I had engaged my passage, namely, a noble Venetian, who was going to Zante in the quality of counsellor, with a numerous and brilliant retinue. The captain of the ship told me that, if I was obliged to take my meals alone, I was not likely to fare very well, and he advised me to obtain an introduction to the nobleman, who would not fail to invite me to share his table. His name was Antonio Dolfin, and he had been nicknamed *Bucentoro,* in consequence of his air of grandeur and the elegance of his toilet. Fortunately I did not require to beg an introduction, for M. Grimani offered, of his own accord, to present me to the magnificent councillor, who received me in the kindest manner, and invited me at once to take my meals at his table. He expressed a desire that I should make the acquaintance of his wife, who was to accompany him in the journey. I called upon her the next day, and I found a lady perfect in manners, but already of a certain age and completely deaf. I had therefore but little pleasure to expect from her conversation. She had a very charming young daughter whom she left in a convent. She became celebrated afterwards, and she is still alive, I believe, the widow of Procurator Iron, whose family is extinct.

I have seldom seen a finer-looking man, or a man of more imposing appearance than M. Dolfin. He was

eminently distinguished for his wit and politeness. He
was eloquent, always cheerful when he lost at cards, the
favourite of ladies, whom he endeavoured to please in
everything, always courageous, and of an equal temper,
whether in good or in adverse fortune.

He had ventured on travelling without permission, and
had entered a foreign service, which had brought him
into disgrace with the government, for a noble son of
Venice cannot be guilty of a greater crime. For this
offence he had been imprisoned in the Leads—a favour
which destiny kept also in reserve for me.

Highly gifted, generous, but not wealthy, M. Dolfin
had been compelled to solicit from the Grand Council
a lucrative governorship, and had been appointed to
Zante; but he started with such a splendid suite that
he was not likely to save much out of his salary. Such
a man as I have just portrayed could not make a fortune in Venice, because an aristocratic government cannot obtain a state of lasting, steady peace at home unless
equality is maintained amongst the nobility, and equality,
either moral or physical, cannot be appreciated in any
other way than by appearances. The result is that the
man who does not want to lay himself open to persecution, and who happens to be superior or inferior to the
others, must endeavour to conceal it by all possible
means. If he is ambitious, he must feign great contempt
for dignities; if he seeks employment, he must not appear to want any; if his features are handsome, he must
be careless of his physical appearance; he must dress
badly, wear nothing in good taste, ridicule every foreign
importation, make his bow without grace, be careless in
his manner; care nothing for the fine arts, conceal his
good breeding, have no foreign cook, wear an uncombed
wig, and look rather dirty. M. Dolfin was not endowed

with any of those eminent qualities, and therefore he had no hope of a great fortune in his native country.

The day before my departure from Venice I did not go out; I devoted the whole of the day to friendship. Madame Orio and her lovely nieces shed many tears, and I joined them in that delightful employment. During the last night that I spent with both of them, the sisters repeated over and over, in the midst of the raptures of love, that they never would see me again. They guessed rightly; but if they had happened to see me again they would have guessed wrongly. Observe how wonderful prophets are!

I went on board, on the 5th of May, with a good supply of clothing, jewels, and ready cash. Our ship carried twenty-four guns and two hundred Sclavonian soldiers. We sailed from Malamacca to the shores of Istria during the night, and we came to anchor in the harbour of Orsera to take ballast. I landed with several others to take a stroll through the wretched place where I had spent three days nine months before, a recollection which caused me a pleasant sensation when I compared my present position to what it was at that time. What a difference in everything—health, social condition, and money! I felt quite certain that in the splendid uniform I was now wearing nobody would recognize the miserable-looking abbé who, but for Friar Stephano, woud have become—God knows what!

CHAPTER XIV

An Amusing Meeting in Orsera—Journey to Corfu—My Stay in Constantinople—Bonneval—My Return to Corfu—Madame F.—The False Prince—I Run Away from Corfu—My Frolics at Casopo—I Surrender Myself a Prisoner—My Speedy Release and Triumph—My Success with Madame F.

I AFFIRM that a stupid servant is more dangerous than a bad one, and a much greater plague, for one can be on one's guard against a wicked person, but never against a fool. You can punish wickedness but not stupidity, unless you send away the fool, male or female, who is guilty of it, and if you do so you generally find out that the change has only thrown you out of the frying-pan into the fire.

This chapter and the two following ones were written; they gave at full length all the particulars which I must now abridge, for my silly servant has taken the three chapters for her own purposes. She pleaded as an excuse that the sheets of paper were old, written upon, covered with scribbling and erasures, and that she had taken them in preference to nice, clean paper, thinking that I would care much more for the last than for the first. I flew into a violent passion, but I was wrong, for the poor girl had acted with a good intent; her judgment alone had misled her. It is well known that the first result of anger is to deprive the angry man of the faculty of reason, for anger and reason do not belong to the same family. Luckily, passion does not keep me long under its sway: *Irasci, celerem tamen et placabilem esse.* After I had wasted my time in hurling at her bitter reproaches, the force of which did not strike her, and in proving to her that she was a stupid fool, she refuted all my arguments by the most complete silence. There was nothing to do but to resign myself, and, although not yet in the best of tempers, I went to work. What I am going to write will probably not be so good as what I had composed when I felt in the proper humour, but my readers must be satisfied with it; they will, like the engineer, gain in time what they lose in strength.

I landed at Orsera while our ship was taking ballast, as a ship cannot sail well when she is too light, and I was walking about when I remarked a man who was looking at me very attentively. As I had no dread of any creditor, I thought that he was interested by my fine appearance; I could not find fault with such a feeling, and kept walking on, but as I passed him, he addressed me:

"Might I presume to enquire whether this is your first visit to Orsera, captain?"

"No, sir, it is my second visit to this city."

"Were you not here last year?"

"I was."

"But you were not in uniform then?"

"True again; but your questions begin to sound rather indiscreet."

"Be good enough to forgive me, sir, for my curiosity is the offspring of gratitude. I am indebted to you for the greatest benefits, and I trust that Providence has brought you here again only to give me the opportunity of making greater still my debt of gratitude to you."

"What on earth have I done, and what can I do for you? I am at a loss to guess your meaning."

"Will you be so kind as to come and breakfast with me? My house is near at hand; my refosco is delicious, please to taste it, and I will convince you in a few words that you are truly my benefactor, and that I have a right to expect that you have returned Orsera to load me with fresh benefits."

I could not suspect the man of insanity; but, as I could not make him out, I fancied that he wanted to make me purchase some of his refosco, and I accepted his invitation. We went up to his room, and he left me for a few moments to order breakfast. I observed several surgical instruments, which made me suppose that he was a surgeon, and I asked him when he returned.

"Yes, captain; I have been practising surgery in this place for twenty years, and in a very poor way, for I had nothing to do, except a few cases of bleeding, of cupping, and occasionally some slight excoriation to dress or a sprained ankle to put to rights. I did not earn even the poorest living. But since last year a great change has taken place; I have made a good deal of money, I have laid it out advantageously, and it is to you, captain, to you (may God bless you!) that I am indebted for my present comforts."

"But how so?"

"In this way, captain. You had a connection with Don Jerome's housekeeper, and you left her, when you went away, a certain souvenir which she communicated to a friend of hers, who, in perfect good faith, made a present of it to his wife. This lady did not wish, I suppose, to be selfish, and she gave the souvenir to a libertine who, in his turn, was so generous with it that, in less

than a month, I had about fifty clients. The following months were not less fruitful, and I gave the benefit of my attendance to everybody, of course, for a consideration. There are a few patients still under my care, but in a short time there will be no more, as the souvenir left by you has now lost all its virtue. You can easily realize now the joy I felt when I saw you; you are a bird of good omen. May I hope that your visit will last long enough to enable you to renew the source of my fortune?"

I laughed heartily, but he was grieved to hear that I was in excellent health. He remarked, however, that I was not likely to be so well off on my return, because, in the country to which I was going, there was abundance of damaged goods, but that no one knew better than he did how to root out the venom left by the use of such bad merchandise. He begged that I would depend upon him, and not trust myself in the hands of quacks, who would be sure to palm their remedies upon me. I promised him everything, and, taking leave of him with many thanks, I returned to the ship. I related the whole affair to M. Dolfin, who was highly amused. We sailed on the following day, but on the fourth day, on the other side of Curzola, we were visited by a storm which very nearly cost me my life. This is how it happened:

The chaplain of the ship was a Sclavonian priest, very ignorant, insolent and coarse-mannered, and, as I turned him into ridicule whenever the opportunity offered, he had naturally become my sworn enemy. *Tant de fiel entre-t-il dans l'âme d'un dévot!* When the storm was at its height, he posted himself on the quarter-deck, and, with book in hand, proceeded to exorcise all the spirits of hell whom he thought he could see in the

clouds, and to whom he pointed for the benefit of the
sailors who, believing themselves lost, were crying, howling, and giving way to despair, instead of attending to
the working of the ship, then in great danger on account of the rocks and of the breakers which surrounded us.

Seeing the peril of our position, and the evil effect
of his stupid incantations upon the minds of the sailors
whom the ignorant priest was throwing into the apathy
of despair, instead of keeping up their·courage, I thought
it prudent to interfere. I went up the rigging, calling
upon the sailors to do their duty cheerfully, telling them
that there were no devils, and that the priest who pretended to see them was a fool. But it was in vain that
I spoke in the most forcible manner, in vain that I went
to work myself, and shewed that safety was only to be
insured by active means, I could not prevent the priest
declaring that I was an Atheist, and he managed to rouse
against me the anger of the greatest part of the crew.
The wind continued to lash the sea into fury for the
two following days, and the knave contrived to persuade
the sailors who listened to him that the hurricane would
not abate as long as I was on board. Imbued with that
conviction, one of the men, thinking he had found a
good opportunity of fulfilling the wishes of the priest,
came up to me as I was standing at the extreme end
of the forecastle, and pushed me so roughly that I was
thrown over. I should have been irretrievably lost, but
the sharp point of an anchor, hanging along the side of
the ship, catching in my clothes, prevented me from falling in the sea, and proved truly my sheet-anchor. Some
men came to my assistance, and I was saved. A corporal then pointed out to me the sailor who had tried
to murder me, and taking a stout stick I treated the

scoundrel to a sound thrashing; but the sailors, headed
by the furious priest, rushed towards us when they heard
his screams, and I should have been killed if the soldiers
had not taken my part. The commander and M. Dolfin
then came on deck, but they were compelled to listen to
the chaplain, and to promise, in order to pacify the vile
rabble, that they would land me at the first opportunity.
But even this was not enough; the priest demanded that
I should give up to him a certain parchment that I had
purchased from a Greek at Malamocco just before sailing. I had no recollection of it, but it was true. I
laughed, and gave it to M. Dolfin; he handed it to the
fanatic chaplain, who, exulting in his victory, called for
a large pan of live coals from the cook's galley, and
made an *auto-da-fé* of the document. The unlucky
parchment, before it was entirely consumed, kept writhing on the fire for half an hour, and the priest did not
fail to represent those contortions as a miracle, and all
the sailors were sure that it was an infernal manuscript
given to me by the devil. The virtue claimed for that
piece of parchment by the man who had sold it to me
was that it insured its lucky possessor the love of all
women, but I trust my readers will do me the justice to
believe that I had no faith whatever in amorous philtres,
talismans, or amulets of any kind: I had purchased it
only for a joke.

You can find throughout Italy, in Greece, and generally in every country the inhabitants of which are yet
wrapped up in primitive ignorance, a tribe of Greeks,
of Jews, of astronomers, and of exorcists, who sell their
dupes rags and toys to which they boastingly attach
wonderful virtues and properties; amulets which render
invulnerable, scraps of cloth which defend from witch-
craft, small bags filled with drugs to keep away goblins,

and a thousand gewgaws of the same description. These wonderful goods have no marketable value whatever in France, in England, in Germany, and throughout the north of Europe generally, but, in revenge, the inhabitants of those countries indulge in knavish practices of a much worse kind.

The storm abated just as the innocent parchment was writhing on the fire, and the sailors, believing that the spirits of hell had been exorcised, thought no more of getting rid of my person, and after a prosperous voyage of a week we cast anchor at Corfu. As soon as I had found a comfortable lodging I took my letters to his eminence the *proveditore-generale,* and to all the naval commanders to whom I was recommended; and after paying my respects to my colonel, and making the acquaintance of the officers of my regiment, I prepared to enjoy myself until the arrival of the Chevalier Vénier, who had promised to take me to Constantinople. He arrived towards the middle of June, but in the mean time I had been playing basset, and had lost all my money, and sold or pledged all my jewellery.

Such must be the fate awaiting every man who has a taste for gambling, unless he should know how to fix fickle fortune by playing with a real advantage derived from calculation or from adroitness, which defies chance. I think that a cool and prudent player can manage both without exposing himself to censure, or deserving to be called a cheat.

During the month that I spent in Corfu, waiting for the arrival of M. Vénier, I did not devote any time to the study, either moral or physical, of the country, for, excepting the days on which I was on duty, I passed my life at the coffee-house, intent upon the game, and sinking, as a matter of course, under the adverse fortune which I braved with obstinacy. I never won, and I had not the moral strength to stop till all my means were gone. The only comfort I had, and a sorry one truly, was to hear the banker himself call me—perhaps sarcastically—a fine player, every time I lost a large stake. My misery was at its height, when new life was infused in me by the booming of the guns fired in honour of the arrival of the *bailo*. He was on board the *Europa,* a frigate of seventy-two guns, and he had taken only eight days to sail from Venice to Corfu. The moment he cast anchor, the *bailo* hoisted his flag of captain-general of the Venetian navy, and the *proveditore* hauled down his own colours. The Republic of Venice has not on the sea any authority greater than that of *Bailo* to the Porte. The Chevalier Vénier had with him a distinguished and brilliant suite; Count Annibal Gambera, Count Charles Zenobio, both Venetian noblemen of the first class, and the Marquis d'Anchotti of Bressan, accompanied him to Constantinople for their own amusement. The *bailo* remained a week in Corfu, and all the naval authorities entertained him and his suite in turn, so that there was a constant succession of balls and suppers. When I presented myself to his excellency, he informed me that he had already spoken to the *proveditore,* who had granted me a furlough of six months to enable me to accompany him to Constantinople as his adjutant; and as soon as the official document for my furlough had been delivered to me, I sent my small stock of worldly goods on board the *Europa,* and we weighed anchor early the next day.

We sailed with a favourable wind which remained steady and brought us in six days to Cerigo, where we stopped to take in some water. Feeling some curiosity to visit the ancient Cythera, I went on shore with the sailors on duty, but it would have been better for me if I had remained on board, for in Cerigo I made a bad acquaintance. I was accompanied by the captain of marines.

The moment we set foot on shore, two men, very poorly dressed and of unprepossessing appearance, came to us and begged for assistance. I asked them who they were, and one, quicker than the other, answered,—

"We are sentenced to live, and perhaps to die, in this island by the despotism of the Council of Ten. There are forty others as unfortunate as ourselves, and we are all born subjects of the Republic.

"The crime of which we have been accused, which is not considered a crime anywhere, is that we were in the habit of living with our mistresses, without being jealous of our friends, when, finding our ladies handsome, they obtained their favours with our ready consent. As we were not rich, we felt no remorse in availing ourselves of the generosity of our friends in such cases, but it was said that we were carrying on an illicit trade, and we have been sent to this place, where we receive every day ten sous in *moneta lunga*. We are called *mangia-marroni*, and are worse off than galley slaves, for we are dying of ennui, and we are often starving without knowing how to stay our hunger. My name is Don Antonio Pocchini, I am of a noble Paduan family, and my mother belongs to the illustrious family of Campo San-Piero."

We gave them some money, and went about the island, returning to the ship after we had visited the fortress. I shall have to speak of that Pocchini in a few years.

The wind continued in our favour, and we reached the Dardanelles in eight or ten days; the Turkish barges met us there to carry us to Constantinople. The sight offered by that city at the distance of a league is truly wonderful; and I believe that a more magnificent panorama cannot be found in any part of the world. It was that splendid view which was the cause of the fall of the Roman, and of the rise of the Greek empire. Constantine the Great, arriving at Byzantium by sea, was so much struck with the wonderful beauty of its position, that he exclaimed, "Here is the proper seat of the empire of the whole world!" and in order to secure the fulfilment of his prediction, he left Rome for Byzantium. If he had known the prophecy of Horace, or rather if he had believed in it, he would not have been guilty of such folly. The poet had said that the downfall of the Roman empire would begin only when one of the successors of Augustus bethought him of removing the capital of the empire to where it had originated. The Troad is not far distant from Thrace.

We arrived at the Venetian Embassy in Pera towards the middle of July, and, for a wonder, there was no talk of the plague in Constantinople just then. We were all provided with very comfortable lodgings, but the intensity of the heat induced the *baili* to seek for a little coolness in a country mansion which had been hired by the Bailo Dona. It was situated at Bouyoudere. The very first order laid upon me was never to go out unknown to the *bailo*, and without being escorted by a janissary, and this order I obeyed to the letter. In those days the Russians had not tamed the insolence of the Turkish people. I am told that foreigners can now go about as much as they please in perfect security.

The day after our arrival, I took a janissary to accompany me to Osman Pacha, of Caramania, the name assumed by Count de Bonneval ever since he had adopted the turban. I sent in my letter, and was immediately shewn into an apartment on the ground floor, furnished in the French fashion, where I saw a stout elderly gentleman, dressed like a Frenchman, who, as I entered the room, rose, came to meet me with a smiling countenance, and asked me how he could serve the *protégé* of a cardinal of the Roman Catholic Church, which he could no longer call his mother. I gave him all the particulars of the circumstances which, in a moment of despair, had induced me to ask the cardinal for letters of introduction for Constantinople, and I added that, the letters once in my possession, my superstitious feelings had made me believe that I was bound to deliver them in person.

"Then, without this letter," he said, "you never would have come to Constantinople, and you have no need of me?"

"True, but I consider myself fortunate in having thus made the acquaintance of a man who has attracted the attention of the whole of Europe, and who still commands that attention."

His excellency made some remark respecting the happiness of young men who, like me, without care, without any fixed purpose, abandon themselves to fortune with that confidence which knows no fear, and telling me that the cardinal's letter made it desirable that he should do something for me, he promised to introduce me to three or four of his Turkish friends who deserved to be known. He invited me to dine with him every Thursday, and undertook to send me a janissary who would protect me from the insults of the rabble, and shew me everything worth seeing.

The cardinal's letter representing me as a literary man, the pacha observed that I ought to see his library.

I followed him through the garden, and we entered a room furnished with grated cupboards; curtains could be seen behind the wirework; the books were most likely behind the curtains.

Taking a key out of his pocket, he opened one of the cupboards, and, instead of folios, I saw long rows of bottles of the finest wines. We both laughed heartily.

"Here are," said the pacha, "my library and my harem. I am old, women would only shorten my life, but good wine will prolong it, or, at least, make it more agreeable."

"I imagine your excellency has obtained a dispensation from the mufti?"

"You are mistaken, for the Pope of the Turks is very far from enjoying as great a power as the Christian Pope. He cannot in any case permit what is forbidden by the Koran; but everyone is at liberty to work out his own damnation if he likes. The Turkish devotees pity the libertines, but they do not persecute them; there is no inquisition in Turkey. Those who do not follow the precepts of religion, say the Turks, will suffer enough in the life to come; there is no need to make them suffer in this life. The only dispensation I have asked and obtained, has been respecting circumcision, although it can hardly be called so, because, at my age, it might have proved dangerous. That ceremony is generally performed, but it is not compulsory."

During the two hours that we spent together, the pacha enquired after several of his friends in Venice, and particularly after Marc Antonio Dieto. I told him that his friends were still faithful to their affection for him, and did not find fault with his apostasy. He answered that he was a Mahometan as he had been a Christian, and that he was not better acquainted with

the Koran than he had been with the Gospel. "I am
certain," he added, "that I shall die calmer and much
happier than Prince Eugène. I have had to say that
God is God, and that Mahomet is the prophet. I have
said it, and the Turks care very little whether I believe
it or not. I wear the turban as the soldier wears the
uniform. I was nothing but a military man; I could
not have turned my hand to any other profession, and
I made up my mind to become lieutenant-general of the
Grand Turk only when I found myself entirely at a loss
how to earn my living. When I left Venice, the pitcher
had gone too often to the well, it was broken at last, and
if the Jews had offered me the command of an army of
fifty thousand men, I would have gone and besieged
Jerusalem.

Bonneval was handsome, but too stout. He had
received a sabre-cut in the lower part of the abdomen,
which compelled him to wear constantly a bandage supported by a silver plate. He had been exiled to Asia,
but only for a short time, for, as he told me, the cabals
are not so tenacious in Turkey as they are in Europe,
and particularly at the court of Vienna. As I was taking
leave of him, he was kind enough to say that, since his
arrival in Turkey, he had never passed two hours as
pleasantly as those he had just spent with me, and that
he would compliment the *bailo* about me.

The Bailo Dona, who had known him intimately
in Venice, desired me to be the bearer of all his friendly
compliments for him, and M. Vénier expressed his deep
regret at not being able to make his acquaintance.

The second day after my first visit to him being
a Thursday, the pacha did not forget to send a janissary
according to his promise. It was about eleven in
the morning when the janissary called for me, I fol-

lowed him, and this time I found Bonneval dressed in the Turkish style. His guests soon arrived, and we sat down to dinner, eight of us, all well disposed to be cheerful and happy. The dinner was entirely French, in cooking and service; his steward and his cook were both worthy French renegades.

He had taken care to introduce me to all his guests and at the same time to let me know who they were, but he did not give me an opportunity of speaking before dinner was nearly over. The conversation was entirely kept up in Italian, and I remarked that the Turks did not utter a single word in their own language, even to say the most ordinary thing. Each guest had near him a bottle which might have contained either white wine or hydromel; all I know is that I drank, as well as M. de Bonneval, next to whom I was seated, some excellent white Burgundy.

The guests got me on the subject of Venice, and particularly of Rome, and the conversation very naturally fell upon religion, but not upon dogmatic questions; the discipline of religion and liturgical questions were alone discussed.

One of the guests, who was addressed as *effendi*, because he had been secretary for foreign affairs, said that the ambassador from Venice to Rome was a friend of his, and he spoke of him in the highest manner. I told him that I shared his admiration for that ambassador, who had given me a letter of introduction for a Turkish nobleman, whom he had represented as an intimate friend. He enquired for the name of the person to whom the letter was addressed, but I could not recollect it, and took the letter out of my pocket-book. The *effendi* was delighted when he found that the letter was for himself. He begged leave to read it at once, and after he had perused it, he kissed the signature and came to embrace me. This scene pleased M. de Bonneval and all his friends. The *effendi*, whose name was Ismail, entreated the pacha to come to dine with him, and to bring me; Bonneval accepted, and fixed a day.

Notwithstanding all the politeness of the *effendi*, I was particularly interested during our charming dinner in a fine elderly man of about sixty, whose countenance breathed at the same time the greatest sagacity and the most perfect kindness. Two years afterwards I found again the same features on the handsome face of M. de Bragadin, a Venetian senator of whom I shall have to speak at length when we come to that period of my life. That elderly gentleman had listened to me with the greatest attention, but without uttering one word. In society, a man whose face and general appearance excite your interest, stimulates strongly your curiosity if he remains silent. When we left the dining-room I enquired from M. de Bonneval who he was; he answered that he was wealthy, a philosopher, a man of acknowledged merit, of great purity of morals, and strongly attached to his religion. He advised me to cultivate his acquaintance if he made any advances to me.

I was pleased with his advice, and when, after a walk under the shady trees of the garden, we returned to a drawing-room furnished in the Turkish fashion, I purposely took a seat near Yusuf Ali. Such was the name of the Turk for whom I felt so much sympathy. He offered me his pipe in a very graceful manner; I refused it politely, and took one brought to me by one of M. de Bonneval's servants. Whenever I have been amongst smokers I have smoked or left the room; otherwise I would have fancied that I was swallowing the smoke of the others, and that idea, which is true and unpleasant, disgusted me. I have never been able to understand how in Germany the ladies, otherwise so polite and delicate, could inhale the suffocating fumes of a crowd of smokers.

Yusuf, pleased to have me near him, at once led the conversation to subjects similar to those which had been discussed at table, and particularly to the reasons which had induced me to give up the peaceful profession of the Church and to choose a military life; and in order to gratify his curiosity without losing his good opinion, I gave him, but with proper caution, some of the particulars of my life, for I wanted him to be satisfied that, if I had at first entered the career of the holy priesthood, it had not been through any vocation of mine. He seemed pleased with my recital, spoke of natural vocations as a Stoic philosopher, and I saw that he was a fatalist; but as I was careful not to attack his system openly, he did not dislike my objections, most likely because he thought himself strong enough to overthrow them.

I must have inspired the honest Mussulman with very great esteem, for he thought me worthy of becoming his disciple; it was not likely that he could entertain the idea of becoming himself the disciple of a young man of nineteen, lost, as he thought, in a false religion.

After spending an hour in examining me, in listening to my principles, he said that he believed me fit to know the real truth, because he saw that I was seeking for it, and that I was not certain of having obtained it so far. He invited me to come and spend a whole day with him, naming the days when I would be certain to find him at home, but he advised me to consult the Pacha Osman before accepting his invitation. I told him that the

pacha had already mentioned him to me and had spoken
very highly of his character; he seemed much pleased.
I fixed a day for my visit, and left him.

I informed M. de Bonneval of all that had occurred;
he was delighted, and promised that his janissary would
be every day at the Venetian palace, ready to execute
my orders.

I received the congratulations of the *baili* upon the
excellent acquaintances I had already made, and M.
Vénier advised me not to neglect such friends in a
country where weariness of life was more deadly to foreigners than the plague.

On the day appointed, I went early to Yusuf's palace,
but he was out. His gardener, who had received his instructions, shewed me every attention, and entertained
me very agreeably for two hours in doing the honours
of his master's splendid garden, where I found the most
beautiful flowers. This gardener was a Neapolitan, and
had belonged to Yusuf for thirty years. His manners
made me suspect that he was well born and well educated, but he told me frankly that he had never been
taught even to read, that he was a sailor when he was
taken in slavery, and that he was so happy in the service
of Yusuf that liberty would be a punishment to him.
Of course I did not venture to address him any questions
about his master, for his reserve might have put my
curiosity to the blush.

Yusuf had gone out on horseback; he returned, and,
after the usual compliments, we dined alone in a summer-house, from which we had a fine view of the sea,
and in which the heat was cooled by a delightful breeze,
which blows regularly at the same hour every day from
the north-west, and is called the *mistral*. We had a good
dinner; there was no prepared dish except the *cauroman*,

a peculiar delicacy of the Turks. I drank water and hydromel, and I told Yusuf that I preferred the last to wine, of which I never took much at that time. "Your hydromel," I said, "is very good, and the Mussulmans who offend against the law by drinking wine do not deserve any indulgence; I believe they drink wine only because it is forbidden." "Many of the true believers," he answered, "think that they can take it as a medicine. The Grank Turk's physician has brought it into vogue as a medicine, and it has been the cause of his fortune, for he has captivated the favour of his master who is in reality constantly ill, because he is always in a state of intoxication." I told Yusuf that in my country drunkards were scarce, and that drunkenness was a vice to be found only among the lowest people; he was much astonished. "I cannot understand," he said, "why wine is allowed by all religions, when its use deprives man of his reason." "All religions," I answered, "forbid excess in drinking wine, and the crime is only in the abuse." I proved him the truth of what I had said by telling him that opium produced the same results as wine, but more powerfully, and consequently Mahomet ought to have forbidden the use of it. He observed that he had never taken either wine or opium in the course of his life.

After dinner, pipes were brought in and we filled them ourseves. I was smoking with pleasure, but, at the same time, was expectorating. Yusuf, who smoked like a Turk, that is to say, without spitting, said,—

"The tobacco you are now smoking is of a very fine quality, and you ought to swallow its balsam which is mixed with the saliva."

"I suppose you are right; smoking cannot be truly enjoyed without the best tobacco."

"That is true to a certain extent, but the enjoyment found in smoking good tobacco is not the principal pleasure, because it only pleases our senses; true enjoyment is that which works upon the soul, and is completely independent of the senses."

"I cannot realize pleasures enjoyed by the soul without the instrumentality of the senses."

"Listen to me. When you fill your pipe do you feel any pleasure?"

"Yes."

"Whence does that pleasure arise, if it is not from your soul? Let us go further. Do you not feel pleased when you give up your pipe after having smoked all the tobacco in it—when you see that nothing is left but some ashes?"

"It is true."

"Well, there are two pleasures in which your senses have certainly nothing to do, but I want you to guess the third, and the most essential."

"The most essential? It is the perfume."

"No; that is a pleasure of the organ of smelling—a sensual pleasure."

"Then I do not know."

"Listen. The principal pleasure derived from tobacco smoking is the sight of the smoke itself. You must never see it go out of the bowl of your pipe, but only from the corner of your mouth, at regular intervals which must not be too frequent. It is so truly the greatest pleasure connected with the pipe, that you cannot find anywhere a blind man who smokes. Try yourself the experiment of smoking a pipe in your room, at night, and without a light; you will soon lay the pipe down."

"It is all perfectly true; yet you must forgive me if I give the preference to several pleasures, in which my senses are interested, over those which afford enjoyment only to my soul."

"Forty years ago I was of the same opinion, and in forty years, if you succeed in acquiring wisdom, you will think like me. Pleasures which give activity to our senses, my dear son, disturb the repose of our soul—a proof that they do not deserve the name of real enjoyments."

"But if I feel them to be real enjoyments, it is enough to prove that they are truly so."

"Granted; but if you would take the trouble of analysing them after you have tasted them, you would not find them unalloyed."

"It may be so, but why should I take a trouble which woud only lessen my enjoyment."

"A time will come when you will feel pleasure in that very trouble."

"It strikes me, dear father, that you prefer mature age to youth."

"You may boldly say old age."

"You surprise me. Must I believe that your early life has been unhappy?"

"Far from it. It was always fortunate in good health, and the master of my own passions; but all I saw in my equals was for me a good school in which I have acquired the knowledge of man, and learned the real road to happiness. The happiest of men is not the most voluptuous, but the one who knows how to choose the highest standards of voluptuousness, which can be found, I say again, not in the pleasures which excite our senses, but in those which give greater repose to the soul."

"That is the voluptuousness which you consider unalloyed."

"Yes, and such is the sight of a vast prairie all covered with grass. The green colour, so strongly recommended by our divine prophet, strikes my eyes, and at the same moment I feel that my soul is wrapped up in a calm so delightful that I fancy myself nearer the Creator. I enjoy the same peace, the same repose, when I am seated on the banks of a river, when I look upon the water so quiet, yet always moving, which flows constantly, yet never disappears from my sight, never loses any of its clearness in spite of its constant motion. It strikes me as the image of my own existence, and of the calm which I require for my life in order to reach, like the water I am gazing upon, the goal which I do not see, and which can only be found at the other end of the journey."

Thus did the Turk reason, and we passed four hours in this sort of conversation. He had buried two wives, and he had two sons and one daughter. The eldest son, having received his patrimony, had established himself in the city of Salonica, where he was a wealthy merchant; the other was in the seraglio, in the service of the Grand Turk, and his fortune was in the hands of a trustee. His daughter, Zelmi, then fifteen years of age, was to inherit all his remaining property. He had given her all the accomplishments which could minister to the happiness of the man whom heaven had destined for her husband. We shall hear more of that daughter anon. The mother of the three children was dead, and five years previous to the time of my visit, Yusuf had taken another wife, a native of Scio, young and very beautiful, but he told me himself that he was now too old, and could not hope to have any child by her. Yet he was only sixty years of age. Before I left, he made me promise to spend at least one day every week with him.

At supper, I told the *baili* how pleasantly the day had passed.

"We envy you," they said, "the prospect you have before you of spending agreeably three or four months in this country, while, in our quality of ministers, we must pine away with melancholy."

A few days afterwards, M. de Bonneval took me with him to dine at Ismail's house, where I saw Asiatic luxury on a grand scale, but there were a great many guests, and the conversation was held almost entirely in the Turkish language—a circumstance which annoyed me and M. de Bonneval also. Ismail saw it, and he invited me to breakfast whenever I felt disposed, assuring me that he would have much pleasure in receiving me. I accepted the invitation, and I went ten or twelve days afterwards. When we reach that period my readers must kindly accompany me to the breakfast. For the present I must return to Yusuf who, during my second visit, displayed a character which inspired me with the greatest esteem and the warmest affection.

We had dined alone as before, and, conversation happening to turn upon the fine arts, I gave my opinion upon one of the precepts in the Koran, by which the Mahometans are deprived of the innocent enjoyment of paintings and statues. He told me that Mahomet, a very sagacious legislator, had been right in removing all images from the sight of the followers of Islam.

"Recollect, my son, that the nations to which the prophet brought the knowledge of the true God were all idolators. Men are weak; if the disciples of the prophet had continued to see the same objects, they might have fallen back into their former errors."

"No one ever worshipped an image as an image; the deity of which the image is a representation is what is worshipped."

"I may grant that, but God cannot be matter, and it is right to remove from the thoughts of the vulgar the idea of a material divinity. You are the only men, you Christians, who believe that you see God."

"It is true, we are sure of it, but observe that faith alone gives us that certainty."

"I know it; but you are idolators, for you see nothing but a material representation, and yet you have a complete certainty that you see God, unless you should tell me that faith disaffirms it."

"God forbid I should tell you such a thing! Faith, on the contrary, affirms our certainty."

"We thank God that we have no need of such self-delusion, and there is not one philosopher in the world who could prove to me that you require it."

"That would not be the province of philosophy, dear father, but of theology—a very superior science."

"You are now speaking the language of our theologians, who differ from yours only in this; they use their science to make clearer the truths we ought to know, whilst your theologians try to render those truths more obscure."

"Recollect, dear father, that they are mysteries."

"The existence of God is a sufficiently important mystery to prevent men from daring to add anything to it. God can only be simple; any kind of combination would destroy His essence; such is the God announced by our prophet, who must be the same for all men and in all times. Agree with me that we can add nothing to the simplicity of God. We say that God is *one;* that is the image of simplicity. You say that He is *one* and *three* at the same time, and such a definition strikes us as contradictory, absurd, and impious."

"It is a mystery."

"Do you mean God or the definition? I am speaking only of the definition, which ought not to be a mystery or absurd. Common sense, my son, must consider as absurd an assertion which is substantially nonsensical. Prove to me that *three* is not a compound, that it cannot be a compound, and I will become a Christian at once."

"My religion tells me to believe without arguing, and I shudder, my dear Yusuf, when I think that, through some specious reasoning, I might be led to renounce the creed of my fathers. I first must be convinced that they lived in error. Tell me whether, respecting my father's memory, I ought to have such a good opinion of myself as to sit in judgment over him, with the intention of giving my sentence against him?"

My lively remonstrance moved Yusuf deeply, but after a few instants of silence he said to me,—

"With such feelings, my son, you are sure to find grace in the eyes of God, and you are, therefore, one of the elect. If you are in error, God alone can convince you of it, for no just man on earth can refute the sentiment you have just given expression to."

We spoke of many other things in a friendly manner, and in the evening we parted with the often repeated assurance of the warmest affection and of the most perfect devotion.

But my mind was full of our conversation, and as I went on pondering over the matter, I thought that Yusuf might be right in his opinion as to the essence of God, for it seemed evident that the Creator of all beings ought to be perfectly simple; but I thought at the same time how impossible it would be for me, because the

Christian religion had made a mistake, to accept the
Turkish creed, which might perhaps have just a conception of God, but which caused me to smile when I recollected that the man who had given birth to it had been
an arrant imposter. I had not the slightest idea, however, that Yusuf wished to make a convert of me.

The third time I dined with him religion was again
the subject of conversation.

"Do you believe, dear father, that the religion of
Mahomet is the only one in which salvation can be
secured?"

"No, my dear son, I am not certain of it, and no man
can have such a certainty; but I am sure that the Christian religion is not the true one, because it cannot be
universal."

"Why not?"

"Because there is neither bread nor wine to be found
in three-fourths of the world. Observe that the precepts
of the Koran can be followed everywhere."

I did not know how to answer, and I would not equiv-
ocate.

"If God cannot be matter," I said, "then He must be
a spirit?"

"We know what He is not, but we do not know what
He is: man cannot affirm that God is a spirit, because
he can only realize the idea in an abstract manner. God
is immaterial; that is the extent of our knowledge, and
it can never be greater."

I was reminded of Plato, who had said exactly the
same, and most certainly Yusuf had never read Plato.

He added that the existence of God could be useful
only to those who did not entertain a doubt of that existence, and that, as a natural consequence, Atheists must
be the most miserable of men. God has made in man

His own image in order that, amongst all the animals
created by Him, there should be one that can understand
and confess the existence of the Creator. Without man,
God would have no witness of His own glory, and man
must therefore understand that his first and highest
duty is to glorify God by practising justice and trusting
to His providence.

"Observe, my son, that God never abandons the man
who, in the midst of misfortunes, falls down in prayer
before Him, and that He often allows the wretch who
has no faith in prayer to die miserably."

"Yet we meet with Atheists who are fortunate and
happy."

"True; but, in spite of their tranquillity, I pity them
because they have no hope beyond this life, and are on
a level with animals. Besides, if they are philosophers,
they must linger in dark ignorance, and, if they never
think, they have no consolation, no resource, when adversity reaches them. God has made man in such a
manner that he cannot be happy unless he entertains no
doubt of the existence of his Divine Creator; in all sta-
tions of life man is naturally prone to believe in that
existence, otherwise man would never have admitted one
God, Creator of all beings and of all things."

"I should like to know why Atheism has only existed
in the systems of the learned, and never as a national
creed."

"Because the poor feel their wants much more than
the rich. There are amongst us a great many impious
men who deride the true believers because they have
faith in the pilgrimage to Mecca. Wretches that they
are! they ought to respect the ancient customs which,
exciting the devotion of fervent souls, feed religious principles, and impart courage under all misfortunes. With-

out such consolation, people would give way to all the excess of despair."

Much pleased with the attention I gave to all he said, Yusuf would thus yield to the inclination he felt to instruct me, and, on my side, feeling myself drawn towards him by the charm which amiable goodness exerts upon all hearts, I would often go and spend the day with him, even without any previous invitation, and Yusuf's friendship soon became one of my most precious treasures.

One morning, I told my janissary to take me to the palace of Ismail Effendi, in order to fulfil my promise to breakfast with him. He gave me the most friendly welcome, and after an excellent breakfast he invited me to take a walk in his garden. We found there a pretty summer-house which we entered, and Ismail attempted some liberties which were not at all to my taste, and which I resented by rising in a very abrupt manner. Seeing that I was angry, the Turk affected to approve my reserve, and said that he had only been joking. I left him after a few minutes, with the intention of not visiting him again, but I was compelled to do so, as I will explain by-and-by.

When I saw M. de Bonneval I told him what had happened and he said that, according to Turkish manners, Ismail had intended to give me a great proof of his friendship, but that I need not be afraid of the offence being repeated. He added that politeness required that I should visit him again, and that Ismail was, in spite of his failing, a perfect gentleman, who had at his disposal the most beautiful female slaves in Turkey.

Five or six weeks after the commencement of our intimacy, Yusuf asked me one day whether I was married. I answered that I was not; the conversation turned upon several moral questions, and at last fell upon chastity, which, in his opinion, could be accounted a virtue only if considered from one point of view, namely, that of total abstinence, but he added that it could not be acceptable to God, because it transgressed against the very first precept He had given to man.

"I would like to know, for instance," he said, "what name can be given to the chastity of your knights of Malta. They take a vow of chastity, but it does not mean that they will renounce women altogether, they renounce marriage only. Their chastity, and therefore chastity in general, is violated only by marriage; yet I observe that marriage is one of your sacraments. Therefore, those knights of Malta promise not to give way to lustful incontinence in the only case in which God might forgive it, but they reserve the license of being lustful unlawfully as often as they please, and whenever an opportunity may offer itself; and that immoral, illicit license is granted to them to such an extent, that they are allowed to acknowledge legally a child which can be born to them only through a double crime! The most revolting part of it all is that these children of crime, who are of course perfectly innocent themselves, are called natural children, as if children born in wedlock came into the world in an unnatural manner! In one word, my dear son, the vow of chastity is so much opposed to Divine precepts and to human nature that it can be agreeable neither to God nor to society, nor to those who pledge themselves to keep it, and, being in such opposition to every divine and human law, it must be a crime."

He enquired for the second time whether I was married; I replied in the negative, and added that I had no idea of ever getting married.

"What!" he exclaimed; "I must then believe that you are not a perfect man, or that you intend to work out your own damnation; unless you should tell me that you are a Christian only outwardly."

"I am a man in the very strongest sense of the word, and I am a true Christian. I must even confess that I adore women, and that I have not the slightest idea of depriving myself of the most delightful of all pleasures."

"According to your religion, damnation awaits you."

"I feel certain of the contrary, because, when we confess our sins, our priests are compelled to give us absolution."

"I know it, but you must agree with me that it is absurd to suppose that God will forgive a crime which you would, perhaps, not commit, if you did not think that, after confession, a priest, a man like you, will give you absolution. God forgives only the repenting sinner."

"No doubt of it, and confession supposes repentance; without it, absolution has no effect."

"Is onanism a crime amongst you?"

"Yes, even greater than lustful and illegitimate copulation."

"I was aware of it, and it has always caused me great surprise, for the legislator who enacts a law, the execution of which is impossible, is a fool. A man in good health, if he cannot have a woman, must necessarily have recourse to onanism, whenever imperious nature demands it, and the man who, from fear of polluting his soul, would abstain from it, would only draw upon himself a mortal disease."

"We believe exactly the reverse; we think that young people destroy their constitutions, and shorten their lives through self-abuse. In several communities they are closely watched, and are as much as possible deprived of every opportunity of indulging in that crime."

"Those who watch them are ignorant fools, and those who pay the watchers for such a service are even more stupid, because prohibition must excite the wish to break through such a tyrannical law, to set at nought an interdiction so contrary to nature."

"Yet it seems to me that self-abuse in excess must be injurious to health, for it must weaken and enervate."

"Certainly, because excess in everything is prejudicial and pernicious; but all such excess is the result of our severe prohibition. If girls are not interfered with in the matter of self-abuse, I do not see why boys should be."

"Because girls are very far from running the same risk; they do not lose a great deal in the action of self-abuse, and what they lose does not come from the same source whence flows the germinal liquid in men."

"I do not know, but we have some physicians who say that chlorosis in girls is the result of that pleasure indulged in to excess."

After many such conversations, in which he seemed to consider me as endowed with reason and talent, even when I was not of his opinion, Yusuf Ali surprised me greatly one day by the following proposition:

"I have two sons and a daughter. I no longer think of my sons, because they have received their share of my fortune. As far as my daughter is concerned she will, after my death, inherit all my possessions, and I am, besides, in a position while I am alive to promote the fortune of the man who may marry her. Five years ago I took a young wife, but she has not given me any progeny, and I know to a certainty that no offspring will bless our union. My daughter, whose name is Zelmi, is now fifteen; she is handsome, her eyes are black and lovely like her mother's, her hair is of the colour of the raven's wing, her complexion is animated alabaster; she is tall, well made, and of a sweet disposition; I have given her an education which would make her worthy of our master, the Sultan. She speaks Greek and Italian fluently, she sings delightfully, and accompanies herself on the harp; she can draw and embroider, and is always contented and cheerful. No living man can boast of having seen her features, and she loves me so dearly that my will is hers. My daughter is a treasure, and I offer her to you if you will consent to go for one year to Adrianople to reside with a relative of mine, who will teach you our religion, our language, and our manners. You will return at the end of one year, and as soon as you have become a Mussulman my daughter shall be your wife. You will find a house ready furnished, slaves of your own, and an income which will enable you to live in comfort. I have no more to say at present. I do not wish you to answer me either to-day, or to-morrow, or on any fixed day. You will give me your decision whenever you feel yourself called upon by your genius to give it, and you need not give me any answer unless you accept my offer, for, should you refuse it, it is not necessary that the subject should be again mentioned. I do not ask you to give full consideration to my proposal, for now that I have thrown the seed in your soul it must fructify. Without hurry, without delay, without anxiety, you can but obey the decrees of God and follow the immutable decision of fate. Such as I know you, I believe that you only require the possession of Zelmi to be competely happy, and that you will become one of the pillars of the Ottoman Empire."

Saying those words, Yusuf pressed me affectionately

in his arms, and left me by myself to avoid any answer I might be inclined to make. I went away in such wonder at all I had just heard, that I found myself at the Venetian Embassy without knowing how I had reached it. The *baili* thought me very pensive, and asked whether anything was the matter with me, but I did not feel disposed to gratify their curiosity. I found that Yusuf had indeed spoken truly: his proposal was of such importance that it was my duty, not only not to mention it to anyone, but even to abstain from thinking it over, until my mind had recovered its calm sufficiently to give me the assurance that no external consideration would weigh in the balance and influence my decision. I had to silence all my passions; prejudices, principles already formed, love, and even self-interest were to remain in a state of complete inaction.

When I awoke the next morning I began to think the matter over, and I soon discovered that, if I wanted to come to a decision, I ought not to ponder over it, as the more I considered the less likely I should be to decide. This was truly a case for the *sequere Deum* of the Stoics.

I did not visit Yusuf for four days, and when I called on him on the fifth day, we talked cheerfully without once mentioning his proposal, although it was very evident that we were both thinking of it. We remained thus for a fortnight, without ever alluding to the matter which engrossed all our thoughts, but our silence was not caused by dissimulation, or by any feeling contrary to our mutual esteem and friendship; and one day Yusuf suggested that very likely I had communicated his proposal to some wise friend, in order to obtain good advice. I immediately assured him it was not so, and that in a matter of so delicate a nature I thought I ought not to ask anybody's advice.

"I have abandoned myself to God, dear Yusuf, and, full of confidence in Him, I feel certain that I shall decide for the best, whether I make up my mind to become your son, or believe that I ought to remain what I am now. In the mean time, my mind ponders over it day and night, whenever I am quiet and feel myself composed and collected. When I come to a decision, I will impart it to you alone, and from that moment you shall have over me the authority of a father."

At these words the worthy Yusuf, his eyes wet with tears, placed his left hand over my head, and the first two fingers of the right hand on my forehead, saying:

"Continue to act in that way, my dear son, and be certain that you can never act wrongly."

"But," I said to him, "one thing might happen, Zelmi might not accept me."

"Have no anxiety about that. My daughter loves you; she, as well as my wife and her nurse, sees you every time that we dine together, and she listens to you with pleasure."

"Does she know that you are thinking of giving her to me as my wife?"

"She knows that I ardently wish you to become a true believer, so as to enable me to link her destiny to yours."

"I am glad that your habits do not permit you to let me see her, because she might dazzle me with her beauty, and then passion would soon have too much weight in the scale; I could no longer flatter myself that my decision had been taken in all the unbiased purity of my soul."

Yusuf was highly delighted at hearing me speak in that manner, and I spoke in perfect good faith. The mere idea of seeing Zelmi caused me to shudder. I felt that, if I had fallen in love with her, I would have be-

come a Mussulman in order to possess her, and that I
might soon have repented such a step, for the religion
of Mahomet presented to my eyes and to my mind nothing but a disagreeable picture, as well for this life as
for a future one. As for wealth, I did not think it deserved the immense sacrifice demanded from me. I could
find equal wealth in Europe, without stamping my forehead with the shameful brand of apostasy. I cared
deeply for the esteem of the persons of distinction who
knew me, and did not want to render myself unworthy
of it. Besides, I felt an immense desire to obtain fame
amongst civilized and polite nations, either in the fine
arts or in literature, or in any other honourable profession, and I could not reconcile myself to the idea of
abandoning to my equals the triumph which I might win
if I lived amongst them. It seemed to me, and I am still
of the same opinion, that the decision of wearing the
turban befits only a Christian despairing of himself and
at the end of his wits, and fortunately I was lost not
in that predicament. My greatest objection was to
spend a year in Adrianople to learn a language for
which I did not feel any liking, and which I should
therefore have learned but imperfectly. How could I, at
my age, renounce the prerogative, so pleasant to my
vanity, of being reputed a fine talker? and I had secured
that reputation wherever I was known. Then I would
often think that Zelmi, the eighth wonder of creation
in the eyes of her father might not appear such in my
eyes, and it would have been enough to make me
miserable, for Yusuf was likely to live twenty years
longer, and I felt that gratitude, as well as respect, would
never have permitted me to give that excellent man any
cause for unhappiness by ceasing to shew myself a devoted and faithful husband to his daughter. Such were

my thoughts, and, as Yusuf could not guess them, it was useless to make a confidant of him.

A few days afterwards, I dined with the Pacha Osman and met my Effendi Ismail. He was very friendly to me, and I reciprocated his attentions, though I paid no attention to the reproaches he addressed to me for not having come to breakfast with him for such a long time. I could not refuse to dine at his house with Bonneval, and he treated me to a very pleasing sight; Neapolitan slaves, men and women, performed a pantomime and some Calabrian dances. M. de Bonneval happened to mention the dance called *forlana,* and Ismail expressing a great wish to know it, I told him that I could give him that pleasure if I had a Venetian woman to dance with and a fiddler who knew the time. I took a violin, and played the *forlana,* but, even if the partner had been found, I could not play and dance at the same time.

Ismail whispered a few words to one of his eunuchs, who went out of the room and returned soon with some message that he delivered to him. The *effendi* told me that he had found the partner I wanted, and I answered that the musician could be had easily, if he would send a note to the Venetian Embassy, which was done at once. The Bailo Dona sent one of his men who played the violin well enough for dancing purposes. As soon as the musician was ready, a door was thrown open, and a fine looking woman came in, her face covered with a black velvet mask, such as we call *moretta* in Venice. The appearance of that beautiful masked woman surprised and delighted every one of the guests, for it was impossible to imagine a more interesting object, not only on account of the beauty of that part of the face which the mask left exposed, but also for the elegance of her shape, the

perfection of her figure, and the exquisite taste displayed
in her costume. The nymph took her place, I did the
same, and we danced the *forlana* six times without stopping.

I was in perspiration and out of breath, for the *forlana* is the most violent of our national dances; but my
beautiful partner stood near me without betraying the
slightest fatigue, and seemed to challenge me to a new
performance. At the round of the dance, which is the
most difficult step, she seemed to have wings. I was
astounded, for I had never seen anyone, even in Venice,
dance the *forlana* so splendidly. After a few minutes
rest, rather ashamed of my feeling tired, I went up to
her, and said, *Ancora sei, e poi basta, se non volete ve-
dermi a morire.* She would have answered me if she
had been able, but she wore one of those cruel masks
which forbid speech. But a pressure of her hand which
nobody could see made me guess all I wanted to know.
The moment we finished dancing the eunuch opened the
door, and my lovely partner disappeared.

Ismail could not thank me enough, but it was I who
owed him my thanks, for it was the only real pleasure
which I enjoyed in Constantinople. I asked him whether
the lady was from Venice, but he only answered by a
significant smile.

"The worthy Ismail," said M. de Bonneval to me, as
we were leaving the house late in the evening, "has been
to-day the dupe of his vanity, and I have no doubt that
he is sorry already for what he has done. To bring out
his beautiful slave to dance with you! According to
the prejudices of this country it is injurious to his dignity, for you are sure to have kindled an amorous flame
in the poor girl's breast. I would advise you to be careful and to keep on your guard, because she will try to

get up some intrigue with you; but be prudent, for intrigues are always dangerous in Turkey."

I promised to be prudent, but I did not keep my promise; for, three or four days afterwards, an old slave woman met me in the street, and offered to sell me for one piaster a tobacco-bag embroidered in gold; and as she put it in my hand she contrived to make me feel that there was a letter in the bag.

I observed that she tried to avoid the eyes of the janissary who was walking behind me; I gave her one piaster, she left me, and I proceeded toward Yusuf's house. He was not at home, and I went to his garden to read the letter with perfect freedom. It was sealed and without any address, and the slave might have made a mistake; but my curiosity was excited to the highest pitch; I broke the seal, and found the following note written in good enough Italian:

"Should you wish to see the person with whom you danced the *forlana*, take a walk towards evening in the garden beyond the fountain, and contrive to become acquainted with the old servant of the gardener by asking her for some lemonade. You may perchance manage to see your partner in the *forlana* without running any risk, even if you should happen to meet Ismail; she is a native of Venice. Be careful not to mention this invitation to any human being."

"I am not such a fool, my lovely countrywoman," I exclaimed, as if she had been present, and put the letter in my pocket. But at that very moment, a fine-looking elderly woman came out of a thicket, pronounced my name, and enquired what I wanted and how I had seen her. I answered that I had been speaking to the wind, not supposing that anyone could hear me, and without any more preparation, she abruptly told me that she was very glad of the opportunity of speaking with me, that she was from Rome, that she had brought up Zelmi, and had taught her to sing and to play the harp. She then praised highly the beauty and the excellent qualities of her pupil, saying that, if I saw her, I would certainly fall in love with her, and expressing how much she regretted that the law should not allow it.

"She sees us at this very moment," she added, "from behind that green window-blind, and we love you ever since Yusuf has informed us that you may, perhaps, become Zelmi's husband."

"May I mention our conversation to Yusuf?" I enquired.

"No."

Her answering in the negative made me understand that, if I had pressed her a little, she would have allowed me to see her lovely pupil, and perhaps it was with that intention that she had contrived to speak to me, but I felt great reluctance to do anything to displease my worthy host. I had another reason of even greater importance: I was afraid of entering an intricate maze in which the sight of a turban hovering over me made me shudder.

Yusuf came home, and far from being angry when he saw me with the woman, he remarked that I must have found much pleasure in conversing with a native of Rome, and he congratulated me upon the delight I must have felt in dancing with one of the beauties from the harem of the voluptuous Ismail.

"Then it must be a pleasure seldom enjoyed, if it is so much talked of?"

"Very seldom indeed, for there is amongst us an invincible prejudice against exposing our lovely women to the eyes of other men; but everyone may do as he

pleases in his own house: Ismail is a very worthy and a
very intelligent man."

"Is the lady with whom I danced known?"

"I believe not. She wore a mask, and everybody
knows that Ismail possesses half a dozen slaves of sur-
passing beauty."

I spent a pleasant day with Yusuf, and when I left
him, I ordered my janissary to take me to Ismail's. As
I was known by his servants, they allowed me to go in,
and I proceeded to the spot described in the letter. The
eunuch came to me, informed me that his master was
out, but that he would be delighted to hear of my having
taken a walk in the garden. I told him that I would
like a glass of lemonade, and he took me to the summer-
house, where I recognized the old woman who had sold
me the tobacco-pouch. The eunuch told her to give me
a glass of some liquid which I found delicious, and would
not allow me to give her any money. We then walked
together towards the fountain, but he told me abruptly
that we were to go back, as he saw three ladies to whom
he pointed, adding that, for the sake of decency, it was
necessary to avoid them. I thanked him for his attentions, left my compliments for Ismail, and went away
not dissatisfied with my first attempt, and with the hope
of being more fortunate another time.

The next morning I received a letter from Ismail inviting me to go fishing with him on the following day,
and stating that he intended to enjoy the sport by moonlight. I immediately gave way to my suppositions, and
I went so far as to fancy that Ismail might be capable
of arranging an interview between me and the lovely
Venetian. I did not mind his being present. I begged
permission of Chevalier Vénier to stop out of the palace
for one night, but he granted it with the greatest dif-

ficulty, because he was afraid of some love affair and of the results it might have. I took care to calm his anxiety as much as I could, but without acquainting him with all the circumstances of the case, for I thought I was wise in being discreet.

I was exact to the appointed time, and Ismail received me with the utmost cordiality, but I was surprised when I found myself alone with him in the boat. We had two rowers and a man to steer; we took some fish, fried in oil, and ate it in the summer-house. The moon shone brightly, and the night was delightful. Alone with Ismail, and knowing his unnatural tastes, I did not feel very comfortable for, in spite of what M. de Bonneval had told me, I was afraid lest the Turk should take a fancy to give me too great a proof of his friendship, and I did not relish our *tête-à-tête*. But my fears were groundless.

"Let us leave this place quietly," said Ismail, "I have just heard a slight noise which heralds something that will amuse us."

He dismissed his attendants, and took my hand, saying,—

"Let us go to a small room, the key of which I luckily have with me, but let us be careful not to make any noise. That room has a window overlooking the fountain where I think that two or three of my beauties have just gone to bathe. We will see them and enjoy a very pleasing sight, for they do not imagine that anyone is looking at them. They know that the place is forbidden to everybody except me."

We entered the room, we went to the window, and, the moon shining right over the basin of the fountain, we saw three nymphs who, now swimming, now standing or sitting on the marble steps, offered themselves to our eyes in every possible position, and in all the attitudes of graceful voluptuousness. Dear reader, I must not paint in too vivid colours the details of that beautiful picture, but if nature has endowed you with an ardent imagination and with equally ardent senses, you will easily imagine the fearful havoc which that unique, wonderful, and enchanting sight must have made upon my poor body.

A few days after that delightful fishing and bathing party by moonlight, I called upon Yusuf early in the morning; as it was raining, I could not go to the garden, and I went into the dining-room, in which I had never seen anyone. The moment I entered the room, a charming female form rose, covering her features with a thick veil which fell to the feet. A slave was sitting near the window, doing some tambour-work, but she did not move. I apologized, and turned to leave the room, but the lady stopped me, observing, with a sweet voice, that Yusuf had commanded her to entertain me before going out. She invited me to be seated, pointing to a rich cushion placed upon two larger ones, and I obeyed, while, crossing her legs, she sat down upon another cushion opposite to me. I thought I was looking upon Zelmi, and fancied that Yusuf had made up his mind to shew me that he was not less courageous than Ismail. Yet I was surprised, for, by such a proceeding, he strongly contradicted his maxims, and ran the risk of impairing the unbiassed purity of my consent by throwing love in the balance. But I had no fear of that, because, to become enamoured, I should have required to see her face.

"I suppose," said the veiled beauty, "that you do not know who I am?"

"I could not guess, if I tried."

"I have been for the last five years the wife of your friend, and I am a native of Scio. I was thirteen years of age when I became his wife."

I was greatly astonished to find that my Mussulman philosopher had gone so far as to allow me to converse with his wife, but I felt more at ease after I had received that information, and fancied that I might carry the adventure further, but it would be necessary to see the lady's face, for a finely-dressed body, the head of which is not seen, excites but feeble desires. The fire lighted by amorous desires is like a fire of straw; the moment it burns up it is near its end. I had before me a magnificent appearance, but I could not see the soul of the image, for a thick gauze concealed it from my hungry gaze. I could see arms as white as alabaster, and hands like those of Alcina, *dove ne nodo apparisce ne vena accede,* and my active imagination fancied that all the rest was in harmony with those beautiful specimens, for the graceful folds of the muslin, leaving the outline all its perfection, hid from me only the living satin of the surface; there was no doubt that everything was lovely, but I wanted to see, in the expression of her eyes, that all that my imagination created had life and was endowed with feeling. The Oriental costume is a beautiful varnish placed upon a porcelain vase to protect from the touch the colours of the flowers and of the design, without lessening the pleasure of the eyes. Yusuf's wife was not dressed like a sultana; she wore the costume of Scio, with a short skirt which concealed neither the perfection of the leg nor the round form of the thigh, nor the voluptuous plump fall of the hips, nor the slender, well-made waist encompassed in a splendid band embroidered in silver and covered with arabesques. Above all those beauties, I could see the shape of two globes

which Apelles would have taken for the model of those
of his lovely Venus, and the rapid, inequal movement
of which proved to me that those ravishing hillocks were
animated. The small valley left between them, and
which my eyes greedily feasted upon, seemed to me a
lake of nectar, in which my burning lips longed to
quench their thirst with more ardour than they would
have drunk from the cup of the gods.

Enraptured, unable to control myself, I thrust my
arm forward by a movement almost independent of my
will, and my hand, too audacious, was on the point of
lifting the hateful veil, but she prevented me by raising
herself quickly on tiptoe, upbraiding me at the same time
for my perfidious boldness, with a voice as commanding
as her attitude.

"Dost thou deserve," she said, "Yusuf's friendship,
when thou abusest the sacred laws of hospitality by insulting his wife?"

"Madam, you must kindly forgive me, for I never had
any intention to insult you. In my country the lowest
of men may fix his eyes upon the face of a queen."

"Yes, but he cannot tear off her veil, if she chooses
to wear it. Yusuf shall avenge me."

The threat, and the tone in which it was pronounced,
frightened me. I threw myself at her feet, and succeeded
in calming her anger.

"Take a seat," she said.

And she sat down herself, crossing her legs with so
much freedom that I caught a glimpse of charms which
would have caused me to lose all control over myself
if the delightful sight had remained one moment longer
exposed to my eyes. I then saw that I had gone the
wrong way to work, and I felt vexed with myself; but it
was too late.

"Art thou excited?" she said.

"How could I be otherwise," I answered, "when thou art scorching me with an ardent fire?"

I had become more prudent, and I sezied her hand without thinking any more of her face.

"Here is my husband," she said, and Yusuf came into the room. We rose, Yusuf embraced me, I complimented him, the slave left the room. Yusuf thanked his wife for having entertained me, and offered her his arm to take her to her own apartment. She took it, but when she reached the door, she raised her veil, and kissing her husband she allowed me to see her lovely face as if it had been done unwittingly. I followed her with my eyes as long as I could, and Yusuf, coming back to me, said with a laugh that his wife had offered to dine with us.

"I thought," I said to him, "that I had Zelmi before me."

"That would have been too much against our established rules. What I have done is not much, but I do not know an honest man who would be bold enough to bring his daughter into the presence of a stranger."

"I think your wife must be handsome; is she more beautiful than Zelmi?"

"My daughter's beauty is cheerful, sweet, and gentle; that of Sophia is proud and haughty. She will be happy after my death. The man who will marry her will find her a virgin."

I gave an account of my adventure to M. de Bonneval, somewhat exaggerating the danger I had run in trying to raise the veil of the handsome daughter of Scio.

"She was laughing at you," said the count, "and you ran no danger. She felt very sorry, believe me, to have to deal with a novice like you. You have been playing

the comedy in the French fashion, when you ought to
have gone straight to the point. What on earth did you
want to see her nose for? She knew very well that she
would have gained nothing by allowing you to see her.
You ought to have secured the essential point. If I
were young I would perhaps manage to give her a revenge, and to punish my friend Yusuf. You have given
that lovely woman a poor opinion of Italian valour.
The most reserved of Turkish women has no modesty
except on her face, and, with her veil over it, she knows
to a certainty that she will not blush at anything. I
am certain that your beauty keeps her face covered
whenever our friend Yusuf wishes to joke with her."

"She is yet a virgin."

"Rather a difficult thing to admit, my good friend;
but I know the daughters of Scio; they have a talent
for counterfeiting virginity."

Yusuf never paid me a similar compliment again, and
he was quite right.

A few days after, I happened to be in the shop of an
Armenian merchant, looking at some beautiful goods,
when Yusuf entered the shop and praised my taste; but,
although I had admired a great many things, I did not
buy, because I thought they were too dear. I said so to
Yusuf, but he remarked that they were, on the contrary, very cheap, and he purchased them all. We parted
company at the door, and the next morning I received all
the beautiful things he had bought; it was a delicate attention of my friend, and to prevent my refusal of such
a splendid present, he had enclosed a note stating that,
on my arrival in Corfu, he would let me know to whom
the goods were to be delivered. He had thus sent me
gold and silver filigrees from Damascus, portfolios,
scarfs, belts, handkerchiefs and pipes, the whole worth

four or five hundred piasters. When I called to thank him, I compelled him to confess that it was a present offered by his friendship.

The day before my departure from Constantinople, the excellent man burst into tears as I bade him adieu, and my grief was as great as his own. He told me that, by not accepting the offer of his daughter's hand, I had so strongly captivated his esteem that his feelings for me could not have been warmer if I had become his son. When I went on board ship with the Bailo Jean Dona, I found another case given to me by him, containing two quintals of the best Mocha coffee, one hundred pounds of tobacco leaves, two large flagons filled, one with Zabandi tobacco, the other with camussa, and a magnificent pipe tube of jessamine wood, covered with gold filigrane, which I sold in Corfu for one hundred sequins. I had not it in my power to give my generous Turk any mark of my gratitude until I reached Corfu, but there I did not fail to do so. I sold all his beautiful presents, which made me the possessor of a small fortune.

Ismail gave me a letter for the Chevalier de Lezze, but I could not forward it to him because I unfortunately lost it; he presented me with a barrel of hydromel, which I turned likewise into money. M. de Bonneval gave me a letter for Cardinal Acquaviva, which I sent to Rome with an account of my journey, but his eminence did not think fit to acknowledge the receipt of either. Bonneval made me a present of twelve bottles of malmsey from Ragusa, and of twelve bottles of genuine scopolo—a great rarity, with which I made a present in Corfu which proved very useful to me, as the reader will discover.

The only foreign minister I saw much in Constantinople was the lord marshal of Scotland, the celebrated

Keith, who represented the King of Prussia, and who, six years later was of great service to me in Paris.

We sailed from Constantinople in the beginning of September in the same man-of-war which had brought us, and we reached Corfu in fourteen days. The Bailo Dona did not land. He had with him eight splendid Turkish horses; I saw two of them still alive in Gorizia in the year 1773.

As soon as I had landed with my luggage, and had engaged a rather mean lodging, I presented myself to M. André Dolfin, the *proveditore-generale,* who promised me again that I should soon be promoted to a lieutenancy. After my visit to him, I called upon M. Camporese, my captain, and was well received by him. My third visit was to the commander of galleases, M. D——R——, to whom M. Antonio Dolfin, with whom I had travelled from Venice to Corfu, had kindly recommended me. After a short conversation, he asked me if I would remain with him with the title of adjutant. I did not hesitate one instant, but accepted, saying how deeply honoured I felt by his offer, and assuring him that he would always find me ready to carry out his orders. He immediately had me taken to my room, and, the next day, I found myself established in his house. I obtained from my captain a French soldier to serve me, and I was well pleased when I found that the man was a hairdresser by trade, and a great talker by nature, for he could take care of my beautiful head of hair, and I wanted to practise French conversation. He was a good-for-nothing fellow, a drunkard and a debauchee, a peasant from Picardy, and he could hardly read or write, but I did not mind all that; all I wanted from him was to serve me, and to talk to me, and his French was pretty good. He was an amusing rogue, knowing by heart a quantity of erotic songs and of smutty stories which he could tell in the most laughable manner.

When I had sold my stock of goods from Constantinople (except the wines), I found myself the owner of nearly five hundred sequins. I redeemed all the articles which I had pledged in the hands of Jews, and turned into money everything of which I had no need. I was determined not to play any longer as a dupe, but to secure in gambling all the advantages which a prudent young man could obtain without sullying his honour.

I must now make my readers acquainted with the sort of life we were at that time leading in Corfu. As to the city itself, I will not describe it, because there are already many descriptions better than the one I could offer in these pages.

We had then in Corfu the *proveditore-generale* who had sovereign authority, and lived in a style of great magnificence. That post was then filled by M. André Dolfin, a man sixty years of age, strict, headstrong, and ignorant. He no longer cared for women, but liked to be courted by them. He received every evening, and the supper-table was always laid for twenty-four persons.

We had three field-officers of the marines who did duty on the galleys, and three field-officers for the troops of the line on board the men-of-war. Each galeass had a captain called *sopracomito,* and we had ten of those captains; we had likewise ten commanders, one for each man-of-war, including three *capi di mare,* or admirals. They all belonged to the nobility of Venice. Ten young Venetian noblemen, from twenty to twenty-two years of age, were at Corfu as midshipmen in the navy. We had, besides, about a dozen civil clerks in the police of the island, or in the administration of justice, entitled *grandi officiali di terra.* Those who were blessed with handsome wives had the pleasure of seeing their houses very much frequented by admirers who aspired to win the favours of the ladies, but there was not much heroic love-making, perhaps for the reason that there were then in Corfu many Aspasias whose favours could be had for money. Gambling was allowed everywhere, and that all absorbing passion was very prejudicial to the emotions of the heart.

The lady who was then most eminent for beauty and gallantry was Madame F——. Her husband, captain of a galley, had come to Corfu with her the year before, and madam had greatly astonished all the naval officers. Thinking that she had the privilege of the choice, she had given the preference to M. D—— R——, and had dismissed all the suitors who presented themselves. M. F—— had married her on the very day she had left the convent; she was only seventeen years of age then, and he had brought her on board his galley immediately after the marriage ceremony.

I saw her for the first time at the dinner-table on the very day of my installation at M. D—— R——'s, and she made a great impression upon me. I thought I was gazing at a supernatural being, so infinitely above all the women I had ever seen, that it seemed impossible to fall in love with her. She appeared to me of a nature different and so greatly superior to mine that I did not see the possibility of rising up to her. I even went so far as to persuade myself that nothing but a Platonic friendship could exist between her and M. D—— R——, and that M. F—— was quite right now not to shew any jealousy. Yet, that M. F—— was a perfect fool, and certainly not worthy of such a woman.

The impression made upon me by Madame F—— was too ridiculous to last long, and the nature of it soon changed, but in a novel manner, at least as far as I was concerned.

My position as adjutant procured me the honour of dining at M. D—— R——'s table, but nothing more. The other adjutant, like me, an ensign in the army, but the greatest fool I had ever seen, shared that honour with me. We were not, however, considered as guests, for nobody ever spoke to us, and, what is more, no one ever honoured us with a look. It used to put me in a rage. I knew very well that people acted in that manner through no real contempt for us, but it went very hard with me. I could very well understand that my colleague, Sanzonio, should not complain of such treatment, because he was a blockhead, but I did not feel disposed to allow myself to be put on a par with him. At the end of eight or ten days, Madame F——, not having condescended to cast one glance upon my person, began to appear disagreeable to me. I felt piqued, vexed, provoked, and the more so because I could not suppose that the lady acted in that manner wilfully and purposely; I would have been highly pleased if there had been premeditation on her part. I felt satisfied that I was a nobody in her estimation, and as I was conscious of being somebody, I wanted her to know it. At last a circumstance offered itself in which, thinking that she could address me, she was compelled to look at me.

M. D—— R—— having observed that a very, very fine turkey had been placed before me, told me to carve it, and I immediately went to work. I was not a skilful carver, and Madame F——, laughing at my want of dexterity, told me that, if I had not been certain of performing my task with credit to myself, I ought not to have undertaken it. Full of confusion, and unable to answer her as my anger prompted, I sat down, with my heart overflowing with spite and hatred against her. To crown my rage, having one day to address me, she asked me what was my name. She had seen me every day for a fortnight, ever since I had been the adjutant of M. D—— R——; therefore she ought to have known my name. Besides, I had been very lucky at the gaming-table, and I had become rather famous in Corfu. My anger against Madame F—— was at its height.

I had placed my money in the hands of a certain Maroli, a major in the army and a gamester by profession, who held the faro bank at the coffee-house. We were partners; I helped him when he dealt, and he rendered me the same office when I held the cards, which was often the case, because he was not generally liked. He used to hold the cards in a way which frightened the punters; my manners were very different, and I was very lucky. Besides I was easy and smiling when my bank was losing, and I won without shewing any avidity, and that is a manner which always pleases the punters.

This Maroli was the man who had won all my money during my first stay in Corfu, and finding, when I returned, that I was resolved not to be duped any more, he judged me worthy of sharing the wise maxims without which gambling must necessarily ruin all those who meddle with it. But as Maroli had won my confidence only to a very slight extent, I was very careful. We made up our accounts every night, as soon as playing was over; the cashier kept the capital of the bank, the winnings were divided, and each took his share away.

Lucky at play, enjoying good health and the friendship of my comrades, who, whenever the opportunity offered, always found me generous and ready to serve them, I would have been well pleased with my position if I had been a little more considered at the table of M. D—— R——, and treated with less haughtiness by his lady who, without any reason, seemed disposed to humiliate me. My self-love was deeply hurt, I hated her, and, with such a disposition of mind, the more I admired the perfection of her charms, the more I found her deficient in wit and intelligence. She might have made the conquest of my heart without bestowing hers upon me, for all I wanted was not to be compelled to hate her, and I could not understand what pleasure it could be for her to be detested, while with only a little kindness she could have been adored. I could not ascribe her manner to a spirit of coquetry, for I had never given her the slightest proof of the opinion I entertained of her beauty, and I could not therefore attribute her behaviour to a passion which might have rendered me disagreeable in her eyes; M. D—— R—— seemed to interest her only in a very slight manner, and as to her husband, she cared nothing for him. In short, that charming woman made me very unhappy, and I was angry with myself because I felt that, if it had not been for the manner in which she treated me, I would not have thought of her, and my vexation was increased by the feeling of hatred entertained by my heart against her, a feeling which until then I had never known to exist in me, and the discovery of which overwhelmed me with confusion.

One day a gentleman handed me, as we were leaving the dinner-table, a roll of gold that he had lost upon trust; Madame F—— saw it, and she said to me very abruptly,—

"What do you do with your money?"

"I keep it, madam, as a provision against possible losses."

"But as you do not indulge in any expense it would be better for you not to play; it is time wasted."

"Time given to pleasure is never time lost, madam; the only time which a young man wastes is that which is consumed in weariness, because when he is a prey to *ennui* he is likely to fall a prey to love, and to be despised by the object of his affection."

"Very likely; but you amuse yourself with hoarding up your money, and shew yourself to be a miser, and a miser is not less contemptible than a man in love. Why do you not buy yourself a pair of gloves?"

You may be sure that at these words the laughter was all on her side, and my vexation was all the greater because I could not deny that she was quite right. It was the adjutant's business to give the ladies an arm to their carriages, and it was not proper to fulfil that duty without gloves. I felt mortified, and the reproach of avarice hurt me deeply. I would a thousand times rather that she had laid my error to a want of education; and yet, so full of contradictions is the human heart, instead of making amends by adopting an appearance of elegance which the state of my finances enabled me to keep up, I did not purchase any gloves, and I resolved to avoid her and to abandon her to the insipid and dull gallantry of Sanzonio, who sported gloves, but whose teeth were rotten, whose breath was putrid, who wore a wig, and whose face seemed to be covered with shrivelled yellow parchment.

I spent my days in a continual state of rage and spite, and the most absurd part of it all was that I felt unhappy because I could not control my hatred for that woman whom, in good conscience, I could not find guilty of anything. She had for me neither love nor dislike, which was quite natural; but being young and disposed

to enjoy myself I had become, without any wilful malice
on her part, an eye-sore to her and the butt of her ban-
tering jokes, which my sensitiveness exaggerated greatly.
For all that I had an ardent wish to punish her and to
make her repent. I thought of nothing else. At one
time I would think of devoting all my intelligence and
all my money to kindling an amorous passion in her
heart, and then to revenge myself by treating her with
contempt. But I soon realized the impracticability of
such a plan, for even supposing that I should succeed in
finding my way to her heart, was I the man to resist
my own success with such a woman? I certainly could
not flatter myself that I was so strong-minded. But
I was the pet child of fortune, and my position was suddenly altered.

M. D—— R—— having sent me with dispatches to
M. de Condulmer, captain of a *galeazza*, I had to wait
until midnight to deliver them, and when I returned I
found that M. D—— R—— had retired to his apartment for the night. As soon as he was visible in the
morning I went to him to render an account of my
mission. I had been with him only a few minutes when
his valet brought a letter saying that Madame F——'s
adjutant was waiting for an answer. M. D—— R——
read the note, tore it to pieces, and in his excitement
stamped with his foot upon the fragments. He walked
up and down the room for a little time, then wrote an
answer and rang for the adjutant, to whom he delivered
it. He then recovered his usual composure, concluded
the perusal of the dispatch sent by M. de Condulmer,
and told me to write a letter. He was looking it over
when the valet came in, telling me that Madame F——
desired to see me. M. D—— R—— told me that he did
not require my services any more for the present, and

that I might go. I left the room, but I had not gone ten yards when he called me back to remind me that my duty was to know nothing; I begged to assure him that I was well aware of that. I ran to Madame F——'s house, very eager to know what she wanted with me. I was introduced immediately, and I was greatly surprised to find her sitting up in bed, her countenance flushed and excited, and her eyes red from the tears she had evidently just been shedding. My heart was beating quickly, yet I did not know why.

"Pray be seated," she said, "I wish to speak with you."

"Madam," I answered, "I am not worthy of so great a favour, and I have not yet done anything to deserve it; allow me to remain standing."

She very likely recollected that she had never been so polite before, and dared not press me any further. She collected her thoughts for an instant or two, and said to me:

"Last evening my husband lost two hundred sequins upon trust at your faro bank; he believed that amount to be in my hands, and I must therefore give it to him immediately, as he is bound in honour to pay his losses to-day. Unfortunately I have disposed of the money, and I am in great trouble. I thought you might tell Maroli that I have paid you the amount lost by my husband. Here is a ring of some value; keep it until the 1st of January, when I will return the two hundred sequins for which I am ready to give you my note of hand."

"I accept the note of hand, madam, but I cannot consent to deprive you of your ring. I must also tell you that M. F—— must go himself to the bank, or send some one there, to redeem his debt. Within ten minutes you shall have the amount you require."

I left her without waiting for an answer, and I returned within a few minutes with the two hundred ducats, which I handed to her, and putting in my pocket her note of hand which she had just written, I bowed to take my leave, but she addressed to me these precious words:

"I believe, sir, that if I had known that you were so well disposed to oblige me, I could not have made up my mind to beg that service from you."

"Well, madam, for the future be quite certain that there is not a man in the world capable of refusing you such an insignificant service whenever you will condescend to ask for it in person."

"What you say is very complimentary, but I trust never to find myself again under the necessity of making such a cruel experiment."

I left Madame F——, thinking of the shrewdness of her answer. She had not told me that I was mistaken, as I had expected she would, for that would have caused her some humiliation: she knew that I was with M. D—— R—— when the adjutant had brought her letter, and she could not doubt that I was aware of the refusal she had met with. The fact of her not mentioning it proved to me that she was jealous of her own dignity; it afforded me great gratification, and I thought her worthy of adoration. I saw clearly that she could have no love for M. D—— R——, and that she was not loved by him, and the discovery made me leap for joy. From that moment I felt I was in love with her, and I conceived the hope that she might return my ardent affection.

The first thing I did, when I returned to my room, was to cross out with ink every word of her note of hand, except her name, in such a manner that it was impossible to guess at the contents, and putting it in an envelope carefully sealed, I deposited it in the hands of a public notary who stated, in the receipt he gave me of the envelope, that he would deliver it only to Madame F——, whenever she should request its delivery.

The same evening M. F—— came to the bank, paid me, played with cash in hand, and won some fifty ducats. What caused me the greatest surprise was that M. D—— R—— continued to be very gracious to Madame F——, and that she remained exactly the same towards him as she used to be before. He did not even enquire what she wanted when she had sent for me. But if she did not seem to change her manner towards my master, it was a very different case with me, for whenever she was opposite to me at dinner, she often addressed herself to me, and she thus gave me many opportunities of shewing my education and my wit in amusing stories or in remarks, in which I took care to blend instruction with witty jests. At that time I had the great talent of making others laugh while I kept a serious countenance myself. I had learnt that accomplishment from M. de Malipiero, my first master in the art of good breeding, who used to say to me,—

"If you wish your audience to cry, you must shed tears yourself, but if you wish to make them laugh, you must contrive to look as serious as a judge."

In everything I did, in every word I uttered, in the presence of Madame F——, the only aim I had was to please her, but I did not wish her to suppose so, and I never looked at her unless she spoke to me. I wanted to force her curiosity, to compel her to suspect—nay, to guess my secret, but without giving her any advantage over me: it was necessary for me to proceed by slow degrees. In the mean time, and until I should have a greater happiness, I was glad to see that my money, that magic talisman, and my good conduct, obtained me a consideration much greater than I could have hoped to obtain either through my position, or from my age, or in consequence of any talent I might have shewn in the profession I had adopted.

Towards the middle of November, the soldier who acted as my servant was attacked with inflammation of the chest; I gave notice of it to the captain of his company, and he was carried to the hospital. On the fourth day I was told that he would not recover, and that he had received the last sacraments; in the evening I happened to be at his captain's when the priest who had attended him came to announce his death, and to deliver a small parcel which the dying man had entrusted to him to be given up to his captain only after his death. The parcel contained a brass seal engraved with ducal arms, a certificate of baptism, and a sheet of paper covered with writing in French. Captain Camporèse, who only spoke Italian, begged me to translate the paper, the contents of which were as follows:

"My will is that this paper, which I have written and signed with my own hand, shall be delivered to my captain only after I have breathed my last: until then, my confessor shall not make any use of it, for I entrust it to his hands only under the seal of confession. I entreat my captain to have me buried in a vault from which my body can be exhumed in case the duke, my father, should request its exhumation. I entreat him likewise to forward my certificate of baptism, the seal with the armorial bearings of my family, and a legal certificate of my birth to the French ambassador in Venice, who will send the whole to the duke, my father, my rights of primogeniture belonging, after my demise, to the prince, my brother. In faith of which I have signed and sealed these presents: François VI. Charles Philippe Louis Foucaud, Prince de la Rochefoucault."

The certificate of baptism, delivered at St. Sulpice gave the same names, and the title of the father was François V. The name of the mother was Gabrielle du Plessis.

As I was concluding my translation I could not help bursting into loud laughter; but the foolish captain, who thought my mirth out of place, hurried out to render an account of the affair to the *proveditore-generale,* and I went to the coffee-house, not doubting for one moment that his excellency would laugh at the captain, and that the post-mortem buffoonery would greatly amuse the whole of Corfu.

I had known in Rome, at Cardinal Acquaviva's, the Abbé de Liancourt, great-grandson of Charles, whose sister, Gabrielle du Plessis, had been the wife of François V., but that dated from the beginning of the last century. I had made a copy from the records of the cardinal of the account of certain circumstances which the Abbé de Liancourt wanted to communicate to the court of Spain, and in which there were a great many particulars respecting the house of Du Plessis. I thought at the same time that the singular imposture of La Valeur (such was the name by which my soldier generally went) was absurd and without a motive, since it was to be known only after his death, and could not therefore prove of any advantage to him.

Half an hour afterwards, as I was opening a fresh pack of cards, the Adjutant Sanzonio came in, and told the important news in the most serious manner. He had just come from the office of the *proveditore,* where Captain Camporèse had run in the utmost hurry to deposit in the hands of his excellency the seal and the papers of the deceased prince. His excellency had immediately issued his orders for the burial of the prince in a vault with all the honours due to his exalted rank. Another half hour passed, and M. Minolto, adjutant of the *proveditore-generale*, came to inform me that his excellency wanted to see me. I passed the cards to Major Maroli, and went to his excellency's house. I found him at supper with several ladies, three or four naval commanders, Madame F——, and M. D—— R——.

"So, your servant was a prince!" said the old general to me.

"Your excellency, I never would have suspected it, and even now that he is dead I do not believe it."

"Why? He is dead, but he was not insane. You have seen his armorial bearings, his certificate of baptism, as well as what he wrote with his own hand. When a man is so near death, he does not fancy practical jokes."

"If your excellency is satisfied of the truth of the story, my duty is to remain silent."

"The story cannot be anything but true, and your doubts surprise me."

"I doubt, monsignor, because I happen to have positive information respecting the families of La Rochefoucault and Du Plessis. Besides, I have seen too much of the man. He was not a madman, but he certainly was an extravagant jester. I have never seen him write, and he has told me himself a score of times that he had never learned."

"The paper he has written proves the contrary. His arms have the ducal bearings; but perhaps you are not aware that M. de la Rochefoucault is a duke and peer of the French realm?"

"I beg your eminence's pardon; I know all about it;
I know even more, for I know that François VI. married
a daughter of the house of Vivonne."

"You know nothing."

When I heard this remark, as foolish as it was rude,
I resolved on remaining silent, and it was with some
pleasure that I observed the joy felt by all the male
guests at what they thought an insult and a blow to my
vanity. An officer remarked that the deceased was a
fine man, a witty man, and had shewn wonderful cleverness in keeping up his assumed character so well that
no one ever had the faintest suspicion of what he really
was. A lady said that, if she had known him, she would
have been certain to find him out. Another flatterer, belonging to that mean, contemptible race always to be
found near the great and wealthy of the earth, assured
us that the late prince had always shewn himself cheerful, amiable, obliging, devoid of haughtiness towards his
comrades, and that he used to sing beautifully. "He
was only twenty-five years of age," said Madame Sagredo, looking me full in the face, "and if he was endowed
with all those qualities, you must have discovered them."

"I can only give you, madam, a true likeness of the
man, such as I have seen him. Always gay, often even
to folly, for he could throw a somersault beautifully;
singing songs of a very erotic kind, full of stories and of
popular tales of magic, miracles, and ghosts, and a thousand marvellous feats which common-sense refused to
believe, and which, for that very reason, provoked the
mirth of his hearers. His faults were that he was
drunken, dirty, quarrelsome, dissolute, and somewhat of
a cheat. I put up with all his deficiences, because he
dressed my hair to my taste, and his constant chattering
offered me the opportunity of practising the colloquial

French which cannot be acquired from books. He has always assured me that he was born in Picardy, the son of a common peasant, and that he had deserted from the French army. He may have deceived me when he said that he could not write."

Just then Camporèse rushed into the room, and announced that La Veleur was yet breathing. The general, looking at me significantly, said that he would be delighted if the man could be saved.

"And I likewise, monsignor, but his confessor will certainly kill him to-night."

"Why should the father confessor kill him?"

"To escape the galleys to which your excellency would not fail to send him for having violated the secrecy of the confessional."

Everybody burst out laughing, but the foolish old general knitted his brows. The guests retired soon afterwards, and Madame F——, whom I had preceded to the carriage, M. D—— R—— having offered her his arm, invited me to get in with her, saying that it was raining. It was the first time that she had bestowed such an honour upon me.

"I am of your opinion about that prince," she said, "but you have incurred the displeasure of the *proveditore*."

"I am very sorry, madam, but it could not have been avoided, for I cannot help speaking the truth openly."

"You might have spared him," remarked M. D—— R——, "the cutting jest of the confessor killing the false prince."

"You are right, sir, but I thought it would make him laugh as well as it made madam and your excellency. In conversation people generally do not object to a witty jest causing merriment and laughter."

"True; only those who have not wit enough to laugh do not like the jest."

"I bet a hundred sequins that the madman will recover, and that, having the general on his side, he will reap all the advantages of his imposture. I long to see him treated as a prince, and making love to Madame Sagredo."

Hearing the last words, Madame F——, who did not like Madame Sagredo, laughed heartily, and, as we were getting out of the carriage, M. D—— R—— invited me to accompany them upstairs. He was in the habit of spending half an hour alone with her at her own house when they had taken supper together with the general, for her husband never shewed himself. It was the first time that the happy couple admitted a third person to their *tête-à-tête*. I felt very proud of the compliment thus paid to me, and I thought it might have important results for me. My satisfaction, which I concealed as well as I could, did not prevent me from being very gay and from giving a comic turn to every subject brought forward by the lady or by her lord.

We kept up our pleasant trio for four hours, and returned to the mansion of M. D—— R—— only at two o'clock in the morning. It was during that night that Madame F—— and M. D—— R—— really made my acquaintance. Madame F—— told him that she had never laughed so much, and that she had never imagined that a conversation, in appearance so simple, could afford so much pleasure and merriment. On my side, I discovered in her so much wit and cheerfulness, that I became deeply enamoured, and went to bed fully satisfied that, in the future, I could not keep up the show of indifference which I had so far assumed towards her.

When I woke up the next morning, I heard from the new soldier who served me that La Valeur was better, and had been pronounced out of danger by the physician. At dinner the conversation fell upon him, but I did not open my lips. Two days afterwards, the general gave orders to have him removed to a comfortable apartment, sent him a servant, clothed him, and the over-credulous *proveditore* having paid him a visit, all the naval commanders and officers thought it their duty to imitate him, and to follow his example: the general curiosity was excited, there was a rush to see the new prince. M. D—— R—— followed his leaders, and Madame Sagredo, having set the ladies in motion, they all called upon him, with the exception of Madame F——, who told me laughingly that she would not pay him a visit unless I would consent to introduce her. I begged to be excused. The knave was called your highness, and the wonderful prince styled Madame Sagredo his princess. M. D—— R—— tried to persuade me to call upon the rogue, but I told him that I had said too much, and that I was neither courageous nor mean enough to retract my words. The whole imposture would soon have been discovered if anyone had possessed a peerage, but it just happened that there was not a copy in Corfu, and the French consul, a fat blockhead, like many other consuls, knew nothing of family trees. The madcap La Valeur began to walk out a week after his metamorphosis into a prince. He dined and had supper every day with the general, and every evening he was present at the reception, during which, owing to his intemperance, he always went fast asleep. Yet, there were two reasons which kept up the belief of his being a prince: the first was that he did not seem afraid of the news expected from Venice, where the *proveditore* had written immediately after the discovery; the second was that he solicited from the bishop the punishment of the priest who had betrayed his secret by violating the seal of confession. The poor priest had already been sent to prison, and the *proveditore* had not the courage to defend him. The new prince had been invited to dinner by all the naval officers, but M. D—— R—— had not made up his mind to imitate them so far, because Madame F—— had clearly warned him that she would dine at her own house on the day he was invited. I had likewise respectfully intimated that, on the same occasion, I would take the liberty of dining somewhere else.

I met the prince one day as I was coming out of the old fortress leading to the esplanade. He stopped, and reproached me for not having called upon him. I laughed, and advised him to think of his safety before the arrival of the news which would expose all the imposture, in which case the *proveditore* was certain to treat him very severely. I offered to help him in his flight from Corfu, and to get a Neapolitan captain, whose ship was ready to sail, to conceal him on board; but the fool, instead of accepting my offer, loaded me with insults.

He was courting Madame Sagredo, who treated him very well, feeling proud that a French prince should have given her the preference over all the other ladies. One day that she was dining in great ceremony at M. D—— R——'s house, she asked me why I had advised the prince to run away.

"I have it from his own lips," she added, "and he cannot make out your obstinacy in believing him an impostor."

"I have given him that advice, madam, because my heart is good, and my judgment sane."

"Then we are all of us as many fools, the *proveditore* included?"

"That deduction would not be right, madam. An opinion contrary to that of another does not necessarily make a fool of the person who entertains it. It might possibly turn out, in ten or twelve days, that I have been entirely mistaken myself, but I should not consider myself a fool in consequence. In the mean time, a lady of your intelligence must have discovered whether that man is a peasant or a prince by his education and manners. For instance, does he dance well?"

"He does not know one step, but he is the first to laugh about it; he says he never would learn dancing."

"Does he behave well at table?"

"Well, he doesn't stand on ceremony. He does not want his plate to be changed, he helps himself with his spoon out of the dishes; he does not know how to check an eructation or a yawn, and if he feels tired he leaves the table. It is evident that he has been very badly brought up."

"And yet he is very pleasant, I suppose. Is he clean and neat?"

"No, but then he is not yet well provided with linen."

"I am told that he is very sober."

"You are joking. He leaves the table intoxicated twice a day, but he ought to be pitied, for he cannot drink wine and keep his head clear. Then he swears like a trooper, and we all laugh, but he never takes offence."

"Is he witty?"

"He has a wonderful memory, for he tells us new stories every day."

"Does he speak of his family?"

"Very often of his mother, whom he loved tenderly. She was a Du Plessis."

"If his mother is still alive she must be a hundred and fifty years old."

"What nonsense!"

"Not at all; she was married in the days of Marie de Médicis."

"But the certificate of baptism names the prince's mother, and his seal——"

"Does he know what armorial bearings he has on that seal?"

"Do you doubt it?"

"Very strongly, or rather I am certain that he knows nothing about it."

We left the table, and the prince was announced. He came in, and Madame Sagredo lost no time in saying to him, "Prince, here is M. Casanova; he pretends that you do not know your own armorial bearings." Hearing these words, he came up to me, sneering, called me a coward, and gave me a smack on the face which almost stunned me. I left the room very slowly, not forgetting my hat and my cane, and went downstairs, while M. D—— R—— was loudly ordering the servants to throw the madman out of the window.

I left the palace and went to the esplanade in order to wait for him. The moment I saw him, I ran to meet him, and I beat him so violently with my cane that one blow alone ought to have killed him. He drew back, and found himself brought to a stand between two walls, where, to avoid being beaten to death, his only resource was to draw his sword, but the cowardly scoundrel did not even think of his weapon, and I left him, on the ground, covered with blood. The crowd formed a line for me to pass, and I went to the coffee-house, where I drank a glass of lemonade, without sugar to precipitate the bitter saliva which rage had brought up from my stomach. In a few minutes, I found myself surrounded by all the young officers of the garrison, who joined in the general opinion that I ought to have killed him, and they at last annoyed me, for it was not my fault if I had not done so, and I would certainly have taken his life if he had drawn his sword.

I had been in the coffee-house for half an hour when the general's adjutant came to tell me that his excellency ordered me to put myself under arrest on board the *bastarda*, a galley on which the prisoners had their legs in irons like galley slaves. The dose was rather too strong to be swallowed, and I did not feel disposed to submit to it. "Very good, adjutant," I replied, "it shall be done." He went away, and I left the coffee-house a moment after him, but when I reached the end of the street, instead of going towards the esplanade, I proceeded quickly towards the sea. I walked along the beach for a quarter of an hour, and finding a boat empty, but with a pair of oars, I got in her, and unfastening her, I rowed as hard as I could towards a large *caicco*, sailing against the wind with six oars. As soon as I had come up to her, I went on board and asked the *carabouchiri* to sail before the wind and to take me to a large wherry which could be seen at some distance, going towards Vido Rock. I abandoned the row-boat, and, after paying the master of the *caicco* generously, I got into the wherry, made a bargain with the skipper who unfurled three sails, and in less than two hours we were fifteen miles away from Corfu. The wind having died away, I made the men row against the current, but towards midnight they told me that they could not row any longer, they were worn out with fatigue. They advised me to sleep until day-break, but I refused to do so, and for a trifle I got them to put me on shore, without asking where I was, in order not to raise their suspicions. It was enough for me to know that I was at a distance of twenty miles from Corfu, and in a place where nobody could imagine me to be. The moon was shining, and I saw a church with a house adjoining, a long barn opened on both sides, a plain of about one hundred yards confined by hills, and nothing more. I found some straw in the barn, and laying myself down, I slept until day-break in spite of the cold. It was the 1st of December, and although the climate is very mild in Corfu I felt benumbed when I awoke, as I had no cloak over my thin uniform.

The bells begin to toll, and I proceed towards the church. The long-bearded *papa*, surprised at my sudden apparition, enquires whether I am *Romeo* (a Greek); I tell him that I am *Fragico* (Italian), but he turns his back upon me and goes into his house, the door of which he shuts without condescending to listen to me.

I then turned towards the sea, and saw a boat leaving a tartan lying at anchor within one hundred yards of the island; the boat had four oars and landed her passengers. I come up to them and meet a good-looking Greek, a woman and a young boy ten or twelve years old. Addressing myself to the Greek, I ask him whether he has had a pleasant passage, and where he comes from. He answers in Italian that he has sailed from Cephalonia with his wife and his son, and that he is bound for Venice; he had landed to hear mass at the Church of Our Lady of Casopo, in order to ascertain whether his father-in-law was still alive, and whether he would pay the amount he had promised him for the dowry of his wife.

"But how can you find it out?"

"The Papa Deldimopulo will tell me; he will communicate faithfully the oracle of the Holy Virgin."

I say nothing and follow him into the church; he speaks to the priest, and gives him some money. The *papa* says the mass, enters the *sanctum sanctorum*, comes out again in a quarter of an hour, ascends the steps of the altar, turns towards his audience, and, after meditating for a minute and stroking his long beard, he delivers his oracle in a dozen words. The Greek of Cephalonia, who certainly could not boast of being as wise as Ulysses, appears very well pleased, and gives more money to the impostor. We leave the church, and I ask him whether he feels satisfied with the oracle.

"Oh! quite satisfied. I know now that my father-in-law is alive, and that he will pay me the dowry, if I consent to leave my child with him. I am aware that it is his fancy and I will give him the boy."

"Does the *papa* know you?"

"No; he is not even acquainted with my name."

"Have you any fine goods on board your tartan?"

"Yes; come and breakfast with me; you can see all I have."

"Very willingly."

Delighted at hearing that oracles were not yet defunct, and satisfied that they will endure as long as there are in this world simple-minded men and deceitful, cunning priests, I follow the good man, who took me to his tartan and treated me to an excellent breakfast. His cargo consisted of cotton, linen, currants, oil, and excellent wines. He had also a stock of night-caps, stockings, cloaks in the Eastern fashion, umbrellas, and sea biscuits, of which I was very fond; in those days I had thirty teeth, and it would have been difficult to find a finer set. Alas! I have but two left now, the other twenty-eight are gone with other tools quite as precious;

but *dum vita super est, bene est.* I bought a small stock of everything he had except cotton, for which I had no use, and without discussing his price I paid him the thirty-five or forty sequins he demanded, and seeing my generosity he made me a present of six beautiful botargoes.

I happened during our conversation to praise the wine of Xante, which he called *generoydes,* and he told me that if I would accompany him to Venice he would give me a bottle of that wine every day including the quarantine. Always superstitious, I was on the point of accepting, and that for the most foolish reason—namely, that there would be no premeditation in that strange resolution, and it might be the impulse of fate. Such was my nature in those days; alas; it is very different now. They say that it is because wisdom comes with old age, but I cannot reconcile myself to cherish the effect of a most unpleasant cause.

Just as I was going to accept his offer he proposes to sell me a very fine gun for ten sequins, saying that in Corfu anyone would be glad of it for twelve. The word Corfu upsets all my ideas on the spot! I fancy I hear the voice of my genius telling me to go back to that city. I purchase the gun for the ten sequins, and my honest Cephalonian, admiring my fair dealing, gives me, over and above our bargain, a beautiful Turkish pouch well filled with powder and shot. Carrying my gun, with a good warm cloak over my uniform and with a large bag containing all my purchases, I take leave of the worthy Greek, and am landed on the shore, determined on obtaining a lodging from the cheating *papa,* by fair means or foul. The good wine of my friend the Cephalonian had excited me just enough to make me carry my determination into immediate execution. I had in my pockets four or five hundred copper gazzette, which were very heavy, but which I had procured from the Greek, foreseeing that I might want them during my stay on the island.

I store my bag away in the barn and I proceed, gun in hand, towards the house of the priest; the church was closed.

I must give my readers some idea of the state I was in at that moment. I was quietly hopeless. The three or four hundred sequins I had with me did not prevent me from thinking that I was not in very great security on the island; I could not remain long, I would soon be found out, and, being guilty of desertion, I should be treated accordingly. I did not know what to do, and that is always an unpleasant predicament. It would be absurd for me to return to Corfu of my own accord; my flight would then be useless, and I should be thought a fool, for my return would be a proof of cowardice or stupidity; yet I did not feel the courage to desert altogether. The chief cause of my decision was not that I had a thousand sequins in the hands of the faro banker, or my well-stocked wardrobe, or the fear of not getting a living somewhere else, but the unpleasant recollection that I should leave behind me a woman whom I loved to adoration, and from whom I had not yet obtained any favour, not even that of kissing her hand. In such distress of mind I could not do anything else but abandon myself to chance, whatever the result might be, and the most essential thing for the present was to secure a lodging and my daily food.

I knock at the door of the priest's dwelling. He looks out of a window and shuts it without listening to me. I knock again, I swear, I call out loudly, all in vain. Giving way to my rage, I take aim at a poor sheep grazing with several others at a short distance, and kill it. The herdsman begins to scream, the *papa* shows himself at the window, calling out, "Thieves! Murder!" and orders the alarm-bell to be rung. Three bells are immediately set in motion, I foresee a general gathering: what is going to happen? I do not know, but happen what will, I load my gun and await coming events.

In less than eight or ten minutes, I see a crowd of peasants coming down the hills, armed with guns, pitchforks, or cudgels: I withdraw inside of the barn, but without the slightest fear, for I cannot suppose that, seeing me alone, these men will murder me without listening to me.

The first ten or twelve peasants come forward, gun in hand and ready to fire: I stop them by throwing down my gazzette, which they lose no time in picking up from the ground, and I keep on throwing money down as the men come forward, until I had no more left. The clowns were looking at each other in great astonishment, not knowing what to make out of a well-dressed young man, looking very peaceful, and throwing his money to them with such generosity. I could not speak to them until the deafening noise of the bells should cease. I quietly sit down on my large bag, and keep still, but as soon as I can be heard I begin to address the men. The priest, however, assisted by his beadle and by the herdsman, interrupts me, and all the more easily that I was speaking Italian. My three enemies, who talked all at once, were trying to excite the crowd against me.

One of the peasants, an elderly and reasonable-looking man, comes up to me and asks me in Italian why I have killed the sheep.

"To eat it, my good fellow, but not before I have paid for it."

"But his holiness, the *papa*, might choose to charge one sequin for it."

"Here is one sequin."

The priest takes the money and goes away: war is over. The peasant tells me that he has served in the campaign of 1716, and that he was at the defence of Corfu. I compliment him, and ask him to find me a lodging and a man able to prepare my meals. He answers that he will procure me a whole house, that he will be my cook himself, but I must go up the hill. No matter! He calls two stout fellows, one takes my bag, the other shoulders my sheep, and forward! As we are walking along, I tell him,——

"My good man, I would like to have in my service twenty-four fellows like these under military discipline. I would give each man twenty gazzette a day, and you would have forty as my lieutenant."

"I will," says the old soldier, "raise for you this very day a body-guard of which you will be proud."

We reach a very convenient house, containing on the ground floor three rooms and a stable, which I immediately turned into a guard-room.

My lieutenant went to get what I wanted, and particularly a needlewoman to make me some shirts. In the course of the day I had furniture, bedding, kitchen utensils, a good dinner, twenty-four well-equipped soldiers, a super-annuated sempstress and several young girls to make my shirts. After supper, I found my position highly pleasant, being surrounded with some thirty persons who looked upon me as their sovereign, although they could not make out what had brought me to their island. The only thing which struck me as disagreeable was that the young girls could not speak Italian, and I did not know Greek enough to enable me to make love to them.

The next morning my lieutenant had the guard relieved, and I could not help bursting into a merry laugh. They were like a flock of sheep: all fine men, well-made and strong; but without uniform and without discipline the finest band is but a herd. However, they quickly learned how to present arms and to obey the orders of their officer. I caused three sentinels to be placed, one before the guard-room, one at my door, and the third where he could have a good view of the sea. This sentinel was to give me warning of the approach of any armed boat or vessel. For the first two or three days I considered all this as mere amusement, but, thinking that I might really want the men to repel force by force, I had some idea of making my army take an oath of allegiance. I did not do so, however, although my lieutenant assured me that I had only to express my wishes, for my generosity had captivated the love of all the islanders.

My sempstress, who had procured some young needle-women to sew my shirts, had expected that I would fall in love with one and not with all, but my amorous zeal overstepped her hopes, and all the pretty ones had their turn; they were all well satisfied with me, and the sempstress was rewarded for her good offices. I was leading a delightful life, for my table was supplied with excellent dishes, juicy mutton, and snipe so delicious that I have never tasted their like except in St. Petersburg. I drank scopolo wine or the best muscatel of the Archipelago. My lieutenant was my only table companion. I never took a walk without him and two of my body-guard, in order to defend myself against the attacks of a few young men who had a spite against me because they fancied, not without some reason, that my needlewomen, their mistresses, had left them on my account. I often thought while I was rambling about the island, that without money I should have been unhappy, and that I was indebted to my gold for all the happiness I was enjoying; but it was right to suppose at the same time that, if I had not felt my purse pretty heavy, I would not have been likely to leave Corfu.

I had thus been playing the petty king with success for a week or ten days, when, towards ten o'clock at night I heard the sentinel's challenge. My lieutenant went out, and returned announcing that an honest-looking man, who spoke Italian, wished to see me on important business. I had him brought in, and, in the presence of my lieutenant, he told me in Italian:

"Next Sunday, the Papa Deldimopulo will fulminate against you the *cataramonachia*. If you do not prevent him, a slow fever will send you into the next world in six weeks."

"I have never heard of such a drug."

"It is not a drug. It is a curse pronounced by a priest with the Host in his hands, and it is sure to be fulfilled."

"What reason can that priest have to murder me?"

"You disturb the peace and discipline of his parish. You have seduced several young girls, and now their lovers refuse to marry them."

I made him drink, and thanking him heartily, wished him good night. His warning struck me as deserving my attention, for, if I had no fear of the *cataramonachia,* in which I had not the slightest faith, I feared certain poisons which might be by far more efficient. I passed a very quiet night, but at day-break I got up, and without saying anything to my lieutenant, I went straight to the church where I found the preist, and addressed him in the following words, uttered in a tone likely to enforce conviction:

"On the first symptom of fever, I will shoot you like a dog. Throw over me a curse which will kill me instantly, or make your will. Farewell!"

Having thus warned him, I returned to my royal palace. Early on the following Monday, the *papa* called on me. I had a slight headache; he enquired after my health, and when I told him that my head felt rather heavy, he made me laugh by the air of anxiety with which he assured me that it could be caused by nothing else than the heavy atmosphere of the island of Casopo.

Three days after his visit, the advanced sentinel gave the war-cry. The lieutenant went out to reconnoitre, and after a short absence he gave me notice that the long boat of an armed vessel had just landed an officer. Danger was at hand.

I go out myself, I call my men to arms, and, advancing a few steps, I see an officer, accompanied by a guide, who was walking towards my dwelling. As he was alone, I had nothing to fear. I return to my room, giving orders to my lieutenant to receive him with all military honours and to introduce him. Then, girding my sword, I wait for my visitor.

In a few minutes, Adjutant Minolto, the same who had brought me the order to put myself under arrest, makes his appearance.

"You are alone," I say to him, "and therefore you come as a friend. Let us embrace."

"I must come as a friend, for, as an enemy, I should not have enough men. But what I see seems a dream."

"Take a seat, and dine with me. I will treat you splendidly."

"Most willingly, and after dinner we will leave the island together."

"You may go alone, if you like; but I will not leave this place until I have the certainty, not only that I shall not be sent to the *bastarda*, but also that I shall have every satisfaction from the knave whom the general ought to send to the galleys."

"Be reasonable, and come with me of your own accord. My orders are to take you by force, but as I have not enough men to do so, I shall make my report, and the general will, of course, send a force sufficient to arrest you."

"Never; I will not be taken alive."

"You must be mad; believe me, you are in the wrong. You have disobeyed the order I brought you to go to the *bastarda;* in that you have acted wrongly, and in that alone, for in every other respect you were perfectly right, the general himself says so."

"Then I ought to have put myself under arrest?"

"Certainly; obedience is necessary in our profession."

"Would you have obeyed, if you had been in my place?"

"I cannot and will not tell you what I would have done, but I know that if I had disobeyed orders I should have been guilty of a crime."

"But if I surrendered now I should be treated like a criminal, and much more severely than if I had obeyed that unjust order."

"I think not. Come with me, and you will know everything."

"What! Go without knowing what fate may be in store for me? Do not expect it. Let us have dinner. If I am guilty of such a dreadful crime that violence must be used against me, I will surrender only to irresistible force. I cannot be worse off, but there may be blood spilled."

"You are mistaken, such conduct would only make you more guilty. But I say like you, let us have dinner. A good meal will very likely render you more disposed to listen to reason."

Our dinner was nearly over, when we heard some noise outside. The lieutenant came in, and informed me that the peasants were gathering in the neighbourhood of my house to defend me, because a rumour had spread through the island that the felucca had been sent with orders to arrest me and take me to Corfu. I told him to undeceive the good fellows, and to send them away, but to give them first a barrel of wine.

The peasants went away satisfied, but, to shew their devotion to me, they all fired their guns.

"It is all very amusing," said the adjutant, "but it will turn out very serious if you let me go away alone, for my duty compels me to give an exact account of all I have witnessed."

"I will follow you, if you will give me your word of honour to land me free in Corfu."

"I have orders to deliver your person to M. Foscari, on board the *bastarda*."

"Well, you shall not execute your orders this time."

"If you do not obey the commands of the general, his honour will compel him to use violence against you, and of course he can do it. But tell me, what would you do if the general should leave you in this island for the sake of the joke? There is no fear of that, however, and, after the report which I must give, the general will certainly make up his mind to stop the affair without shedding blood."

"Without a fight it will be difficult to arrest me, for

with five hundred peasants in such a place as this I would not be afraid of three thousand men."

"One man will prove enough; you will be treated as a leader of rebels. All these peasants may be devoted to you, but they cannot protect you against one man who will shoot you for the sake of earning a few pieces of gold. I can tell you more than that: amongst all those men who surround you there is not one who would not murder you for twenty sequins. Believe me, go with me. Come to enjoy the triumph which is awaiting you in Corfu. You will be courted and applauded. You will narrate yourself all your mad frolics, people will laugh, and at the same time will admire you for having listened to reason the moment I came here. Everybody feels esteem for you, and M. D.—— R—— thinks a great deal of you. He praises very highly the command you have shewn over your passion in refraining from thrusting your sword through that insolent fool, in order not to forget the respect you owed to his house. The general himself must esteem you, for he cannot forget what you told him of that knave."

"What has become of him?"

"Four days ago Major Sardina's frigate arrived with dispatches, in which the general must have found all the proof of the imposture, for he has caused the false duke or prince to disappear very suddenly. Nobody knows where he has been sent to, and nobody ventures to mention the fellow before the general, for he made the most egregious blunder respecting him."

"But was the man received in society after the thrashing I gave him?"

"God forbid! Do you not recollect that he wore a sword? From that moment no one would receive him. His arm was broken and his jaw shattered to pieces.

But in spite of the state he was in, in spite of what he must have suffered, his excellency had him removed a week after you had treated him so severely. But your flight is what everyone has been wondering over. It was thought for three days that M. D—— R—— had concealed you in his house, and he was openly blamed for doing so. He had to declare loudly at the general's table that he was in the most complete ignorance of your whereabouts. His excellency even expressed his anxiety about your escape, and it was only yesterday that your place of refuge was made known by a letter addressed by the priest of this island to the Proto-Papa Bulgari, in which he complained that an Italian officer had invaded the island of Casopo a week before, and had committed unheard-of violence. He accused you of seducing all the girls, and of threatening to shoot him if he dared to pronounce *cataramonachia* against you. This letter, which was read publicly at the evening reception, made the general laugh, but he ordered me to arrest you all the same."

"Madame Sagredo is the cause of it all."

"True, but she is well punished for it. You ought to call upon her with me to-morrow."

"To-morrow? Are you then certain that I shall not be placed under arrest?"

"Yes, for I know that the general is a man of honour."

"I am of the same opinion. Well, let us go on board your felucca. We will embark together after midnight."

"Why not now?"

"Because I will not run the risk of spending the night on board M. Foscari's *bastarda*. I want to reach Corfu by daylight, so as to make your victory more brilliant."

"But what shall we do for the next eight hours?"

"We will pay a visit to some beauties of a species unknown in Corfu, and have a good supper."

I ordered my lieutenant to send plenty to eat and to drink to the men on board the felucca, to prepare a splendid supper, and to spare nothing, as I should leave the island at midnight. I made him a present of all my provisions, except such as I wanted to take with me; these I sent on board. My janissaries, to whom I gave a week's pay, insisted upon escorting me, fully equipped, as far as the boat, which made the adjutant laugh all the way.

We reached Corfu by eight o'clock in the morning, and we went alongside the *bastarda*. The adjutant consigned me to M. Foscari, assuring me that he would immediately give notice of my arrival to M. D——R——, send my luggage to his house, and report the success of his expedition to the general.

M. Foscari, the commander of the *bastarda*, treated me very badly. If he had been blessed with any delicacy of feeling, he would not have been in such a hurry to have me put in irons. He might have talked to me, and have thus delayed for a quarter of an hour that operation which greatly vexed me. But, without uttering a single word, he sent me to the *capo di scalo* who made me sit down, and told me to put my foot forward to receive the irons, which, however, do not dishonour anyone in that country, not even the galley slaves, for they are better treated than soldiers.

My right leg was already in irons, and the left one was in the hands of the man for the completion of that unpleasant ceremony, when the adjutant of his excellency came to tell the executioner to set me at liberty and to return me my sword. I wanted to present my compliments to the noble M. Foscari, but the adjutant, rather ashamed, assured me that his excellency did not expect me to do so.

The first thing I did was to pay my respects to the general, without saying one word to him, but he told me with a serious countenance to be more prudent for the future, and to learn that a soldier's first duty was to obey, and above all to be modest and discreet. I understood perfectly the meaning of the two last words, and acted accordingly.

When I made my appearance at M. D—— R——'s, I could see pleasure on everybody's face. Those moments have always been so dear to me that I have never forgotten them, they have afforded me consolation in the time of adversity. If you would relish pleasure you must endure pain, and delights are in proportion to the privations we have suffered. M. D—— R—— was so glad to see me that he came up to me and warmly embraced me. He presented me with a beautiful ring which he took from his own finger, and told me that I had acted quite rightly in not letting anyone, and particularly himself, know where I had taken refuge.

"You can't think," he added, frankly, "how interested Madame F—— was in your fate. She would be really delighted if you called on her immediately."

How delightful to receive such advice from his own lips! But the word "immediately" annoyed me, because, having passed the night on board the felucca, I was afraid that the disorder of my toilet might injure me in her eyes. Yet I could neither refuse M. D—— R——, nor tell him the reason of my refusal, and I bethought myself that I could make a merit of it in the eyes of Madame F——.

I therefore went at once to her house; the goddess

was not yet visible, but her attendant told me to come in, assuring me that her mistress's bell would soon be heard, and that she would be very sorry if I did not wait to see her. I spent half an hour with that young and indiscreet person, who was a very charming girl, and learned from her many things which caused me great pleasure, and particularly all that had been said respecting my escape. I found that throughout the affair my conduct had met with general approbation.

As soon as Madame F—— had seen her maid, she desired me to be shewn in. The curtains were drawn aside, and I thought I saw Aurora surrounded with the roses and the pearls of morning. I told her that, if it had not been for the order I received from M. D—— R——, I would not have presumed to present myself before her in my travelling costume; and in the most friendly tone she answered that M. D—— R——, knowing all the interest she felt in me, had been quite right to tell me to come, and she assured me that M. D—— R—— had the greatest esteem for me.

"I do not know, madam, how I have deserved such great happiness, for all I dared aim at was toleration."

"We all admired the control you kept over your feelings when you refrained from killing that insolent madman on the spot; he would have been thrown out of the window if he had not beat a hurried retreat."

"I should certainly have killed him, madam, if you had not been present."

"A very pretty compliment, but I can hardly believe that you thought of me in such a moment."

I did not answer, but cast my eyes down, and gave a deep sigh. She observed my new ring, and in order to change the subject of conversation she praised M. D—— R—— very highly, as soon as I had told her how he had offered it to me. She desired me to give her an account of my life on the island, and I did so, but allowed my pretty needlewomen to remain under a veil, for I had already learnt that in this world the truth must often remain untold.

All my adventures amused her much, and she greatly admired my conduct.

"Would you have the courage," she said, "to repeat all you have just told me, and exactly in the same terms, before the *proveditore-generale?*"

"Most certainly, madam, provided he asked me himself."

"Well, then, prepare to redeem your promise. I want our excellent general to love you and to become your warmest protector, so as to shield you against every injustice and to promote your advancement. Leave it all to me."

Her reception fairly overwhelmed me with happiness, and on leaving her house I went to Major Maroli to find out the state of my finances. I was glad to hear that after my escape he had no longer considered me a partner in the faro bank. I took four hundred sequins from the cashier, reserving the right to become again a partner, should circumstances prove at any time favourable.

In the evening I made a careful toilet, and called for the Adjutant Minolto in order to pay with him a visit to Madame Sagredo, the general's favourite. With the exception of Madame F—— she was the greatest beauty of Corfu. My visit surprised her, because, as she had been the cause of all that had happened, she was very far from expecting it. She imagined that I had a spite against her. I undeceived her, speaking to her very candidly, and she treated me most kindly, inviting me to come now and then to spend the evening at her house.

But I neither accepted nor refused her amiable invitation, knowing that Madame F—— disliked her; and how could I be a frequent guest at her house with such a knowledge! Besides, Madame Sagredo was very fond of gambling, and, to please her, it was necessary either to lose or make her win, but to accept such conditions one must be in love with the lady or wish to make her conquest, and I had not the slightest idea of either. The Adjutant Minolto never played, but he had captivated the lady's good graces by his services in the character of Mercury.

When I returned to the palace I found Madame F—— alone, M. D—— R—— being engaged with his correspondence. She asked me to sit near her, and to tell her all my adventures in Constantinople. I did so, and I had no occasion to repent it. My meeting with Yusuf's wife pleased her extremely, but the bathing scene by moonlight made her blush with excitement. I veiled as much as I could the too brilliant colours of my picture, but, if she did not find me clear, she would oblige me to be more explicit, and if I made myself better understood by giving to my recital a touch of voluptuousness which I borrowed from her looks more than from my recollection, she would scold me and tell me that I might have disguised a little more. I felt that the way she was talking would give her a liking for me, and I was satisfied that the man who can give birth to amorous desires is easily called upon to gratify them: it was the reward I was ardently longing for, and I dared to hope it would be mine, although I could see it only looming in the distance.

It happened that, on that day, M. D—— R—— had invited a large company to supper. I had, as a matter of course, to engross all conversation, and to give the

fullest particulars of all that had taken place from the
moment I received the order to place myself under arrest up to the time of my release from the *bastarda*. M.
Foscari was seated next to me, and the last part of my
narrative was not, I suppose, particularly agreeable to
him.

The account I gave of my adventures pleased everybody, and it was decided that the *proveditore-generale*
must have the pleasure of hearing my tale from my own
lips. I mentioned that hay was very plentiful in Casopo,
and as that article was very scarce in Corfu, M. D——
R—— told me that I ought to seize the opportunity of
making myself agreeable to the general by informing
him of that circumstance without delay. I followed his
advice the very next day, and was very well received,
for his excellency immediately ordered a squad of men
to go to the island and bring large quantities of hay to
Corfu.

A few days later the Adjutant Minolto came to me
in the coffee-house, and told me that the general wished
to see me: this time I promptly obeyed his commands.

CHAPTER XV

Progress of My Amour—My Journey to Otranto—I Enter the Service of Madame F.—A Fortunate Excoriation

THE room I entered was full of people. His excellency, seeing me, smiled and drew upon me the attention of all his guests by saying aloud, "Here comes the young man who is a good judge of princes."

"My lord, I have become a judge of nobility by frequenting the society of men like you."

"The ladies are curious to know all you have done from the time of your escape from Corfu up to your return."

"Then you sentence me, monsignor, to make a public confession?"

"Exactly; but, as it is to be a confession, be careful not to omit the most insignificant circumstance, and suppose that I am not in the room."

"On the contrary, I wish to receive absolution only from your excellency. But my history will be a long one."

"If such is the case, your confessor gives you permission to be seated."

I gave all the particulars of my adventures, with the exception of my dalliance with the nymphs of the island.

"Your story is a very instructive one," observed the general.

"Yes, my lord, for the adventures shew that a young man is never so near his utter ruin than when, excited by some great passion, he finds himself able to minister to it, thanks to the gold in his purse."

I was preparing to take my leave, when the major-domo came to inform me that his excellency desired me to remain to supper. I had therefore the honour of a seat at his table, but not the pleasure of eating, for I was obliged to answer the questions addressed to me from all quarters, and I could not contrive to swallow a single mouthful. I was seated next to the Proto-Papa Bulgari, and I entreated his pardon for having ridiculed Deldimopulo's oracle. "It is nothing else but regular cheating," he said, "but it is very difficult to put a stop to it; it is an old custom."

A short time afterwards, Madame F—— whispered a few words to the general, who turned to me and said that he would be glad to hear me relate what had occurred to me in Constantinople with the wife of the Turk Yusuf, and at another friend's house, where I had seen bathing by moonlight. I was rather surprised at such an invitation, and told him that such frolics were not worth listening to, and the general not pressing me no more was said about it. But I was astonished at Madame F——'s indiscretion; she had no business to make my confidences public. I wanted her to be jealous of her own dignity, which I loved even more than her person.

Two or three days later, she said to me,—

"Why did you refuse to tell your adventures in Constantinople before the general?"

"Because I do not wish everybody to know that you allow me to tell you such things. What I may dare, madam, to say to you when we are alone, I would certainly not say to you in public."

"And why not? It seems to me, on the contrary, that if you are silent in public out of respect for me, you ought to be all the more silent when we are alone."

"I wanted to amuse you, and have exposed myself to the danger of displeasing you, but I can assure you, madam, that I will not run such a risk again."

"I have no wish to pry into your intentions, but it strikes me that if your wish was to please me, you ought not to have run the risk of obtaining the opposite result. We take supper with the general this evening, and M. D—— R—— has been asked to bring you. I feel certain that the general will ask you again for your adventures in Constantinople, and this time you cannot refuse him."

M. D—— R—— came in and we went to the general's. I thought as we were driving along that, although Madame F—— seemed to have intended to humiliate me, I ought to accept it all as a favour of fortune, because, by compelling me to explain my refusal to the general, Madame F—— had, at the same time, compelled me to a declaration of my feelings, which was not without importance.

The *proveditore-generale* gave me a friendly welcome, and kindly handed me a letter which had come with the official dispatches from Constantinople. I bowed my thanks, and put the letter in my pocket: but he told me that he was himself a great lover of news, and that I could read my letter. I opened it; it was from Yusuf, who announced the death of Count de Bonneval. Hearing the name of the worthy Yusuf, the general asked me to tell him my adventure with his wife. I could not now refuse, and I began a story which amused and interested the general and his friends for an hour or so, but which was from beginning to end the work of my imagination.

Thus I continued to respect the privacy of Yusuf, to
avoid implicating the good fame of Madame F——, and
to shew myself in a light which was tolerably advantageous to me. My story, which was full of sentiment,
did me a great deal of honour, and I felt very happy
when I saw from the expression of Madame F——'s face
that she was pleased with me, although somewhat surprised.

When we found ourselves again in her house she told
me, in the presence of M. D—— R——, that the story
I had related to the general was certainly very pretty,
although purely imaginary, that she was not angry with
me, because I had amused her, but that she could not
help remarking my obstinacy in refusing compliance
with her wishes. Then, turning to M. D—— R——, she
said,——

"M. Casanova pretends that if he had given an account of his meeting with Yusuf's wife without changing
anything everybody would think that I allowed him to
entertain me with indecent stories. I want you to give
your opinion about it. Will you," she added, speaking
to me, "be so good as to relate immediately the adventure in the same words which you have used when you
told me of it?"

"Yes, madam, if you wish me to do so."

Stung to the quick by an indiscretion which, as I did
not yet know women thoroughly, seemed to me without
example, I cast all fears of displeasing to the winds,
related the adventure with all the warmth of an impas-
sioned poet, and without disguising or attenuating in the
least the desires which the charms of the Greek beauty
had inspired me with.

"Do you think," said M. D—— R—— to Madame
F——, "that he ought to have related that adventure

before all our friends as he has just related it to us?"

"If it be wrong for him to tell it in public, it is also wrong to tell it to me in private."

"You are the only judge of that: yes, if he has displeased you; no, if he has amused you. As for my own opinion, here it is: He has just now amused me very much, but he would have greatly displeased me if he had related the same adventure in public."

"Then," exclaimed Madame F——, "I must request you never to tell me in private anything that you cannot repeat in public."

"I promise, madam, to act always according to your wishes."

"It being understood," added M. D—— R——, smiling, "that madam reserves all rights of repealing that order whenever she may think fit."

I was vexed, but I contrived not to shew it. A few minutes more, and we took leave of Madame F——.

I was beginning to understand that charming woman, and to dread the ordeal to which she would subject me. But love was stronger than fear, and, fortified with hope, I had the courage to endure the thorns, so as to gather the rose at the end of my sufferings. I was particularly pleased to find that M. D—— R—— was not jealous of me, even when she seemed to dare him to it. This was a point of the greatest importance.

A few days afterwards, as I was entertaining her on various subjects, she remarked how unfortunate it had been for me to enter the lazzaretto at Ancona without any money.

"In spite of my distress," I said, "I fell in love with a young and beautiful Greek slave, who very nearly contrived to make me break through all the sanitary laws."

"How so?"

"You are alone, madam, and I have not forgotten your orders."

"Is it a very improper story?"

"No: yet I would not relate it to you in public."

"Well," she said, laughing, "I repeal my order, as M. D—— R—— said I would. Tell me all about it."

I told my story, and, seeing that she was pensive, I exaggerated the misery I had felt at not being able to complete my conquest.

"What do you mean by your misery? I think that the poor girl was more to be pitied than you. You have never seen her since?"

"I beg your pardon, madam; I met her again, but I dare not tell you when or how."

"Now you must go on; it is all nonsense for you to stop. Tell me all; I expect you have been guilty of some black deed."

"Very far from it, madam, for it was a very sweet, although incomplete, enjoyment."

"Go on! But do not call things exactly by their names. It is not necessary to go into details."

Emboldened by the renewal of her order, I told her, without looking her in the face, of my meeting with the Greek slave in the presence of Bellino, and of the act which was cut short by the appearance of her master. When I had finished my story, Madame F—— remained silent, and I turned the conversation into a different channel, for though I felt myself on an excellent footing with her, I knew likewise that I had to proceed with great prudence. She was too young to have lowered herself before, and she would certainly look upon a connection with me as a lowering of her dignity.

Fortune which had always smiled upon me in the most hopeless cases, did not intend to ill-treat me on this occasion, and procured me, on that very same day, a favour of a very peculiar nature. My charming lady-love having pricked her finger rather severely, screamed loudly, and stretched her hand towards me, entreating me to suck the blood flowing from the wound. You may judge, dear reader, whether I was long in seizing that beautiful hand, and if you are, or if you have ever been in love, you will easily guess the manner in which I performed my delightful work. What is a kiss? Is it not an ardent desire to inhale a portion of the being we love? Was not the blood I was sucking from that charming wound a portion of the woman I worshipped? When I had completed my work, she thanked me affectionately, and told me to spit out the blood I had sucked.

"It is here," I said, placing my hand on my heart, "and God alone knows what happiness it has given me."

"You have drunk my blood with happiness! Are you then a cannibal?"

"I believe not, madam; but it would have been sacrilege in my eyes if I had suffered one single drop of your blood to be lost."

One evening, there was an unusually large attendance at M. D—— R——'s assembly, and we were talking of the carnival which was near at hand. Everybody was regretting the lack of actors, and the impossibility of enjoying the pleasures of the theatre. I immediately offered to procure a good company at my expense, if the boxes were at once subscribed for, and the monopoly of the faro bank granted to me. No time was to be lost, for the carnival was approaching, and I had to go to Otranto to engage a troop. My proposal was accepted with great joy, and the *proveditore-generale* placed a felucca at my disposal. The boxes were all taken in three days, and a Jew took the pit, two nights a week excepted, which I reserved for my own profit.

The carnival being very long that year, I had every chance of success. It is said generally that the profession of theatrical manager is difficult, but, if that is the case, I have not found it so by experience, and am bound to affirm the contrary.

I left Corfu in the evening, and having a good breeze in my favour, I reached Otranto by day-break the following morning, without the oarsmen having had to row a stroke. The distance from Corfu to Otranto is only about fifteen leagues.

I had no idea of landing, owing to the quarantine which is always enforced for any ship or boat coming to Italy from the east. I only went to the parlour of the lazaretto, where, placed behind a grating, you can speak to any person who calls, and who must stand behind another grating placed opposite, at a distance of six feet.

As soon as I announced that I had come for the purpose of engaging a troupe of actors to perform in Corfu, the managers of the two companies then in Otranto came to the parlour to speak to me. I told them at once that I wished to see all the performers, one company at a time.

The two rival managers gave me then a very comic scene, each manager wanting the other to bring his troupe first. The harbour-master told me that the only way to settle the matter was to say myself which of the two companies I would see first: one was from Naples, the other from Sicily. Not knowing either I gave the preference to the first. Don Fastidio, the manager, was very vexed, while Battipaglia, the director of the second, was delighted because he hoped that, after seeing the Neapolitan troupe, I would engage his own.

An hour afterwards, Fastidio returned with all his performers, and my surprise may be imagined when amongst them I recognized Petronio and his sister Marina, who, the moment she saw me, screamed for joy, jumped over the grating, and threw herself in my arms. A terrible hubbub followed, and high words passed between Fastidio and the harbour-master. Marina being in the service of Fastidio, the captain compelled him to confine her to the lazaretto, where she would have to perform quarantine at his expense. The poor girl cried bitterly, but I could not remedy her imprudence.

I put a stop to the quarrel by telling Fastidio to shew me all his people, one after the other. Petronio belonged to his company, and performed the lovers. He told me that he had a letter for me from Thérèse. I was also glad to see a Venetian of my acquaintance who played the pantaloon in the pantomime, three tolerably pretty actresses, a *pulcinella*, and a scaramouch. Altogether, the troupe was a decent one.

I told Fastidio to name the lowest salary he wanted for all his company, assuring him that I would give the preference to his rival, if he should ask me too much.

"Sir," he answered, "we are twenty, and shall require six rooms with ten beds, one sitting-room for all of us, and thirty Neapolitan ducats a day, all travelling expenses paid. Here is my stock of plays, and we will perform those that you may choose."

Thinking of poor Marina who would have to remain in the lazaretto before she could reappear on the stage at Otranto, I told Fastidio to get the contract ready, as I wanted to go away immediately.

I had scarcely pronounced these words than war broke

out again between the manager-elect and his unfortunate competitor. Battipaglia, in his rage, called Marina a harlot, and said that she had arranged beforehand with Fastidio to violate the rules of the lazaretto in order to compel me to choose their troupe. Petronio, taking his sister's part, joined Fastidio, and the unlucky Battipaglia was dragged outside and treated to a generous dose of blows and fisticuffs, which was not exactly the thing to console him for a lost engagement.

Soon afterwards, Petronio brought me Thérèse's letter. She was ruining the duke, getting rich accordingly, and waiting for me in Naples.

Everything being ready towards evening, I left Otranto with twenty actors, and six large trunks containing their complete wardrobes. A light breeze which was blowing from the south might have carried us to Corfu in ten hours, but when we had sailed about one hour my *carabouchiri* informed me that he could see by the moonlight a ship which might prove to be a corsair, and get hold of us. I was unwilling to risk anything, so I ordered them to lower the sails and return to Otranto. At day-break we sailed again with a good westerly wind, which would also have taken us to Corfu; but after we had gone two or three hours, the captain pointed out to me a brigantine, evidently a pirate, for she was shaping her course so as to get to windward of us. I told him to change the course, and to go by starboard, to see if the brigantine would follow us, but she immediately imitated our manœuvre. I could not go back to Otranto, and I had no wish to go to Africa, so I ordered the men to shape our course, so as to land on the coast of Calabria, by hard rowing and at the nearest point. The sailors, who were frightened to death, communicated their fears to my comedians, and soon I heard nothing but weeping and sobbing. Every one of them was calling earnestly upon some saint, but not one single prayer to God did I hear. The bewailings of scaramouch, the dull and spiritless despair of Fastidio, offered a picture which would have made me laugh heartily if the danger had been imaginary and not real. Marina alone was cheerful and happy, because she did not realize the danger we were running, and she laughed at the terror of the crew and of her companions.

A strong breeze sprang up towards evening, so I ordered them to clap on all sail and scud before the wind, even if it should get stronger. In order to escape the pirate, I had made up my mind to cross the gulf. We took the wind through the night, and in the morning we were eighty miles from Corfu, which I determined to reach by rowing. We were in the middle of the gulf, and the sailors were worn out with fatigue, but I had no longer any fear. A gale began to blow from the north, and in less than an hour it was blowing so hard that we were compelled to sail close to the wind in a fearful manner. The felucca looked every moment as if it must capsize. Every one looked terrified but kept complete silence, for I had enjoined it on penalty of death. In spite of our dangerous position, I could not help laughing when I heard the sobs of the cowardly scaramouch. The helmsman was a man of great nerve, and the gale being steady I felt we would reach Corfu without mishap. At day-break we sighted the town, and at nine in the morning we landed at Mandrachia. Everybody was surprised to see us arrive that way.

As soon as my company was landed, the young officers naturally came to inspect the actresses, but they did not find them very desirable, with the exception of Marina, who received uncomplainingly the news that I

could not renew my acquaintance with her. I felt
certain that she would not lack admirers. But my actresses, who had appeared ugly at the landing, produced
a very different effect on the stage, and particularly the
pantaloon's wife. M. Duodo, commander of a man-of-
war, called upon her, and, finding master pantaloon intolerant on the subject of his better-half, gave him a
few blows with his cane. Fastidio informed me the
next day that the pantaloon and his wife refused to perform any more, but I made them alter their mind by
giving them a benefit night.

The pantaloon's wife was much applauded, but she
felt insulted because, in the midst of the applause, the
pit called out, "Bravo, Duodo!" She presented herself
to the general in his own box, in which I was generally,
and complained of the manner in which she was treated.
The general promised her, in my name, another benefit
night for the close of the carnival, and I was of course
compelled to ratify his promise. The fact is, that, to
satisfy the greedy actors, I abandoned to my comedians,
one by one, the seventeen nights I had reserved for
myself. The benefit I gave to Marina was at the special
request of Madame F——, who had taken her into great
favour since she had had the honour of breakfasting
alone with M. D—— R—— in a villa outside of the
city.

My generosity cost me four hundred sequins, but the
faro bank brought me a thousand and more, although
I never held the cards, my management of the theatre
taking up all my time. My manner with the actresses
gained me great kindness; it was clearly seen that I
carried on no intrigue with any of them, although I
had every facility for doing so. Madame F—— complimented me, saying that she had not entertained such a

good opinion of my discretion. I was too busy through the carnival to think of love, even of the passion which filled my heart. It was only at the beginning of Lent, and after the departure of the comedians, that I could give rein to my feelings.

One morning Madame F—— sent a messenger who summoned me to her presence. It was eleven o'clock; I immediately went to her, and enquired what I could do for her service.

"I wanted to see you," she said, "to return the two hundred sequins which you lent me so nobly. Here they are; be good enough to give me back my note of hand."

"Your note of hand, madam, is no longer in my possession. I have deposited it in a sealed envelope with the notary . . . who, according to this receipt of his, can return it only to you."

"Why did you not keep it yourself?"

"Because I was afraid of losing it, or of having it stolen. And in the event of my death I did not want such a document to fall into any other hands but yours."

"A great proof of your extreme delicacy, certainly, but I think you ought to have reserved the right of taking it out of the notary's custody yourself."

"I did not forsee the possibility of calling for it myself."

"Yet it was a very likely thing. Then I can send word to the notary to transmit it to me?"

"Certainly, madam; you alone can claim it."

She sent to the notary, who brought the envelope himself.

She tore the envelope open, and found only a piece of paper besmeared with ink, quite illegible, except her own name, which had not been touched.

"You have acted," she said, "most nobly; but you must agree with me that I cannot be certain that this piece of paper is really my note of hand, although I see my name on it."

"True, madam; and if you are not certain of it, I confess myself in the wrong."

"I must be certain of it, and I am so; but you must grant that I could not swear to it."

"Granted, madam."

During the following days it struck me that her manner towards me was singularly altered. She never received me in her dishabille, and I had to wait with great patience until her maid had entirely dressed her before being admitted into her presence.

If I related any story, any adventure, she pretened not to understand, and affected not to see the point of an anecdote or a jest; very often she would purposely not look at me, and then I was sure to relate badly. If M. D——— R——— laughed at something I had just said, she would ask what he was laughing for, and when he had told her, she would say it was insipid or dull. If one of her bracelets became unfastened, I offered to fasten it again, but either she would not give me so much trouble, or I did not understand the fastening, and the maid was called to do it. I could not help shewing my vexation, but she did not seem to take the slightest notice of it. If M. D——— R——— excited me to say something amusing or witty, and I did not speak immediately, she would say that my budget was empty, laughing, and adding that the wit of poor M. Casanova was worn out. Full of rage, I would plead guilty by my silence to her taunting accusation, but I was thoroughly miserable, for I did not see any cause for that extraordinary change in her feelings, being conscious that I had not given her any motive for it. I wanted to shew her openly my indifference and contempt, but whenever an opportunity offered, my courage would forsake me, and I would let it escape.

One evening M. D—— R—— asking me whether I had often been in love, I answered,——

"Three times, my lord."

"And always happily, of course."

"Always unhappily. The first time, perhaps, because, being an ecclesiastic, I durst not speak openly of my love. The second, because a cruel, unexpected event compelled me to leave the woman I loved at the very moment in which my happiness would have been complete. The third time, because the feeling of pity, with which I inspired the beloved object, induced her to cure me of my passion, instead of crowning my felicity."

"But what specific remedies did she use to effect your cure?"

"She has ceased to be kind."

"I understand she has treated you cruelly, and you call that pity, do you? You are mistaken."

"Certainly," said Madame F——, "a woman may pity the man she loves, but she would not think of ill-treating him to cure him of his passion. That woman has never felt any love for you."

"I cannot, I will not believe it, madam."

"But are you cured?"

"Oh! thoroughly; for when I happen to think of her, I feel nothing but indifference and coldness. But my recovery was long."

"Your convalescence lasted, I suppose, until you fell in love with another."

"With another, madam? I thought I had just told you that the third time I loved was the last."

A few days after that conversation, M. D—— R——
told me that Madame F—— was not well, that he could
not keep her company, and that I ought to go to her,
as he was sure she would be glad to see me. I obeyed,
and told Madame F—— what M. D—— R——
had said. She was lying on a sofa. Without looking at me, she told me she was feverish, and would
not ask me to remain with her, because I would feel
weary.

"I could not experience any weariness in your society, madam; at all events, I can leave you only by
your express command, and, in that case, I must spend
the next four hours in your ante-room, for M. D——
R—— has told me to wait for him here."

"If so, you may take a seat."

Her cold and distant manner repelled me, but I loved
her, and I had never seen her so beautiful, a slight fever
animating her complexion which was then truly dazzling in its beauty. I kept where I was, dumb and as
motionless as a statue, for a quarter of an hour. Then
she rang for her maid, and asked me to leave her alone
for a moment. I was called back soon after, and she
said to me,——

"What has become of your cheerfulness?"

"If it has disappeared, madam, it can only be by your
will. Call it back, and you will see it return in full
force."

"What must I do to obtain that result?"

"Only be towards me as you were when I returned
from Casopo. I have been disagreeable to you for the
last four months, and as I do not know why, I feel
deeply grieved."

"I am always the same: in what do you find me
changed?"

"Good heavens! In everything, except in beauty. But I have taken my decision."

"And what is it?"

"To suffer in silence, without allowing any circumstance to alter the feelings with which you have inspired me; to wish ardently to convince you of my perfect obedience to your commands; to be ever ready to give you fresh proofs of my devotion."

"I thank you, but I cannot imagine what you can have to suffer in silence on my account. I take an interest in you, and I always listen with pleasure to your adventures. As a proof of it, I am extremely curious to hear the history of your three loves."

I invented on the spot three purely imaginary stories, making a great display of tender sentiments and of ardent love, but without alluding to amorous enjoyment, particularly when she seemed to expect me to do so. Sometimes delicacy, sometimes respect or duty, interfered to prevent the crowning pleasure, and I took care to observe, at such moments of disappointment, that a true lover does not require that all important item to feel perfectly happy. I could easily see that her imagination was travelling farther than my narrative, and that my reserve was agreeable to her. I believed I knew her nature well enough to be certain that I was taking the best road to induce her to follow me where I wished to lead her. She expressed a sentiment which moved me deeply, but I was careful not to shew it. We were talking of my third love, of the woman who, out of pity, had undertaken to cure me, and she remarked,——

"If she truly loved you, she may have wished not to cure you, but to cure herself."

On the day following this partial reconciliation, M.

F——, her husband, begged my commanding officer, D—— R——, to let me go with him to Butintro for an excursion of three days, his own adjutant being seriously ill.

Butintro is seven miles from Corfu, almost opposite to that city; it is the nearest point to the island from the mainland. It is not a fortress, but only a small village of Epirus, or Albania, as it is now called, and belonging to the Venetians. Acting on the political axiom that "neglected right is lost right," the Republic sends every year four galleys to Butintro with a gang of galley slaves to fell trees, cut them, and load them on the galleys, while the military keep a sharp look-out to prevent them from escaping to Turkey and becoming Mussulmans. One of the four galleys was commanded by M. F—— who, wanting an adjutant for the occasion, chose me.

I went with him, and on the fourth day we came back to Corfu with a large provision of wood. I found M. D—— R—— alone on the terrace of his palace. It was Good Friday. He seemed thoughtful, and, after a silence of a few minutes, he spoke the following words, which I can never forget:

"M. F——, whose adjutant died yesterday, has just been entreating me to give you to him until he can find another officer. I have told him that I had no right to dispose of your person, and that he ought to apply to you, assuring him that, if you asked me leave to go with him, I would not raise any objection, although I require two adjutants. Has he not mentioned the matter to you?"

"No, monsignor, he has only tendered me his thanks for having accompanied him to Butintro, nothing else."

"He is sure to speak to you about it. What do you intend to say?"

"Simply that I will never leave the service of your excellency without your express command to do so."

"I never will give you such an order."

As M. D—— R—— was saying the last word, M. and Madame F—— came in. Knowing that the conversation would most likely turn upon the subject which had just been broached, I hurried out of the room. In less than a quarter of an hour I was sent for, and M. F—— said to me, confidentially,——

"Well, M. Casanova, would you not be willing to live with me as my adjutant?"

"Does his excellency dismiss me from his service?"

"Not at all," observed M. D—— R——, "but I leave you the choice."

"My lord, I could not be guilty of ingratitude."

And I remained there standing, uneasy, keeping my eyes on the ground, not even striving to conceal my mortification, which was, after all, very natural in such a position. I dreaded looking at Madame F——, for I knew that she could easily guess all my feelings. An instant after, her foolish husband coldly remarked that I should certainly have a more fatiguing service with him than with M. D—— R——, and that, of course, it was more honourable to serve the general governor of the *galeazze* than a simple *sopra-committo*. I was on the point of answering, when Madame F—— said, in a graceful and easy manner, "M. Casanova is right," and she changed the subject. I left the room, revolving in my mind all that had just taken place.

My conclusion was that M. F—— had asked M. D—— R—— to let me go with him at the suggestion of his wife, or, at least with her consent, and it was highly

flattering to my love and to my vanity. But I was
bound in honour not to accept the post, unless I had a
perfect assurance that it would not be disagreeable to
my present patron. "I will accept," I said to myself,
"if M. D—— R—— tells me positively that I shall please
him by doing so. It is for M. F—— to make him
say it."

On the same night I had the honour of offering my
arm to Madame F—— during the procession which takes
place in commemoration of the death of our Lord and
Saviour, which was then attended on foot by all the
nobility. I expected she would mention the matter, but
she did not. My love was in despair, and through the
night I could not close my eyes. I feared she had been
offended by my refusal, and was overwhelmed with grief.
I passed the whole of the next day without breaking my
fast, and did not utter a single word during the evening
reception. I felt very unwell, and I had an attack of
fever which kept me in bed on Easter Sunday. I was
very weak on the Monday, and intended to remain in
my room, when a messenger from Madame F—— came
to inform me that she wished to see me. I told the
messenger not to say that he had found me in bed, and
dressing myself rapidly I hurried to her house. I entered her room, pale, looking very ill: yet she did not
enquire after my health, and kept silent a minute or
two, as if she had been trying to recollect what she had
to say to me.

"Ah! yes, you are aware that our adjutant is dead,
and that we want to replace him. My husband, who
has a great esteem for you, and feels that M. D——
R—— leaves you perfectly free to make your choice, has
taken the singular fancy that you will come, if I ask
you myself to do us that pleasure. Is he mistaken? If

you would come to us, you would have that room."

She was pointing to a room adjoining the chamber in which she slept, and so situated that, to see her in every part of her room, I should not even require to place myself at the window.

"M. D—— R——," she continued, "will not love you less, and as he will see you here every day, he will not be likely to forget his interest in your welfare. Now, tell me, will you come or not?"

"I wish I could, madam, but indeed I cannot."

"You cannot? That is singular. Take a seat, and tell me what there is to prevent you, when, in accepting my offer, you are sure to please M. D—— R—— as well as us."

"If I were certain of it, I would accept immediately; but all I have heard from his lips was that he left me free to make a choice."

"Then you are afraid to grieve him, if you come to us?"

"It might be, and for nothing on earth. . . ."

"I am certain of the contrary."

"Will you be so good as to obtain that he says so to me himself?"

"And then you will come?"

"Oh, madam! that very minute!"

But the warmth of my exclamation might mean a great deal, and I turned my head round so as not to embarrass her. She asked me to give her her mantle to go to church, and we went out. As we were going down the stairs, she placed her ungloved hand upon mine. It was the first time that she had granted me such a favour, and it seemed to me a good omen. She took off her hand, asking me whether I was feverish. "Your hand," she said, "is burning."

When we left the church, M. D—— R——'s carriage happened to pass, and I assisted her to get in, and as soon as she had gone, hurried to my room in order to breathe freely and to enjoy all the felicity which filled my soul; for I no longer doubted her love for me, and I knew that, in this case, M. D—— R—— was not likely to refuse her anything.

What is love? I have read plenty of ancient verbiage on that subject, I have read likewise most of what has been said by modern writers, but neither all that has been said, nor what I have thought about it, when I was young and now that I am no longer so, nothing, in fact, can make me agree that love is a trifling vanity. It is a sort of madness, I grant that, but a madness over which philosophy is entirely powerless; it is a disease to which man is exposed at all times, no matter at what age, and which cannot be cured, if he is attacked by it in his old age. Love being sentiment which cannot be explained! God of all nature!—bitter and sweet feeling! Love!—charming monster which cannot be fathomed! God who, in the midst of all the thorns with which thou plaguest us, strewest so many roses on our path that, without thee, existence and death would be united and blended together!

Two days afterwards, M. D—— R——, told me to go and take orders from M. F—— on board his galley, which was ready for a five or six days' voyage. I quickly packed a few things, and called for my new patron who received me with great joy. We took our departure without seeing madam, who was not yet visible. We returned on the sixth day, and I went to establish myself in my new home, for, as I was preparing to go to M. D—— R——, to take his orders, after our landing, he came himself, and after asking M. F—— and me whether we were pleased with each other, he said to me,——

"Casanova, as you suit each other so well, you may be certain that you will greatly please me by remaining in the service of M. F——."

I obeyed respectfully, and in less than one hour I had taken possession of my new quarters. Madame F—— told me how delighted she was to see that great affair ended according to her wishes, and I answered with a deep reverence.

I found myself like the salamander, in the very heart of the fire for which I had been longing so ardently.

Almost constantly in the presence of Madame F——, dining often alone with her, accompanying her in her walks, even when M. D—— R—— was not with us, seeing her from my room, or conversing with her in her chamber, always reserved and attentive without pretension, the first night passed by without any change being brought about by that constant intercourse. Yet I was full of hope, and to keep up my courage I imagined that love was not yet powerful enough to conquer her pride. I expected everything from some lucky chance, which I promised myself to improve as soon as it should present itself, for I was persuaded that a lover is lost if he does not catch fortune by the forelock.

But there was one circumstance which annoyed me. In public, she seized every opportunity of treating me with distinction, while, when we were alone, it was exactly the reverse. In the eyes of the world I had all the appearance of a happy lover, but I would rather have had less of the appearance of happiness and more of the reality. My love for her was disinterested; vanity had no share in my feelings.

One day, being alone with me, she said,——

"You have enemies, but I silenced them last night."

"They are envious, madam, and they would pity me if they could read the secret pages of my heart. You could easily deliver me from those enemies."

"How can you be an object of pity for them, and how could I deliver you from them?"

"They believe me happy, and I am miserable; you would deliver me from them by ill-treating me in their presence."

"Then you would feel my bad treatment less than the envy of the wicked?"

"Yes, madam, provided your bad treatment in public were compensated by your kindness when we are alone, for there is no vanity in the happiness I feel in belonging to you. Let others pity me, I will be happy on condition that others are mistaken."

"That's a part that I can never play."

I would often be indiscreet enough to remain behind the curtain of the window in my room, looking at her when she thought herself perfectly certain that nobody saw her; but the liberty I was thus guilty of never proved of great advantage to me. Whether it was because she doubted my discretion or from habitual reserve, she was so particular that, even when I saw her in bed, my longing eyes never could obtain a sight of anything but her head.

One day, being present in her room while her maid was cutting off the points of her long and beautiful hair, I amused myself in picking up all those pretty bits, and put them all, one after the other, on her toilet-table, with the exception of one small lock which I slipped into my pocket, thinking that she had not taken any notice of my keeping it; but the moment we were alone she told me quietly, but rather too seriously, to take out of my pocket the hair I had picked up from the floor. Thinking she was going too far, and such rigour appearing to me as cruel as it was unjust and absurd, I obeyed, but threw the hair on the toilet-table with an air of supreme contempt.

"Sir, you forget yourself."

"No, madam, I do not, for you might have feigned not to have observed such an innocent theft."

"Feigning is tiresome."

"Was such petty larceny a very great crime?"

"No crime, but it was an indication of feelings which you have no right to entertain for me."

"Feelings which you are at liberty not to return, madam, but which hatred or pride can alone forbid my heart to experience. If you had a heart you would not be the victim of either of those two fearful passions, but you have only head, and it must be a very wicked head, judging by the care it takes to heap humiliation upon me. You have surprised my secret, madam, you may use it as you think proper, but in the meantime I have learned to know you thoroughly. That knowledge will prove more useful than your discovery, for perhaps it will help me to become wiser."

After this violent tirade I left her, and as she did not call me back retired to my room. In the hope that sleep would bring calm, I undressed and went to bed. In such moments a lover hates the object of his love, and his heart distils only contempt and hatred. I could not go to sleep, and when I was sent for at supper-time I answered that I was ill. The night passed off without my eyes being visited by sleep, and feeling weak and low I thought I would wait to see what ailed me, and refused to have my dinner, sending word that I was still very unwell. Towards evening I felt my heart leap for joy when I heard my beautiful lady-love enter my room. Anxiety, want of food and sleep, gave me truly the appearance of being ill, and I was delighted that it should be so. I sent her away very soon, by telling her with perfect indifference that it was nothing but a bad headache, to which I was subject, and that repose and diet would effect a speedy cure.

But at eleven o'clock she came back with her friend, M. D—— R——, and coming to my bed she said, affectionately,——

"What ails you, my poor Casanova?"

"A very bad headache, madam, which will be cured to-morrow."

"Why should you wait until to-morrow? You must get better at once. I have ordered a basin of broth and two new-laid eggs for you."

"Nothing, madam; complete abstinence can alone cure me."

"He is right," said M. D—— R——, "I know those attacks."

I shook my head slightly. M. D—— R—— having just then turned round to examine an engraving, she took my hand, saying that she would like me to drink some broth, and I felt that she was giving me a small parcel. She went to look at the engraving with M. D—— R——.

I opened the parcel, but feeling that it contained hair, I hurriedly concealed it under the bed-clothes: at the same moment the blood rushed to my head with such violence that it actually frightened me. I begged for some water, she came to me, with M. D—— R——, and then were both frightened to see me so red, when they had seen me pale and weak only one minute before. Madame F—— gave me a glass of water in which she

put some *Eau des carmes* which instantly acted as a
violent emetic. Two or three minutes after I felt better,
and asked for something to eat. Madame F—— smiled.
The servant came in with the broth and the eggs, and
while I was eating I told the history of Pandolfin. M.
D—— R—— thought it was all a miracle, and I could
read, on the countenance of the charming woman, love,
affection, and repentance. If M. D—— R—— had not
been present, it would have been the moment of my
happiness, but I felt certain that I should not have long
to wait. M. D—— R—— told Madame F—— that, if
he had not seen me so sick, he would have believed my
illness to be all sham, for he did not think it possible
for anyone to rally so rapidly.

"It is all owing to my *Eau des carmes*," said Madame
F——, looking at me, "and I will leave you my bottle."

"No, madam, be kind enough to take it with you,
for the water would have no virtue without your presence."

"I am sure of that," said M. D—— R——, "so I will
leave you here with your patient."

"No, no, he must go to sleep now."

I slept all night, but in my happy dreams I was with
her, and the reality itself would hardly have procured
me greater enjoyment than I had during my happy
slumbers. I saw I had taken a very long stride forward,
for twenty-four hours of abstinence gave me the right
to speak to her openly of my love, and the gift of her
hair was an irrefutable confession of her own feelings.

On the following day, after presenting myself before
M. F——, I went to have a little chat with the maid,
to wait until her mistress was visible, which was not
long, and I had the pleasure of hearing her laugh when
the maid told her I was there. As soon as I went in,

without giving me time to say a single word, she told me how delighted she was to see me looking so well, and advised me to call upon M. D—— R——.

It is not only in the eyes of a lover, but also in those of every man of taste, that a woman is a thousand times more lovely at the moment she comes out of the arms of Morpheus than when she has completed her toilet. Around Madame F—— more brilliant beams were blazing than around the sun when he leaves the embrace of Aurora. Yet the most beautiful woman thinks as much of her toilet as the one who cannot do without it; very likely because the more human creatures possess the more they want.

In the order given to me by Madame F—— to call on M. D—— R——, I saw another reason to be certain of approaching happiness, for I thought that, by dismissing me so quickly, she had only tried to postpone the consummation which I might have pressed upon her, and which she could not have refused.

Rich in the possession of her hair, I held a consultation with my love to decide what I ought to do with it, for Madame F——, very likely in her wish to atone for the miserly sentiment which had refused me a small bit, had given me a splendid lock, full a yard and a half long. Having thought it over, I called upon a Jewish confectioner whose daughter was a skilful embroiderer, and I made her embroider before me, on a bracelet of green satin, the four initial letters of our names, and make a very thin chain with the remainder. I had a piece of black ribbon added to one end of the chain, in the shape of a sliding noose, with which I could easily strangle myself if ever love should reduce me to despair, and I passed it round my neck. As I did not want to lose even the smallest particle of so precious a treasure, I cut with a pair of scissors all the small bits which were left, and devoutly gathered them together. Then I reduced them into a fine powder, and ordered the Jewish confectioner to mix the powder in my presence with a paste made of amber, sugar, vanilla, angelica, alkermes and storax, and I waited until the comfits prepared with that mixture were ready. I had some more made with the same composition, but without any hair; I put the first in a beautiful sweetmeat box of fine crystal, and the second in a tortoise-shell box.

From the day when, by giving me her hair, Madame F—— had betrayed the secret feelings of her heart, I no longer lost my time in relating stories or adventures; I only spoke to her of my love, of my ardent desires; I told her that she must either banish me from her presence, or crown my happiness, but the cruel, charming woman would not accept that alternative. She answered that happiness could not be obtained by offending every moral law, and by swerving from our duties. If I threw myself at her feet to obtain by anticipation her forgiveness for the loving violence I intended to use against her, she would repulse me more powerfully than if she had had the strength of a female Hercules, for she would say, in a voice full of sweetness and affection,——

"My friend, I do not entreat you to respect my weakness, but be generous enough to spare me for the sake of all the love I feel for you."

"What! you love me, and you refuse to make me happy! It is impossible! it is unnatural. You compel me to believe that you do not love me. Only allow me to press my lips one moment upon your lips, and I ask no more."

"No, dearest, no; it would only excite the ardour of

your desires, shake my resolution, and we should then find ourselves more miserable than we are now."

Thus did she every day plunge me in despair, and yet she complained that my wit was no longer brilliant in society, that I had lost that elasticity of spirits which had pleased her so much after my arrival from Constantinople. M. D—— R——, who often jestingly waged war against me, used to say that I was getting thinner and thinner every day. Madame F—— told me one day that my sickly looks were very disagreeable to her, because wicked tongues would not fail to say that she treated me with cruelty. Strange, almost unnatural thought! On it I composed an idyll which I cannot read, even now, without feeling tears in my eyes.

"What!" I answered, "you acknowledge your cruelty towards me? You are afraid of the world guessing all your heartless rigour, and yet you continue to enjoy it! You condemn me unmercifully to the torments of Tantalus! You would be delighted to see me gay, cheerful, happy, even at the expense of a judgment by which the world would find you guilty of a supposed but false kindness towards me, and yet you refuse me even the slightest favours!"

"I do not mind people believing anything, provided it is not true."

"What a contrast! Would it be possible for me not to love you, for you to feel nothing for me? Such contradictions strike me as unnatural. But you are growing thinner yourself, and I am dying. It must be so; we shall both die before long, you of consumption, I of exhausting decline; for I am now reduced to enjoying your shadow during the day, during the night, always, everywhere, except when I am in your presence."

At that passionate declaration, delivered with all the

ardour of an excited lover, she was surprised, deeply moved, and I thought that the happy hour had struck. I folded her in my arms, and was already tasting the first fruits of enjoyment. . . . The sentinel knocked twice! . . . Oh! fatal mischance! I recovered my composure and stood in front of her . . . M. D—— R—— made his appearance, and this time he found me in so cheerful a mood that he remained with us until one o'clock in the morning.

My comfits were beginning to be the talk of our society. M. D—— R——, Madame F——, and I were the only ones who had a box full of them. I was stingy with them, and no one durst beg any from me, because I had said that they were very expensive, and that in all Corfu there was no confectioner who could make or physician who could analyse them. I never gave one out of my crystal box, and Madame F—— remarked it. I certainly did not believe them to be amorous philtre, and I was very far from supposing that the addition of the hair made them taste more delicious; but a superstition, the offspring of my love, caused me to cherish them, and it made me happy to think that a small portion of the woman I worshipped was thus becoming a part of my being.

Influenced perhaps by some secret sympathy, Madame F—— was exceedingly fond of the comfits. She asserted before all her friends that they were the universal panacea, and knowing herself perfect mistress of the inventor, she did not enquire after the secret of the composition. But having observed that I gave away only the comfits which I kept in my tortoise-shell box, and that I never eat any but those from the crystal box, she one day asked me what reason I had for that. Without taking time to think, I told her that in those I kept for myself there was a certain ingredient which made the partaker love her.

"I do not believe it," she answered; "but are they different from those I eat myself?"

"They are exactly the same, with the exception of the ingredient I have just mentioned, which has been put only in mine."

"Tell me what the ingredient is."

"It is a secret which I cannot reveal to you."

"Then I will never eat any of your comfits."

Saying which, she rose, emptied her box, and filled it again with chocolate drops; and for the next few days she was angry with me, and avoided my company. I felt grieved, I became low-spirited, but I could not make up my mind to tell her that I was eating her hair!

She enquired why I looked so sad.

"Because you refuse to take my comfits."

"You are master of your secret, and I am mistress of my diet."

"That is my reward for having taken you into my confidence."

And I opened my box, emptied its contents in my hand, and swallowed the whole of them, saying, "Two more doses like this, and I shall die mad with love for you. Then you will be revenged for my reserve. Farewell, madam."

She called me back, made me take a seat near her, and told me not to commit follies which would make her unhappy; that I knew how much she loved me, and that it was not owing to the effect of any drug. "To prove to you," she added, "that you do not require anything of the sort to be loved, here is a token of my affection." And she offered me her lovely lips, and upon them mine remained pressed until I was compelled to draw a breath. I threw myself at her feet, with tears of love and gratitude blinding my eyes, and told her that I would confess my crime, if she would promise to forgive me.

"Your crime! You frighten me. Yes, I forgive you, but speak quickly, and tell me all."

"Yes, everything. My comfits contain your hair reduced to a powder. Here on my arm, see this bracelet on which our names are written with your hair, and round my neck this chain of the same material, which will help me to destroy my own life when your love fails me. Such is my crime, but I would not have been guilty of it, if I had not loved you."

She smiled, and, bidding me rise from my kneeling position, she told me that I was indeed the most criminal of men, and she wiped away my tears, assuring me that I should never have any reason to strangle myself with the chain.

After that conversation, in which I had enjoyed the sweet nectar of my divinity's first kiss, I had the courage to behave in a very different manner. She could see the ardour which consumed me; perhaps the same fire burned in her veins, but I abstained from any attack.

"What gives you," she said one day, "the strength to control yourself?"

"After the kiss which you granted to me of your own accord, I felt that I ought not to wish any favour unless your heart gave it as freely. You cannot imagine the happiness that kiss has given me."

"I not imagine it, you ungrateful man! Which of us has given that happiness?"

"Neither you nor I, angel of my soul! That kiss so tender, so sweet, was the child of love!"

"Yes, dearest, of love, the treasures of which are in-exhaustible."

The words were scarcely spoken, when our lips were engaged in happy concert. She held me so tight against her bosom that I could not use my hands to secure other pleasures, but I felt myself perfectly happy. After that delightful skirmish, I asked her whether we were never to go any further.

"Never, dearest friend, never. Love is a child which must be amused with trifles; too substantial food would kill it."

"I know love better than you; it requires that sub-stantial food, and unless it can obtain it, love dies of exhaustion. Do not refuse me the consolation of hope."

"Hope as much as you please, if it makes you happy."

"What should I do, if I had no hope? I hope, because I know you have a heart."

"Ah! yes. Do you recollect the day, when, in your anger, you told me that I had only a head, but no heart, thinking you were insulting me grossly!"

"Oh! yes, I recollect it."

"How heartily I laughed, when I had time to think! Yes, dearest, I have a heart, or I should not feel as happy as I feel now. Let us keep our happiness, and be satisfied with it, as it is, without wishing for anything more."

Obedient to her wishes, but every day more deeply enamoured, I was in hope that nature at last would prove stronger than prejudice, and would cause a fortu-nate crisis. But, besides nature, fortune was my friend, and I owed my happiness to an accident.

Madame F—— was walking one day in the garden, leaning on M. D—— R——'s arm, and was caught by a large rose-bush, and the prickly thorns left a deep cut on her leg. M. D—— R—— bandaged the wound with his handkerchief, so as to stop the blood which was flowing abundantly, and she had to be carried home in a palanquin.

In Corfu, wounds on the legs are dangerous when they are not well attended to, and very often the wounded are compelled to leave the city to be cured.

Madame F—— was confined to her bed, and my lucky position in the house condemned me to remain constantly at her orders. I saw her every minute; but, during the first three days, visitors succeeded each other without intermission, and I never was alone with her. In the evening, after everybody had gone, and her husband had retired to his own apartment, M. D—— R—— remained another hour, and for the sake of propriety I had to take my leave at the same time that he did. I had much more liberty before the accident, and I told her so half seriously, half jestingly. The next day, to make up for my disappointment, she contrived a moment of happiness for me.

An elderly surgeon came every morning to dress her wound, during which operation her maid only was present, but I used to go, in my morning dishabille, to the girl's room, and to wait there, so as to be the first to hear how my dear one was.

That morning, the girl came to tell me to go in as the surgeon was dressing the wound.

"See, whether my leg is less inflamed."

"To give an opinion, madam, I ought to have seen it yesterday."

"True. I feel great pain, and I am afraid of erysipelas."

"Do not be afraid, madam," said the surgeon, "keep your bed, and I answer for your complete recovery."

The surgeon being busy preparing a poultice at the other end of the room, and the maid out, I enquired whether she felt any hardness in the calf of the leg, and whether the inflammation went up the limb; and naturally, my eyes and my hands kept pace with my questions. . . . I saw no inflammation, I felt no hardness, but . . . and the lovely patient hurriedly let the curtain fall, smiling, and allowing me to take a sweet kiss, the perfume of which I had not enjoyed for many days. It was a sweet moment; a delicious ecstacy. From her mouth my lips descended to her wound, and satisfied in that moment that my kisses were the best of medicines, I would have kept my lips there, if the noise made by the maid coming back had not compelled me to give up my delightful occupation.

When we were left alone, burning with intense desires, I entreated her to grant happiness at least to my eyes.

"I feel humiliated," I said to her, "by the thought that the felicity I have just enjoyed was only a theft."

"But supposing you were mistaken?"

The next day I was again present at the dressing of the wound, and as soon as the surgeon had left, she asked me to arrange her pillows, which I did at once. As if to make that pleasant office easier, she raised the bed-clothes to support herself, and she thus gave me a sight of beauties which intoxicated my eyes, and I protracted the easy operation without her complaining of my being too slow.

When I had done I was in a fearful state, and I threw myself in an arm-chair opposite her bed, half dead, in a sort of trance. I was looking at that lovely being who, almost artless, was continually granting me greater and still greater favours, and yet never allowed me to reach the goal for which I was so ardently longing.

"What are you thinking of?" she said.

"Of the supreme felicity I have just been enjoying."

"You are a cruel man."

"No, I am not cruel, for, if you love me, you must not blush for your indulgence. You must know, too, that, loving you passionately, I must not suppose that it is to be a surprise that I am indebted for my happiness in the enjoyment of the most ravishing sights, for if I owed it only to mere chance I should be compelled to believe that any other man in my position might have had the same happiness, and such an idea would be misery to me. Let me be indebted to you for having proved to me this morning how much enjoyment I can derive from one of my senses. Can you be angry with my eyes?"

"Yes."

"They belong to you; tear them out."

The next day, the moment the doctor had gone, she sent her maid out to make some purchases.

"Ah!" she said a few minutes after, "my maid has forgotten to change my chemise."

"Allow me to take her place."

"Very well, but recollect that I give permission only to your eyes to take a share in the proceedings."

"Agreed!"

She unlaced herself, took off her stays and her chemise, and told me to be quick and put on the clean one, but I was not speedy enough, being too much engaged by all I could see.

"Give me my chemise," she exclaimed; "it is there on that small table."

"Where?"

"There, near the bed. Well, I will take it myself."

She leaned over towards the table, and exposed almost everything I was longing for, and, turning slowly

round, she handed me the chemise which I could hardly
hold, trembling all over with fearful excitement. She
took pity on me, my hands shared the happiness of my
eyes; I fell in her arms, our lips fastened together, and,
in a voluptuous, ardent pressure, we enjoyed an amorous
exhaustion not sufficient to allay our desires, but delightful enough to deceive them for the moment.

With greater control over herself than women have
generally under similar circumstances, she took care to
let me reach only the porch of the temple, without granting me yet a free entrance to the sanctuary.

CHAPTER XVI

*A Fearful Misfortune Befalls Me—Love Cools Down—
I Leave Corfu and Return to Venice—I Give Up the
Army and Become a Fiddler*

THE wound was rapidly healing up, and I saw near
at hand the moment when Madame F—— would
leave her bed, and resume her usual avocations.

The governor of the galeasses having issued orders for
a general review at Gouyn, M. F——, left for that place
in his galley, telling me to join him there early on the
following day with the felucca. I took supper alone
with Madame F——, and I told her how unhappy it
made me to remain one day away from her.

"Let us make up to-night for to-morrow's disappointment," she said, "and let us spend it together in conversation. Here are the keys; when you know that my
maid has left me, come to me through my husband's
room."

I did not fail to follow her instructions to the letter,
and we found ourselves alone with five hours before us.
It was the month of June, and the heat was intense. She
had gone to bed; I folded her in my arms, she pressed me
to her bosom, but, condemning herself to the most cruel
torture, she thought I had no right to complain, if I was
subjected to the same privation which she imposed upon
herself. My remonstrances, my prayers, my entreaties
were of no avail.

"Love," she said, "must be kept in check with a tight hand, and we can laugh at him, since, in spite of the tyranny which we force him to obey, we succeed all the same in gratifying our desires."

After the first ecstacy, our eyes and lips unclosed to- gether, and a little apart from each other we take de- light in seeing the mutual satisfaction beaming on our features.

Our desires revive; she casts a look upon my state of innocence entirely exposed to her sight. She seems vexed at my want of excitement, and, throwing off everything which makes the heat unpleasant and inter- feres with our pleasure, she bounds upon me. It is more than amorous fury, it is desperate lust. I share her frenzy, I hug her with a sort of delirium, I enjoy a felic- ity which is on the point of carrying me to the regions of bliss . . . but, at the very moment of completing the offering, she fails me, moves off, slips away, and comes back to work off my excitement with a hand which strikes me as cold as ice.

"Ah, thou cruel, beloved woman! Thou art burning with the fire of love, and thou deprivest thyself of the only remedy which could bring calm to thy senses! Thy lovely hand is more humane than thou art, but thou has not enjoyed the felicity that thy hand has given me. My hand must owe nothing to thine. Come, darling light of my heart, come! Love doubles my existence in the hope that I will die again, but only in that charming retreat from which you have ejected me in the very moment of my greatest enjoyment."

While I was speaking thus, her very soul was breath- ing forth the most tender sighs of happiness, and as she pressed me tightly in her arms I felt that she was welter- ing in an ocean of bliss.

Silence lasted rather a long time, but that unnatural felicity was imperfect, and increased my excitement.

"How canst thou complain," she said tenderly, "when it is to that very imperfection of our enjoyment that we are indebted for its continuance? I loved thee a few minutes since, now I love thee a thousand times more, and perhaps I should love thee less if thou hadst carried my enjoyment to its highest limit."

"Oh! how much art thou mistaken, lovely one! How great is thy error! Thou art feeding upon sophisms, and thou leavest reality aside; I mean nature which alone can give real felicity. Desires constantly renewed and never fully satisfied are more terrible than the torments of hell."

"But are not these desires happiness when they are always accompanied by hope?"

"No, if that hope is always disappointed. It becomes hell itself, because there is no hope, and hope must die when it is killed by constant deception."

"Dearest, if hope does not exist in hell, desires cannot be found there either; for to imagine desires without hopes would be more than madness."

"Well, answer me. If you desire to be mine entirely, and if you feel the hope of it, which, according to your way of reasoning, is a natural consequence, why do you always raise an impediment to your own hope? Cease, dearest, cease to deceive yourself by absurd sophisms. Let us be as happy as it is in nature to be, and be quite certain that the reality of happiness will increase our love, and that love will find a new life in our very enjoyment."

"What I see proves the contrary; you are alive with excitement now, but if your desires had been entirely satisfied, you would be dead, benumbed, motionless. I know it by experience: if you had breathed the full ecstacy of enjoyment, as you desired, you would have found a weak ardour only at long intervals."

"Ah! charming creature, your experience is but very small; do not trust to it. I see that you have never known love. That which you call love's grave is the sanctuary in which it receives life, the abode which makes it immortal. Give way to my prayers, my lovely friend, and then you shall know the difference between Love and Hymen. You shall see that, if Hymen likes to die in order to get rid of life, Love on the contrary expires only to spring up again into existence, and hastens to revive, so as to savour new enjoyment. Let me undeceive you, and believe me when I say that the full gratification of desires can only increase a hundred-fold the mutual ardour of two beings who adore each other."

"Well, I must believe you; but let us wait. In the meantime let us enjoy all the trifles, all the sweet preliminaries of love. Devour thy mistress, dearest, but abondon to me all thy being. If this night is too short we must console ourselves to-morrow by making arrangements for another one."

"And if our intercourse should be discovered?"

"Do we make a mystery of it? Everybody can see that we love each other, and those who think that we do not enjoy the happiness of lovers are precisely the only persons we have to fear. We must only be careful to guard against being surprised in the very act of proving our love. Heaven and nature must protect our affection, for there is no crime when two hearts are blended in true love. Since I have been conscious of my own existence, Love has always seemed to me the god of my being, for every time I saw a man I was delighted; I thought that I was looking upon one-half of myself, because I felt I was made for him and he for me. I longed to be married. It was that uncertain longing of the heart which occupies exclusively a young girl of fifteen. I had no conception of love, but I fancied that it naturally accompanied marriage. You can therefore imagine my surprise when my husband, in the very act of making a woman of me, gave me a great deal of pain without giving me the slightest idea of pleasure! My imagination in the convent was much better than the reality I had been condemned to by my husband! The result has naturally been that we have become very good friends, but a very indifferent husband and wife, without any desires for each other. He has every reason to be pleased with me, for I always shew myself docile to his wishes, but enjoyment not being in those cases seasoned by love, he must find it without flavour, and he seldom comes to me for it.

"When I found out that you were in love with me, I felt delighted, and gave you every opportunity of becoming every day more deeply enamoured of me, thinking myself certain of never loving you myself. As soon as I felt that love had likewise attacked my heart, I illtreated you to punish you for having made my heart sensible. Your patience and constancy have astonished me, and have caused me to be guilty, for after the first kiss I gave you I had no longer any control over myself. I was indeed astounded when I saw the havoc made by one single kiss, and I felt that my happiness was wrapped up in yours. That discovery flattered and delighted me, and I have found out, particularly to-night, that I cannot be happy unless you are so yourself."

"That is, my beloved, the most refined of all sentiments experienced by love, but it is impossible for you to render me completely happy without following in everything the laws and the wishes of nature."

The night was spent in tender discussions and in exquisite voluptuousness, and it was not without some grief that at day-break I tore myself from her arms to go to Gouyn. She wept for joy when she saw that I left her without having lost a particle of my vigour, for she did not imagine such a thing possible.

After that night, so rich in delights, ten or twelve days passed without giving us any opportunity of quenching even a small particle of the amorous thirst which devoured us, and it was then that a fearful misfortune befell me.

One evening after supper, M. D—— R—— having retired, M. F—— used no ceremony, and, although I was present, told his wife that he intended to pay her a visit after writing two letters which he had to dispatch early the next morning. The moment he had left the room we looked at each other, and with one accord fell into each other's arms. A torrent of delights rushed through our souls without restraint, without reserve, but when the first ardour had been appeased, without giving me time to think or to enjoy the most complete, the most delicious victory, she drew back, repulsed me, and threw hrself, panting, distracted, upon a chair near her bed. Rooted to the spot, astonished, almost mad, I tremblingly looked at her, trying to understand what had caused such an extraordinary action. She turned round towards me and said, her eyes flashing with the fire of love,——

"My darling, we were on the brink of the precipice."

"The precipice! Ah! cruel woman, you have killed me, I feel myself dying, and perhaps you will never see me again."

I left her in a state of frenzy, and rushed out, towards the esplanade, to cool myself, for I was choking. Any man who has not experienced the cruelty of an action like that of Madame F——, and especially in the situation I found myself in at that moment, mentally and bodily, can hardly realize what I suffered, and, although I have felt that suffering, I could not give an idea of it.

I was in that fearful state, when I heard my name called from a window, and unfortunately I condescended to answer. I went near the window, and I saw, thanks to the moonlight, the famous Melulla standing on her balcony.

"What are you doing there at this time of night?" I enquired.

"I am enjoying the cool evening breeze. Come up for a little while."

This Melulla, of fatal memory, was a courtezan from Zante, of rare beauty, who for the last four months had been the delight and the rage of all the young men in Corfu. Those who had known her agreed in extolling her charms: she was the talk of all the city. I had seen her often, but, although she was very beautiful, I was very far from thinking her as lovely as Madame F——, putting my affection for the latter on one side. I recollect seeing in Dresden, in the year 1790, a very handsome woman who was the image of Melulla.

I went upstairs mechanically, and she took me to a voluptuous boudoir; she complained of my being the only one who had never paid her a visit, when I was the man she would have preferred to all others, and I had the infamy to give way. . . . I became the most criminal of men.

It was neither desire, nor imagination, nor the merit

of the woman which caused me to yield, for Melulla was
in no way worthy of me; no, it was weakness, indolence,
and the state of bodily and mental irritation in which I
then found myself: it was a sort of spite, because the
angel whom I adored had displeased me by a caprice,
which, had I not been unworthy of her, would only have
caused me to be still more attached to her.

Melulla, highly pleased with her success, refused the
gold I wanted to give her, and allowed me to go after I
had spent two hours with her.

When I recovered my composure, I had but one feeling—hatred for myself and for the contemptible creature
who had allured me to be guilty of so vile an insult to
the loveliest of her sex. I went home the prey to fearful
remorse, and went to bed, but sleep never closed my eyes
throughout that cruel night.

In the morning, worn out with fatigue and sorrow, I
got up, and as soon as I was dressed I went to M. F——,
who had sent for me to give me some orders. After I
had returned, and had given him an account of my mission, I called upon Madame F——, and finding her at
her toilet I wished her good morning, observing that her
lovely face was breathing the cheerfulness and the calm
of happiness; but, suddenly, her eyes meeting mine, I
saw her countenance change, and an expression of sadness replace her looks of satisfaction. She cast her eyes
down as if she was deep in thought, raised them again
as if to read my very soul, and breaking our painful silence, as soon as she had dismissed her maid, she said
to me, with an accent full of tenderness and of solem-
nity,——

"Dear one, let there be no concealment either on my
part or on yours. I felt deeply grieved when I saw you
leave me last night, and a little consideration made me

understand all the evil which might accrue to you in consequence of what I had done. With a nature like yours, such scenes might cause very dangerous disorders, and I have resolved not to do again anything by halves. I thought that you went out to breathe the fresh air, and I hoped it would do you good. I placed myself at my window, where I remained more than an hour without seeing a light in your room. Sorry for what I had done, loving you more than ever, I was compelled, when my husband came to my room, to go to bed with the sad conviction that you had not come home. This morning, M. F—— sent an officer to tell you that he wanted to see you, and I heard the messenger inform him that you were not yet up, and that you had come home very late. I felt my heart swell with sorrow. I am not jealous, dearest, for I know that you cannot love anyone but me; I only felt afraid of some misfortune. At last, this morning, when I heard you coming, I was happy, because I was ready to shew my repentance, but I looked at you, and you seemed a different man. Now, I am still looking at you, and, in spite of myself, my soul reads upon your countenance that you are guilty, that you have outraged my love. Tell me at once, dearest, if I am mistaken; if you have deceived me, say so openly. Do not be unfaithful to love and to truth. Knowing that I was the cause of it, I should never forgive myself, but there is an excuse for you in my heart, in my whole being."

More than once, in the course of my life, I have found myself under the painful necessity of telling falsehoods to the woman I loved; but in this case, after so true, so touching an appeal, how could I be otherwise than sincere? I felt myself sufficiently debased by my crime, and I could not degrade myself still more by falsehood. I was so far from being disposed to such a line of conduct that I could not speak, and I burst out crying.

"What, my darling! you are weeping! Your tears make me miserable. You ought not to have shed any with me but tears of happiness and love. Quick, my beloved, tell me whether you have made me wretched. Tell me what fearful revenge you have taken on me, who would rather die than offend you. If I have caused you any sorrow, it has been in the innocence of a loving and devoted heart."

"My own darling angel, I never thought of revenge, for my heart, which can never cease to adore you, could never conceive such a dreadful idea. It is against my own heart that my cowardly weakness has allured me to the commission of a crime which, for the remainder of my life, makes me unworthy of you."

"Have you, then, given yourself to some wretched woman?"

"Yes, I have spent two hours in the vilest debauchery, and my soul was present only to be the witness of my sadness, of my remorse, of my unworthiness."

"Sadness and remorse! Oh, my poor friend! I believe it. But it is my fault; I alone ought to suffer; it is I who must beg you to forgive me."

Her tears made mine flow again.

"Divine soul," I said, "the reproaches you are addressing to yourself increase twofold the gravity of my crime. You would never have been guilty of any wrong against me if I had been really worthy of your love."

I felt deeply the truth of my words.

We spent the remainder of the day apparently quiet and composed, concealing our sadness in the depths of our hearts. She was curious to know all the circumstances of my miserable adventure, and, accepting it as an expiation, I related them to her. Full of kindness, she assured me that we were bound to ascribe that accident to fate, and that the same thing might have happened to the best of men. She added that I was more to be pitied than condemned, and that she did not love me less. We both were certain that we would seize the first favourable opportunity, she of obtaining her pardon, I of atoning for my crime, by giving each other new and complete proofs of our mutual ardour. But Heaven in its justice had ordered differently, and I was cruelly punished for my disgusting debauchery.

On the third day, as I got up in the morning, an awful pricking announced the horrid state into which the wretched Melulla had thrown me. I was thunderstruck! And when I came to think of the misery which I might have caused if, during the last three days, I had obtained some new favour from my lovely mistress, I was on the point of going mad. What would have been her feelings if I had made her unhappy for the remainder of her life! Would anyone, then, knowing the whole case, have condemned me if I had destroyed my own life in order to deliver myself from everlasting remorse? No, for the man who kills himself from sheer despair, thus performing upon himself the execution of the sentence he would have deserved at the hands of justice cannot be blamed either by a virtuous philosopher or by a tolerant Christian. But of one thing I am quite certain: if such a misfortune had happened, I should have committed suicide.

Overwhelmed with grief by the discovery I had just made, but thinking that I should get rid of the inconvenience as I had done three times before, I prepared myself for a strict diet, which would restore my health in

six weeks without anyone having any suspicion of my
illness, but I soon found out that I had not seen the end
of my troubles; Melulla had communicated to my system all the poisons which corrupt the source of life. I
was acquainted with an elderly doctor of great experience in those matters; I consulted him, and he promised
to set me to rights in two months; he proved as good
as his word. At the beginning of September I found
myself in good health, and it was about that time that I
returned to Venice.

The first thing I resolved on, as soon as I discovered
the state I was in, was to confess everything to Madame
F——. I did not wish to wait for the time when a
compulsory confession would have made her blush for
her weakness, and given her cause to think of the fearful consequences which might have been the result of
her passion for me. Her affection was too dear to me
to run the risk of losing it through a want of confidence in her. Knowing her heart, her candour, and
the generosity which had prompted her to say that I
was more to be pitied than blamed, I thought myself
bound to prove by my sincerity that I deserved her
esteem.

I told her candidly my position and the state I had
been thrown in, when I thought of the dreadful consequences it might have had for her. I saw her shudder
and tremble, and she turned pale with fear when I added
that I would have avenged her by killing myself.

"Villainous, infamous Melulla!" she exclaimed.

And I repeated those words, but turning them against
myself when I realized all I had sacrificed through the
most disgusting weakness.

Everyone in Corfu knew of my visit to the wretched
Melulla, and everyone seemed surprised to see the ap-

pearance of health on my countenance; for many were the victims that she had treated like me.

My illness was not my only sorrow; I had others which, although of a different nature, were not less serious. It was written in the book of fate that I should return to Venice a simple ensign as when I left: the general did not keep his word, and the bastard son of a nobleman was promoted to the lieutenancy instead of myself. From that moment the military profession, the one most subject to arbitrary despotism, inspired me with disgust, and I determined to give it up. But I had another still more important motive for sorrow in the fickleness of fortune which had completely turned against me. I remarked that, from the time of my degradation with Melulla, every kind of misfortune befell me. The greatest of all—that which I felt most, but which I had the good sense to try and consider a favour—was that a week before the departure of the army M. D—— R—— took me again for his adjutant, and M. F—— had to engage another in my place. On the occasion of that change Madame F—— told me, with an appearance of regret, that in Venice we could not, for many reasons, continue our intimacy. I begged her to spare me the reasons, as I foresaw that they would only throw humiliation upon me. I began to discover that the goddess I had worshipped was, after all, a poor human being like all other women, and to think that I should have been very foolish to give up my life for her. I probed in one day the real worth of her heart, for she told me, I cannot recollect in reference to what, that I excited her pity. I saw clearly that she no longer loved me; pity is a debasing feeling which cannot find a home in a heart full of love, for that dreary sentiment is too near a relative of contempt. Since that time I never found myself alone with Madame F——. I loved her still; I could easily have made her blush, but I did not do it.

As soon as we reached Venice she became attached to M. F—— R——, whom she loved until death took him from her. She was unhappy enough to lose her sight twenty years after. I believe she is still alive.

During the last two months of my stay in Corfu, I learned the most bitter and important lessons. In after years I often derived useful hints from the experience I acquired at that time.

Before my adventure with the worthless Melulla, I enjoyed good health, I was rich, lucky at play, liked by everybody, beloved by the most lovely woman of Corfu. When I spoke, everybody would listen and admire my wit; my words were taken for oracles, and everyone coincided with me in everything. After my fatal meeting with the courtezan I rapidly lost my health, my money, my credit; cheerfulness, consideration, wit, everything, even the faculty of eloquence vanished with fortune. I would talk, but people knew that I was unfortunate, and I no longer interested or convinced my hearers. The influence I had over Madame F—— faded away little by little, and, almost without her knowing it, the lovely woman became completely indifferent to me.

I left Corfu without money, although I had sold or pledged everything I had of any value. Twice I had reached Corfu rich and happy, twice I left it poor and miserable. But this time I had contracted debts which I have never paid, not through want of will but through carelessness.

Rich and in good health, everyone received me with open arms; poor and looking sick, no one shewed me any consideration. With a full purse and the tone of a conqueror, I was thought witty, amusing; with an empty purse and a modest air, all I said appeared dull and insipid. If I had become rich again, how soon I would have been again accounted the eighth wonder of the world! Oh, men! oh, fortune! Everyone avoided me as if the ill luck which crushed me down was infectious.

We left Corfu towards the end of September, with five galleys, two galeasses, and several smaller vessels, under the command of M. Renier. We sailed along the shores of the Adriatic, towards the north of the gulf, where there are a great many harbours, and we put in one of them every night. I saw Madame F—— every evening; she always came with her husband to take supper on board our galeass. We had a fortunate voyage, and cast anchor in the harbour of Venice on the 14th of October, 1745, and after having performed quarantine on board our ships, we landed on the 25th of November. Two months afterwards, the galeasses were set aside altogether. The use of these vessels could be traced very far back in ancient times; their maintenance was very expensive, and they were useless. A galeass had the frame of a frigate with the rowing apparatus of the galley, and when there was no wind, five hundred slaves had to row.

Before simple good sense managed to prevail and to enforce the suppression of these useless carcasses, there were long discussions in the senate, and those who opposed the measure took their principal ground of opposition in the necessity of respecting and conserving all the institutions of olden times. That is the disease of persons who can never identify themselves with the successive improvements born of reason and experience;

worthy persons who ought to be sent to China, or to the
dominions of the Grand Lama, where they would certainly be more at home than in Europe.

That ground of opposition to all improvements, however absurd it may be, is a very powerful one in a republic, which must tremble at the mere idea of novelty
either in important or in trifling things. Superstition
has likewise a great part to play in these conservative
views.

There is one thing that the Republic of Venice will
never alter: I mean the galleys, because the Venetians
truly require such vessels to ply, in all weathers and in
spite of the frequent calms, in a narrow sea, and because
they would not know what to do with the men sentenced
to hard labour.

I have observed a singular thing in Corfu, where
there are often as many as three thousand galley slaves;
it is that the men who row on the galleys, in consequence
of a sentence passed upon them for some crime, are held
in a kind of opprobrium, whilst those who are there voluntarily are, to some extent, respected. I have always
thought it ought to be the reverse, because misfortune,
whatever it may be, ought to inspire some sort of respect; but the vile fellow who condemns himself voluntarily and as a trade to the position of a slave seems to
me contemptible in the highest degree. The convicts of
the Republic, however, enjoy many privileges, and are,
in every way, better treated than the soldiers. It very
often occurs that soldiers desert and give themselves up
to a *sopracomito* to become galley slaves. In those
cases, the captain who loses a soldier has nothing to do
but to submit patiently, for he would claim the man in
vain. The reason of it is that the Republic has always
believed galley slaves more necessary than soldiers. The

Venetians may perhaps now (I am writing these lines in the year 1797) begin to realize their mistake.

A galley slave, for instance, has the privilege of stealing with impunity. It is considered that stealing is the least crime they can be guilty of, and that they ought to be forgiven for it.

"Keep on your guard," says the master of the galley slave; "and if you catch him in the act of stealing, thrash him, but be careful not to cripple him; otherwise you must pay me the one hundred ducats the man has cost me."

A court of justice could not have a galley slave taken from a galley, without paying the master the amount he has disbursed for the man.

As soon as I had landed in Venice, I called upon Madame Orio, but I found the house empty. A neighbour told me that she had married the Procurator Rosa, and had removed to his house. I went immediately to M. Rosa and was well received. Madame Orio informed me that Nanette had become Countess R., and was living in Guastalla with her husband.

Twenty-four years afterwards, I met her eldest son, then a distinguished officer in the service of the Infante of Parma.

As for Marton, the grace of Heaven had touched her, and she had become a nun in the convent at Muran. Two years afterwards, I received from her a letter full of unction in which she adjured me, in the name of Our Saviour and of the Holy Virgin, never to present myself before her eyes. She added that she was bound by Christian charity to forgive me for the crime I had committed in seducing her, and she felt certain of the reward of the elect, and she assured me that she would ever pray earnestly for my conversion.

I never saw her again, but she saw me in 1754, as I will mention when we reach that year.

I found Madame Manzoni still the same. She had predicted that I would not remain in the military profession, and when I told her that I had made up my mind to give it up, because I could not be reconciled to the injustice I had experienced, she burst out laughing. She enquired about the profession I intended to follow after giving up the army, and I answered that I wished to become an advocate. She laughed again, saying that it was too late. Yet I was only twenty years old.

When I called upon M. Grimani I had a friendly welcome from him, but, having enquired after my brother François, he told me that he had had him confined in Fort Saint André, the same to which I had been sent before the arrival of the Bishop of Martorano.

"He works for the major there," he said; "he copies Simonetti's battle-pieces, and the major pays him for them; in that manner he earns his living, and is becoming a good painter."

"But he is not a prisoner?"

"Well, very much like it, for he cannot leave the fort. The major, whose name is Spiridion, is a friend of Razetta, who could not refuse him the pleasure of taking care of your brother."

I felt it a dreadful curse that the fatal Razetta should be the tormentor of all my family, but I concealed my anger.

"Is my sister," I enquired, "still with him?"

"No, she has gone to your mother in Dresden."

This was good news.

I took a cordial leave of the Abbé Grimani, and I proceeded to Fort Saint André. I found my brother hard at work, neither pleased nor displeased with his position, and enjoying good health. After embracing him affectionately, I enquired what crime he had committed to be thus a prisoner.

"Ask the major," he said, "for I have not the faintest idea."

The major came in just then, so I gave him the military salute, and asked by what authority he kept my brother under arrest.

"I am not accountable to you for my actions."

"That remains to be seen."

I then told my brother to take his hat, and to come and dine with me. The major laughed, and said that he had no objection provided the sentinel allowed him to pass.

I saw that I should only waste my time in discussion, and I left the fort fully bent on obtaining justice.

The next day I went to the war office, where I had the pleasure of meeting my dear Major Pelodoro, who was then commander of the Fortress of Chiozza. I informed him of the complaint I wanted to prefer before the secretary of war respecting my brother's arrest, and of the resolution I had taken to leave the army. He promised me that, as soon as the consent of the secretary for war could be obtained, he would find a purchaser for my commission at the same price I had paid for it.

I had not long to wait. The war secretary came to the office, and everything was settled in half an hour. He promised his consent to the sale of my commission as soon as he ascertained the abilities of the purchaser, and Major Spiridion happening to make his appearance in the office while I was still there, the secretary ordered him rather angrily, to set my brother at liberty immediately, and cautioned him not to be guilty again of such reprehensible and arbitrary acts.

I went at once for my brother, and we lived together in furnished lodgings.

A few days afterwards, having received my discharge and one hundred sequins, I threw off my uniform, and found myself once more my own master.

I had to earn my living in one way or another, and I decided for the profession of gamester. But Dame Fortune was not of the same opinion, for she refused to smile upon me from the very first step I took in the career, and in less than a week I did not possess a groat. What was to become of me? One must live, and I turned fiddler. Doctor Gozzi had taught me well enough to enable me to scrape on the violin in the orchestra of a theatre, and having mentioned my wishes to M. Grimani he procured me an engagement at his own theatre of Saint Samuel, where I earned a crown a day, and supported myself while I awaited better things.

Fully aware of my real position, I never shewed myself in the fashionable circles which I used to frequent before my fortune had sunk so low. I knew that I was considered as a worthless fellow, but I did not care. People despised me, as a matter of course; but I found comfort in the consciousness that I was worthy of contempt. I felt humiliated by the position to which I was reduced after having played so brilliant a part in society; but as I kept the secret to myself I was not degraded, even if I felt some shame. I had not exchanged my last word with Dame Fortune, and was still in hope of reckoning with her some day, because I was young, and youth is dear to Fortune.

CHAPTER XVII

I Turn Out A Worthless Fellow—My Good Fortune—
I Become A Rich Nobleman

WITH an education which ought to have ensured me an honourable standing in the world, with some intelligence, wit, good literary and scientific knowledge, and endowed with those accidental physical qualities which are such a good passport into society, I found myself, at the age of twenty, the mean follower of a sublime art, in which, if great talent is rightly admired, mediocrity is as rightly despised. I was compelled by poverty to become a member of a musical band, in which I could expect neither esteem nor consideration, and I was well aware that I should be the laughing-stock of the persons who had known me as a doctor in divinity, as an ecclesiastic, and as an officer in the army, and had welcomed me in the highest society.

I knew all that, for I was not blind to my position; but contempt, the only thing to which I could not have remained indifferent, never shewed itself anywhere under a form tangible enough for me to have no doubt of my being despised, and I set it at defiance, because I was satisfied that contempt is due only to cowardly, mean actions, and I was conscious that I had never been guilty of any. As to public esteem, which I had ever been anxious to secure, my ambition was slumbering, and satisfied with being my own master I enjoyed my independence without puzzling my head about the future. I felt that in my first profession, as I was not blessed with the vocation necessary to it, I should have succeeded only by dint of hypocrisy, and I should have been despicable in my own estimation, even if I had seen the purple mantle on my shoulders, for the greatest dignities cannot silence a man's own conscience. If, on the other hand, I had continued to seek fortune in a military career, which is surrounded by a halo of glory, but is otherwise the worst of professions for the constant self-abnegation, for the complete surrender of one's will which passive obedience demands, I should have required a patience to which I could not lay any claim, as every kind of injustice was revolting to me, and as I could not bear to feel myself dependent. Besides, I was of opinion that a man's profession, whatever it might be, ought to supply him with enough money to satisfy all his wants; and the very poor pay of an officer would never have been sufficient to cover my expenses, because my education had given me greater wants than those of officers in general. By scraping my violin I earned enough to keep myself without requiring anybody's assistance, and I have always thought that the man who can support himself is happy. I grant that my profession was not a brilliant one, but I did not mind it, and, calling prejudices all the feelings which rose in my breast against myself, I was not long in sharing all the habits of my degraded comrades. When the play was over, I went with them to the drinking-booth, which we often left intoxicated to spend the night in houses of ill-fame. When we happened to find those places already tenanted by other men, we forced them by violence to quit the premises, and defrauded the miserable victims of prostitution of the mean salary the law allows them, after compelling them to yield to our brutality. Our scandalous proceedings often exposed us to the greatest danger.

We would very often spend the whole night rambling about the city, inventing and carrying into execution the most impertinent, practical jokes. One of our favourite pleasures was to unmoor the patricians' gondolas, and to let them float at random along the canals, enjoying by anticipation all the curses that gondoliers would not fail to indulge in. We would rouse up hurriedly, in the middle of the night, an honest midwife, telling her to hasten to Madame So-and-so, who, not being even pregnant, was sure to tell her she was a fool when she called at the house. We did the same with physicians, whom we often sent half dressed to some nobleman who was enjoying excellent health. The priests fared no better; we would send them to carry the last sacraments to married men who were peacefully slumbering near their wives, and not thinking of extreme unction.

We were in the habit of cutting the wires of the bells in every house, and if we chanced to find a gate open we would go up the stairs in the dark, and frighten the sleeping inmates by telling them very loudly that the house door was not closed, after which we would go down, making as much noise as we could, and leave the house with the gate wide open.

During a very dark night we formed a plot to overturn the large marble table of St. Angelo's Square, on which it was said that in the days of the League of Cambray the commissaries of the Republic were in the habit of paying the bounty to the recruits who engaged to fight under the standard of St. Mark—a circumstance which secured for the table a sort of public veneration.

Whenever we could contrive to get into a church

tower we thought it great fun to frighten all the parish by ringing the alarm bell, as if some fire had broken out; but that was not all, we always cut the bell ropes, so that in the morning the churchwardens had no means of summoning the faithful to early mass. Sometimes we would cross the canal, each of us in a different gondola, and take to our heels without paying as soon as we landed on the opposite side, in order to make the gondoliers run after us.

The city was alive with complaints, and we laughed at the useless search made by the police to find out those who disturbed the peace of the inhabitants. We took good care to be careful, for if we had been discovered we stood a very fair chance of being sent to practice rowing at the expense of the Council of Ten.

We were seven, and sometimes eight, because, being much attached to my brother François, I gave him a share now and then in our nocturnal orgies. But at last fear put a stop to our criminal jokes, which in those days I used to call only the frolics of young men. This is the amusing adventure which closed our exploits.

In every one of the seventy-two parishes of the city of Venice, there is a large public-house called *magazzino*. It remains open all night, and wine is retailed there at a cheaper price than in all the other drinking houses. People can likewise eat in the *magazzino*, but they must obtain what they want from the pork butcher near by, who has the exclusive sale of eatables, and likewise keeps his shop open throughout the night. The pork butcher is usually a very poor cook, but as he is cheap, poor people are willingly satisfied with him, and these resorts are considered very useful to the lower class. The nobility, the merchants, even workmen in good circumstances, are never seen in the *magazzini*, for cleanliness is not exactly worshipped in such places. Yet there are a few private rooms which contain a table surrounded with benches, in which a respectable family or a few friends can enjoy themselves in a decent way.

It was during the Carnival of 1745, after midnight; we were, all the eight of us, rambling about together with our masks on, in quest of some new sort of mischief to amuse us, and we went into the *magazzino* of the parish of the Holy Cross to get something to drink. We found the public room empty, but in one of the private chambers we discovered three men quietly conversing with a young and pretty woman, and enjoying their wine.

Our chief, a noble Venetian belonging to the Balbi family, said to us, "It would be a good joke to carry off those three blockheads, and to keep the pretty woman in our possession." He immediately explained his plan, and under cover of our masks we entered their room, Balbi at the head of us. Our sudden appearance rather surprised the good people, but you may fancy their astonishment when they heard Balbi say to them: "Under penalty of death, and by order of the Council of Ten, I command you to follow us immediately, without making the slightest noise; as to you, my good woman, you need not be frightened, you will be escorted to your house." When he had finished his speech, two of us got hold of the woman to take her where our chief had arranged beforehand, and the others seized the three poor fellows, who were trembling all over, and had not the slightest idea of opposing any resistance.

The waiter of the *magazzino* came to be paid, and our chief gave him what was due, enjoining silence under penalty of death. We took our three prisoners to a large boat. Balbi went to the stern, ordered the boat-

man to stand at the bow, and told him that he need
not enquire where we were going, that he would steer
himself whichever way he thought fit. Not one of us
knew where Balbi wanted to take the three poor devils.

He sails all along the canal, gets out of it, takes several turnings, and in a quarter of an hour, we reach
Saint George where Balbi lands our prisoners, who àre
delighted to find themselves at liberty. After this, the
boatman is ordered to take us to Saint Geneviève, where
we land, after paying for the boat.

We proceed at once to Palombo Square, where my
brother and another of our band were waiting for us
with our lovely prisoner, who was crying.

"Do not weep, my beauty," says Balbi to her, "we
will not hurt you. We intend only to take some re-
freshment at the Rialto, and then we will take you
home in safety."

"Where is my husband?"

"Never fear; you shall see him again to-morrow."

Comforted by that promise, and as gentle as a lamb,
she follows us to the "Two Swords." We ordered a
good fire in a private room, and, everything we wanted
to eat and to drink having been brought in, we send
the waiter away, and remain alone. We take off our
masks, and the sight of eight young, healthy faces seems
to please the beauty we had so unceremoniously carried
off. We soon manage to reconcile her to her fate by
the gallantry of our proceedings; encouraged by a good
supper and by the stimulus of wine, prepared by our
compliments and by a few kisses, she realizes what is
in store for her, and does not seem to have any unconquerable objection. Our chief, as a matter of right,
claims the privilege of opening the ball; and by dint
of sweet words he overcomes the very natural repug-

nance she feels at consummating the sacrifice in so numerous company. She, doubtless, thinks the offering agreeable, for, when I present myself as the priest appointed to sacrifice a second time to the god of love, she receives me almost with gratitude, and she cannot conceal her joy when she finds out that she is destined to make us all happy. My brother François alone exempted himself from paying the tribute, saying that he was ill, the only excuse which could render his refusal valid, for we had established as a law that every member of our society was bound to do whatever was done by the others.

After that fine exploit, we put on our masks, and, the bill being paid, escorted the happy victim to Saint Job, where she lived, and did not leave her till we had seen her safe in her house, and the street door closed.

My readers may imagine whether we felt inclined to laugh when the charming creature bade us good night, thanking us all with perfect good faith!

Two days afterwards, our nocturnal orgy began to be talked of. The young woman's husband was a weaver by trade, and so were his two friends. They joined together to address a complaint to the Council of Ten. The complaint was candidly written and contained nothing but the truth, but the criminal portion of the truth was veiled by a circumstance which must have brought a smile on the grave countenances of the judges, and highly amused the public at large: the complaint setting forth that the eight masked men had not rendered themselves guilty of any act disagreeable to the wife. It went on to say that the two men who had carried her off had taken her to such a place, where they had, an hour later, been met by the other six, and that they had all repaired to the "Two Swords," where they had spent an hour in drinking. The said lady having been handsomely entertained by the eight masked men, had been escorted to her house, where she had been politely requested to excuse the joke perpetrated upon her husband. The three plaintiffs had not been able to leave the island of Saint George until day-break, and the husband, on reaching his house, had found his wife quietly asleep in her bed. She had informed him of all that had happened; she complained of nothing but of the great fright she had experienced on account of her husband, and on that count she entreated justice and the punishment of the guilty parties.

That complaint was comic throughout, for the three rogues shewed themselves very brave in writing, stating that they would certainly not have given way so easily if the dread authority of the council had not been put forth by the leader of the band. The document produced three different results; in the first place, it amused the town; in the second, all the idlers of Venice went to Saint Job to hear the account of the adventure from the lips of the heroine herself, and she got many presents from her numerous visitors; in the third place, the Council of Ten offered a reward of five hundred ducats to any person giving such information as would lead to the arrest of the perpetrators of the practical joke, even if the informer belonged to the band, provided he was not the leader.

The offer of that reward would have made us tremble if our leader, precisely the one who alone had no interest in turning informer, had not been a patrician. The rank of Balbi quieted my anxiety at once, because I knew that, even supposing one of us were vile enough to betray our secret for the sake of the reward, the tribunal would have done nothing in order not to implicate a patrician. There was no cowardly traitor amongst us, although we were all poor; but fear had its effect, and our nocturnal pranks were not renewed.

Three or four months afterwards the chevalier Nicolas Iron, then one of the inquisitors, astonished me greatly by telling me the whole story, giving the names of all the actors. He did not tell me whether any one of the band had betrayed the secret, and I did not care to know; but I could clearly see the characteristic spirit of the aristocracy, for which the *solo mihi* is the supreme law.

Towards the middle of April of the year 1746 M. Girolamo Cornaro, the eldest son of the family Cornaro de la Reine, married a daughter of the house of Soranzo de St. Pol, and I had the honour of being present at the wedding . . . as a fiddler. I played the violin in one of the numerous bands engaged for the balls which were given for three consecutive days in the Soranzo Palace.

On the third day, towards the end of the dancing, an hour before day-break, feeling tired, I left the orchestra abruptly; and as I was going down the stairs I observed a senator, wearing his red robes, on the point of getting into a gondola. In taking his handkerchief out of his pocket he let a letter drop on the ground. I picked it up, and coming up to him just as he was going down the steps I handed it to him. He received it with many thanks, and enquired where I lived. I told him, and he insisted upon my coming with him in the gondola saying that he would leave me at my house. I accepted gratefully, and sat down near him. A few minutes afterwards he asked me to rub his left arm, which, he said, was so benumbed that he could not feel it. I rubbed it with all my strength, but he told me in a sort of indistinct whisper that the numbness was spreading all along the left side, and that he was dying.

I was greatly frightened; I opened the curtain, took the lantern, and found him almost insensible, and the mouth drawn on one side. I understood that he was seized with an apoplectic stroke, and called out to the gondoliers to land me at once, in order to procure a surgeon to bleed the patient.

I jumped out of the gondola, and found myself on the very spot where three years before I had taught Razetta such a forcible lesson; I enquired for a surgeon at the first coffee-house, and ran to the house that was pointed out to me. I knocked as hard as I could; the door was at last opened, and I made the surgeon follow me in his dressing-gown as far as the gondola, which was waiting; he bled the senator while I was tearing my shirt to make the compress and the bandage.

The operation being performed, I ordered the gondoliers to row as fast as possible, and we soon reached St. Marina; the servants were roused up, and taking the sick man out of the gondola we carried him to his bed almost dead.

Taking everything upon myself, I ordered a servant to hurry out for a physician, who came in a short time, and ordered the patient to be bled again, thus approving the first bleeding prescribed by me. Thinking I had a right to watch the sick man, I settled myself near his bed to give him every care he required.

An hour later, two noblemen, friends of the senator, came in, one a few minutes after the other. They were in despair; they had enquired about the accident from the gondoliers, and having been told that I knew more than they did, they loaded me with questions which I answered. They did not know who I was, and did not like to ask me; whilst I thought it better to preserve a modest silence.

The patient did not move; his breathing alone shewed that he was still alive; fomentations were constantly applied, and the priest who had been sent for, and was of very little use under such circumstances, seemed to be there only to see him die. All visitors were sent away by my advice, and the two noblemen and myself were the only persons in the sick man's room. At noon we partook silently of some dinner which was served in the sick room.

In the evening one of the two friends told me that if I had any business to attend to I could go, because they would both pass the night on a mattress near the patient.

"And I, sir," I said, "will remain near his bed in this arm-chair, for if I went away the patient would die, and he will live as long as I am near him."

This sententious answer struck them with astonishment, as I expected it would, and they looked at each other in great surprise.

We had supper, and in the little conversation we had I gathered the information that the senator, their friend, was M. de Bragadin, the only brother of the procurator of that name. He was celebrated in Venice not only for his eloquence and his great talents as a statesman, but also for the gallantries of his youth. He had been very extravagant with women, and more than one of them had committed many follies for him. He had gambled and lost a great deal, and his brother was his most bitter enemy, because he was infatuated with the idea that he had tried to poison him. He had accused him of that crime before the Council of Ten, which, after an investigation of eight months, had brought in a verdict of not guilty: but that just sentence, although given unanimously by that high tribunal, had not had the effect of destroying his brother's prejudices against him.

M. de Bragadin, who was perfectly innocent of such a crime and oppressed by an unjust brother who deprived him of half of his income, spent his days like an amiable philosopher, surrounded by his friends, amongst whom were the two noblemen who were then watching him; one belonged to the Dandolo family, the other was a Barbaro, and both were excellent men. M. de Bragadin was handsome, learned, cheerful, and most kindly disposed; he was then about fifty years old.

The physician who attended him was named Terro; he thought, by some peculiar train of reasoning, that he could cure him by applying a mercurial ointment to the chest, to which no one raised any objection. The rapid effect of the remedy delighted the two friends, but it frightened me, for in less than twenty-four hours the patient was labouring under great excitement of the brain. The physician said that he had expected that effect, but that on the following day the remedy would act less on the brain, and diffuse its beneficial action through the whole of the system, which required to be invigorated by a proper equilibrium in the circulation of the fluids.

At midnight the patient was in a state of high fever, and in a fearful state of irritation. I examined him closely, and found him hardly able to breathe. I roused up his two friends, and declared that in my opinion the patient would soon die unless the fatal ointment was at once removed. And without waiting for their answer, I bared his chest, took off the plaster, washed the skin carefully with lukewarm water, and in less than three minutes he breathed freely and fell into a quiet sleep. Delighted with such a fortunate result, we lay down again.

The physician came very early in the morning, and was much pleased to see his patient so much better, but when M. Dandolo informed him of what had been done, he was angry, said it was enough to kill his patient, and asked who had been so audacious as to destroy the effect of his prescription. M. de Bragadin, speaking for the first time, said to him:

"Doctor, the person who has delivered me from your mercury, which was killing me, is a more skilful physician than you;" and, saying these words, he pointed to me.

It would be hard to say who was the more astonished: the doctor, when he saw an unknown young man, whom he must have taken for an impostor, declared more learned than himself; or I, when I saw myself transformed into a physician, at a moment's notice. I kept silent, looking very modest, but hardly able to control my mirth, whilst the doctor was staring at me with a mixture of astonishment and of spite, evidently thinking me some bold quack who had tried to supplant him. At last, turning towards M. de Bragadin, he told him coldly that he would leave him in my hands; he was taken at his word, he went away, and behold! I had become the physician of one of the most illustrious members of the Venetian Senate! I must confess that I was very glad of it, and I told my patient that a proper diet was all he needed, and that nature, assisted by the approaching fine season, would do the rest.

The dismissed physician related the affair through the town, and, as M. de Bragadin was rapidly improving, one of his relations, who came to see him, told him that everybody was astonished at his having chosen for his physician a fiddler from the theatre; but the senator put a stop to his remarks by answering that a fiddler could know more than all the doctors in Venice, and that he owed his life to me.

The worthy nobleman considered me as his oracle, and his two friends listened to me with the deepest attention. Their infatuation encouraging me, I spoke like a learned physician, I dogmatized, I quoted authors whom I had never read.

M. de Bragadin, who had the weakness to believe in the occult sciences, told me one day that, for a young man of my age, he thought my learning too extensive, and that he was certain I was the possessor of some supernatural endowment. He entreated me to tell him the truth.

What extraordinary things will sometimes occur from mere chance, or from the force of circumstances! Unwilling to hurt his vanity by telling him that he was mistaken, I took the wild resolution of informing him, in the presence of his two friends, that I possessed a certain numeral calculus which gave answers (also in numbers), to any questions I liked to put.

M. de Bragadin said that it was Solomon's key, vulgarly called cabalistic science, and he asked me from whom I learnt it.

"From an old hermit," I answered, "who lives on the Carpegna Mountain, and whose acquaintance I made quite by chance when I was a prisoner in the Spanish army."

"The hermit," remarked the senator, "has without informing you of it, linked an invisible spirit to the calculus he has taught you, for simple numbers can not have the power of reason. You possess a real treasure, and you may derive great advantages from it."

"I do not know," I said, "in what way I could make my science useful, because the answers given by the numerical figures are often so obscure that I have felt discouraged, and I very seldom tried to make any use of my calculus. Yet, it is very true that, if I had not formed my pyramid, I never should have had the happiness of knowing your excellency."

"How so?"

"On the second day, during the festivities at the Soranzo Palace, I enquired of my oracle whether I would meet at the ball anyone whom I should not care to see. The answer I obtained was this: 'Leave the ball-room precisely at four o'clock.' I obeyed implicitly, and met your excellency."

The three friends were astounded. M. Dandolo asked me whether I would answer a question he would ask, the interpretation of which would belong only to him, as he was the only person acquainted with the subject of the question.

I declared myself quite willing, for it was necessary to brazen it out, after having ventured as far as I had done. He wrote the question, and gave it to me; I read it, I could not understand either the subject or the meaning of the words, but it did not matter, I had to give an answer. If the question was so obscure that I could not make out the sense of it, it was natural that I should not understand the answer. I therefore answered, in ordinary figures, four lines of which he alone could be the interpreter, not caring much, at least in appearance, how they would be understood. M. Dandolo read them twice over, seemed astonished, said that it was all very plain to him; it was Divine, it was unique, it was a gift from Heaven, the numbers being

only the vehicle, but the answer emanating evidently
from an immortal spirit.

M. Dandolo was so well pleased that his two friends
very naturally wanted also to make an experiment.
They asked questions on all sorts of subjects, and my
answers, perfectly unintelligible to myself, were all held
as Divine by them. I congratulated them on their success, and congratulated myself in their presence upon
being the possessor of a thing to which I had until then
attached no importance whatever, but which I promised
to cultivate carefully, knowing that I could thus be of
some service to their excellencies.

They all asked me how long I would require to teach
them the rules of my sublime calculus. "Not very long,"
I answered, "and I will teach you as you wish, although
the hermit assured me that I would die suddenly within
three days if I communicated my science to anyone,
but I have no faith whatever in that prediction." M.
de Bragadin who believed in it more than I did, told
me in a serious tone that I was bound to have faith in
it, and from that day they never asked me again to
teach them. They very likely thought that, if they
could attach me to them, it would answer the purpose
as well as if they possessed the science themselves. Thus
I became the hierophant of those three worthy and
talented men, who, in spite of their literary accomplishments, were not wise, since they were infatuated with
occult and fabulous sciences, and believed in the existence of phenomena impossible in the moral as well as
in the physical order of things. They believed that
through me they possessed the philosopher's stone, the
universal panacea, the intercourse with all the elemen-
tary, heavenly, and infernal spirits; they had no doubt
whatever that, thanks to my sublime science, they

could find out the secrets of every government in Europe.

After they had assured themselves of the reality of my cabalistic science by questions respecting the past, they decided to turn it to some use by consulting it upon the present and upon the future. I had no difficulty in shewing myself a good guesser, because I always gave answers with a double meaning, one of the meanings being carefully arranged by me, so as not to be understood until after the event; in that manner, my cabalistic science, like the oracle of Delphi, could never be found in fault. I saw how easy it must have been for the ancient heathen priests to impose upon ignorant, and therefore credulous mankind. I saw how easy it will always be for impostors to find dupes, and I realized, even better than the Roman orator, why two augurs could never look at each other without laughing; it was because they had both an equal interest in giving importance to the deceit they perpetrated, and from which they derived such immense profits. But what I could not, and probably never shall, understand, was the reason for which the Fathers, who were not so simple or so ignorant as our Evangelists, did not feel able to deny the divinity of oracles, and, in order to get out of the difficulty, ascribed them to the devil. They never would have entertained such a strange idea if they had been acquainted with cabalistic science. My three worthy friends were like the holy Fathers; they had intelligence and wit, but they were superstitious, and no philosophers. But, although believing fully in my oracles, they were too kind-hearted to think them the work of the devil, and it suited their natural goodness better to believe my answers inspired by some heavenly spirit. They were not only good Christians and faithful to the Church, but even real devotees and full of scruples. They were not married, and, after having renounced all commerce with women, they had become the enemies of the female sex; perhaps a strong proof of the weakness of their minds. They imagined that chastity was the condition *sine quâ non* exacted by the spirits from those who wished to have intimate communication or intercourse with them: they fancied that spirits excluded women, and *vice versâ*.

With all these oddities, the three friends were truly intelligent and even witty, and, at the beginning of my acquaintance with them, I could not reconcile these antagonistic points. But a prejudiced mind cannot reason well, and the faculty of reasoning is the most important of all. I often laughed when I heard them talk on religious matters; they would ridicule those whose intellectual faculties were so limited that they could not understand the mysteries of religion. The incarnation of the Word, they would say, was a trifle for God, and therefore easy to understand, and the resurrection was so comprehensible that it did not appear to them wonderful, because, as God cannot die, Jesus Christ was naturally certain to rise again. As for the Eucharist, transubstantiation, the real presence, it was all no mystery to them, but palpable evidence, and yet they were not Jesuits. They were in the habit of going to confession every week, without feeling the slightest trouble about their confessors, whose ignorance they kindly regretted. They thought themselves bound to confess only what was a sin in their own opinion, and in that, at least, they reasoned with good sense.

With those three extraordinary characters, worthy of esteem and respect for their moral qualities, their honesty, their reputation, and their age, as well as for their

noble birth, I spent my days in a very pleasant manner; although, in their thirst for knowledge, they often kept me hard at work for ten hours running, all four of us being locked up together in a room, and unapproachable to everybody, even to friends or relatives.

I completed the conquest of their friendship by relating to them the whole of my life, only with some proper reserve, so as not to lead them into any capital sins. I confess candidly that I deceived them, as the Papa Deldimopulo used to deceive the Greeks who applied to him for the oracles of the Virgin. I certainly did not act towards them with a true sense of honesty, but if the reader to whom I confess myself is acquainted with the world and with the spirit of society, I entreat him to think before judging me, and perhaps I may meet with some indulgence at his hands.

I might be told that if I had wished to follow the rules of pure morality I ought either to have declined intimate intercourse with them or to have undeceived them. I cannot deny these premises, but I will answer that I was only twenty years of age, I was intelligent, talented, and had just been a poor fiddler. I should have lost my time in trying to cure them of their weakness; I should not have succeeded, for they would have laughed in my face, deplored my ignorance, and the result of it all would have been my dismissal. Besides, I had no mission, no right, to constitute myself an apostle, and if I had heroically resolved on leaving them as soon as I knew them to be foolish visionaries, I should have shewn myself a misanthrope, the enemy of those worthy men for whom I could procure innocent pleasures, and my own enemy at the same time; because, as a young man, I liked to live well, to enjoy all the pleasures natural to youth and to a good constitution.

By acting in that manner I should have failed in common politeness, I should perhaps have caused or allowed M. de Bragadin's death, and I should have exposed those three honest men to becoming the victims of the first bold cheat who, ministering to their monomania, might have won their favour, and would have ruined them by inducing them to undertake the chemical operations of the Great Work. There is also another consideration, dear reader, and as I love you I will tell you what it is. An invincible self-love would have prevented me from declaring myself unworthy of their friendship either by my ignorance or by my pride; and I should have been guilty of great rudeness if I had ceased to visit them.

I took, at least it seems to me so, the best, the most natural, and the noblest decision, if we consider the disposition of their mind, when I decided upon the plan of conduct which insured me the necessaries of life: and of those necessaries who could be a better judge than your very humble servant?

Through the friendship of those three men, I was certain of obtaining consideration and influence in my own country. Besides, I found it very flattering to my vanity to become the subject of the speculative chattering of empty fools who, having nothing else to do, are always trying to find out the cause of every moral phenomenon they meet with, which their narrow intellect cannot understand.

People racked their brain in Venice to find out how my intimacy with three men of that high character could possibly exist; they were wrapped up in heavenly aspirations, I was a world's devotee; they were very strict in their morals, I was thirsty of all pleasures!

At the beginning of summer, M. de Bragadin was once

more able to take his seat in the senate, and, the day before he went out for the first time, he spoke to me thus:

"Whoever you may be, I am indebted to you for my life. Your first protectors wanted to make you a priest, a doctor, an advocate, a soldier, and ended by making a fiddler of you; those persons did not know you. God had evidently instructed your guardian angel to bring you to me. I know you and appreciate you. If you will be my son, you have only to acknowledge me for your father, and, for the future, until my death, I will treat you as my own child. Your apartment is ready, you may send your clothes: you shall have a servant, a gondola at your orders, my own table, and ten sequins a month. It is the sum I used to receive from my father when I was your age. You need not think of the future; think only of enjoying yourself, and take me as your adviser in everything that may happen to you, in everything you may wish to undertake, and you may be certain of always finding me your friend."

I threw myself at his feet to assure him of my gratitude, and embraced him calling him my father. He folded me in his arms, called me his dear son; I promised to love and to obey him; his two friends, who lived in the same palace, embraced me affectionately, and we swore eternal fraternity.

Such is the history of my metamorphosis, and of the lucky stroke which, taking me from the vile profession of a fiddler, raised me to the rank of a grandee.

OF JACQUES CASANOVA
559

CHAPTER XVIII

*I lead a dissolute life—Zawoiski—Rinaldi—L'Abbadie
—the young countess—the Capuchin friar Z. Steffani
—Ancilla—La Ramon—I take a gondola at St. Job to
go to Mestra.*

FORTUNE, which had taken pleasure in giving me
a specimen of its despotic caprice, and had insured
my happiness through means which sages would dis-
avow, had not the power to make me adopt a system of
moderation and prudence which alone could establish
my future welfare on a firm basis.

My ardent nature, my irresistible love of pleasure, my
unconquerable independence, would not allow me to submit to the reserve which my new position in life demanded from me. I began to lead a life of complete
freedom, caring for nothing but what ministered to my
tastes, and I thought that, as long as I respected the
laws, I could trample all prejudices under my feet. I
fancied that I could live free and independent in a country ruled entirely by an aristocratic government, but
this was not the case, and would not have been so even
if fortune had raised me to a seat in that same government, for the Republic of Venice, considering that its
primary duty is to preserve its own integrity, finds itself the slave of its own policy, and is bound to sacrifice
everything to self-preservation, before which the laws
themselves cease to be inviolable.

But let us abandon the discussion of a principle now too trite, for humankind, at least in Europe, is satisfied that unlimited liberty is nowhere consistent with a properly-regulated state of society. I have touched lightly on the matter, only to give to my readers some idea of my conduct in my own country, where I began to tread a path which was to lead me to a state prison as inscrutable as it was unconstitutional.

With enough money, endowed by nature with a pleasing and commanding physical appearance, a confirmed gambler, a true spendthrift, a great talker, very far from modest, intrepid, always running after pretty women, supplanting my rivals, and acknowledging no good company but that which ministered to my enjoyment, I was certain to be disliked; but, ever ready to expose myself to any danger, and to take the responsibility of all my actions, I thought I had a right to do anything I pleased, for I always broke down abruptly every obstacle I found in my way.

Such conduct could not but be disagreeable to the three worthy men whose oracle I had become, but they did not like to complain. The excellent M. de Bragadin would only tell me that I was giving him a repetition of the foolish life he had himself led at my age, but that I must prepare to pay the penalty of my follies, and to feel the punishment when I should reach his time of life. Without wanting in the respect I owed him, I would turn his terrible forebodings into jest, and continue my course of extravagance. However, I must mention here the first proof he gave me of his true wisdom.

At the house of Madame Avogadro, a woman full of wit in spite of her sixty years, I had made the acquaintance of a young Polish nobleman called Zawoiski. He was expecting money from Poland, but in the mean time the Venetian ladies did not let him want for any, being all very much in love with his handsome face and his Polish manners. We soon became good friends, my purse was his, but, twenty years later, he assisted me to a far greater extent in Munich. Zawoiski was honest, he had only a small dose of intelligence, but it was enough for his happiness. He died in Trieste five or six years ago, the ambassador of the Elector of Trèves. I will speak of him in another part of these Memoirs.

This amiable young man, who was a favourite with everybody and was thought a free-thinker because he frequented the society of Angelo Querini and Lunardo Vénier, presented me one day, as we were out walking, to an unknown countess who took my fancy very strongly. We called on her in the evening, and, after introducing me to her husband, Count Rinaldi, she invited us to remain and have supper.

The count made a faro bank in the course of the evening, I punted with his wife as a partner, and won some fifty ducats.

Very much pleased with my new acquaintance, I called alone on the countess the next morning. The count, apologizing for his wife who was not up yet, took me to her room. She received me with graceful ease, and, her husband having left us alone, she had the art to let me hope for every favour, yet without committing herself; when I took leave of her, she invited me to supper for the evening. After supper I played, still in partnership with her, won again, and went away very much in love. I did not fail to pay her another visit the next morning, but when I presented myself at the house I was told that she had gone out.

I called again in the evening, and, after she had excused herself for not having been at home in the morning, the faro bank began, and I lost all my money, still having the countess for my partner. After supper, and when the other guests had retired, I remained with Zawoiski, Count Rinaldi having offered to give us our revenge. As I had no more money, I played upon trust, and the count threw down the cards after I had lost five hundred sequins. I went away in great sorrow. I was bound in honour to pay the next morning, and I did not possess a groat. Love increased my despair, for I saw myself on the point of losing the esteem of a woman by whom I was smitten, and the anxiety I felt did not escape M. de Bragadin when we met in the morning. He kindly encouraged me to confess my troubles to him. I was conscious that it was my only chance, and candidly related the whole affair, and I ended by saying that I should not survive my disgrace. He consoled me by promising that my debt would be cancelled in the course of the day, if I would swear never to play again upon trust. I took an oath to that effect, and kissing his hand, I went out for a walk, relieved from a great load. I had no doubt that my excellent father would give me five hundred sequins during the day, and I enjoyed my anticipation the honour I would derive, in the opinion of the lovely countess, by my exactitude and prompt discharge of my debt. I felt that it gave new strength to my hopes, and that feeling prevented me from regretting my heavy loss, but grateful for the great generosity of my benefactor I was fully determined on keeping my promise.

I dined with the three friends, and the matter was not even alluded to; but, as we were rising from the table, a servant brought M. de Bragadin a letter and a parcel.

He read the letter, asked me to follow him into his study, and the moment we were alone, he said,—

"Here is a parcel for you."

I opened it, and found some forty sequins. Seeing my surprise, M. de Bragadin laughed merrily and handed me the letter, the contents of which ran thus:

"M. de Casanova may be sure that our playing last night was only a joke: he owes me nothing. My wife begs to send him half of the gold which he has lost in cash.

"COUNT RINALDI."

I looked at M. de Bragadin, perfectly amazed, and he burst out laughing. I guessed the truth, thanked him, and embracing him tenderly I promised to be wiser for the future. The mist I had before my eyes was dispelled, I felt that my love was defunct, and I remained rather ashamed, when I realized that I had been the dupe of the wife as well as of the husband.

"This evening," said my clever physician, "you can have a gay supper with the charming countess."

"This evening, my dear, respected benefactor, I will have supper with you. You have given me a masterly lesson."

"The next time you lose money upon trust, you had better not pay it."

"But I should be dishonoured."

"Never mind. The sooner you dishonour yourself, the more you will save, for you will always be compelled to accept your dishonour whenever you find yourself utterly unable to pay your losses. It is therefore more prudent not to wait until then."

"It is much better still to avoid that fatal impossibility by never playing otherwise than with money in hand."

"No doubt of it, for then you will save both your honour and your purse. But, as you are fond of games of chance, I advise you never to punt. Make the bank, and the advantage must be on your side."

"Yes, but only a slight advantage."

"As slight as you please, but it will be on your side, and when the game is over you will find yourself a winner and not a loser. The punter is excited, the banker is calm. The last says, 'I bet you do not guess,' while the first says, 'I bet I can guess.' Which is the fool, and which is the wise man? The question is easily answered. I adjure you to be prudent, but if you should punt and win, recollect that you are only an idiot if at the end you lose."

"Why an idiot? Fortune is very fickle."

"It must necessarily be so; it is a natural consequence. Leave off playing, believe me, the very moment you see luck turning, even if you should, at that moment, win but one groat."

I had read Plato, and I was astonished at finding a man who could reason like Socrates.

The next day, Zawoiski called on me very early to tell me that I had been expected to supper, and that Count Rinaldi had praised my promptness in paying my debts of honour. I did not think it necessary to undeceive him, but I did not go again to Count Rinaldi's, whom I saw sixteen years afterwards in Milan. As to Zawoiski, I did not tell him the story till I met him in Carlsbad, old and deaf, forty years later.

Three or four months later, M. de Bragadin taught me another of his masterly lessons. I had become acquainted, through Zawoiski, with a Frenchman called L'Abbadie, who was then soliciting from the Venetian Government the appointment of inspector of the armies of the Republic. The senate appointed, and I presented him to my protector, who promised him his vote; but the circumstance I am going to relate prevented him from fulfilling his promise.

I was in need of one hundred sequins to discharge a few debts, and I begged M. de Bragadin to give them to me.

"Why, my dear son, do you not ask M. de l'Abbadie to render you that service?"

"I should not dare to do so, dear father."

"Try him; I am certain that he will be glad to lend you that sum."

"I doubt it, but I will try."

I called upon L'Abbadie on the following day, and after a short exchange of compliments I told him the service I expected from his friendship. He excused himself in a very polite manner, drowning his refusal in that sea of commonplaces which people are sure to repeat when they cannot or will not oblige a friend. Zawoiski came in as he was still apologizing, and I left them together. I hurried at once to M. de Bragadin, and told him my want of success. He merely remarked that the Frenchman was deficient in intelligence.

It just happened that it was the very day on which the appointment of the inspectorship was to be brought before the senate. I went out to attend to my business (I ought to say to my pleasure), and as I did not return home till after midnight I went to bed without seeing my father. In the morning I said in his presence that I intended to call upon L'Abbadie to congratulate him upon his appointment.

"You may spare yourself that trouble; the senate has rejected his nomination."

"How so? Three days ago L'Abbadie felt sure of his success."

"He was right then, for he would have been appointed if I had not made up my mind to speak against him. I have proved to the senate that a right policy forbade the government to trust such an important post to a foreigner."

"I am much surprised, for your excellency was not of that opinion the day before yesterday."

"Very true, but then I did not know M. de l'Abbadie. I found out only yesterday that the man was not sufficiently intelligent to fill the position he was soliciting. Is he likely to possess a sane judgment when he refuses to lend you one hundred sequins? That refusal has cost him an important appointment and an income of three thousand crowns, which would now be his."

When I was taking my walk on the same day I met Zawoiski with L'Abbadie, and did not try to avoid them. L'Abbadie was furious, and he had some reason to be so.

"If you had told me," he said angrily, "that the one hundred sequins were intended as a gag to stop M. de Bragadin's mouth, I would have contrived to procure them for you."

"If you had had an inspector's brains you would have easily guessed it."

The Frenchman's resentment proved very useful to me, because he related the circumstance to everybody. The result was that from that time those who wanted the patronage of the senator applied to me. Comment is needless; this sort of thing has long been in existence, and will long remain so, because very often, to obtain the highest of favours, all that is necessary is to obtain the good-will of a minister's favourite or even of his valet. My debts were soon paid.

It was about that time that my brother Jean came to Venice with Guarienti, a converted Jew, a great judge of paintings, who was travelling at the expense of His Majesty the King of Poland, and Elector of Saxony. It was the converted Jew who had purchased for His Majesty the gallery of the Duke of Modena for one hundred thousand sequins. Guarienti and my brother left Venice for Rome, where Jean remained in the studio of the celebrated painter Raphael Mengs, whom we shall meet again hereafter.

Now, as a faithful historian, I must give my readers the story of a certain adventure in which were involved the honour and happiness of one of the most charming women in Italy, who would have been unhappy if I had not been a thoughtless fellow.

In the early part of October, 1746, the theatres being opened, I was walking about with my mask on when I perceived a woman, whose head was well enveloped in the hood of her mantle, getting out of the Ferrara barge which had just arrived. Seeing her alone, and observing her uncertain walk, I felt myself drawn towards her as if an unseen hand had guided me.

I come up to her, and offer my services if I can be of any use to her. She answers timidly that she only wants to make some enquiries.

"We are not here in the right place for conversation," I say to her; "but if you would be kind enough to come with me to a café, you would be able to speak and to explain your wishes."

She hesitates, I insist, and she gives way. The tavern was close at hand; we go in, and are alone in a private room. I take off my mask, and out of politeness she must put down the hood of her mantle. A large muslin head-dress conceals half of her face, but her eyes, her nose, and her pretty mouth are enough to let me see on her features beauty, nobleness, sorrow, and that candour which gives youth such an undefinable charm. I need not say that, with such a good letter of introduction, the unknown at once captivated my warmest interest. After wiping away a few tears which are flowing, in spite of all her efforts, she tells me that she belongs to a noble family, that she has run away from her father's house, alone, trusting in God, to meet a Venetian nobleman who had seduced her and then deceived her, thus sealing her everlasting misery.

"You have then some hope of recalling him to the path of duty? I suppose he has promised you marriage?"

"He has engaged his faith to me in writing. The only favour I claim from your kindness is to take me to his house, to leave me there, and to keep my secret."

"You may trust, madam, to the feelings of a man of honour. I am worthy of your trust. Have entire confidence in me, for I already take a deep interest in all your concerns. Tell me his name."

"Alas! sir, I give way to fate."

With these words, she takes out of her bosom a paper which she gives me; I recognize the handwriting of Zanetto Steffani. It was a promise of marriage by which he engaged his word of honour to marry within a week, in Venice, the young countess A—— S——. When I have read the paper, I return it to her, saying that I knew the writer quite well, that he was connected with the chancellor's office, known as a great libertine, and deeply in debt, but that he would be rich after his mother's death.

"For God's sake take me to his house."

"I will do anything you wish; but have entire confidence in me, and be good enough to hear me. I advise you not to go to his house. He has already done you great injury, and, even supposing that you should happen to find him at home, he might be capable of receiving you badly; if he should not be at home, it is most likely that his mother would not exactly welcome you, if you should tell her who you are and what is your errand. Trust to me, and be quite certain that God has sent me on your way to assist you. I promise you that to-morrow at the latest you shall know whether Steffani is in Venice, what he intends to do with you, and what we may compel him to do. Until then my advice is not to let him know your arrival in Venice."

"Good God! where shall I go to-night?"

"To a respectable house, of course."

"I will go to yours, if you are married."

"I am a bachelor."

I knew an honest widow who resided in a lane, and who had two furnished rooms. I persuade the young countess to follow me, and we take a gondola. As we are gliding along, she tells me that, one month before, Steffani had stopped in her neighbourhood for necessary repairs to his travelling-carriage, and that, on the same day he had made her acquaintance at a house where she had gone with her mother for the purpose of offering their congratulations to a newly-married lady.

"I was unfortunate enough," she continued, "to inspire him with love, and he postponed his departure. He remained one month in C——, never going out but in the evening, and spending every night under my windows conversing with me. He swore a thousand times that he adored me, that his intentions were honourable. I entreated him to present himself to my parents to ask me in marriage, but he always excused himself by alleging some reason, good or bad, assuring me that he could not be happy unless I shewed him entire confidence. He would beg of me to make up my mind to run away with him, unknown to everybody, promising that my honour should not suffer from such a step, because, three days after my departure, everybody should receive notice of my being his wife, and he assured me that he would bring me back on a visit to my native place shortly after our marriage. Alas, sir! what shall I say now? Love blinded me; I fell into the abyss; I believed him; I agreed to everything. He gave me the paper which you have read, and the following night I allowed him to come into my room through the window under which he was in the habit of conversing with me. I consented to be guilty of a crime which I believed would be atoned for within three days, and he left me, promising that the next night he would be again under my window, ready to receive me in his arms. Could I possibly entertain any doubt after the fearful crime I had committed for him? I prepared a small parcel, and waited for his coming, but in vain. Oh! what a cruel long night it was! In the morning I heard that the monster had gone away with his servant one hour after sealing my shame. You may imagine my despair! I adopted the only plan that despair could suggest, and that, of course, was not the right one. One hour before midnight I left my father's roof, alone, thus completing my dishonour, but resolved on death, if the man who has cruelly robbed me of my most precious treasure, and whom a natural instinct told me I could find here, does not restore me the honour which he alone can give me back. I walked all night and nearly the whole day, without taking any food, until I got into the barge, which brought me here in twenty-four hours. I travelled in the boat with five men and two women, but no one saw my face or heard my voice, I kept constantly sitting down in a corner, holding my head down, half asleep, and with this prayer-book in my hands. I was left alone, no one spoke to me, and I thanked God for it. When I landed on the wharf, you did not give me time to think how I could find out the dwelling of my perfidious seducer, but you may imagine the impression produced upon me by the sudden apparition of a masked man who, abruptly, and as if placed there purposely by Providence, offered me his services; it seemed to me that you had guessed my distress, and, far from experiencing any repugnance, I felt that I was acting rightly in trusting myself in your hands, in spite of all prudence which, perhaps, ought to have made me turn a deaf ear to your words, and refuse the invitation to enter alone with you the house to which you took me.

"You know all now, sir; but I entreat you not to judge me too severely; I have been virtuous all through my life; one month ago I had never committed a fault which could call a blush upon my face, and the bitter tears which I shed every day will, I hope, wash out my crime in the eyes of God. I have been carefully brought up, but love and the want of experience have thrown me into the abyss. I am in your hands, and I feel certain that I shall have no cause to repent it."

I needed all she had just told me to confirm me in the interest which I had felt in her from the first moment. I told her unsparingly that Steffani had seduced and abandoned her of malice aforethought, and that she ought to think of him only to be revenged of his perfidy. My words made her shudder, and she buried her beautiful face in her hands.

We reached the widow's house. I established her in a

pretty, comfortable room, and ordered some supper for her, desiring the good landlady to shew her every attention and to let her want for nothing. I then took an affectionate leave of her, promising to see her early in the morning.

On leaving this interesting but hapless girl, I proceeded to the house of Steffani. I heard from one of his mother's gondoliers that he had returned to Venice three days before, but that, twenty-four hours after his return, he had gone away again without any servant, and nobody knew his whereabouts, not even his mother. The same evening, happening to be seated next to an abbé from Bologna at the theatre, I asked him several questions respecting the family of my unfortunate *protégée*.

The abbé being intimately acquainted with them, I gathered from him all the information I required, and, amongst other things, I heard that the young countess had a brother, then an officer in the papal service.

Very early the next morning I called upon her. She was still asleep. The widow told me that she had made a pretty good supper, but without speaking a single word, and that she had locked herself up in her room immediately afterwards. As soon as she had opened her door, I entered her room, and, cutting short her apologies for having kept me waiting, I informed her of all I had heard.

Her features bore the stamp of deep sorrow, but she looked calmer, and her complexion was no longer pale. She thought it unlikely that Steffani would have left for any other place but for C——. Admitting the possibility that she might be right, I immediately offered to go to C—— myself, and to return without loss of time to fetch her, in case Steffani should be there. Without giving her time to answer I told her all the particulars I had learned concerning her honourable family, which caused her real satisfaction.

"I have no objection," she said, "to your going to C——, and I thank you for the generosity of your offer, but I beg you will postpone your journey. I still hope that Steffani will return, and then I can take a decision."

"I think you are quite right," I said. "Will you allow me to have some breakfast with you?"

"Do you suppose I could refuse you?"

"I should be very sorry to disturb you in any way. How did you use to amuse yourself at home?"

"I am very fond of books and music; my harpsichord was my delight."

I left her after breakfast, and in the evening I came back with a basket full of good books and music, and I sent her an excellent harpsichord. My kindness confused her, but I surprised her much more when I took out of my pocket three pairs of slippers. She blushed, and thanked me with great feeling. She had walked a long distance, her shoes were evidently worn out, her feet sore, and she appreciated the delicacy of my present. As I had no improper design with regard to her, I enjoyed her gratitude, and felt pleased at the idea she evidently entertained of my kind attentions. I had no other purpose in view but to restore calm to her mind, and to obliterate the bad opinion which the unworthy Steffani had given her of men in general. I never thought of inspiring her with love for me, and I had not the slightest idea that I could fall in love with her. She was unhappy, and her unhappiness—a sacred thing in my eyes—called all the more for my most honourable sympathy, because, without knowing me, she had given me her entire confidence. Situated as she was, I could not suppose her heart susceptible of harbouring a new affection, and I would have despised myself if I had tried to seduce her by any means in my power.

I remained with her only a quarter of an hour, being unwilling that my presence should trouble her at such a moment, as she seemed to be at a loss how to thank me and to express all her gratitude.

I was thus engaged in a rather delicate adventure, the end of which I could not possibly foresee, but my warmth for my *protégée* did not cool down, and having no difficulty in procuring the means to keep her I had no wish to see the last scene of the romance. That singular meeting, which gave me the useful opportunity of finding myself endowed with generous dispositions, stronger even than my love for pleasure, flattered my self-love more than I could express. I was then trying a great experiment, and conscious that I wanted sadly to study myself, I gave up all my energies to acquire the great science of the γνῶθι σεαύτον.

On the third day, in the midst of expressions of gratitude which I could not succeed in stopping she told me that she could not conceive why I shewed her so much sympathy, because I ought to have formed but a poor opinion of her in consequence of the readiness with which she had followed me into the café. She smiled when I answered that I could not understand how I had succeeded in giving her so great a confidence in my virtue, when I appeared before her with a mask on my face, in a costume which did not indicate a very virtuous character.

"It was easy for me, madam," I continued, "to guess that you were a beauty in distress, when I observed your youth, the nobleness of your countenance, and, more than all, your candour. The stamp of truth was so well affixed to the first words you uttered that I could not have the shadow of a doubt left in me as to your being the unhappy victim of the most natural of all feelings, and as to your having abandoned your home through a sentiment of honour. Your fault was that of a warm heart seduced by love, over which reason could have no sway, and your flight—the action of a soul crying for reparation or for revenge—fully justifies you. Your cowardly seducer must pay with his life the penalty due to his crime, and he ought never to receive, by marrying you, an unjust reward, for he is not worthy of possessing you after degrading himself by the vilest conduct."

"Everything you say is true. My brother, I hope, will avenge me."

"You are greatly mistaken if you imagine that Steffani will fight your brother; Steffani is a coward who will never expose himself to an honourable death."

As I was speaking, she put her hand in her pocket and drew forth, after a few moments' consideration, a stiletto six inches long, which she placed on the table.

"What is this?" I exclaimed.

"It is a weapon upon which I reckoned until now to use against myself in case I should not succeed in obtaining reparation for the crime I have committed. But you have opened my eyes. Take away, I entreat you, this stiletto, which henceforth is useless to me. I trust in your friendship, and I have an inward certainty that I shall be indebted to you for my honour as well as for my life."

I was struck by the words she had just uttered, and I felt that those words, as well as her looks, had found their way to my heart, besides enlisting my generous sympathy. I took the stiletto, and left her with so much agitation that I had to acknowledge the weakness of my heroism, which I was very near turning into ridicule; yet I had the wonderful strength to perform, at least by halves, the character of a Cato until the seventh day.

I must explain how a certain suspicion of the young lady arose in my mind. That doubt was heavy on my heart, for, if it had proved true, I should have been a dupe, and the idea was humiliating. She had told me that she was a musician; I had immediately sent her a harpsichord, and, yet, although the instrument had been at her disposal for three days, she had not opened it once, for the widow had told me so. It seemed to me that the best way to thank me for my attentive kindness would have been to give me a specimen of her musical talent. Had she deceived me? If so, she would lose my esteem. But, unwilling to form a hasty judgment, I kept on my guard, with a firm determination to make good use of the first opportunity that might present itself to clear up my doubts.

I called upon her the next day after dinner, which was not my usual time, having resolved on creating the opportunity myself. I caught her seated before a toilet-glass, while the widow dressed the most beautiful auburn hair I had ever seen. I tendered my apologies for my sudden appearance at an unusual hour; she excused herself for not having completed her toilet, and the widow went on with her work. It was the first time I had seen the whole of her face, her neck, and half of her arms, which the graces themselves had moulded. I remained in silent contemplation. I praised, quite by chance, the perfume of the pomatum, and the widow took the opportunity of telling her that she had spent in combs, powder, and pomatum the three livres she had received from her. I recollected then that she had told me the first day that she had left C—— with ten paoli.

I blushed for very shame, for I ought to have thought of that.

As soon as the widow had dressed her hair, she left the room to prepare some coffee for us. I took up a ring which had been laid by her on the toilet-table, and I saw that it contained a portrait exactly like her; I was amused at the singular fancy she had had of having her likeness taken in a man's costume, with black hair. "You are mistaken," she said, "it is a portrait of my brother. He is two years older than I, and is an officer in the papal army."

I begged her permission to put the ring on her finger; she consented, and when I tried, out of mere gallantry, to kiss her hand, she drew it back, blushing. I feared she might be offended, and I assured her of my respect.

"Ah, sir!" she answered, "in the situation in which I am placed, I must think of defending myself against my own self much more than against you."

The compliment struck me as so fine, and so complimentary to me, that I thought it better not to take it up, but she could easily read in my eyes that she would never find me ungrateful for whatever feelings she might entertain in my favour. Yet I felt my love taking such proportions that I did not know how to keep it a mystery any longer.

Soon after that, as she was again thanking me for the books I had given her, saying that I had guessed her taste exactly, because she did not like novels, she added, "I owe you an apology for not having sung to you yet, knowing that you are fond of music." These words made me breathe freely; without waiting for any answer, she sat down before the instrument and played several pieces with a facility, with a precision, with an expression of which no words could convey any idea. I was in ecstacy. I entreated her to sing; after some little ceremony, she took one of the music books I had given her, and she sang at sight in a manner which fairly ravished me. I begged that she would allow me to kiss her hand, and she did not say yes, but when I took it and pressed my lips on it, she did not oppose any resistance; I had the courage to smother my ardent desires, and the kiss I imprinted on her lovely hand was a mixture of tenderness, respect, and admiration.

I took leave of her, smitten, full of love, and almost determined on declaring my passion. Reserve becomes silliness when we know that our affection is returned by the woman we love, but as yet I was not quite sure.

The disappearance of Steffani was the talk of Venice, but I did not inform the charming countess of that circumstance. It was generally supposed that his mother had refused to pay his debts, and that he had run away to avoid his creditors. It was very possible. But, whether he returned or not, I could not make up my mind to lose the precious treasure I had in my hands. Yet I did not see in what manner, in what quality, I could enjoy that treasure, and I found myself in a regular maze. Sometimes I had an idea of consulting my kind father, but I would soon abandon it with fear, for I had made a trial of his empiric treatment in the Rinaldi affair, and still more in the case of l'Abbadie. His remedies frightened me to that extent that I would rather remain ill than be cured by their means.

One morning I was foolish enough to enquire from the widow whether the lady had asked her who I was. What an egregious blunder! I saw it when the good woman, instead of answering me, said,——

"Does she not know who you are?"

"Answer me, and do not ask questions," I said, in order to hide my confusion.

The worthy woman was right; through my stupidity she would now feel curious; the tittle-tattle of the neighbourhood would of course take up the affair and discuss it; and all through my thoughtlessness! It was an unpardonable blunder. One ought never to be more careful than in addressing questions to half-educated persons. During the fortnight that she had passed under my protection, the countess had shewn me no curiosity whatever to know anything about me, but it did not prove that she was not curious on the subject. If I had been wise, I should have told her the very first day who I was, but I made up for my mistake that evening better than anybody else could have done it, and, after having told her all about myself, I entreated her forgiveness for not having done so sooner. Thanking me for my confidence, she confessed how curious she had been to know me better, and she assured me that she would never have been imprudent enough to ask any questions about me from her landlady. Women have a more delicate, a surer tact than men, and her last words were a home-thrust for me.

Our conversation having turned to the extraordinary absence of Steffani, she said that her father must necessarily believe her to be hiding with him somewhere. "He must have found out," she added, "that I was in the habit of conversing with him every night from my window, and he must have heard of my having embarked for Venice on board the Ferrara barge. I feel certain that my father is now in Venice, making secretly every effort to discover me. When he visits this city he always puts up at Boncousin; will you ascertain whether he is there?"

She never pronounced Steffani's name without disgust and hatred, and she said she would bury herself in a convent, far away from her native place, where no one could be acquainted with her shameful history.

I intended to make some enquiries the next day, but it was not necessary for me to do so, for in the evening, at supper-time, M. Barbaro said to us,——

"A nobleman, a subject of the Pope, has been recommended to me, and wishes me to assist him with my influence in a rather delicate and intricate matter. One of our citizens has, it appears, carried off his daughter, and has been hiding somewhere with her for the last fortnight, but nobody knows where. The affair ought to be brought before the Council of Ten, but the mother of the ravisher claims to be a relative of mine, and I do not intend to interfere."

I pretended to take no interest in M. Barbaro's words, and early the next morning I went to the young countess to tell her the interesting news. She was still asleep; but, being in a hurry, I sent the widow to say that I wanted to see her only for two minutes in order to communicate something of great importance. She received me, covering herself up to the chin with the bed-clothes.

As soon as I had informed her of all I knew, she entreated me to enlist M. Barbaro as a mediator between herself and her father, assuring me that she would rather die than become the wife of the monster who had dishonoured her. I undertook to do it, and she gave me the promise of marriage used by the deceiver to seduce her, so that it could be shewn to her father.

In order to obtain M. Barbaro's mediation in favour of the young countess, it would have been necessary to tell him that she was under my protection, and I felt it would injure my *protégée*. I took no determination at first, and most likely one of the reasons for my hesitation was that I saw myself on the point of losing her, which was particularly repugnant to my feelings.

After dinner Count A—— S—— was announced as wishing to see M. Barbaro. He came in with his son, the living portrait of his sister. M. Barbaro took them to his study to talk the matter over, and within an hour they had taken leave. As soon as they had gone, the excellent M. Barbaro asked me, as I had expected, to consult my heavenly spirit, and to ascertain whether he would be right in interfering in favour of Count A—— S——. He wrote the question himself, and I gave the following answer with the utmost coolness:

"You ought to interfere, but only to advise the father to forgive his daughter and to give up all idea of compelling her to marry her ravisher, for Steffani has been sentenced to death by the will of God."

The answer seemed wonderful to the three friends, and I was myself surprised at my boldness, but I had a foreboding that Steffani was to meet his death at the hands of somebody; love might have given birth to that presentiment. M. de Bragadin, who believed my oracle infallible, observed that it had never given such a clear answer, and that Steffani was certainly dead. He said to M. de Barbaro,——

"You had better invite the count and his son to dinner here to-morrow. You must act slowly and prudently; it would be necessary to know where the daughter is before you endeavour to make the father forgive her."

M. Barbaro very nearly made me drop my serious countenance by telling me that if I would try my oracle I could let them know at once where the girl was. I answered that I would certainly ask my spirit on the morrow, thus gaining time in order to ascertain beforehand the disposition of the father and of his son. But I could not help laughing, for I had placed myself under the necessity of sending Steffani to the next world, if the reputation of my oracle was to be maintained.

I spent the evening with the young countess, who entertained no doubt either of her father's indulgence or of the entire confidence she could repose in me.

What delight the charming girl experienced when she heard that I would dine the next day with her father and brother, and that I would tell her every word that would be said about her! But what happiness it was for me to see her convinced that she was right in loving me, and that, without me, she would certainly have been lost in a town where the policy of the government tolerates debauchery as a solitary species of individual freedom. We congratulated each other upon our fortuitous meeting and upon the conformity in our tastes, which we thought truly wonderful. We were greatly pleased that her easy acceptance of my invitation, or my promptness in persuading her to follow and to trust me, could not be ascribed to the mutual attraction of our features, for I was masked, and her hood was then as good as a mask. We entertained no doubt that everything had been arranged by Heaven to get us acquainted, and to fire us both, even unknown to ourselves, with love for each other.

"Confess," I said to her, in a moment of enthusiasm, and as I was covering her hand with kisses, "confess that if you found me to be in love with you you would fear me."

"Alas! my only fear is to lose you."

That confession, the truth of which was made evident by her voice and by her looks, proved the electric spark which ignited the latent fire. Folding her rapidly in

my arms, pressing my mouth on her lips, reading in her
beautiful eyes neither a proud indignation nor the cold
compliance which might have been the result of a fear
of losing me, I gave way entirely to the sweet inclination
of love, and swimming already in a sea of delights I felt
my enjoyment increased a hundredfold when I saw, on
the countenance of the beloved creature who shared it,
the expression of happiness, of love, of modesty, and of
sensibility, which enhances the charm of the greatest
triumph.

She had scarcely recovered her composure when she
cast her eyes down and sighed deeply. Thinking that
I knew the cause of it, I threw myself on my knees
before her, and speaking to her words of the warmest
affection I begged, I entreated her, to forgive me.

"What offence have I to forgive you for, dear friend?
You have not rightly interpreted my thoughts. Your
love caused me to think of my happiness, and in that
moment a cruel recollection drew that sigh from me.
Pray rise from your knees."

Midnight had struck already; I told her that her good
fame made it necessary for me to go away; I put my
mask on and left the house. I was so surprised, so
amazed at having obtained a felicity of which I did not
think myself worthy, that my departure must have
appeared rather abrupt to her. I could not sleep. I
passed one of those disturbed nights during which the
imagination of an amorous young man is unceasingly
running after the shadows of reality. I had tasted, but
not savoured, that happy reality, and all my being was
longing for her who alone could make my enjoyment
complete. In that nocturnal drama love and imagination were the two principal actors; hope, in the back-
ground, performed only a dumb part. People may say

what they please on that subject but hope is in fact
nothing but a deceitful flatterer accepted by reason only
because it is often in need of palliatives. Happy are
those men who, to enjoy life to the fullest extent, require
neither hope nor foresight.

In the morning, recollecting the sentence of death
which I had passed on Steffani, I felt somewhat embarrassed about it. I wished I could have recalled it, as
well for the honour of my oracle, which was seriously im-
plicated by it, as for the sake of Steffani himself, whom
I did not hate half so much since I was indebted to him
for the treasure in my possession.

The count and his son came to dinner. The father
was simple, artless, and unceremonious. It was easy to
read on his countenance the grief he felt at the unpleasant adventure of his daughter, and his anxiety to
settle the affair honourably, but no anger could be traced
on his features or in his manners. The son, as handsome
as the god of love, had wit and great nobility of manner. His easy, unaffected carriage pleased me, and wishing to win his friendship I shewed him every attention.

After the dessert, M. Barbaro contrived to persuade
the count that we were four persons with but one head
and one heart, and the worthy nobleman spoke to us
without any reserve. He praised his daughter very
highly. He assured us that Steffani had never entered
his house, and therefore he could not conceive by what
spell, speaking to his daughter only at night and from
the street under the window, he had succeeded in seducing her to such an extent as to make her leave her home
alone, on foot, two days after he had left himself in his
post-chaise.

"Then," observed M. Barbaro, "it is impossible to be

certain that he actually seduced her, or to prove that she went off with him."

"Very true, sir, but although it cannot be proved, there is no doubt of it, and now that no one knows where Steffani is, he can be nowhere but with her. I only want him to marry her."

"It strikes me that it would be better not to insist upon a compulsory marriage which would seal your daughter's misery, for Steffani is, in every respect, one of the most worthless young men we have amongst our government clerks."

"Were I in your place," said M. de Bragadin, "I would let my daughter's repentance disarm my anger, and I would forgive her."

"Where is she? I am ready to fold her in my arms, but how can I believe in her repentance when it is evident that she is still with him."

"Is it quite certain that in leaving C—— she proceeded to this city?"

"I have it from the master of the barge himself, and she landed within twenty yards of the Roman gate. An individual wearing a mask was waiting for her, joined her at once, and they both disappeared without leaving any trace of their whereabouts."

"Very likely it was Steffani waiting there for her."

"No, for he is short, and the man with the mask was tall. Besides, I have heard that Steffani had left Venice two days before the arrival of my daughter. The man must have been some friend of Steffani, and he has taken her to him."

"But, my dear count, all this is mere supposition."

"There are four persons who have seen the man with the mask, and pretend to know him, only they do not agree. Here is a list of four names, and I will accuse these four persons before the Council of Ten, if Steffani should deny having my daughter in his possession."

The list, which he handed to M. Barbaro, gave not only the names of the four accused persons, but likewise those of their accusers. The last name, which M. Barbaro read, was mine. When I heard it, I shrugged my shoulders in a manner which caused the three friends to laugh heartily.

M. de Bragadin, seeing the surprise of the count at such uncalled-for mirth, said to him,——

"This is Casanova my son, and I give you my word of honour that, if your daughter is in his hands, she is perfectly safe, although he may not look exactly the sort of man to whom young girls should be trusted."

The surprise, the amazement, and the perplexity of the count and his son were an amusing picture. The loving father begged me to excuse him, with tears in his eyes, telling me to place myself in his position. My only answer was to embrace him most affectionately.

The man who had recognized me was a noted pimp whom I had thrashed some time before for having deceived me. If I had not been there just in time to take care of the young countess, she would not have escaped him, and he would have ruined her for ever by taking her to some house of ill-fame.

The result of the meeting was that the count agreed to postpone his application to the Council of Ten until Steffani's place of refuge should be discovered.

"I have not seen Steffani for six months, sir," I said to the count, "but I promise you to kill him in a duel as soon as he returns."

"You shall not do it," answered the young count, very coolly, "unless he kills me first."

"Gentlemen," exclaimed M. de Bragadin, "I can assure you that you will neither of you fight a duel with him, for Steffani is dead."

"Dead!" said the count.

"We must not," observed the prudent Barbaro, "take that word in its literal sense, but the wretched man is dead to all honour and self-respect."

After that truly dramatic scene, during which I could guess that the *dénouement* of the play was near at hand, I went to my charming countess, taking care to change my gondola three times—a necessary precaution to baffle spies.

I gave my anxious mistress an exact account of all the conversation. She was very impatient for my coming, and wept tears of joy when I repeated her father's words of forgiveness; but when I told her that nobody knew of Steffani having entered her chamber, she fell on her knees and thanked God. I then repeated her brother's words, imitating his coolness: "You shall not kill him, unless he kills me first." She kissed me tenderly, calling me her guardian angel, her saviour, and weeping in my arms. I promised to bring her brother on the following day, or the day after that at the latest. We had our supper, but we did not talk of Steffani, or of revenge, and after that pleasant meal we devoted two hours to the worship of the god of love.

I left her at midnight, promising to return early in the morning—my reason for not remaining all night with her was that the landlady might, if necessary, swear without scruple that I had never spent a night with the young girl. It proved a very lucky inspiration of mine, for, when I arrived home, I found the three friends waiting impatiently for me in order to impart to me wonderful news which M. de Bragadin had heard at the sitting of the senate.

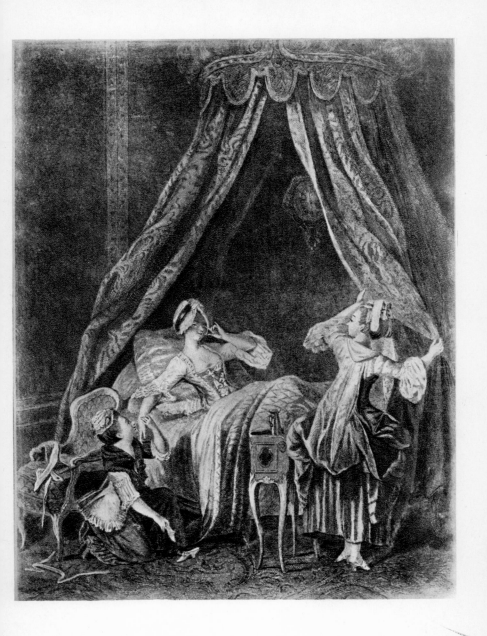

"Steffani," said M. de Bragadin to me, "is dead, as our angel Paralis revealed it to us; he is dead to the world, for he has become a Capuchin friar. The senate, as a matter of course, has been informed of it. We alone are aware that it is a punishment which God has visited upon him. Let us worship the Author of all things, and the heavenly hierarchy which renders us worthy of knowing what remains a mystery to all men. Now we must achieve our undertaking, and console the poor father. We must enquire from Paralis where the girl is. She cannot now be with Steffani. Of course, God has not condemned her to become a Capuchin nun."

"I need not consult my angel, dearest father, for it is by his express orders that I have been compelled until now to make a mystery of the refuge found by the young countess."

I related the whole story, except what they had no business to know, for, in the opinion of the worthy men, who had paid heavy tribute to Love, all intrigues were fearful crimes. M. Dandolo and M. Barbaro expressed their surprise when they heard that the young girl had been under my protection for a fortnight, but M. de Bragadin said that he was not astonished, that it was according to cabalistic science, and that he knew it.

"We must only," he added, "keep up the mystery of his daughter's place of refuge for the count, until we know for a certainty that he will forgive her, and that he will take her with him to C——, or to any other place where he may wish to live hereafter."

"He cannot refuse to forgive her," I said, "when he finds that the amiable girl would never have left C—— if her seducer had not given her this promise of marriage in his own handwriting. She walked as far as the barge, and she landed at the very moment I was passing the

Roman gate. An inspiration from above told me to accost her and to invite her to follow me. She obeyed, as if she was fulfilling the decree of Heaven, I took her to a refuge impossible to discover, and placed her under the care of a God-fearing woman."

My three friends listened to me so attentively that they looked like three statues. I advised them to invite the count to dinner for the day after next, because I needed some time to consult Paralis *de modo tenendi*. I then told M. Barbaro to let the count know in what sense he was to understand Steffani's death. He undertook to do it, and we retired to rest.

I slept only four or five hours, and, dressing myself quickly, hurried to my beloved mistress. I told the widow not to serve the coffee until we called for it, because we wanted to remain quiet and undisturbed for some hours, having several important letters to write.

I found the lovely countess in bed, but awake, and her eyes beaming with happiness and contentment. For a fortnight I had only seen her sad, melancholy, and thoughtful. Her pleased countenance, which I naturally ascribed to my influence, filled me with joy. We commenced as all happy lovers always do, and we were both unsparing of the mutual proofs of our love, tenderness, and gratitude.

After our delightful amorous sport, I told her the news, but love had so completely taken possession of her pure and sensitive soul, that what had been important was now only an accessory. But the news of her seducer having turned a Capuchin friar filled her with amazement, and, passing very sensible remarks on the extraordinary event, she pitied Steffani. When we can feel pity, we love no longer, but a feeling of pity succeeding love is the characteristic only of a great and generous mind. She was much pleased with me for having informed my three friends of her being under my protection, and she left to my care all the necessary arrangements for obtaining a reconciliation with her father.

Now and then we recollected that the time of our separation was near at hand, our grief was bitter, but we contrived to forget it in the ecstacy of our amorous enjoyment.

"Ah! why can we not belong for ever to each other?" the charming girl would exclaim. "It is not my acquaintance with Steffani, it is your loss which will seal my eternal misery."

But it was necessary to bring our delightful interview to a close, for the hours were flying with fearful rapidity. I left her happy, her eyes wet with tears of intense felicity.

At the dinner-table M. Barbaro told me that he had paid a visit to his relative, Steffani's mother, and that she had not appeared sorry at the decision taken by her son, although he was her only child.

"He had the choice," she said, "between killing himself and turning friar, and he took the wiser course."

The woman spoke like a good Christian, and she professed to be one; but she spoke like an unfeeling mother, and she was truly one, for she was wealthy, and if she had not been cruelly avaricious her son would not have been reduced to the fearful alternative of committing suicide or of becoming a Capuchin friar.

The last and most serious motive which caused the despair of Steffani, who is still alive, remained a mystery for everybody. My Memoirs will raise the veil when no one will care anything about it.

The count and his son were, of course, greatly surprised, and the event made them still more desirous of discovering the young lady. In order to obtain a clue to her place of refuge, the count had resolved on summoning before the Council of Ten all the parties, accused and accusing, whose names he had on his list, with the exception of myself. His determination made it necessary for us to inform him that his daughter was in my hands, and M. de Bragadin undertook to let him know the truth.

We were all invited to supper by the count, and we went to his hostelry, with the exception of M. de Bragadin, who had declined the invitation. I was thus prevented from seeing my divinity that evening, but early the next morning I made up for lost time, and as it had been decided that her father would on that very day be informed of her being under my care, we remained together until noon. We had no hope of contriving another meeting, for I had promised to bring her brother in the afternoon.

The count and his son dined with us, and after dinner M. de Bragadin said,——

"I have joyful news for you, count; your beloved daughter has been found!"

What an agreeable surprise for the father and son! M. de Bragadin handed them the promise of marriage written by Steffani, and said,——

"This, gentlemen, evidently brought your lovely young lady to the verge of madness when she found that he had gone from C—— without her. She left your house alone on foot, and as she landed in Venice Providence threw her in the way of this young man, who induced her to follow him, and has placed her under the care of an honest woman, whom she has not left since, whom she will leave only to fall in your arms as soon as she is certain of your forgiveness for the folly she has committed."

"Oh! let her have no doubt of my forgiving her," exclaimed the father, in the ecstacy of joy, and turning to me, "Dear sir, I beg of you not to delay the fortunate moment on which the whole happiness of my life depends."

I embraced him warmly, saying that his daughter would be restored to him on the following day, and that I would let his son see her that very afternoon, so as to give him an opportunity of preparing her by degrees for that happy reconciliation. M. Barbaro desired to accompany us, and the young man, approving all my arrangements, embraced me, swearing everlasting friendship and gratitude.

We went out all three together, and a gondola carried us in a few minutes to the place where I was guarding a treasure more precious than the golden apples of the Hesperides. But, alas! I was on the point of losing that treasure, the remembrance of which causes me, even now, a delicious trembling.

I preceded my two companions in order to prepare my lovely young friend for the visit, and when I told her that, according to my arrangements, her father would not see her till on the following day:

"Ah!" she exclaimed with the accent of true happiness, "then we can spend a few more hours together! Go, dearest, go and bring my brother."

I returned with my companions, but how can I paint that truly dramatic situation? Oh! how inferior art must ever be to nature! The fraternal love, the delight beaming upon those two beautiful faces, with a slight shade of confusion on that of the sister, the pure joy shining in the midst of their tender caresses, the most eloquent exclamations followed by a still more eloquent silence, their loving looks which seem like flashes of lightning in the midst of a dew of tears, a thought of politeness which brings blushes on her countenance, when she recollects that she has forgotten her duty towards a nobleman whom she sees for the first time, and finally there was my part, not a speaking one, but yet the most important of all. The whole formed a living picture to which the most skilful painter could not have rendered full justice.

We sat down at last, the young countess between her brother and M. Barbaro, on the sofa, I, opposite to her, on a low foot-stool.

"To whom, dear sister, are we indebted for the happiness of having found you again?"

"To my guardian angel," she answered, giving me her hand, "to this generous man who was waiting for me, as if Heaven had sent him with the special mission of watching over your sister; it is he who has saved me, who has prevented me from falling into the gulf which yawned under my feet, who has rescued me from the shame threatening me, of which I had then no conception; it is to him I am indebted for all, to him who, as you see, kisses my hand now for the first time."

And she pressed her handkerchief to her beautiful eyes to dry her tears, but ours were flowing at the same time.

Such is true virtue, which never loses its nobleness, even when modesty compels it to utter some innocent falsehood. But the charming girl had no idea of being guilty of an untruth. It was a pure, virtuous soul which was then speaking through her lips, and she allowed it to speak. Her virtue seemed to whisper to her that, in spite of her errors, it had never deserted her. A young girl who gives way to a real feeling of love cannot be guilty of a crime, or be exposed to remorse.

Towards the end of our friendly visit, she said that she longed to throw herself at her father's feet, but that she wished to see him only in the evening, so as not to give any opportunity to the gossips of the place, and it was agreed that the meeting, which was to be the last scene of the drama, should take place the next day towards the evening.

We returned to the count's hostelry for supper, and the excellent man, fully persuaded that he was indebted to me for his honour as well as for his daughter's, looked at me with admiration, and spoke to me with gratitude. Yet he was not sorry to have ascertained himself, and before I had said so, that I had been the first man who had spoken to her after landing. Before parting in the evening, M. Barbaro invited them to dinner for the next day.

I went to my charming mistress very early the following morning, and, although there was some danger in protracting our interview, we did not give it a thought, or, if we did, it ouly caused us to make good use of the short time that we could still devote to love.

After having enjoyed, until our strength was almost expiring, the most delightful, the most intense voluptuousness in which mutual ardour can enfold two young, vigorous, and passionate lovers, the young countess dressed herself, and, kissing her slippers, said she would never part with them as long as she lived. I asked her to give me a lock of her hair, which she did at once. I meant to have it made into a chain like the one woven with the hair of Madame F——, which I still wore round my neck.

Towards dusk, the count and his son, M. Dandolo, M.

Barbaro, and myself, proceeded together to the abode of the young countess. The moment she saw her father, she threw herself on her knees before him, but the count, bursting into tears, took her in his arms, covered her with kisses, and breathed over her words of forgiveness, of love and blessing. What a scene for a man of sensibility! An hour later we escorted the family to the inn, and, after wishing them a pleasant journey, I went back with my two friends to M. de Bragadin, to whom I gave a faithful account of what had taken place.

We thought that they had left Venice, but the next morning they called at the place in a *peotta* with six rowers. The count said that they could not leave the city without seeing us once more; without thanking us again, and me particularly, for all we had done for them. M. de Bragadin, who had not seen the young countess before, was struck by her extraordinary likeness to her brother.

They partook of some refreshments, and embarked in their *peotta*, which was to carry them, in twenty-four hours, to Ponte di Lago Oscuro, on the River Po, near the frontiers of the papal states. It was only with my eyes that I could express to the lovely girl all the feelings which filled my heart, but she understood the language, and I had no difficulty in interpreting the meaning of her looks.

Never did an introduction occur in better season than that of the count to M. Barbaro. It saved the honour of a respectable family; and it saved me from the unpleasant consequences of an interrogatory in the presence of the Council of Ten, during which I should have been convicted of having taken the young girl with me, and compelled to say what I had done with her.

A few days afterwards we all proceeded to Padua to

remain in that city until the end of autumn. I was
grieved not to find Doctor Gozzi in Padua; he had been
appointed to a benefice in the country, and he was living
there with Bettina; she had not been able to remain with
the scoundrel who had married her only for the sake
of her small dowry, and had treated her very ill.

I did not like the quiet life of Padua, and to avoid
dying from ennui I fell in love with a celebrated Venetian
courtezan. Her name was Ancilla; sometime after, the
well-known dancer, Campioni, married her and took her
to London, where she caused the death of a very worthy
Englishman. I shall have to mention her again in four
years; now I have only to speak of a certain circumstance which brought my love adventure with her to a
close after three or four weeks.

Count Medini, a young, thoughtless fellow like myself, and with inclinations of much the same cast, had
introduced me to Ancilla. The count was a confirmed
gambler and a thorough enemy of fortune. There was
a good deal of gambling going on at Ancilla's, whose favourite lover he was, and the fellow had presented me to
his mistress only to give her the opportunity of making
a dupe of me at the card-table.

And, to tell the truth, I was a dupe at first; not thinking of any foul play, I accepted ill luck without complaining; but one day I caught them cheating. I took
a pistol out of my pocket, and, aiming at Medini's
breast, I threatened to kill him on the spot unless he
refunded at once all the gold they had won from me.
Ancilla fainted away, and the count, after refunding the
money, challenged me to follow him out and measure
swords. I placed my pistols on the table, and we went
out. Reaching a convenient spot, we fought by the
bright light of the moon, and I was fortunate enough

to give him a gash across the shoulder. He could not move his arm, and he had to cry for mercy.

After that meeting, I went to bed and slept quietly, but in the morning I related the whole affair to my father, and he advised me to leave Padua immediately, which I did.

Count Medini remained my enemy through all his life. I shall have occasion to speak of him again when I reach Naples.

The remainder of the year 1746 passed off quietly, without any events of importance. Fortune was now favourable to me and now adverse.

Towards the end of January, 1747, I received a letter from the young countess A—— S——, who had married the Marquis of ——. She entreated me not to appear to know her, if by chance I visited the town in which she resided, for she had the happiness of having linked her destiny to that of a man who had won her heart after he had obtained her hand.

I had already heard from her brother that, after their return to C——, her mother had taken her to the city from which her letter was written, and there, in the house of a relative with whom she was residing, she had made the acquaintance of the man who had taken upon himself the charge of her future welfare and happiness. I saw her one year afterwards, and if it had not been for her letter, I should certainly have solicited an introduction to her husband. Yet, peace of mind has greater charms even than love; but, when love is in the way, we do not think so.

For a fortnight I was the lover of a young Venetian girl, very handsome, whom her father, a certain Ramon, exposed to public admiration as a dancer at the theatre. I might have remained longer her captive, if marriage

had not forcibly broken my chains. Her protectress,
Madame Cecilia Valmarano, found her a very proper
husband in the person of a French dancer, called Binet,
who had assumed the name of Binetti, and thus his
young wife had not to become a French woman; she
soon won great fame in more ways than one. She was
strangely privileged; time with its heavy hand seemed
to have no power over her. She always appeared young,
even in the eyes of the best judges of faded, bygone
female beauty. Men, as a general rule, do not ask for
anything more, and they are right in not racking their
brain for the sake of being convinced that they are the
dupes of external appearance. The last lover that the
wonderful Binetti killed by excess of amorous enjoyment
was a certain Mosciuski, a Pole, whom fate brought to
Venice seven or eight years ago: she had then reached
her sixty-third year!

My life in Venice would have been pleasant and happy,
if I could have abstained from punting at basset. The
ridotti were only open to noblemen who had to appear
without masks, in their patrician robes, and wearing the
immense wig which had become indispensable since the
beginning of the century. I would play, and I was
wrong, for I had neither prudence enough to leave off
when fortune was adverse, nor sufficient control over
myself to stop when I had won. I was then gambling
through a feeling of avarice. I was extravagant by taste,
and I always regretted the money I had spent, unless
it had been won at the gaming-table, for it was only in
that case that the money had, in my opinion, cost me
nothing.

At the end of January, finding myself under the necessity of procuring two hundred sequins, Madame Manzoni contrived to obtain for me from another woman

the loan of a diamond ring worth five hundred. I made up my mind to go to Treviso, fifteen miles distant from Venice, to pawn the ring at the Mont-de-pieté, which there lends money upon valuables at the rate of five per cent. That useful establishment does not exist in Venice, where the Jews have always managed to keep the monopoly in their hands.

I got up early one morning, and walked to the end of the *canale regio,* intending to engage a gondola to take me as far as Mestra, where I could take post horses, reach Treviso in less than two hours, pledge my diamond ring, and return to Venice the same evening.

As I passed along St. Job's Quay, I saw in a two-oared gondola a country girl beautifully dressed. I stopped to look at her; the gondoliers, supposing that I wanted an opportunity of reaching Mestra at a cheap rate, rowed back to the shore.

Observing the lovely face of the young girl, I do not hesitate, but jump into the gondola, and pay double fare, on condition that no more passengers are taken. An elderly priest was seated near the young girl, he rises to let me take his place, but I politely insist upon his keeping it.

CHAPTER XIX

I Fall in Love with Christine, and Find a Husband Worthy of Her—Christine's Wedding

"THOSE gondoliers," said the elderly priest, addressing me in order to begin the conversation, "are very fortunate. They took us up at the Rialto for thirty soldi, on condition that they would be allowed to embark other passengers, and here is one already; they will certainly find more."

"When I am in a gondola, reverend sir, there is no room left for any more passengers."

So saying, I give forty more soldi to the gondoliers, who, highly pleased with my generosity, thank me and call me excellency. The good priest, accepting that title as truly belonging to me, entreats my pardon for not having addressed me as such.

"I am not a Venetian nobleman, reverend sir, and I have no right to the title of *Eccellenza*."

"Ah!" says the young lady, "I am very glad of it."

"Why so, signora?"

"Because when I find myself near a nobleman I am afraid. But I suppose that you are an *illustrissimo*."

"Not even that, signora; I am only an advocate's clerk."

"So much the better, for I like to be in the company of persons who do not think themselves above me. My father was a farmer, brother of my uncle here, rector of

601

P——, where I was born and bred. As I am an only daughter I inherited my father's property after his death, and I shall likewise be heiress to my mother, who has been ill a long time and cannot live much longer, which causes me a great deal of sorrow; but it is the doctor who says it. Now, to return to my subject, I do not suppose that there is much difference between an advocate's clerk and the daughter of a rich farmer. I only say so for the sake of saying something, for I know very well that, in travelling, one must accept all sorts of companions: is it not so, uncle?"

"Yes, my dear Christine, and as a proof you see that this gentleman has accepted our company without knowing who or what we are."

"But do you think I would have come if I had not been attracted by the beauty of your lovely niece?"

At these words the good people burst out laughing. As I did not think that there was anything very comic in what I had said, I judged that my travelling companions were rather simple, and I was not sorry to find them so.

"Why do you laugh so heartily, beautiful *demigella?* Is it to shew me your fine teeth? I confess that I have never seen such a splendid set in Venice."

"Oh! it is not for that, sir, although everyone in Venice has paid me the same compliment. I can assure you that in P—— all the girls have teeth as fine as mine. Is it not a fact, uncle?"

"Yes, my dear niece."

"I was laughing, sir, at a thing which I will never tell you."

"Oh! tell me, I entreat you."

"Oh! certainly not, never."

"I will tell you myself," says the curate.

"You will not," she exclaims, knitting her beautiful eyebrows. "If you do I will go away."

"I defy you to do it, my dear. Do you know what she said, sir, when she saw you on the wharf? 'Here is a very handsome young man who is looking at me, and would not be sorry to be with us.' And when she saw that the gondoliers were putting back for you to embark she was delighted."

While the uncle was speaking to me, the indignant niece was slapping him on the shoulder.

"Why are you angry, lovely Christine, at my hearing that you liked my appearance, when I am so glad to let you know how truly charming I think you?"

"You are glad for a moment. Oh! I know the Venetians thoroughly now. They have all told me that they were charmed with me, and not one of those I would have liked ever made a declaration to me."

"What sort of declaration did you want?"

"There's only one sort for me, sir; the declaration leading to a good marriage in church, in the sight of all men. Yet we remained a fortnight in Venice; did we not, uncle?"

"This girl," said the uncle, "is a good match, for she possesses three thousand crowns. She has always said that she would marry only a Venetian, and I have accompanied her to Venice to give her an opportunity of being known. A worthy woman gave us hospitality for a fortnight, and has presented my niece in several houses where she made the acquaintance of marriageable young men, but those who pleased her would not hear of marriage, and those who would have been glad to marry her did not take her fancy."

"But do you imagine, reverend sir, that marriages can be made like omelets? A fortnight in Venice, that is nothing; you ought to live there at least six months. Now, for instance, I think your niece sweetly pretty, and I should consider myself fortunate if the wife whom God intends for me were like her, but, even if she offered me now a dowry of fifty thousand crowns on condition that our wedding takes place immediately, I would refuse her. A prudent young man wants to know the character of a girl before he marries her, for it is neither money nor beauty which can ensure happiness in married life."

"What do you mean by character?" asked Christine; "is it a beautiful hand-writing?"

"No, my dear. I mean the qualities of the mind and the heart. I shall most likely get married sometime, and I have been looking for a wife for the last three years, but I am still looking in vain. I have known several young girls almost as lovely as you are, and all with a good marriage portion, but after an acquaintance of two or three months I found out that they could not make me happy."

"In what were they deficient?"

"Well, I will tell you, because you are not acquainted with them, and there can be no indiscretion on my part. One whom I certainly would have married, for I loved her dearly, was extremely vain. She would have ruined me in fashionable clothes and by her love for luxuries. Fancy! she was in the habit of paying one sequin every month to the hair-dresser, and as much at least for pomatum and perfumes."

"She was a giddy, foolish girl. Now, I spend only ten soldi in one year on wax which I mix with goat's grease, and there I have an excellent pomatum."

"Another, whom I would have married two years ago, laboured under a disease which would have made me unhappy; as soon as I knew of it, I ceased my visits."

"What disease was it?"

"A disease which would have prevented her from being a mother, and, if I get married, I wish to have children."

"All that is in God's hands, but I know that my health is excellent. Is it not, uncle?"

"Another was too devout, and that does not suit me. She was so over-scrupulous that she was in the habit of going to her confessor twice a week, and every time her confession lasted at least one hour. I want my wife to be a good Christian, but not bigoted."

"She must have been a great sinner, or else she was very foolish. I confess only once a month, and get through everything in two minutes. Is it not true, uncle? and if you were to ask me any questions, uncle, I should not know what more to say."

"One young lady thought herself more learned than I, although she would, every minute, utter some absurdity. Another was always low-spirited, and my wife must be cheerful."

"Hark to that, uncle! You and my mother are always chiding me for my cheerfulness."

"Another, whom I did not court long, was always afraid of being alone with me, and if I gave her a kiss she would run and tell her mother."

"How silly she must have been! I have never yet listened to a lover, for we have only rude peasants in P——, but I know very well that there are some things which I would not tell my mother."

"One had a rank breath; another painted her face, and, indeed, almost every young girl is guilty of that fault. I am afraid marriage is out of the question for me, because I want, for instance, my wife to have black eyes, and in our days almost every woman colours them by art; but I cannot be deceived, for I am a good judge."

"Are mine black?"

"Ah! Ah!"

"You are laughing?"

"I laugh because your eyes certainly appear to be black, but they are not so in reality. Never mind, you are very charming in spite of that."

"Now, that is amusing. You pretend to be a good judge, yet you say that my eyes are dyed black. My eyes, sir, whether beautiful or ugly, are now the same as God made them. Is it not so, uncle?"

"I never had any doubt of it, my dear niece."

"And you do not believe me, sir?"

"No, they are too beautiful for me to believe them natural."

"Oh, dear me! I cannot bear it."

"Excuse me, my lovely *damigella*, I am afraid I have been too sincere."

After that quarrel we remained silent. The good curate smiled now and then, but his niece found it very hard to keep down her sorrow.

At intervals I stole a look at her face, and could see that she was very near crying. I felt sorry, for she was a charming girl. In her hair, dressed in the fashion of wealthy countrywomen, she had more than one hundred sequins' worth of gold pins and arrows which fastened the plaits of her long locks as dark as ebony. Heavy gold ear-rings, and a long chain, which was wound twenty times round her snowy neck, made a fine contrast to her complexion, on which the lilies and the roses were admirably blended. It was the first time that I had seen a country beauty in such splendid apparel. Six years before, Lucie at Paséan had captivated me, but in a different manner.

Christine did not utter a single word, she was in despair, for her eyes were truly of the greatest beauty, and I was cruel enough to attack them. She evidently hated me, and her anger alone kept back her tears. Yet I would not undeceive her, for I wanted her to bring matters to a climax.

When the gondola had entered the long canal of Marghera, I asked the clergyman whether he had a carriage to go to Treviso, through which place he had to pass to reach P——.

"I intended to walk," said the worthy man, "for my parish is poor and I am the same, but I will try to obtain a place for Christine in some carriage travelling that way."

"You would confer a real kindness on me if you would both accept a seat in my chaise; it holds four persons, and there is plenty of room."

"It is a good fortune which we were far from expecting."

"Not at all, uncle; I will not go with this gentleman."

"Why not, my dear niece?"

"Because I will not."

"Such is the way," I remarked, without looking at her, "that sincerity is generally rewarded."

"Sincerity, sir! nothing of the sort," she exclaimed, angrily, "it is sheer wickedness. There can be no true black eyes now for you in the world, but, as you like them, I am very glad of it."

"You are mistaken, lovely Christine, for I have the means of ascertaining the truth."

"What means?"

"Only to wash the eyes with a little lukewarm rose-water; or if the lady cries, the artificial colour is certain to be washed off."

At those words, the scene changed as if by the wand of a conjuror. The face of the charming girl, which had expressed nothing but indignation, spite and disdain, took an air of contentment and of placidity delightful to witness. She smiled at her uncle who was much pleased with the change in her countenance, for the offer of the carriage had gone to his heart.

"Now you had better cry a little, my dear niece, and *il signore* will render full justice to your eyes."

Christine cried in reality, but it was immoderate laughter that made her tears flow.

That species of natural originality pleased me greatly, and as we were going up the steps at the landing-place, I offered her my full apologies; she accepted the carriage. I ordered breakfast, and told a *vetturino* to get a very handsome chaise ready while we had our meal, but the curate said that he must first of all go and say his mass.

"Very well, reverend sir, we will hear it, and you must say it for my intention."

I put a silver ducat in his hand.

"It is what I am in the habit of giving," I observed.

My generosity surprised him so much that he wanted to kiss my hand. We proceeded towards the church, and I offered my arm to the niece who, not knowing whether she ought to accept it or not, said to me,——

"Do you suppose that I cannot walk alone?"

"I have no such idea, but if I do not give you my arm, people will think me wanting in politeness."

"Well, I will take it. But now that I have your arm, what will people think?"

"Perhaps that we love each other and that we make a very nice couple."

"And if anyone should inform your mistress that we are in love with each other, or even that you have given your arm to a young girl?"

"I have no mistress, and I shall have none in future, because I could not find a girl as pretty as you in all Venice."

"I am very sorry for you, for we cannot go again to Venice; and even if we could, how could we remain there six months? You said that six months were necessary to know a girl well."

"I would willingly defray all your expenses."

"Indeed? Then say so to my uncle, and he will think it over, for I could not go alone."

"In six months you would know me likewise."

"Oh! I know you very well already."

"Could you accept a man like me?"

"Why not?"

"And will you love me?"

"Yes, very much, when you are my husband."

I looked at the young girl with astonishment. She seemed to me a princess in the disguise of a peasant girl. Her dress, made of *gros de Tours* and all embroidered in gold, was very handsome, and cost certainly twice as much as the finest dress of a Venetian lady. Her bracelets, matching the neckchain, completed her rich toilet. She had the figure of a nymph, and the new fashion of wearing a mantle not having yet reached her village, I could see the most magnificent bosom, although her dress was fastened up to the neck. The end of the richly-embroidered skirt did not go lower than the ankles, which allowed me to admire the neatest little foot and the lower part of an exquisitely moulded leg. Her firm and easy walk, the natural freedom of all her movements, a charming look which seemed to say, "I am very glad that you think me pretty," everything, in short, caused the ardent fire of amorous desires to circulate through my veins. I could not conceive how such a lovely girl could have spent a fortnight in Venice without finding a man to marry or to deceive her. I was particularly delighted with her simple, artless way of talking, which in the city might have been taken for silliness.

Absorbed in my thoughts, and having resolved in my own mind on rendering brilliant homage to her charms, I waited impatiently for the end of the mass.

After breakfast I had great difficulty in convincing the curate that my seat in the carriage was the last one, but I found it easier to persuade him on our arrival in Treviso to remain for dinner and for supper at a small, unfrequented inn, as I took all the expense upon myself. He accepted very willingly when I added that immediately after supper a carriage would be in readiness to convey him to P——, where he would arrive in an hour after a pleasant journey by moonlight. He had nothing to hurry him on, except his wish to say mass in his own church the next morning.

I ordered a fire and a good dinner, and the idea struck me that the curate himself might pledge the ring for me, and thus give me the opportunity of a short interview with his niece. I proposed it to him, saying that I could not very well go myself, as I did not wish to be known. He undertook the commission at once, expressing his pleasure at doing something to oblige me.

He left us, and I remained alone with Christine. I spent an hour with her without trying to give her even a kiss, although I was dying to do so, but I prepared her heart to burn with the same desires which were already burning in me by those words which so easily inflame the imagination of a young girl.

The curate came back and returned me the ring, saying that it could not be pledged until the day after the morrow, in consequence of the Festival of the Holy Virgin. He had spoken to the cashier, who had stated that if I liked the bank would lend double the sum I had asked.

"My dear sir," I said, "you would greatly oblige me if you would come back here from P—— to pledge the ring yourself. Now that it has been offered once by you, it might look very strange if it were brought by another person. Of course I will pay all your expenses."

"I promise you to come back."

I hoped he would bring his niece with him.

I was seated opposite to Christine during the dinner, and discovered fresh charms in her every minute, but, fearing I might lose her confidence if I tried to obtain some slight favour, I made up my mind not to go to work too quickly, and to contrive that the curate should take her again to Venice. I thought that there only I could manage to bring love into play and to give it the food it requires.

"Reverend sir," I said, "let me advise you to take your niece again to Venice. I undertake to defray all expenses, and to find an honest woman with whom your Christine will be as safe as with her own mother. I want to know her well in order to make her my wife, and if she comes to Venice our marriage is certain."

"Sir, I will bring my niece myself to Venice as soon as you inform me that you have found a worthy woman with whom I can leave her in safety."

While we were talking I kept looking at Christine, and I could see her smile with contentment.

"My dear Christine," I said, "within a week I shall have arranged the affair. In the meantime, I will write to you. I hope that you have no objection to correspond with me."

"My uncle will write for me, for I have never been taught writing."

"What, my dear child! you wish to become the wife of a Venetian, and you cannot write."

"Is it then necessary to know how to write in order to become a wife? I can read well."

"That is not enough, and although a girl can be a wife and a mother without knowing how to trace one letter, it is generally admitted that a young girl ought to be able to write. I wonder you never learned."

"There is no wonder in that, for not one girl in our village can do it. Ask my uncle."

"It is perfectly true, but there is not one who thinks of getting married in Venice, and as you wish for a Venetian husband you must learn."

"Certainly," I said, "and before you come to Venice, for everybody would laugh at you, if you could not write. I see that it makes you sad, my dear, but it cannot be helped."

"I am sad, because I cannot learn writing in a week."

"I undertake," said her uncle, "to teach you in a fortnight, if you will only practice diligently. You will then know enough to be able to improve by your own exertions."

"It is a great undertaking, but I accept it; I promise you to work night and day, and to begin to-morrow."

After dinner, I advised the priest not to leave that evening, to rest during the night, and I observed that, by going away before day-break, he would reach P—— in good time, and feel all the better for it. I made the same proposal to him in the evening, and when he saw that his niece was sleepy, he was easily persuaded to remain. I called for the innkeeper, ordered a carriage for the clergyman, and desired that a fire might be lit for me in the next room where I would sleep, but the good priest said that it was unnecessary, because there were two large beds in our room, that one would be for me and the other for him and his niece.

"We need not undress," he added, "as we mean to leave very early, but you can take off your clothes, sir, because you are not going with us, and you will like to remain in bed to-morrow morning."

"Oh!" remarked Christine, "I must undress myself, otherwise I could not sleep, but I only want a few minutes to get ready in the morning."

I said nothing, but I was amazed. Christine then, lovely and charming enough to wreck the chastity of a Xenocrates, would sleep naked with her uncle! True, he was old, devout, and without any of the ideas which might render such a position dangerous, yet the priest was a man, he had evidently felt like all men, and he ought to have known the danger he was exposing himself to. My carnal-mindedness could not realize such a state of innocence. But it was truly innocent, so much so that he did it openly, and did not suppose that anyone could see anything wrong in it. I saw it all plainly, but I was not accustomed to such things, and felt lost in wonderment. As I advanced in age and in experience, I have seen the same custom established in many countries amongst honest people whose good morals were in no way debased by it, but it was amongst good people, and I do not pretend to belong to that worthy class.

We had had no meat for dinner, and my delicate

palate was not over-satisfied. I went down to the kitchen myself, and I told the landlady that I wanted the best that could be procured in Treviso for supper, particularly in wines.

"If you do not mind the expense, sir, trust to me, and I undertake to please you. I will give you some Gatta wine."

"All right, but let us have supper early."

When I returned to our room, I found Christine caressing the cheeks of her old uncle, who was laughing; the good man was seventy-five years old.

"Do you know what is the matter?" he said to me; "my niece is caressing me because she wants me to leave her here until my return. She tells me that you were like brother and sister during the hour you have spent alone together this morning, and I believe it, but she does not consider that she would be a great trouble to you."

"Not at all, quite the reverse, she will afford me great pleasure, for I think her very charming. As to our mutual behaviour, I believe you can trust us both to do our duty."

"I have no doubt of it. Well, I will leave her under your care until the day after to-morrow. I will come back early in the morning so as to attend to your business."

This extraordinary and unexpected arrangement caused the blood to rush to my head with such violence that my nose bled profusely for a quarter of an hour. It did not frighten me, because I was used to such accidents, but the good priest was in a great fright, thinking that it was a serious hæmorrhage.

When I had allayed his anxiety, he left us on some business of his own, saying that he would return at night-fall. I remained alone with the charming, artless Christine, and lost no time in thanking her for the confidence she placed in me.

"I can assure you," she said, "that I wish you to have a thorough knowledge of me; you will see that I have none of the faults which have displeased you so much in the young ladies you have known in Venice, and I promise to learn writing immediately."

"You are charming and true; but you must be discreet in P——, and confide to no one that we have entered into an agreement with each other. You must act according to your uncle's instructions, for it is to him that I intend to write to make all arrangements."

"You may rely upon my discretion. I will not say anything even to my mother, until you give me permission to do so."

I passed the afternoon, in denying myself even the slightest liberties with my lovely companion, but falling every minute deeper in love with her. I told her a few love stories which I veiled sufficiently not to shock her modesty. She felt interested, and I could see that, although she did not always understand, she pretended to do so, in order not to appear ignorant.

When her uncle returned, I had arranged everything in my mind to make her my wife, and I resolved on placing her, during her stay in Venice, in the house of the same honest widow with whom I had found a lodging for my beautiful Countess A—— S——.

We had a delicious supper. I had to teach Christine how to eat oysters and truffles, which she then saw for the first time. Gatta wine is like champagne, it causes merriment without intoxicating, but it cannot be kept for more than one year. We went to bed before midnight, and it was broad daylight when I awoke. The curate had left the room so quietly that I had not heard him.

I looked towards the other bed, Christine was asleep. I wished her good morning, she opened her eyes, and leaning on her elbow, she smiled sweetly.

"My uncle has gone. I did not hear him."

"Dearest Christine, you are as lovely as one of God's angels. I have a great longing to give you a kiss."

"If you long for a kiss, my dear friend, come and give me one."

I jump out of my bed, decency makes her hide her face. It was cold, and I was in love. I find myself in her arms by one of those spontaneous movements which sentiment alone can cause, and we belong to each other without having thought of it, she happy and rather confused, I delighted, yet unable to realize the truth of a victory won without any contest.

An hour passed in the midst of happiness, during which we forgot the whole world. Calm followed the stormy gusts of passionate love, and we gazed at each other without speaking.

Christine was the first to break the silence:

"What have we done?" she said, softly and lovingly.

"We have become husband and wife."

"What will my uncle say to-morrow?"

"He need not know anything about it until he gives us the nuptial benediction in his own church."

"And when will he do so?"

"As soon as we have completed all the arrangements necessary for a public marriage."

"How long will that be?"

"About a month."

"We cannot be married during Lent."

"I will obtain permission."

"You are not deceiving me?"

"No, for I adore you."

"Then, you no longer want to know me better?"

"No, I know you thoroughly now, and I feel certain that you will make me happy."

"And will you make me happy, too?"

"I hope so."

"Let us get up and go to church. Who could have believed that, to get a husband, it was necessary not to go to Venice, but to come back from that city!"

We got up, and, after partaking of some breakfast, we went to hear mass. The morning passed off quickly, but towards dinner-time I thought that Christine looked different to what she did the day before, and I asked her the reason of that change.

"It must be," she said, "the same reason which causes you to be thoughtful."

"An air of thoughtfulness, my dear, is proper to love when it finds itself in consultation with honour. This affair has become serious, and love is now compelled to think and consider. We want to be married in the church, and we cannot do it before Lent, now that we are in the last days of carnival; yet we cannot wait until Easter, it would be too long. We must therefore obtain a dispensation in order to be married. Have I not reason to be thoughtful?"

Her only answer was to come and kiss me tenderly. I had spoken the truth, yet I had not told her all my reasons for being so pensive. I found myself drawn into an engagement which was not disagreeable to me, but I wished it had not been so very pressing. I could not conceal from myself that repentance was beginning to creep into my amorous and well-disposed mind, and I was grieved at it. I felt certain, however, that the charming girl would never have any cause to reproach me for her misery.

We had the whole evening before us, and as she had told me that she had never gone to a theatre, I resolved on affording her that pleasure. I sent for a Jew from whom I procured everything necessary to disguise her, and we went to the theatre. A man in love enjoys no pleasure but that which he gives to the woman he loves. After the performance was over, I took her to the Casino, and her astonishment made me laugh when she saw for the first time a faro bank. I had not money enough to play myself, but I had more than enough to amuse her and to let her play a reasonable game. I gave her ten sequins, and explained what she had to do. She did not even know the cards, yet in less than an hour she had won one hundred sequins. I made her leave off playing, and we returned to the inn. When we were in our room, I told her to see how much money she had, and when I assured her that all that gold belonged to her, she thought it was a dream.

"Oh! what will my uncle say?" she exclaimed.

We had a light supper, and spent a delightful night, taking good care to part by day-break, so as not to be caught in the same bed by the worthy ecclesiastic. He arrived early and found us sleeping soundly in our respective beds. He woke me, and I gave him the ring which he went to pledge immediately. When he returned two hours later, he saw us dressed and talking quietly near the fire. As soon as he came in, Christine rushed to embrace him, and she shewed him all the gold she had in her possession. What a pleasant surprise for the good old priest! He did not know how to express his wonder! He thanked God for what he called a miracle, and he concluded by saying that we were made to insure each other's happiness.

The time to part had come. I promised to pay them a visit in the first days of Lent, but on condition that on my arrival in P—— I would not find anyone informed of my name or of my concerns. The curate gave me the certificate of birth of his niece and the account of her possessions. As soon as they had gone I took my departure for Venice, full of love for the charming girl, and determined on keeping my engagement with her. I knew how easy it would be for me to convince my three friends that my marriage had been irrevocably written in the great book of fate.

My return caused the greatest joy to the three excellent men, because, not being accustomed to see me three days absent, M. Dandolo and M. Barbaro were afraid of some accident having befallen me; but M. de Bragadin's faith was stronger, and he allayed their fears, saying to them that, with Paralis watching over me, I could not be in any danger.

The very next day I resolved on insuring Christine's happiness without making her my wife. I had thought of marrying her when I loved her better than myself, but after obtaining possession the balance was so much on my side that my self-love proved stronger than my love for Christine. I could not make up my mind to renounce the advantages, the hopes which I thought were attached to my happy independence. Yet I was the slave of sentiment. To abandon the artless, innocent girl seemed to me an awful crime of which I could not be guilty, and the mere idea of it made me shudder. I was aware that she was, perhaps, bearing in her womb a living token of our mutual love, and I shivered at the bare possibility that her confidence in me might be re-paid by shame and everlasting misery.

I bethought myself of finding her a husband in every way better than myself; a husband so good that she would not only forgive me for the insult I should thus be guilty of towards her, but also thank me at the end, and like me all the better for my deceit.

To find such a husband could not be very difficult, for Christine was not only blessed with wonderful beauty, and with a well-established reputation for virtue, but she was also the possessor of a fortune amounting to four thousand Venetian ducats.

Shut up in a room with the three worshippers of my oracle, I consulted Paralis upon the affair which I had so much at heart. The answer was:

"Serenus must attend to it."

Serenus was the cabalistic name of M. de Bragadin, and the excellent man immediately expressed himself ready to execute all the orders of Paralis. It was my duty to inform him of those orders.

"You must," I said to him, "obtain from the Holy Father a dispensation for a worthy and virtuous girl, so as to give her the privilege of marrying during Lent in the church of her village; she is a young country girl. Here is her certificate of birth. The husband is not yet known; but it does not matter, Paralis undertakes to find one."

"Trust to me," said my father, "I will write at once to our ambassador in Rome, and I will contrive to have my letter sent by special express. You need not be anxious, leave it all to me, I will make it a business of state, and I must obey Paralis all the more readily that I foresee that the intended husband is one of us four. Indeed, we must prepare ourselves to obey."

I had some trouble in keeping my laughter down, for it was in my power to metamorphose Christine into a grand Venetian lady, the wife of a senator; but that was not my intention. I again consulted the oracle in order to ascertain who would be the husband of the young girl, and the answer was that M. Dandolo was entrusted with the care of finding one, young, handsome, virtuous, and able to serve the Republic, either at home or abroad. M. Dandolo was to consult me before concluding any arrangements. I gave him courage for his task by informing him that the girl had a dowry of four thousand ducats, but I added that his choice was to be made within a fortnight. M. de Bragadin, delighted at not being entrusted with the commission, laughed heartily.

Those arrangements made me feel at peace with myself. I was certain that the husband I wanted would be found, and I only thought of finishing the carnival gaily, and of contriving to find my purse ready for a case of emergency.

Fortune soon rendered me possessor of a thousand sequins. I paid my debts, and the licence for the marriage having arrived from Rome ten days after M. de Bragadin had applied for it, I gave him one hundred ducats, that being the sum it had cost. The dispensation gave Christine the right of being married in any church in Christendom, she would only have to obtain the seal of the episcopal court of the diocese in which the marriage was to take place, and no publication of banns was required. We wanted, therefore, but one thing—a trifling one, namely, the husband. M. Dandolo had already proposed three or four to me, but I had refused them for excellent reasons. At last he offered one who suited me exactly.

I had to take the diamond ring out of pledge, and not

wishing to do it myself, I wrote to the priest making an appointment in Treviso. I was not, of course, surprised when I found that he was accompanied by his lovely niece, who, thinking that I had come to complete all arrangements for our marriage, embraced me without ceremony, and I did the same. If the uncle had not been present, I am afraid that those kisses would have caused all my heroism to vanish. I gave the curate the dispensation, and the handsome features of Christine shone with joy. She certainly could not imagine that I had been working so actively for others, and, as I was not yet certain of anything, I did not undeceive her then. I promised to be in P—— within eight or ten days, when we would complete all necessary arrangements. After dinner, I gave the curate the ticket for the ring and the money to take it out of pledge, and we retired to rest. This time, very fortunately, there was but one bed in the room, and I had to take another chamber for myself.

The next morning, I went into Christine's room, and found her in bed. Her uncle had gone out for my diamond ring, and alone with that lovely girl, I found that I had, when necessary, complete control over my passions. Thinking that she was not to be my wife, and that she would belong to another, I considered it my duty to silence my desires. I kissed her, but nothing more.

I spent one hour with her, fighting like Saint Anthony against the carnal desires of my nature. I could see the charming girl full of love and of wonder at my reserve, and I admired her virtue in the natural modesty which prevented her from making the first advances. She got out of bed and dressed herself without shewing any disappointment. She would, of course, have felt mortified

if she had had the slightest idea that I despised her, or
that I did not value her charms.

Her uncle returned, gave me the ring, and we had
dinner, after which he treated me to a wonderful exhibition. Christine had learned how to write, and, to give
me a proof of her talent, she wrote very fluently and
very prettily in my presence.

We parted, after my promising to come back again
within ten days, and I returned to Venice.

On the second Sunday in Lent, M. Dandolo told me
with an air of triumph that the fortunate husband had
been found, and that there was no doubt of my approval
of the new candidate. He named Charles ——, whom
I knew by sight—a very handsome young man, of irreproachable conduct, and about twenty-two years of
age. He was clerk to M. Ragionato and god-son of
Count Algarotti, a sister of whom had married M. Dandolo's brother.

"Charles ——," said M. Dandolo to me, "has lost his
father and his mother, and I feel satisfied that his god-
father will guarantee the dowry brought by his wife.
I have spoken to him, and I believe him disposed to
marry an honest girl whose dowry would enable him to
purchase M. Ragionato's office."

"It seems to promise very well, but I cannot decide
until I have seen him."

"I have invited him to dine with us to-morrow."

The young man came, and I found him worthy of all
M. Dandolo's praise. We became friends at once; he
had some taste for poetry, I read some of my productions to him, and having paid him a visit the following
day, he shewed me several pieces of his own composition
which were well written. He introduced me to his aunt,
in whose house he lived with his sister, and I was much

pleased with their friendly welcome. Being alone with him in his room, I asked him what he thought of love.

"I do not care for love," he answered: "but I should like to get married in order to have a house of my own."

When I returned to the palace, I told M. Dandolo that he might open the affair with Count Algarotti, and the count mentioned it to Charles, who said that he could not give any answer, either one way or the other, until he should have seen the young girl, talked with her, and enquired about her reputation. As for Count Algarotti, he was ready to be answerable for his god-son, that is to guarantee four thousand ducats to the wife, provided her dowry was worth that amount. Those were only the preliminaries; the rest belonged to my province.

Dandolo having informed Charles that the matter was entirely in my hands, he called on me and enquired when I would be kind enough to introduce him to the young person. I named the day, adding that it was necessary to devote a whole day to the visit, as she resided at a distance of twenty miles from Venice, that we would dine with her and return the same evening. He promised to be ready for me by day-break. I immediately sent an express to the curate to inform him of the day on which I would call with a friend of mine whom I wished to introduce to his niece.

On the appointed day, Charles was punctual. I took care to let him know along the road that I had made the acquaintance of the young girl and of her uncle as travelling companions from Venice to Mestra about one month before, and that I would have offered myself as a husband, if I had been in a position to guarantee the dowry of four thousand ducats. I did not think it necessary to go any further in my confidences.

We arrived at the good priest's house two hours before

mid-day, and soon after our arrival, Christine came in with an air of great ease, expressing all her pleasure at seeing me. She only bowed to Charles, enquiring from me whether he was likewise a clerk.

Charles answered that he was clerk at Ragionato.

She pretended to understand, in order not to appear ignorant.

"I want you to look at my writing," she said to me, "and afterwards we will go and see my mother."

Delighted at the praise bestowed upon her writing by Charles, when he heard that she had learned only one month, she invited us to follow her. Charles asked her why she had waited until the age of nineteen to study writing.

"Well, sir, what does it matter to you? Besides, I must tell you that I am seventeen, and not nineteen years of age."

Charles entreated her to excuse him, smiling at the quickness of her answer.

She was dressed like a simple country girl, yet very neatly, and she wore her handsome gold chains round her neck and on her arms. I told her to take my arm and that of Charles, which she did, casting towards me a look of loving obedience. We went to her mother's house; the good woman was compelled to keep her bed owing to sciatica. As we entered the room, a respecta-ble-looking man, who was seated near the patient, rose at the sight of Charles, and embraced him affectionately. I heard that he was the family physician, and the cir-cumstance pleased me much.

After we had paid our compliments to the good woman, the doctor enquired after Charles's aunt and sister; and alluding to the sister who was suffering from a secret disease, Charles desired to say a few words to

him in private; they left the room together. Being alone
with the mother and Christine, I praised Charles, his excellent conduct, his high character, his business abilities,
and extolled the happiness of the woman who would be
his wife. They both confirmed my praises by saying
that everything I said of him could be read on his features. I had no time to lose, so I told Christine to be
on her guard during dinner, as Charles might possibly
be the husband whom God had intended for her.

"For me?"

"Yes, for you. Charles is one of a thousand; you
would be much happier with him than you could be
with me; the doctor knows him, and you could ascertain
from him everything which I cannot find time to tell
you now about my friend."

The reader can imagine all I suffered in making this
declaration, and my surprise when I saw the young girl
calm and perfectly composed! Her composure dried
the tears already gathering in my eyes. After a short
silence, she asked me whether I was certain that such a
handsome young man would have her. That question
gave me an insight into Christine's heart and feelings,
and quieted all my sorrow, for I saw that I had not
known her well. I answered that, beautiful as she was,
there was no doubt of her being loved by everybody.

"It will be at dinner, my dear Christine, that my
friend will examine and study you; do not fail to shew
all the charms and qualities with which God has endowed you, but do not let him suspect our intimacy."

"It is all very strange. Is my uncle informed of this
wonderful change?"

"No."

"If your friend should feel pleased with me, when
would he marry me?"

"Within ten days. I will take care of everything, and you will see me again in the course of the week."

Charles came back with the doctor, and Christine, leaving her mother's bedside, took a chair opposite to us. She answered very sensibly all the questions addressed to her by Charles, often exciting his mirth by her artlessness, but not shewing any silliness.

Oh! charming simplicity! offspring of wit and of ignorance! thy charm is delightful, and thou alone hast the privilege of saying anything without ever giving offence! But how unpleasant thou art when thou art not natural! and thou art the masterpiece of art when thou art imitated with perfection!

We dined rather late, and I took care not to speak to Christine, not even to look at her, so as not to engross her attention, which she devoted entirely to Charles, and I was delighted to see with what ease and interest she kept up the conversation. After dinner, and as we were taking leave, I heard the following words uttered by Charles, which went to my very heart:

"You are made, lovely Christine, to minister to the happiness of a prince."

And Christine? This was her answer:

"I should esteem myself fortunate, sir, if you should judge me worthy of ministering to yours."

These words excited Charles so much that he embraced me!

Christine was simple, but her artlessness did not come from her mind, only from her heart. The simplicity of mind is nothing but silliness, that of the heart is only ignorance and innocence; it is a quality which subsists even when the cause has ceased to be. This young girl, almost a child of nature, was simple in her manners, but graceful in a thousand trifling ways which cannot be described. She was sincere, because she did not know that to conceal some of our impressions is one of the precepts of propriety, and as her intentions were pure, she was a stranger to that false shame and mock modesty which cause pretended innocence to blush at a word or at a movement said or made very often without any wicked purpose.

During our journey back to Venice Charles spoke of nothing but of his happiness. He had decidedly fallen in love.

"I will call to-morrow morning upon Count Algarotti," he said to me, "and you may write to the priest to come with all the necessary documents to make the contract of marriage which I long to sign."

His delight and his surprise were intense when I told him that my wedding present to Christine was a dispensation from the Pope for her to be married in Lent.

"Then," he exclaimed, "we must go full speed ahead!"

In the conference which was held the next day between my young substitute, his god-father, and M. Dandolo, it was decided that the parson should be invited to come with his niece. I undertook to carry the message, and leaving Venice two hours before morning I reached P—— early. The priest said he would be ready to start immediately after mass. I then called on Christine, and I treated her to a fatherly and sentimental sermon, every word of which was intended to point out to her the true road to happiness in the new condition which she was on the point of adopting. I told her how she ought to behave towards her husband, towards his aunt and his sister, in order to captivate their esteem and their love. The last part of my discourse was pathetic and rather disparaging to myself, for, as I enforced upon her the necessity of being faithful to her husband, I was necessarily led to entreat her pardon for having seduced her.

"When you promised to marry me, after we had both been weak enough to give way to our love, did you intend to deceive me?"

"Certainly not."

"Then you have not deceived me. On the contrary, I owe you some gratitude for having thought that, if our union should prove unhappy, it was better to find another husband for me, and I thank God that you have succeeded so well. Tell me, now, what I can answer to your friend in case he should ask me, during the first night, why I am so different to what a virgin ought to be?"

"It is not likely that Charles, who is full of reserve and propriety, would ask you such a thing, but if he should, tell him positively that you never had a lover, and that you do not suppose yourself to be different to any other girl."

"Will he believe me?"

"He would deserve your contempt, and entail punishment on himself if he did not. But dismiss all anxiety; that will not occur. A sensible man, my dear Christine, when he has been rightly brought up, never ventures upon such a question, because he is not only certain to displease, but also sure that he will never know the truth, for if the truth is likely to injure a woman in the opinion of her husband, she would be very foolish, indeed, to confess it."

"I understand your meaning perfectly, my dear friend; let us, then, embrace each other for the last time."

"No, for we are alone and I am very weak. I adore thee as much as ever."

"Do not cry, dear friend, for, truly speaking, I have no wish for it."

That simple and candid answer changed my disposition suddenly, and, instead of crying, I began to laugh. Christine dressed herself splendidly, and after breakfast we left P——. We reached Venice in four hours. I lodged them at a good inn, and going to the palace, I told M. Dandolo that our people had arrived, that it would be his province to bring them and Charles together on the following day, and to attend to the matter altogether, because the honour of the future husband and wife, the respect due to their parents and to propriety, forbade any further interference on my part.

He understood my reasons, and acted accordingly. He brought Charles to me, I presented both of them to the curate and his niece, and then left them to complete their business.

I heard afterwards from M. Dandolo that they all called upon Count Algarotti, and at the office of a notary, where the contract of marriage was signed, and that, after fixing a day for the wedding, Charles had escorted his intended back to P——.

On his return, Charles paid me a visit. He told me that Christine had won by her beauty and pleasing manners the affection of his aunt, of his sister, and of his god-father, and that they had taken upon themselves all the expense of the wedding.

"We intend to be married," he added, "on such a day at P——, and I trust that you will crown your work of kindness by being present at the ceremony."

I tried to excuse myself, but he insisted with such a feeling of gratitude, and with so much earnestness, that I was compelled to accept. I listened with real pleasure to the account he gave me of the impression produced upon all his family and upon Count Algarotti by the beauty, the artlessness, the rich toilet, and especially by the simple talk of the lovely country girl.

"I am deeply in love with her," Charles said to me, "and I feel that it is to you that I shall be indebted for the happiness I am sure to enjoy with my charming wife. She will soon get rid of her country way of talking in Venice, because here envy and slander will but too easily shew her the absurdity of it."

His enthusiasm and happiness delighted me, and I congratulated myself upon my own work. Yet I felt inwardly some jealousy, and I could not help envying a lot which I might have kept for myself.

M. Dandolo and M. Barbaro having been also invited by Charles, I went with them to P——. We found the dinner-table laid out in the rector's house by the servants of Count Algarotti, who was acting as Charles's father, and having taken upon himself all the expense of the wedding, had sent his cook and his major-domo to P——.

When I saw Christine, the tears filled my eyes, and I had to leave the room. She was dressed as a country girl, but looked as lovely as a nymph. Her husband, her uncle, and Count Algarotti had vainly tried to make her adopt the Venetian costume, but she had very wisely refused.

"As soon as I am your wife," she had said to Charles, "I will dress as you please, but here I will not appear before my young companions in any other costume than the one in which they have always seen me. I shall thus avoid being laughed at, and accused of pride, by the girls among whom I have been brought up."

There was in these words something so noble, so just, and so generous, that Charles thought his sweetheart a supernatural being. He told me that he had enquired,

from the woman with whom Christine had spent a fortnight, about the offers of marriage she had refused at
that time, and that he had been much surprised, for two
of those offers were excellent ones.

"Christine," he added, "was evidently destined by
Heaven for my happiness, and to you I am indebted for
the precious possession of that treasure."

His gratitude pleased me, and I must render myself
the justice of saying that I entertained no thought of
abusing it. I felt happy in the happiness I had thus
given.

We repaired to the church towards eleven o'clock, and
were very much astonished at the difficulty we experienced in getting in. A large number of the nobility of
Treviso, curious to ascertain whether it was true that
the marriage ceremony of a country girl would be publicly performed during Lent when, by waiting only one
month, a dispensation would have been useless, had
come to P——. Everyone wondered at the permission
having been obtained from the Pope, everyone imagined
that there was some extraordinary reason for it, and was
in despair because it was impossible to guess that reason.
In spite of all feelings of envy, every face beamed with
pleasure and satisfaction when the young couple made
their appearance, and no one could deny that they deserved that extraordinary distinction, that exception to
all established rules.

A certain Countess of Tos. . . ., from Treviso, Christine's god-mother, went up to her after the ceremony,
and embraced her most tenderly, complaining that the
happy event had not been communicated to her in Treviso. Christine, in her artless way, answered with as
much modesty as sweetness, that the countess ought to
forgive her if she had failed in her duty towards her, on

account of the marriage having been decided on so hastily. She presented her husband, and begged Count Algarotti to atone for her error towards her god-mother by inviting her to join the wedding respast, an invitation which the countess accepted with great pleasure. That behaviour, which is usually the result of a good education and a long experience of society, was in the lovely peasant-girl due only to a candid and well-balanced mind which shone all the more because it was all nature and not art.

As they returned from the church, Charles and Christine knelt down before the young wife's mother, who gave them her blessing with tears of joy.

Dinner was served, and, of course, Christine and her happy spouse took the seats of honour. Mine was the last, and I was very glad of it, but although everything was delicious, I ate very little, and scarcely opened my lips.

Christine was constantly busy, saying pretty things to every one of her guests, and looking at her husband to make sure that he was pleased with her.

Once or twice she addressed his aunt and sister in such a gracious manner that they could not help leaving their places and kissing her tenderly, congratulating Charles upon his good fortune. I was seated not very far from Count Algarotti, and I heard him say several times to Christine's god-mother that he had never felt so delighted in his life.

When four o'clock struck, Charles whispered a few words to his lovely wife, she bowed to her god-mother, and everybody rose from the table. After the usual compliments—and in this case they bore the stamp of sincerity—the bride distributed among all the girls of the village, who were in the adjoining room, packets full of sugar-plums which had been prepared before hand,

and she took leave of them, kissing them all without any pride. Count Algarotti invited all the guests to sleep at a house he had in Treviso, and to partake there of the dinner usually given the day after the wedding. The uncle alone excused himself, and the mother could not come, owing to her disease which prevented her from moving. The good woman died three months after Christine's marriage.

Christine therefore left her village to follow her husband, and for the remainder of their lives they lived together in mutual happiness.

Count Algarotti, Christine's god-mother and my two noble friends, went away together. The bride and bridegroom had, of course, a carriage to themselves, and I kept the aunt and the sister of Charles company in another. I could not help envying the happy man somewhat, although in my inmost heart I felt pleased with his happiness.

The sister was not without merit. She was a young widow of twenty-five, and still deserved the homage of men, but I gave the preference to the aunt, who told me that her new niece was a treasure, a jewel which was worthy of everybody's admiration, but that she would not let her go into society until she could speak the Venetian dialect well.

"Her cheerful spirits," she added, "her artless simplicity, her natural wit, are like her beauty, they must be dressed in the Venetian fashion. We are highly pleased with my nephew's choice, and he has incurred everlasting obligations towards you. I hope that for the future you will consider our house as your own."

The invitation was polite, perhaps it was sincere, yet I did not avail myself of it, and they were glad of it. At the end of one year Christine presented her husband with a living token of their mutual love, and that circumstance increased their conjugal felicity.

We all found comfortable quarters in the count's house in Treviso, where, after partaking of some refreshments, the guests retired to rest.

The next morning I was with Count Algarotti and my two friends when Charles came in, handsome, bright, and radiant. While he was answering with much wit some jokes of the count, I kept looking at him with some anxiety, but he came up to me and embraced me warmly. I confess that a kiss never made me happier.

People wonder at the devout scoundrels who call upon their saint when they think themselves in need of heavenly assistance, or who thank him when they imagine that they have obtained some favour from him, but people are wrong, for it is a good and right feeling, which preaches against Atheism.

At the invitation of Charles, his aunt and his sister had gone to pay a morning visit to the young wife, and they returned with her. Happiness never shone on a more lovely face!

M. Algarotti, going towards her, enquired from her affectionately whether she had had a good night. Her only answer was to rush to her husband's arms. It was the most artless, and at the same time the most eloquent, answer she could possible give. Then turning her beautiful eyes towards me, and offering me her hand, she said,—

"M. Casanova, I am happy, and I love to be indebted to you for my happiness."

The tears which were flowing from my eyes, as I kissed her hand, told her better than words how truly happy I was myself.

The dinner passed off delightfully. We then left for

Mestra and Venice. We escorted the married couple to their house, and returned home to amuse M. Bragadin with the relation of our expedition. This worthy and particularly learned man said a thousand things about the marriage, some of great profundity and others of great absurdity.

I laughed inwardly. I was the only one who had the key to the mystery, and could realize the secret of the comedy.

CHAPTER XX

*Slight Misfortunes Compel Me to Leave Venice—My
Adventures in Milan and Mantua*

ON Low Sunday Charles paid us a visit with his
lovely wife, who seemed totally indifferent to what
Christine used to be. Her hair dressed with powder did
not please me as well as the raven black of her beautiful locks, and her fashionable town attire did not, in my
eyes, suit her as well as her rich country dress. But the
countenances of husband and wife bore the stamp of happiness. Charles reproached me in a friendly manner because I had not called once upon them, and, in order to
atone for my apparent negligence, I went to see them the
next day with M. Dandolo. Charles told me that his
wife was idolized by his aunt and his sister who had
become her bosom friend; that she was kind, affectionate, unassuming, and of a disposition which enforced
affection. I was no less pleased with this favourable
state of things than with the facility with which Christine was learning the Venetian dialect.

When M. Dandolo and I called at their house, Charles
was not at home; Christine was alone with his two relatives. The most friendly welcome was proffered to us,
and in the course of conversation the aunt praised the
progress made by Christine in her writing very highly,
and asked her to let me see her copy-book. I followed
her to the next room, where she told me that she was

very happy; that every day she discovered new virtues
in her husband. He had told her, without the slightest
appearance of suspicion of displeasure, that he knew
that we had spent two days together in Treviso, and that
he had laughed at the well-meaning fool who had given
him that piece of information in the hope of raising a
cloud in the heaven of their felicity.

Charles was truly endowed with all the virtues, with
all the noble qualities of an honest and distinguished
man. Twenty-six years afterwards I happened to require the assistance of his purse, and found him my
true friend. I never was a frequent visitor at his house,
and he appreciated my delicacy. He died a few months
before my last departure from Venice, leaving his widow
in easy circumstances, and three well-educated sons, all
with good positions, who may, for what I know, be still
living with their mother.

In June I went to the fair at Padua, and made the
acquaintance of a young man of my own age, who was
then studying mathematics under the celebrated Professor Succi. His name was Tognolo, but thinking it
did not sound well, he changed it for that of Fabris.
He became, in after years, Comte de Fabris, lieutenant-
general under Joseph II., and died Governor of Transyl-
vania. This man, who owed his high fortune to his
talents, would, perhaps, have lived and died unknown
if he had kept his name of Tognolo, a truly vulgar one.
He was from Uderzo, a large village of the Venetian
Friuli. He had a brother in the Church, a man of parts,
and a great gamester, who, having a deep knowledge of
the world, had taken the name of Fabris, and the younger
brother had to assume it likewise. Soon afterwards he
bought an estate with the title of count, became a Venetian nobleman, and his origin as a country bumpkin

was forgotten. If he had kept his name of Tognolo it would have injured him, for he could not have pronounced it without reminding his hearers of what is called, by the most contemptible of prejudices, low extraction, and the privileged class, through an absurd error, does not admit the possibility of a peasant having talent or genius. No doubt a time will come when society, more enlightened, and therefore more reasonable, will acknowledge that noble feelings, honour, and heroism can be found in every condition of life as easily as in a class, the blood of which is not always exempt from the taint of a misalliance.

The new count, while he allowed others to forget his origin, was too wise to forget it himself, and in legal documents he always signed his family name as well as the one he had adopted. His brother had offered him two ways to win fortune in the world, leaving him perfectly free in his choice. Both required an expenditure of one thousand sequins, but the abbé had put the amount aside for that purpose. My friend had to choose between the sword of Mars and the bird of Minerva. The abbé knew that he could purchase for his brother a company in the army of his Imperial and Apostolic Majesty, or obtain for him a professorship at the University of Padua; for money can do everything. But my friend, who was gifted with noble feelings and good sense, knew that in either profession talents and knowledge were essentials, and before making a choice he was applying himself with great success to the study of mathematics. He utlimately decided upon the military profession, thus imitating Achilles, who preferred the sword to the distaff, and he paid for it with his life like the son of Peleus; though not so young, and not through a wound inflicted by an arrow, but from the plague, which he caught in the unhappy country in which the indolence of Europe allows the Turks to perpetuate that fearful disease.

The distinguished appearance, the noble sentiments, the great knowledge, and the talents of Fabris would have been turned into ridicule in a man called Tognolo, for such is the force of prejudices, particularly of those which have no ground to rest upon, that an ill-sounding name is degrading in this our stupid society. My opinion is that men who have an ill-sounding name, or one which presents an indecent or ridiculous idea, are right in changing it if they intend to win honour, fame, and fortune either in arts or sciences. No one can reasonably deny them that right, provided the name they assume belongs to nobody. The alphabet is general property, and everyone has the right to use it for the creation of a word forming an appellative sound. But he must truly create it. Voltaire, in spite of his genius, would not perhaps have reached posterity under his name of *Arouet*, especially amongst the French, who always give way so easily to their keen sense of ridicule and equivocation. How could they have imagined that a writer *à rouet* could be a man of genius? And *D'Alembert*, would he have attained his high fame, his universal reputation, if he had been satisfied with his name of *M. Le Rond*, or Mr. Allround? What would have become of *Metastasio* under his true name of *Trapasso?* What impression would *Melanchthon* have made with his name of *Schwarzerd?* Would he then have dared to raise the voice of a moralist philosopher, of a reformer of the Eucharist, and so many other holy things? Would not M. de Beauharnais have caused some persons to laugh and others to blush if he had kept his name of *Beauvit*, even if the first founder of his family had been indebted for his fortune to the fine quality expressed by that name?

Would the *Bourbeux* have made as good a figure on the throne as the Bourbons? I think that King Poniatowski ought to have abdicated the name of *Augustus,* which he had taken at the time of his accession to the throne, when he abdicated royalty. The *Coleoni* of Bergamo, however, would find it rather difficult to change their name, because they would be compelled at the same time to change their coat of arms (the two generative glands), and thus to annihilate the glory of their ancestor, the hero Bartholomeo.

Towards the end of autumn my friend Fabris introduced me to a family in the midst of which the mind and the heart could find delicious food. That family resided in the country on the road to Zero. Card-playing, love-making, and practical jokes were the order of the day. Some of those jokes were rather severe ones, but the order of the day was never to get angry and to laugh at everything, for one was to take every jest pleasantly or be thought a bore. Bedsteads would at night tumble down under their occupants, ghosts were personated, diuretic pills or sugar-plums were given to young ladies, as well as comfits who produced certain winds rising from the *netherlands,* and impossible to keep under control. These jokes would sometimes go rather too far, but such was the spirit animating all the members of that circle; they would laugh. I was not less inured than the others to the war of offence and defence, but at last there was such a bitter joke played upon me that it suggested to me another, the fatal consequences of which put a stop to the mania by which we were all possessed.

We were in the habit of walking to a farm which was about half a league distant by the road, but the distance could be reduced by half by going over a deep and miry ditch across which a narrow plank was thrown, and I always insisted upon going that way, in spite of the fright of the ladies who always trembled on the narrow bridge, although I never failed to cross the first, and to offer my hand to help them over. One fine day, I crossed first so as to give them courage, but suddenly, when I reached the middle of the plank, it gave way under me, and there I was in the ditch, up to the chin in stinking mud, and, in spite of my inward rage, obliged, according to the general understanding, to join in the merry laughter of all my companions. But the merriment did not last long, for the joke was too bad, and everyone declared it to be so. Some peasants were called to the rescue, and with much difficulty they dragged me out in the most awful state. An entirely new dress, embroidered with spangles, my silk stockings, my lace, everything, was of course spoiled, but not minding it, I laughed more heartily that anybody else, although I had already made an inward vow to have the most cruel revenge. In order to know the author of that bitter joke I had only to appear calm and indifferent about it. It was evident that the plank had been purposely sawn. I was taken back to the house, a shirt, a coat, a complete costume, were lent me, for I had come that time only for twenty-four hours, and had not brought anything with me. I went to the city the next morning, and towards the evening I returned to the gay company. Fabris, who had been as angry as myself, observed to me that the perpetrator of the joke evidently felt his guilt, because he took good care not to discover himself. But I unveiled the mystery by promising one sequin to a peasant woman if she could find out who had sawn the plank. She contrived to discover the young man who had done the work. I called on him, and the offer of a sequin, together with my threats, compelled him to confess that he had been paid for his work by Signor Demetrio, a Greek, dealer in spices, a good and amiable man of between forty-five and fifty years, on whom I never played any trick, except in the case of a pretty, young servant girl whom he was courting, and whom I had juggled from him.

Satisfied with my discovery, I was racking my brain to invent a good practical joke, but to obtain complete revenge it was necessary that my trick should prove worse than the one he had played upon me. Unfortunately my imagination was at bay. I could not find anything. A funeral put an end to my difficulties.

Armed with my hunting-knife, I went alone to the cemetery a little after midnight, and opening the grave of the dead man who had been buried that very day, I cut off one of the arms near the shoulder, not without some trouble, and after I had re-buried the corpse, I returned to my room with the arm of the defunct. The next day, when supper was over, I left the table and retired to my chamber as if I intended to go to bed, but taking the arm with me I hid myself under Demetrio's bed. A short time after, the Greek comes in, undresses himself, put his light out, and lies down. I give him time to fall nearly asleep; then, placing myself at the foot of the bed, I pull away the clothes little by little until he is half naked. He laughs and calls out,——

"Whoever you may be, go away and let me sleep quietly, for I do not believe in ghosts;" he covers himself again and composes himself to sleep.

I wait five or six minutes, and pull again at the bed-clothes; but when he tries to draw up the sheet, saying that he does not care for ghosts, I oppose some resistance. He sits up so as to catch the hand which is pulling

at the clothes, and I take care that he should get hold of
the dead hand. Confident that he has caught the man
or the woman who was playing the trick, he pulls it
towards him, laughing all the time; I keep tight hold of
the arm for a few instants, and then let it go suddenly;
the Greek falls back on his pillow without uttering a
single word.

The trick was played, I leave the room without any
noise, and, reaching my chamber, go to bed.

I was fast asleep, when towards morning I was awoke
by persons going about, and not understanding why they
should be up so early, I got up. The first person I met
—the mistress of the house—told me that I had played
an abominable joke.

"I? What have I done?"

"M. Demetrio is dying."

"Have I killed him?"

She went away without answering me. I dressed myself, rather frightened, I confess, but determined upon
pleading complete ignorance of everything, and I proceeded to Demetrio's room; and I was confronted with
horror-stricken countenances and bitter reproaches. I
found all the guests around him. I protested my innocence, but everyone smiled. The archpriest and the
beadle, who had just arrived, would not bury the arm
which was lying there, and they told me that I had been
guilty of a great crime.

"I am astonished, reverend sir," I said to the priest,
"at the hasty judgment which is thus passed upon me,
when there is no proof to condemn me."

"You have done it," exclaimed all the guests, "you
alone are capable of such an abomination; it is just
like you. No one but you would have dared to do such
a thing!"

"I am compelled," said the archpriest, "to draw up an official report."

"As you please, I have not the slightest objection," I answered, "I have nothing to fear."

And I left the room.

I continued to take it coolly, and at the dinner-table I was informed that M. Demetrio had been bled, that he had recovered the use of his eyes, but not of his tongue or of his limbs. The next day he could speak, and I heard, after I had taken leave of the family, that he was stupid and spasmodic. The poor man remained in that painful state for the rest of his life. I felt deeply grieved, but I had not intended to injure him so badly. I thought that the trick he had played upon me might have cost my life, and I could not help deriving consolation from that idea.

On the same day, the archpriest made up his mind to have the arm buried, and to send a formal denunciation against me to the episcopal chancellorship of Treviso.

Annoyed at the reproaches which I received on all sides, I returned to Venice. A fortnight afterwards I was summoned to appear before the *magistrato alla blasfemia*. I begged M. Barbaro to enquire the cause of the aforesaid summons, for it was a formidable court. I was surprised at the proceedings being taken against me, as if there had been a certainty of my having desecrated a grave, whilst there could be nothing but suspicion. But I was mistaken, the summons was not relating to that affair. M. Barbaro informed me in the evening that a woman had brought a complaint against me for having violated her daughter. She stated in her complaint that, having decoyed her child to the Zuecca, I had abused her by violence, and she adduced as a proof that her daughter was confined to her bed, owing to the bad treatment she had received from me in my endeavours to ravish her.

It was one of those complaints which are often made, in order to give trouble and to cause expense, even against innocent persons. I was innocent of violation, but it was quite true that I had given the girl a sound thrashing. I prepared my defence, and begged M. Barbaro to deliver it to the magistrate's secretary.

DECLARATION

I hereby declare that, on such a day, having met the woman —— with her daughter, I accosted them and offered to give them some refreshments at a coffee-house near by; that the daughter refused to accept my caresses, and that the mother said to me,—

"My daughter is yet a virgin, and she is quite right not to lose her maidenhood without making a good profit by it."

"If so," I answered, "I will give you ten sequins for her virginity."

"You may judge for yourself," said the mother.

Having assured myself of the fact by the assistance of the sense of feeling, and having ascertained that it might be true, I told the mother to bring the girl in the afternoon to the Zuecca, and that I would give her the ten sequins. My offer was joyfully accepted, the mother brought her daughter to me, she received the money, and leaving us together in the Garden of the Cross, she went away.

When I tried to avail myself of the right for which I had paid, the girl, most likely trained to the business by her mother, contrived to prevent me. At first the game amused me, but at last, being tired of it, I told her to have done. She answered quietly that it was not her

fault if I was not able to do what I wanted. Vexed and
annoyed, I placed her in such a position that she found
herself at bay, but, making a violent effort, she managed
to change her position and debarred me from making
any further attempts.

"Why," I said to her, "did you move?"

"Because I would not have it in that position."

"You would not?"

"No."

Without more ado, I got hold of a broomstick, and
gave her a good lesson, in order to get something for the
ten sequins which I had been foolish enough to pay in
advance. But I have broken none of her limbs, and I
took care to apply my blows only on her posteriors, on
which spot I have no doubt that all the marks may be
seen. In the evening I made her dress herself again,
and sent her back in a boat which chanced to pass, and
she was landed in safety. The mother received ten
sequins, the daughter has kept her hateful maidenhood,
and, if I am guilty of anything, it is only of having given
a thrashing to an infamous girl, the pupil of a still more
infamous mother.

My declaration had no effect. The magistrate was acquainted with the girl, and the mother laughed at having
duped me so easily. I was summoned, but did not appear before the court, and a writ was on the point of
being issued against my body, when the complaint of
the profanation of a grave was filed against me before
the same magistrate. It would have been less serious
for me if the second affair had been carried before the
Council of Ten, because one court might have saved me
from the other.

The second crime, which, after all, was only a joke,
was high felony in the eyes of the clergy, and a great

deal was made of it. I was summoned to appear within twenty-four hours, and it was evident that I would be arrested immediately afterwards. M. de Bragadin, who always gave good advice, told me that the best way to avoid the threatening storm was to run away. The advice was certainly wise, and I lost no time in getting ready.

I have never left Venice with so much regret as I did then, for I had some pleasant intrigues on hand, and I was very lucky at cards. My three friends assured me that, within one year at the furthest, the cases against me would be forgotten, and in Venice, when public opinion has forgotten anything, it can be easily arranged.

I left Venice in the evening and the next day I slept at Verona. Two days afterwards I reached Mantua. I was alone, with plenty of clothes and jewels, without letters of introduction, but with a well-filled purse, enjoying excellent health and my twenty-three years.

In Mantua I ordered an excellent dinner, the very first thing one ought to do at a large hotel, and after dinner I went out for a walk. In the evening, after I had seen the coffee-houses and the places of resort, I went to the theatre, and I was delighted to see Marina appear on the stage as a comic dancer, amid the greatest applause, which she deserved, for she danced beautifully. She was tall, handsome, very well made and very graceful. I immediately resolved on renewing my acquaintance with her, if she happened to be free, and after the opera I engaged a boy to take me to her house. She had just sat down to supper with someone, but the moment she saw me she threw her napkin down and flew to my arms. I returned her kisses, judging by her warmth that her guest was a man of no consequence.

The servant, without waiting for orders, had already laid a plate for me, and Marina invited me to sit down near her. I felt vexed, because the aforesaid individual had not risen to salute me, and before I accepted Marina's invitation I asked her who the gentleman was, begging her to introduce me.

"This gentleman," she said, "is Count Celi, of Rome; he is my lover."

"I congratulate you," I said to her, and turning towards the so-called count, "Sir," I added, "do not be angry at our mutual affection, Marina is my daughter."

"She is a prostitute."

"True," said Marina, "and you can believe the count, for he is my procurer."

At those words, the brute threw his knife at her face, but she avoided it by running away. The scoundrel followed her, but I drew my sword, and said,—

"Stop, or you are a dead man."

I immediately asked Marina to order her servant to light me out, but she hastily put a cloak on, and taking my arm she entreated me to take her with me.

"With pleasure," I said.

The count then invited me to meet him alone, on the following day, at the Casino of Pomi, to hear what he had to say.

"Very well, sir, at four in the afternoon," I answered.

I took Marina to my inn, where I lodged her in the room adjoining mine, and we sat down to supper.

Marina, seeing that I was thoughtful, said,—

"Are you sorry to have saved me from the rage of that brute?"

"No, I am glad to have done so, but tell me truly who and what he is."

"He is a gambler by profession, and gives himself out

as Count Celi. I made his acquaintance here. He courted me, invited me to supper, played after supper, and, having won a large sum from an Englishman whom he had decoyed to his supper by telling him that I would be present, he gave me fifty guineas, saying that he had given me an interest in his bank. As soon as I had become his mistress, he insisted upon my being compliant with all the men he wanted to make his dupes, and at last he took up his quarters at my lodgings. The welcome I gave you very likely vexed him, and you know the rest. Here I am, and here I will remain until my departure for Mantua where I have an engagement as first dancer. My servant will bring me all I need for to-night, and I will give him orders to move all my luggage to-morrow. I will not see that scoundrel any more. I will be only yours, if you are free as in Corfu, and if you love me still."

"Yes, my dear Marina, I do love you, but if you wish to be my mistress, you must be only mine."

"Oh! of course. I have three hundred sequins, and I will give them to you to-morrow if you will take me as your mistress."

"I do not want any money; all I want is yourself. Well, it is all arranged; to-morrow evening we shall feel more comfortable."

"Perhaps you are thinking of a duel for to-morrow? But do not imagine such a thing, dearest. I know that man; he is an arrant coward."

"I must keep my engagement with him."

"I know that, but he will not keep his, and I am very glad of it."

Changing the conversation and speaking of our old acquaintances, she informed me that she had quarreled with her brother Petronio, that her sister was prima donna in Genoa, and that Bellino Thérèse was still in Naples, where she continued to ruin dukes. She concluded by saying,—

"I am the most unhappy of the family."

"How so? You are beautiful, and you have become an excellent dancer. Do not be so prodigal of your favours, and you cannot fail to meet with a man who will take care of your fortune."

"To be sparing of my favours is very difficult; when I love, I am no longer mine, but when I do not love, I cannot be amiable. Well, dearest, I could be very happy with you."

"Dear Marina, I am not wealthy, and my honour would not allow me . . . ."

"Hold your tongue; I understand you."

"Why have you not a lady's maid with you instead of a male servant?"

"You are right. A maid would look more respectable, but my servant is so clever and so faithful!"

"I can guess all his qualities, but he is not a fit servant for you."

The next day after dinner I left Marina getting ready for the theatre, and having put everything of value I possessed in my pocket, I took a carriage and proceeded to the Casino of Pomi. I felt confident of disabling the false count, and sent the carriage away. I was conscious of being guilty of great folly in exposing my life with such an adversary. I might have broken my engagement with him without implicating my honour, but, the fact is that I felt well disposed for a fight, and as I was certainly in the right I thought the prospect of a duel very delightful. A visit to a dancer, a brute professing to be a nobleman, who insults her in my presence, who wants to kill her, who allows her to be carried off in his very teeth, and whose only opposition is to give me an appointment! It seemed to me that if I had failed to come, I should have given him the right to call me a coward.

The count had not yet arrived. I entered the coffee-room to wait for him. I met a good-looking Frenchman there, and I addressed him. Being pleased with his conversation, I told him that I expected the arrival of a man, and that as my honour required that he should find me alone I would feel grateful if he would go away as soon as I saw the man approaching. A short time afterwards I saw my adversary coming along, but with a second. I then told the Frenchman that he would oblige me by remaining, and he accepted as readily as if I had invited him to a party of pleasure. The count came in with his follower, who was sporting a sword at least forty inches long, and had all the look of a cut-throat. I advanced towards the count, and said to him dryly,—

"You told me that you would come alone."

"My friend will not be in the way, as I only want to speak to you."

"If I had known that, I would not have gone out of my way. But do not let us be noisy, and let us go to some place where we can exchange a few words without being seen. Follow me."

I left the coffee-room with the young Frenchman, who, being well acquainted with the place, took me to the most favourable spot, and we waited there for the two other champions, who were walking slowly and talking together. When they were within ten paces I drew my sword and called upon my adversary to get ready. My Frenchman had already taken out his sword, but he kept it under his arm.

"Two to one!" exclaimed Celi.

"Send your friend away, and this gentleman will go likewise; at all events, your friend wears a sword, therefore we are two against two."

"Yes," said the Frenchman, "let us have a four-handed game."

"I do not cross swords with a dancer," said the cutthroat.

He had scarcely uttered those words when my friend, going up to him, told him that a dancer was certainly as good as a blackleg, and gave him a violent bow with the flat of his sword on the face. I followed his example with Celi, who began to beat a retreat, and said that he only wanted to tell me something, and that he would fight afterwards.

"Well, speak."

"You know me and I do not know you. Tell me who you are."

My only answer was to resume laying my sword upon the scoundrel, while the Frenchman was shewing the same dexterity upon the back of his companion, but the two cowards took to their heels, and there was nothing for us to do but to sheathe our weapons. Thus did the duel end in a manner even more amusing than Marina herself had anticipated.

My brave Frenchman was expecting someone at the casino. I left him after inviting him to supper for that evening after the opera. I gave him the name which I had assumed for my journey and the address of my hotel.

I gave Marina a full description of the adventure.

"I will," she said, "amuse everybody at the theatre this evening with the story of your meeting. But that which pleases me most is that, if your second is really a dancer, he can be no other than M. Baletti, who is engaged with me for the Mantua Theatre."

I stored all my valuables in my trunk again, and went to the opera, where I saw Baletti, who recognized me, and pointed me out to all his friends, to whom he was relating the adventure. He joined me after the performance, and accompanied me to the inn. Marina, who had already returned, came to my room as soon as she heard my voice, and I was amused at the surprise of the amiable Frenchman, when he saw the young artist with whom he had engaged to dance the comic parts. Marina, although an excellent dancer, did not like the serious style. Those two handsome adepts of Terpsichore had never met before, and they began an amorous warfare which made me enjoy my supper immensely, because, as he was a fellow artist, Marina assumed towards Baletti a tone well adapted to the circumstances, and very different to her usual manner with other men. She shone with wit and beauty that evening, and was in an excellent temper, for she had been much applauded by the public, the true version of the Celi business being already well known.

The theatre was to be open only for ten more nights, and as Marina wished to leave Milan immediately after the last performance, we decided on travelling together. In the mean time, I invited Baletti (it was an Italian name which he had adopted for the stage) to be our guest during the remainder of our stay in Milan. The friendship between us had a great influence upon all the subsequent events of my life, as the reader will see in these Memoirs. He had great talent as a dancer, but that was the least of his excellent qualities. He was honest, his feelings were noble, he had studied much, and he had received the best education that could be given in those days in France to a nobleman.

On the third day I saw plainly that Marina wished to make a conquest of her colleague, and feeling what great advantage might accrue to her from it I resolved on helping her. She had a post-chaise for two persons, and I easily persuaded her to take Baletti with her, saying that I wished to arrive alone in Mantua for several reasons which I could not confide to her. The fact was that if I had arrived with her, people would have naturally supposed that I was her lover, and I wished to avoid that. Baletti was delighted with the proposal; he insisted upon paying his share of the expenses, but Marina would not hear of it. The reasons alleged by the young man for paying his own expenses were excellent ones, and it was with great difficulty that I prevailed upon him to accept Marina's offer, but I ultimately succeeded. I promised to wait for them on the road, so as to take dinner and supper together, and on the day appointed for our departure I left Milan one hour before them.

Reaching the city of Cremona very early, where we intended to sleep, I took a walk about the streets, and, finding a coffee-house, I went in. I made there the acquaintance of a French officer, and we left the coffee-room together to take a short ramble. A very pretty woman happened to pass in a carriage, and my companion stopped her to say a few words. Their conversation was soon over, and the officer joined me again.

"Who is that lovely lady?" I enquired.

"She is a truly charming woman, and I can tell you an anecdote about her worthy of being transmitted to posterity. You need not suppose that I am going to exaggerate, for the adventure is known to everybody in Cremona. The charming woman whom you have just seen is gifted with wit greater even than her beauty, and here is a specimen of it. A young officer, one amongst many military men who were courting her, when Marshal de Richelieu was commanding in Genoa, boasted of being treated by her with more favour than all the others, and one day, in the very coffee-room where we met, he advised a brother officer not to lose his time in courting her, because he had no chance whatever of obtaining any favour.

" 'My dear fellow,' said the other officer, 'I have a much better right to give you that piece of advice, for I have already obtained from her everything which can be granted to a lover.'

" 'I am certain that you are telling a lie,' exclaimed the young man, 'and I request you to follow me out.'

" 'Most willingly,' said the indiscreet swain, 'but what is the good of ascertaining the truth through a duel and of cutting our throats, when I can make the lady herself certify the fact in your presence.'

" 'I bet twenty-five louis that it is all untrue,' said the incredulous officer.

" 'I accept your bet. Let us go.'

"The two contending parties proceeded together towards the dwelling of the lady whom you saw just now, who was to name the winner of the twenty-five louis.

"They found her in her dressing-room. 'Well gentlemen,' she said, 'what lucky wind has brought you here together at this hour?'

" 'It is a bet, madam,' answered the unbelieving officer, 'and you alone can be the umpire in our quarrel. This gentleman has been boasting of having obtained from you everything a woman can grant to the most

favoured lover. I have given him the lie in the most
impressive manner, and a duel was to ensue, when he
offered to have the truth of his boast certified by you.
I have bet twenty-five louis that you would not admit
it, and he has taken my bet. Now, madam, you can say
which of us two is right.'

"You have lost, sir," she said to him; 'but now I beg
both of you to quit my house, and I give you fair warning that if you ever dare to shew your faces here again,
you will be sorry for it.'

"The two heedless fellows went away dreadfully mortified. The unbeliever paid the bet, but he was deeply
vexed, called the other a coxcomb, and a week afterwards
killed him in a duel.

"Since that time the lady goes to the casino, and con-
tinues to mix in society, but does not see company at
her own house, and lives in perfect accord with her husband."

"How did the husband take it all?"

"Quite well, and like an intelligent, sensible man. He
said that, if his wife had acted differently, he would have
applied for a divorce, because in that case no one would
have entertained a doubt of her being guilty."

"That husband is indeed a sensible fellow. It is certain that, if his wife had given the lie to the indiscreet
officer, he would have paid the bet, but he would have
stood by what he had said, and everybody would have
believed him. By declaring him the winner of the bet
she has cut the matter short, and she has avoided a judgment by which she would have been dishonoured. The
inconsiderate boaster was guilty of a double mistake for
which he paid the penalty of his life, but his adversary
was as much wanting in delicacy, for in such matters

rightly-minded men do not venture upon betting. If the one who says *yes* is imprudent, the one who says *no* is a dupe. I like the lady's presence of mind."

"But what sentence would you pass on her. Guilty or not guilty?"

"Not guilty."

"I am of the same opinion, and it has been the verdict of the public likewise, for she has since been treated even better than before the affair. You will see, if you go to the casino, and I shall be happy to introduce you to her."

I invited the officer to sup with us, and we spent a very pleasant evening. After he had gone, I remarked with pleasure that Marina was capable of observing the rules of propriety. She had taken a bedroom to herself, so as not to hurt the feelings of her respectable fellow-dancer.

When I arrived in Mantua, I put up at St. Mark's hotel. Marina, to whom I had given a notice that my intention was to call on her but seldom, took up her abode in the house assigned to her by the theatrical manager.

In the afternoon of the same day, as I was walking about, I went into a bookseller's shop to ascertain whether there was any new work out. I remained there without perceiving that the night had come, and on being told that the shop was going to be closed, I went out. I had only gone a few yards when I was arrested by a patrol, the officer of which told me that, as I had no lantern and as eight o'clock had struck, his duty was to take me to the guardhouse. It was in vain that I observed that, having arrived only in the afternoon, I could not know that order of the police. I was compelled to follow him.

When we reached the guardhouse, the officer of the patrol introduced me to his captain, a tall, fine-looking young man who received me in the most cheerful manner. I begged him to let me return to my hotel as I needed rest after my journey. He laughed and answered, "No, indeed, I want you to spend a joyous night with me, and in good company." He told the officer to give me back my sword, and, addressing me again, he said, "I only consider you, my dear sir, as my friend and guest."

I could not help being amused at such a novel mode of invitation, and I accepted it. He gave some orders to a German soldier, and soon afterwards the table was laid out for four persons. The two other officers joined us, and we had a very gay supper. When the desert had been served the company was increased by the arrival of two disgusting, dissolute females. A green cloth was spread over the table, and one of the officers began a faro bank. I punted so as not to appear unwilling to join the game, and after losing a few sequins I went out to breathe the fresh air, for we had drunk freely. One of the two females followed me, teased me, and finally contrived, in spite of myself, to make me a present which condemned me to a regimen of six weeks. After that fine exploit, I went in again.

A young and pleasant officer, who had lost some fifteen or twenty sequins, was swearing like a trooper because the banker had pocketed his money and was going. The young officer had a great deal of gold before him on the table, and he contended that the banker ought to have warned him that it would be the last game.

"Sir," I said to him, politely, "you are in the wrong,

for faro is the freest of games. Why do you not take the bank yourself?"

"It would be too much trouble, and these gentlemen do not punt high enough for me, but if that sort of thing amuses you, take the bank and I will punt."

"Captain," I said, "will you take a fourth share in my bank?"

"Willingly."

"Gentlemen, I beg you to give notice that I will lay the cards down after six games."

I asked for new packs of cards, and put three hundred sequins on the table. The captain wrote on the back of a card, *"Good for a hundred sequins, O'Neilan,"* and placing it with my gold I began my bank.

The young officer was delighted, and said to me,—

"Your bank might be defunct before the end of the sixth game."

I did not answer, and the play went on.

At the beginning of the fifth game, my bank was in the pangs of death; the young officer was in high glee. I rather astonished him by telling him that I was glad to lose, for I thought him a much more agreeable companion when he was winning.

There are some civilities which very likely prove unlucky for those to whom they are addressed, and it turned out so in this case, for my compliment turned his brain. During the fifth game, a run of adverse cards made him lose all he had won, and as he tried to do violence to Dame Fortune in the sixth round, he lost every sequin he had.

"Sir," he said to me, "you have been very lucky, but I hope you will give me my revenge to-morrow."

"It would be with the greatest pleasure, sir, but I never play except when I am under arrest."

I counted my money, and found that I had won two hundred and fifty sequins, besides a debt of fifty sequins due by an officer who played on trust which Captain O'Neilan took on his own account. I completed his share, and at day-break he allowed me to go away.

As soon as I got to my hotel, I went to bed, and when I awoke, I had a visit from Captain Laurent, the officer who had played on trust. Thinking that his object was to pay me what he had lost, I told him that O'Neilan had taken his debt on himself, but he answered that he had only called for the purpose of begging of me a loan of six sequins on his note of hand, by which he would pledge his honour to repay me within one week. I gave him the money, and he begged that the matter might remain between us.

"I promise it," I said to him, "but do not break your word."

The next day I was ill, and the reader is aware of the nature of my illness. I immediately placed myself under a proper course of diet, however unpleasant it was at my age; but I kept to my system, and it cured me rapidly.

Three or four days afterwards Captain O'Neilan called on me, and when I told him the nature of my sickness he laughed, much to my surprise.

"Then you were all right before that night?" he enquired.

"Yes, my health was excellent."

"I am sorry that you should have lost your health in such an ugly place. I would have warned you if I had thought you had any intentions in that quarter."

"Did you know of the woman having . . . ?"

"Zounds! Did I not? It is only a week since I paid

a visit to the very same place myself, and I believe the creature was all right before my visit."

"Then I have to thank you for the present she has bestowed upon me."

"Most likely; but it is only a trifle, and you can easily get cured if you care to take the trouble."

"What! Do you not try to cure yourself?"

"Faith, no. It would be too much trouble to follow a regular diet, and what is the use of curing such a trifling inconvenience when I am certain of getting it again in a fortnight. Ten times in my life I have had that patience, but I got tired of it, and for the last two years I have resigned myself, and now I put up with it."

"I pity you, for a man like you would have great success in love."

"I do not care a fig for love; it requires cares which would bother me much more than the slight inconvenience to which we were alluding, and to which I am used now."

"I am not of your opinion, for the amorous pleasure is insipid when love does not throw a little spice in it. Do you think, for instance, that the ugly wretch I met at the guard-room is worth what I now suffer on her account?"

"Of course not, and that is why I am sorry for you. If I had known, I could have introduced you to something better."

"The very best in that line is not worth my health, and health ought to be sacrificed only for love."

"Oh! you want women worthy of love? There are a few here; stop with us for some time, and when you are cured there is nothing to prevent you from making conquests."

O'Neilan was only twenty-three years old; his father,

who was dead, had been a general, and the beautiful Countess Borsati was his sister. He presented me to the Countess Zanardi Nerli, still more lovely than his sister, but I was prudent enough not to burn my incense before either of them, for it seemed to me that everybody could guess the state of my health.

I have never met a young man more addicted to debauchery than O'Neilan. I have often spent the night rambling about with him, and I was amazed at his cynical boldness and impudence. Yet he was noble, generous, brave, and honourable. If in those days young officers were often guilty of so much immorality, of so many vile actions, it was not so much their fault as the fault of the privileges which they enjoyed through custom, indulgence, or party spirit. Here is an example:

One day O'Neilan, having drunk rather freely, rides through the city at full speed. A poor old woman who was crossing the street has no time to avoid him, she falls, and her head is cut open by the horse's feet. O'Neilan places himself under arrest, but the next day he is set at liberty. He had only to plead that it was an accident.

The officer Laurent not having called upon me to redeem his promisory note of six sequins during the week, I told him in the street that I would no longer consider myself bound to keep the affair secret. Instead of excusing himself, he said,—

"I do not care!"

The answer was insulting, and I intended to compel him to give me reparation, but the next day O'Neilan told me that Captain Laurent had gone mad and had been locked up in a mad-house. He subsequently recovered his reason, but his conduct was so infamous that he was cashiered.

O'Neilan, who was as brave as Bayard, was killed a
few years afterwards at the battle of Prague. A man
of his complexion was certain to fall the victim of Mars
or of Venus. He might be alive now if he had been endowed only with the courage of the fox, but he had the
courage of the lion. It is a virtue in a soldier, but almost a fault in an officer. Those who brave danger with
a full knowledge of it are worthy of praise, but those
who do not realize it escape only by a miracle, and without any merit attaching itself to them. Yet we must
respect those great warriors, for their unconquerable
courage is the offspring of a strong soul, of a virtue
which places them above ordinary mortals.

Whenever I think of Prince Charles de Ligne I cannot restrain my tears. He was as brave as Achilles, but
Achilles was invulnerable. He would be alive now if he
had remembered during the fight that he was mortal.
Who are they that, having known him, have not shed
tears in his memory? He was handsome, kind, polished,
learned, a lover of the arts, cheerful, witty in his conversation, a pleasant companion, and a man of perfect
equability. Fatal, terrible revolution! A cannon ball
took him from his friends, from his family, from the
happiness which surrounded him.

The Prince de Waldeck has also paid the penalty of
his intrepidity with the loss of one arm. It is said that
he consoles himself for that loss with the consciousness
that with the remaining one he can yet command an
army.

O you who despise life, tell me whether that contempt
of life renders you worthy of it?

The opera opened immediately after Easter, and I was
present at every performance. I was then entirely cured,
and had resumed my usual life. I was pleased to see

that Baletti shewed off Marina to the best advantage. I never visited her, but Baletti was in the habit of breakfasting with me almost every morning.

He had often mentioned an old actress who had left the stage for more than twenty years, and pretended to have been my father's friend. One day I took a fancy to call upon her, and he accompanied me to her house.

I saw an old, broken-down crone whose toilet astonished me as much as her person. In spite of her wrinkles, her face was plastered with red and white, and her eyebrows were indebted to India ink for their black appearance. She exposed one-half of her flabby, disgusting bosom, and there could be no doubt as to her false set of teeth. She wore a wig which fitted very badly, and allowed the intrusion of a few gray hairs which had survived the havoc of time. Her shaking hands made mine quiver when she pressed them. She diffused a perfume of amber at a distance of twenty yards, and her affected, mincing manner amused and sickened me at the same time. Her dress might possibly have been the fashion twenty years before. I was looking with dread at the fearful havoc of old age upon a face which, before merciless time had blighted it, had evidently been handsome, but what amazed me was the childish effrontery with which this time-withered specimen of womankind was still waging war with the help of her blasted charms.

Baletti, who feared lest my too visible astonishment should vex her, told her that I was amazed at the fact that the beautiful strawberry which bloomed upon her chest had not been withered by the hand of Time. It was a birth-mark which was really very much like a strawberry. "It is that mark," said the old woman, simpering, "which gave me the name of 'La Fragoletta.'"

Those words made me shudder.

I had before my eyes the fatal phantom which was the cause of my existence. I saw the woman who had thirty years before, seduced my father: if it had not been for her, he would never have thought of leaving his father's house, and would never have engendered me in the womb of a Venetian woman. I have never been of the opinion of the old author who says, *Nemo vitam vellet si daretur scientibus*.

Seeing how thoughtful I was, she politely enquired my name from Baletti, for he had presented me only as a friend, and without having given her notice of my visit. When he told her that my name was Casanova, she was extremely surprised.

"Yes, madam," I said, "I am the son of Gaetan Casanova, of Parma."

"Heavens and earth! what is this? Ah! my friend, I adored your father! He was jealous without cause, and abandoned me. Had he not done so, you would have been my son! Allow me to embrace you with the feelings of a loving mother."

I expected as much, and, for fear she should fall, I went to her, received her kiss, and abandoned myself to her tender recollections. Still an actress, she pressed her handkerchief to her eyes, pretending to weep, and assuring me that I was not to doubt the truth of what she said.

"Although," she added, "I do not look an old woman yet."

"The only fault of your dear father," she continued, "was a want of gratitude."

I have no doubt that she passed the same sentence upon the son, for, in spite of her kind invitation, I never paid her another visit.

My purse was well filled, and as I did not care for

Mantua, I resolved on going to Naples, to see again my dear Thérèse, Donna Lucrezia, Palo father and son, Don Antonio Casanova, and all my former acquaintances. However, my good genius did not approve of that decision, for I was not allowed to carry it into execution. I should have left Mantua three days later, had I not gone to the opera that night.

I lived like an anchorite during my two months' stay in Mantua, owing to the folly I committed on the night of my arrival. I played only that time, and then I had been lucky. My slight erotic inconvenience, by compelling me to follow the diet necessary to my cure, most likely saved me from greater misfortunes which, perhaps, I should not have been able to avoid.

CHAPTER XXI

My Journey to Cesena in Search of Treasure—I Take Up My Quarters in Franzia's House—His Daughter Javotte

THE opera was nearly over when I was accosted by a young man who, abruptly, and without any introduction, told me that as a stranger I had been very wrong in spending two months in Mantua without paying a visit to the natural history collection belonging to his father, Don Antonio Capitani, commissary and prebendal president.

"Sir," I answered, "I have been guilty only through ignorance, and if you would be so good as to call for me at my hotel to-morrow morning, before the evening I shall have atoned for my error, and you will no longer have the right to address me the same reproach."

The son of the prebendal commissary called for me, and I found in his father a most eccentric, whimsical sort of man. The curiosities of his collection consisted of his family tree, of books of magic, relics, coins which he believed to be antediluvian, a model of the ark taken from nature at the time when Noah arrived in that extraordinary harbour, Mount Ararat, in Armenia. He had several medals, one of Sesostris, another of Semiramis, and an old knife of a queer shape, covered with rust. Besides all those wonderful treasures, he possessed, but under lock and key, all the paraphernalia of freemasonry.

"Pray, tell me," I said to him, "what relation there is between this collection and natural history? I see nothing here representing the three kingdoms."

"What! You do not see the antediluvian kingdom, that of Sesostris and that of Semiramis? Are not those the three kingdoms?"

When I heard that answer I embraced him with an exclamation of delight, which was sarcastic in its intent, but which he took for admiration, and he at once unfolded all the treasures of his whimsical knowledge respecting his possessions, ending with the rusty blade which he said was the very knife with which Saint Peter cut off the ear of Malek.

"What!" I exclaimed, "you are the possessor of this knife, and you are not as rich as Crœsus?"

"How could I be so through the possession of the knife?"

"In two ways. In the first place, you could obtain possession of all the treasures hidden under ground in the States of the Church."

"Yes, that is a natural consequence, because St. Peter has the keys."

"In the second place, you might sell the knife to the Pope, if you happen to possess proof of its authenticity."

"You mean the parchment. Of course I have it; do you think I would have bought one without the other?"

"All right, then. In order to get possession of that knife, the Pope would, I have no doubt, make a cardinal of your son, but you must have the sheath too."

"I have not got it, but it is unnecessary. At all events I can have one made."

"That would not do, you must have the very one in which Saint Peter himself sheathed the knife when God said, *Mitte gladium tuum in vaginam.* That very sheath does exist, and it is now in the hands of a person who might sell it to you at a reasonable price, or you might sell him your knife, for the sheath without the knife is of no use to him, just as the knife is useless to you without the sheath."

"How much would it cost me?"

"One thousand sequins."

"And how much would that person give me for the knife?"

"One thousand sequins, for one has as much value as the other."

The commissary, greatly astonished, looked at his son, and said, with the voice of a judge on the bench,—

"Well, son, would you ever have thought that I would be offered one thousand sequins for this knife?"

He then opened a drawer and took out of it an old piece of paper, which he placed before me. It was written in Hebrew, and a facsimile of the knife was drawn on it. I pretended to be lost in admiration, and advised him very strongly to purchase the sheath.

"It is not necessary for me to buy it, or for your friend to purchase the knife. We can find out and dig up the treasures together."

"Not at all. The rubric says in the most forcible manner that the owner of the blade, *in vaginam,* shall be one. If the Pope were in possession of it he would be able, through a magical operation known to me, to cut off one of the ears of every Christian king who might be thinking of encroaching upon the rights of the Church."

"Wonderful, indeed! But it is very true, for it is said in the Gospel that Saint Peter did cut off the ear of somebody."

"Yes, of a king."

"Oh, no! not of a king."

"Of a king, I tell you. Enquire whether Malek or Melek does not mean king."

"Well! in case I should make up my mind to sell the knife, who would give me the thousand sequins?"

"I would; one half to-morrow, cash down; the balance of five hundred in a letter of exchange payable one month after date."

"Ah! that is like business. Be good enough to accept a dish of macaroni with us to-morrow, and under a solemn pledge of secrecy we will discuss this important affair."

I accepted and took my leave, firmly resolved on keeping up the joke. I came back on the following day, and the very first thing he told me was that, to his certain knowledge, there was an immense treasure hidden somewhere in the Papal States, and that he would make up his mind to purchase the sheath. This satisfied me that there was no fear of his taking me at my word, so I produced a purse full of gold, saying I was quite ready to complete our bargain for the purchase of the knife.

"The Treasure," he said, "is worth millions; but let us have dinner. You are not going to be served in silver plates and dishes, but in real Raphael mosaic."

"My dear commissary, your magnificence astonishes me; mosaic is, indeed, by far superior to silver plate, although an ignorant fool would only consider it ugly earthen ware."

The compliment delighted him.

After dinner, he spoke as follows:

"A man in very good circumstances, residing in the Papal States, and owner of the country house in which he lives with all his family, is certain that there is a treasure in his cellar. He has written to my son, declaring himself ready to undertake all expenses necessary to possess himself of that treasure, if we could procure a magician powerful enough to unearth it."

The son then took a letter out of his pocket, read me some passages, and begged me to excuse him if, in consequence of his having pledged himself to keep the secret, he could not communicate all the contents of the letter; but I had, unperceived by him, read the word Cesena, the name of the village, and that was enough for me.

"Therefore all that is necessary is to give me the possibility of purchasing the sheath on credit, for I have no ready cash at present. You need not be afraid of endorsing my letters of exchange, and if you should know the magician you might go halves with him."

"The magician is ready; it is I, but unless you give me five hundred sequins cash down we cannot agree."

"I have no money."

"Then sell me the knife."

"No."

"You are wrong, for now that I have seen it I can easily take it from you. But I am honest enough not to wish to play such a trick upon you."

"You could take my knife from me? I should like to be convinced of that, but I do not believe it."

"You do not? Very well, to-morrow the knife will be in my possession, but when it is once in my hands you need not hope to see it again. A spirit which is under my orders will bring it to me at midnight, and the same spirit will tell me where the treasure is buried."

"Let the spirit tell you that, and I shall be convinced."

"Give me a pen, ink and paper."

I asked a question from my oracle, and the answer I had was that the treasure was to be found not far from the Rubicon.

"That is," I said, "a torrent which was once a river."

They consulted a dictionary, and found that the Rubicon flowed through Cesena. They were amazed, and, as I wished them to have full scope for wrong reasoning, I left them.

I had taken a fancy, not to purloin five hundred sequins from those poor fools, but to go and unearth the amount at their expense in the house of another fool, and to laugh at them all into the bargain. I longed to play the part of a magician. With that idea, when I left the house of the ridiculous antiquarian, I proceeded to the public library, where, with the assistance of a dictionary, I wrote the following specimen of facetious erudition:

"The treasure is buried in the earth at a depth of seventeen and a half fathoms, and has been there for six centuries. Its value amounts to two millions of sequins, enclosed in a casket, the same which was taken by Godfrey de Bouillon from Mathilda, Countess of Tuscany, in the year 1081, when he endeavoured to assist Henry IV. against that princess. He buried the box himself in the very spot where it now is, before he went to lay siege to Jerusalem. Gregory VII., who was a great magician, having been informed of the place where it had been hidden, had resolved on getting possession of it himself, but death prevented him from carrying out his intentions. After the death of the Countess Mathilda, in the year 1116, the genius presiding over all hidden treasures appointed seven spirits to guard the box. During a night with a full moon, a learned magician can raise the treasure to the surface of the earth by placing himself in the middle of the magical ring called *maximus*."

I expected to see the father and son, and they came early in the morning. After some rambling conversation, I gave them what I had composed at the library, namely, the history of the treasure taken from the Countess Mathilda.

I told them that I had made up my mind to recover the treasure, and I promised them the fourth part of it, provided they would purchase the sheath; I concluded by threatening again to possess myself of their knife.

"I cannot decide," said the commissary, "before I have seen the sheath."

"I pledge my word to shew it to you to-morrow," I answered.

We parted company, highly pleased with each other.

In order to manufacture a sheath, such as the wonderful knife required, it was necessary to combine the most whimsical idea with the oddest shape. I recollected very well the form of the blade, and, as I was revolving in my mind the best way to produce something very extravagant but well adapted to the purpose I had in view, I spied in the yard of the hotel an old piece of leather, the remnant of what had been a fine gentleman's boot; it was exactly what I wanted.

I took that old sole, boiled it, and made in it a slit in which I was certain that the knife would go easily. Then I pared it carefully on all sides to prevent the possibility of its former use being found out; I rubbed it with pumice stone, sand, and ochre, and finally I succeeded in imparting to my production such a queer, old-fashioned shape that I could not help laughing in looking at my work.

When I presented it to the commissary, and he had found it an exact fit for the knife, the good man remained astounded. We dined together, and after dinner it was decided that his son should accompany me, and introduce me to the master of the house in which the treasure was buried, that I was to receive a letter of exchange for one thousand Roman crowns, drawn by the son on Bologna, which would be made payable to my name only after I should have found the treasure, and that the knife with the sheath would be delivered into my hands only when I should require it for the great operation; until then the son was to retain possession of it.

Those conditions having been agreed upon, we made an agreement in writing, binding upon all parties, and our departure was fixed for the day after the morrow.

As we left Mantua, the father pronounced a fervent blessing over his son's head, and told me that he was count palatine, shewing me the diploma which he had received from the Pope. I embraced him, giving him his title of count, and pocketed his letter of exchange.

After bidding adieu to Marina, who was then the acknowledged mistress of Count Arcorati, and to Baletti whom I was sure of meeting again in Venice before the end of the year, I went to sup with my friend O'Neilan.

We started early in the morning, travelled through Ferrara and Bologna, and reached Cesena, where we put up at the posting-house. We got up early the next day and walked quietly to the house of George Franzia, a wealthy peasant, who was owner of the treasure. It was only a quarter of a mile from the city, and the good man was agreeably surprised by our arrival. He embraced Capitani, whom he knew already, and leaving me with his family he went out with my companion to talk business.

Observant as usual, I passed the family in review, and fixed my choice upon the eldest daughter. The youngest girl was ugly, and the son looked a regular fool. The mother seemed to be the real master of the household, and there were three or four servants going about the premises.

The eldest daughter was called Geneviève, or Javotte, a very common name among the girls of Cesena. I told her that I thought her eighteen, but she answered, in a tone half serious, half vexed, that I was very much mistaken, for she had only just completed her fourteenth year.

"I am very glad it is so, my pretty child."

These words brought back her smile.

The house was well situated, and there was not another dwelling around it for at least four hundred yards. I was glad to see that I should have comfortable quarters, but I was annoyed by a very unpleasant stink which tainted the air, and which could certainly not be agreeable to the spirits I had to evoke.

"Madame Franzia," said I, to the mistress of the house, "what is the cause of that bad smell?"

"Sir, it arises from the hemp which we are macerating."

I concluded that if the cause were removed, I should get rid of the effect.

"What is that hemp worth, madam?" I enquired.

"About forty crowns."

"Here they are; the hemp belongs to me now, and I must beg your husband to have it removed immediately."

Capitani called me, and I joined him. Franzia shewed me all the respect due to a great magician, although I had not much the appearance of one.

We agreed that he should receive one-fourth of the treasure, Capitani another fourth, and that the remainder should belong to me. We certainly did not shew much respect for the rights of Saint Peter.

I told Franzia that I should require a room with two

beds for myself alone, and an ante-room with bathing apparatus. Capitani's room was to be in a different part of the house, and my room was to be provided with three tables, two of them small and one large. I added that he must at once procure me a sewing-girl between the ages of fourteen and eighteen, she was to be a virgin, and it was necessary that she should, as well as every person in the house, keep the secret faithfully, in order that no suspicion of our proceedings should reach the Inquisition, or all would be lost.

"I intend to take up my quarters here to-morrow," I added; "I require two meals every day, and the only wine I can drink is Jévêse. For my breakfast I drink a peculiar kind of chocolate which I make myself, and which I have brought with me. I promise to pay my own expenses in case we do not succeed. Please remove the hemp to a place sufficiently distant from the house, so that its bad smell may not annoy the spirits to be evoked by me, and let the air be purified by the discharge of gunpowder. Besides, you must send a trusty servant to-morrow to convey our luggage from the hotel here, and keep constantly in the house and at my disposal one hundred new wax candles and three torches."

After I had given those instructions to Franzia, I left him, and went towards Cesena with Capitani, but we had not gone a hundred yards when we heard the good man running after us.

"Sir," he said to me, "be kind enough to take back the forty crowns which you paid to my wife for the hemp."

"No, I will not do anything of the sort, for I do not want you to sustain any loss."

"Take them back, I beg. I can sell the hemp in the course of the day for forty crowns without difficulty."

"In that case I will, for I have confidence in what you say."

Such proceedings on my part impressed the excellent man very favourably, and he entertained the deepest veneration for me, which was increased, when, against Capitani's advice, I resolutely refused one hundred sequins which he wanted to force upon me for my travelling expenses. I threw him into raptures by telling him that on the eve of possessing an immense treasure, it was unnecessary to think of such trifles.

The next morning our luggage was sent for, and we found ourselves comfortably located in the house of the wealthy and simple Franzia.

He gave us a good dinner, but with too many dishes, and I told him to be more economical, and to give only some good fish for our supper, which he did. After supper he told me that, as far as the young maiden was concerned, he thought he could recommend his daughter Javotte, as he had consulted his wife, and had found I could rely upon the girl being a virgin.

"Very good," I said; "now tell me what grounds you have for supposing that there is a treasure in your house?"

"In the first place, the oral tradition transmitted from father to son for the last eight generations; in the second, the heavy sounds which are heard under ground during the night. Besides, the door of the cellar opens and shuts of itself every three or four minutes; which must certainly be the work of the devils seen every night wandering through the country in the shape of pyramidal flames."

"If it is as you say, it is evident that you have a treasure hidden somewhere in your house; it is as certain as the fact that two and two are four. Be very careful not to put a lock to the door of the cellar to prevent its opening and shutting of itself; otherwise you would have an earthquake, which would destroy everything here. Spirits will enjoy perfect freedom, and they break through every obstacle raised against them."

"God be praised for having sent here, forty years ago, a learned man who told my father exactly the same thing! That great magician required only three days more to unearth the treasure when my father heard that the Inquisition had given orders to arrest him, and he lost no time in insuring his escape. Can you tell me how it is that magicians are not more powerful than the Inquisitors?"

"Because the monks have a greater number of devils under their command than we have. But I feel certain that your father had already expended a great deal of money with that learned man."

"About two thousand crowns."

"Oh! more, more."

I told Franzia to follow me, and, in order to accomplish something in the magic line, I dipped a towel in some water, and uttering fearful words which belonged to no human language, I washed the eyes, the temples, and the chest of every person in the family, including Javotte, who might have objected to it if I had not begun with her father, mother, and brother. I made them swear upon my pocket-book that they were not labouring under any impure disease, and I concluded the ceremony by compelling Javotte to swear likewise that she had her maidenhood. As I saw that she was blushing to the very roots of her hair in taking the oath, I was cruel enough to explain to her what it meant; I then asked her to swear again, but she answered that there was no need of it now that she knew what it was. I ordered all the family to kiss me, and finding that Javotte had eaten garlic I forbade the use of it entirely, which order Franzia promised should be complied with.

Geneviève was not a beauty as far as her features were concerned; her complexion was too much sunburnt, and her mouth was too large, but her teeth were splendid, and her under lip projected slightly as if it had been formed to receive kisses. Her bosom was well made and as firm as a rock, but her hair was too light, and her hands too fleshy. The defects, however, had to be overlooked, and altogether she was not an unpleasant morsel. I did not purpose to make her fall in love with me; with a peasant girl that task might have been a long one; all I wanted was to train her to perfect obedience, which, in default of love, has always appeared to me the essential point. True that in such a case one does not enjoy the ecstatic raptures of love, but one finds a compensation in the complete control obtained over the woman.

I gave notice to the father, to Capitani, and to Javotte, that each would, in turn and in the order of their age, take supper with me, and that Javotte would sleep every night in my ante-room, where was to be placed a bath in which I would bathe my guest one half hour before sitting down to supper, and the guest was not to have broken his fast throughout the day.

I prepared a list of all the articles of which I pretended to be in need, and giving it to Franzia I told him to go to Cesena himself the next day, and to purchase everything without bargaining to obtain a lower price. Among other things, I ordered a piece, from twenty to thirty yards long, of white linen, thread, scissors, needles, storax, myrrh, sulphur, olive oil, camphor, one ream of paper, pens and ink, twelve sheets of parchment, brushes, and a branch of olive tree to make a stick of eighteen inches in length.

After I had given all my orders very seriously and without any wish to laugh, I went to bed highly pleased with my personification of a magician, in which I was astonished to find myself so completely successful.

The next morning, as soon as I was dressed, I sent for Capitani, and commanded him to proceed every day to Cesena, to go to the best coffee-house, to learn carefully every piece of news and every rumour, and to report them to me.

Franzia, who had faithfully obeyed my orders, returned before noon from the city with all the articles I had asked for.

"I have not bargained for anything," he said to me, "and the merchants must, I have no doubt, have taken me for a fool, for I have certainly paid one-third more than the things are worth."

"So much the worse for them if they have deceived you, but you would have spoilt everything if you had beaten them down in their price. Now, send me your daughter and let me be alone with her."

As soon as Javotte was in my room, I made her cut the linen in seven pieces, four of five feet long, two of two feet, and one of two feet and a half; the last one was intended to form the hood of the robe I was to wear for the great operation. Then I said to Javotte:

"Sit down near my bed and begin sewing. You will dine here and remain at work until the evening. When your father comes, you must let us be alone, but as soon as he leaves me, come back and go to bed."

She dined in my room, where her mother waited on her without speaking, and gave her nothing to drink except St. Jévêse wine. Towards evening her father came, and she left us.

I had the patience to wash the good man while he was in the bath, after which he had supper with me; he ate voraciously, telling me that it was the first time in his life that he had remained twenty-four hours without breaking his fast. Intoxicated with the St. Jévêse wine he had drunk, he went to bed and slept soundly until morning, when his wife brought me my chocolate. Javotte was kept sewing as on the day before; she left the room in the evening when Capitani came in, and I treated him in the same manner as Franzia; on the third day, it was Javotte's turn, and that had been the object I had kept in view all the time.

When the hour came, I said to her,——

"Go, Javotte, get into the bath and call me when you are ready, for I must purify you as I have purified your father and Capitani."

She obeyed, and within a quarter of an hour she called me. I performed a great many ablutions on every part of her body, making her assume all sorts of positions, for she was perfectly docile, but, as I was afraid of betraying myself, I felt more suffering than enjoyment, and my indiscreet hands, running over every part of her person, and remaining longer and more willingly on a certain spot, the sensitiveness of which is extreme, the poor girl was excited by an ardent fire which was at last quenched by the natural result of that excitement. I made her get out of the bath soon after that, and as I was drying her I was very near forgetting magic to follow the impulse of nature, but, quicker than I, nature relieved itself, and I was thus enabled to reach the end of the scene without anticipating the *dénoue-*

ment. I told Javotte to dress herself, and to come back to me as soon as she was ready.

She had been fasting all day, and her toilet did not take a long time. She ate with a ferocious appetite, and the St. Jévêse wine, which she drank like water, imparted so much animation to her complexion that it was no longer possible to see how sunburnt she was. Being alone with her after supper, I said to her,——

"My dear Javotte, have you been displeased at all I have compelled you to submit to this evening?"

"Not at all; I liked it very much."

"Then I hope that you will have no objection to get in the bath with me to-morrow, and to wash me as I have washed you."

"Most willingly, but shall I know how to do it well?"

"I will teach you, and for the future I wish you to sleep every night in my room, because I must have a complete certainty that on the night of the great operation I shall find you such as you ought to be."

From that time Javotte was at her ease with me, all her restraint disappeared, she would look at me and smile with entire confidence. Nature had operated, and the mind of a young girl soon enlarges its sphere when pleasure is her teacher. She went to bed, and as she knew that she had no longer anything to conceal from me, her modesty was not alarmed when she undressed herself in my presence. It was very warm, any kind of covering is unpleasant in the hot weather, so she stripped to the skin and soon fell asleep. I did the same, but I could not help feeling some regret at having engaged myself not to take advantage of the position before the night of the great incantation. I knew that the operation to unearth the treasure would be a complete failure, but I knew likewise that it would not fail because Javotte's virginity was gone.

At day-break the girl rose and began sewing. As soon as she had finished the robe, I told her to make a crown of parchment with seven long points, on which I painted some fearful figures and hieroglyphs.

In the evening, one hour before supper, I got into the bath, and Javotte joined me as soon as I called her. She performed upon me with great zeal the same ceremonies that I had done for her the day before, and she was as gentle and docile as possible. I spent a delicious hour in that bath, enjoying everything, but respecting the essential point.

My kisses making her happy, and seeing that I had no objection to her caresses, she loaded me with them. I was so pleased at all the amorous enjoyment her senses were evidently experiencing, that I made her easy by telling her that the success of the great magic operation depended upon the amount of pleasure she enjoyed. She then made extraordinary efforts to persuade me that she was happy, and without overstepping the limits where I had made up my mind to stop, we got out of the bath highly pleased with each other.

As we were on the point of going to bed, she said to me,——

"Would it injure the success of your operation if we were to sleep together?"

"No, my dear girl; provided you are a virgin on the day of the great incantation, it is all I require."

She threw herself in my arms, and we spent a delightful night, during which I had full opportunity of admiring the strength of her constitution as well as my own restraint, for I had sufficient control over myself not to break through the last obstacle.

I passed a great part of the following night with Franzia and Capitani in order to see with my own eyes the wonderful things which the worthy peasant had mentioned to me. Standing in the yard, I heard distinctly heavy blows struck under the ground at intervals of three or four minutes. It was like the noise which would be made by a heavy pestle falling in a large copper mortar. I took my pistols and placed myself near the self-moving door of the cellar, holding a dark lantern in my hand. I saw the door open slowly, and in about thirty seconds closing with violence. I opened and closed it myself several times, and, unable to discover any hidden physical cause for the phenomenon, I felt satisfied that there was some unknown roguery at work, but I did not care much to find it out.

We went upstairs again, and, placing myself on the balcony, I saw in the yard several shadows moving about. They were evidently caused by the heavy and damp atmosphere, and as to the pyramidal flames which I could see hovering over the fields, it was a phenomenon well known to me. But I allowed my two companions to remain persuaded that they were the spirits keeping watch over the treasure.

That phenomenon is very common throughout southern Italy where the country is often at night illuminated by those meteors which the people believe to be devils, and ignorance has called night spirits, or will-o'-the-wisps.

Dear reader, the next chapter will tell you how my magic undertaking ended, and perhaps you will enjoy a good laugh at my expense, but you need not be afraid of hurting my feelings.

CHAPTER XXII

The Incantation—A Terrible Storm—My Fright—
Javotte's Virginity Is Saved—I Give Up the Under-
taking, and Sell the Sheath to Capitani—I Meet
Juliette and Count Alfani, Alias Count Celi—I Make
Up My Mind to Go to Naples—Why I Take a Dif-
ferent Road

MY great operation had to be performed on the following day; otherwise, according to all established rules, I would have had to wait until the next full
moon. I had to make the gnomes raise the treasure to
the surface of the earth at the very spot on which my incantations would be performed. Of course, I knew well
enough that I should not succeed, but I knew likewise
that I could easily reconcíle Franzia and Capitani to
a failure, by inventing some excellent reasons for our
want of success. In the mean time I had to play my
part of a magician, in which I took a real delight. I
kept Javotte at work all day, sewing together, in the
shape of a ring, some thirty sheets of paper on which
I painted the most wonderful designs. That ring, which
I called *maximus,* had a diameter of three geometric
paces. I had manufactured a sort of sceptre or magic
wand with the branch of olive brought by Franzia from
Cesena. Thus prepared, I told Javotte that, at twelve
o'clock at night, when I came out of the magic ring,
she was to be ready for everything. The order did not

seem repugnant to her; she longed to give me that proof of her obedience, and, on my side, considering myself as her debtor, I was in a hurry to pay my debt and to give her every satisfaction.

The hour having struck, I ordered Franzia and Capitani to stand on the balcony, so as to be ready to come to me if I called for them, and also to prevent anyone in the house seeing my proceedings. I then threw off all profane garments. I clothe myself in the long white robe, the work of a virgin's innocent hands. I allow my long hair to fall loosely. I place the extraordinary crown on my head, the circle *maximus* on my shoulders, and, seizing the sceptre with one hand, the wonderful knife with the other, I go down into the yard. There I spread my circle on the ground, uttering the most barbarous words, and after going round it three times I jump into the middle.

Squatting down there, I remain a few minutes motionless, then I rise, and I fix my eyes upon a heavy, dark cloud coming from the west, whilst from the same quarter the thunder is rumbling loudly. What a sublime genius I should have appeared in the eyes of my two fools, if, having a short time before taken notice of the sky in that part of the horizon, I had announced to them that my operation would be attended by that phenomenon!

The cloud spreads with fearful rapidity, and soon the sky seems covered with a funeral pall, on which the most vivid flashes of lightning keep blazing every moment.

Such a storm was a very natural occurrence, and I had no reason to be astonished at it, but somehow, fear was beginning to creep into me, and I wished myself in my room. My fright soon increased at the sight of the lightning, and on hearing the claps of thunder which succeeded each other with fearful rapidity and seemed to roar over my very head. I then realized what extraordinary effect fear can have on the mind, for I fancied that, if I was not annihilated by the fires of heaven which were flashing all around me, it was only because they could not enter my magic ring. Thus was I admiring my own deceitful work! That foolish reason prevented me from leaving the circle in spite of the fear which caused me to shudder. If it had not been for that belief, the result of a cowardly fright, I would not have remained one minute where I was, and my hurried flight would no doubt have opened the eyes of my two dupes, who could not have failed to see that, far from being a magician, I was only a poltroon. The violence of the wind, the claps of thunder, the piercing cold, and above all, fear, made me tremble all over like an aspen leaf. My system, which I thought proof against every accident, had vanished: I acknowledged an avenging God who had waited for this opportunity of punishing me at one blow for all my sins, and of annihilating me, in order to put an end to my want of faith. The complete immobility which paralyzed all my limbs seemed to me a proof of the uselessness of my repentance, and that conviction only increased my consternation.

But the roaring of the thunder dies away, the rain begins to fall heavily, danger vanishes, and I feel my courage reviving. Such is man! or at all events, such was I at that moment. It was raining so fast that, if it had continued pouring with the same violence for a quarter of an hour, the country would have been inundated. As soon as the rain had ceased, the wind abated, the clouds were dispersed, and the moon shone in all its splendour, like silver in the pure, blue sky. I take up my magic ring, and telling the two friends to retire to their beds without speaking to me, I hurry to my room. I still felt rather shaken, and, casting my eyes on Javotte, I thought her so pretty that I felt positively frightened. I allowed her to dry me, and after that necessary operation I told her piteously to go to bed. The next morning she told me that, when she saw me come in, shaking all over in spite of the heat, she had herself shuddered with fear.

After eight hours of sound sleep I felt all right, but I had had enough of the comedy, and to my great surprise the sight of Geneviève did not move me in any way. The obedient Javotte had certainly not changed, but I was not the same. I was for the first time in my life reduced to a state of apathy, and in consequence of the superstitious ideas which had crowded in my mind the previous night I imagined that the innocence of that young girl was under the special protection of Heaven, and that if I had dared to rob her of her virginity the most rapid and terrible death would have been my punishment.

At all events, thanks to my youth and my exalted ideas, I fancied that through my self-denying resolutions the father would not be so great a dupe, and the daughter not so unhappy, unless the result should prove as unfortunate for her as it had been for poor Lucy, of Paséan.

The moment that Javotte became in my eyes an object of holy horror, my departure was decided. The resolution was all the more irrevocable because I fancied some old peasant might have witnessed all my tricks in the middle of the magic ring, in which case the most Holy, or, if you like, the most infernal, Inquisition, receiving information from him, might very well have caught me and enhanced my fame by some splendid *auto-da-fé* in which I had not the slightest wish to be the principal actor. It struck me as so entirely within the limits of probability that I sent at once for Franzia and Capitani, and in the presence of the unpolluted virgin I told them that I had obtained from the seven spirits watching over the treasure all the necessary particulars, but that I had been compelled to enter into an agreement with them to delay the extraction of the treasure placed under their guardianship. I told Franzia that I would hand to him in writing all the information which I had compelled the spirits to give me. I produced, in reality, a few minutes afterwards, a document similar to the one I had concocted at the public library in Mantua, adding that the treasure consisted of diamonds, rubies, emeralds, and one hundred thousand pounds of gold dust. I made him take an oath on my pocket-book to wait for me, and not to have faith in any magician unless he gave him an account of the treasure in every way similar to the one which, as a great favor, I was leaving in his hands. I ordered him to burn the crown and the ring, but to keep the other things carefully until my return.

"As for you, Capitani," I said to my companion, "proceed at once to Cesena, and remain at the inn until our luggage has been brought by the man whom Franzia is going to send with it."

Seeing that poor Javotte looked miserable, I went up to her, and, speaking to her very tenderly, I promised to see her again before long. I told her at the same time that, the great operation having been performed successfully, her virginity was no longer necessary, and that she was at liberty to marry as soon as she pleased, or whenever a good opportunity offered itself.

I at once returned to the city, where I found Capitani making his preparations to go to the fair of Lugo, and then to Mantua. He told me, crying like a child, that his father would be in despair when he saw him come back without the knife of Saint Peter.

"You may have it," I said, "with the sheath, if you will let me have the one thousand Roman crowns, the amount of the letter of exchange."

He thought it an excellent bargain, and accepted it joyfully. I gave him back the letter of exchange, and made him sign a paper by which he undertook to return the sheath whenever I brought the same amount, but he is still waiting for it.

I did not know what to do with the wonderful sheath, and I was not in want of money, but I should have considered myself dishonoured if I had given it to him for nothing; besides, I thought it a good joke to levy a contribution upon the ignorant credulity of a count palatine created by the grace of the Pope. In after days, however, I would willingly have refunded his money, but, as fate would have it, we did not see each other for a long time, and when I met him again I was not in a position to return the amount. It is, therefore, only to chance that I was indebted for the sum, and certainly Capitani never dreamed of complaining, for being the possessor of *gladium cum vaginâ* he truly believed himself the master of every treasure concealed in the Papal States.

Capitani took leave of me on the following day, and I intended to proceed at once to Naples, but I was again prevented; this is how it happened.

As I returned to the inn after a short walk, mine host handed me the bill of the play announcing four performances of the *Didone* of Metastasio at the Spada. Seeing no acquaintance of mine among the actors or actresses, I made up my mind to go to the play in the evening, and to start early the next day with post-horses. A remnant of my fear of the Inquisition urged me on, and I could not help fancying that spies were at my heels.

Before entering the house I went into the actresses' dressing-room, and the leading lady struck me as rather good-looking. Her name was Narici, and she was from Bologna. I bowed to her, and after the common-place conversation usual in such cases, I asked her whether she was free.

"I am only engaged with the manager," she answered.

"Have you any lover?"

"No."

"I offer myself for the post, if you have no objection."

She smiled jeeringly, and said,——

"Will you take four tickets for the four performances?"

I took two sequins out of my purse, taking care to let her see that it was well filled, and when she gave me the four tickets, presented them to the maid who was dressing her and was prettier than the mistress, and so left the room without uttering a single word. She called me back; I pretended not to hear her, and took a ticket for the pit. After the first ballet, finding the whole performance very poor, I was thinking of going away, when, happening to look towards the chief box, I saw to my astonishment that it was tenanted by the Venetian Manzoni and the celebrated Juliette. The reader will doubtless remember the ball she gave at my house in Venice, and the smack with which she saluted my cheek on that occasion.

They had not yet noticed me, and I enquired from the person seated next to me who was that beautiful lady wearing so many diamonds. He told me that she was Madame Querini, from Venice, whom Count Spada, the owner of the theatre, who was sitting near her, had brought with him from Faenza. I was glad to hear that M. Querini had married her at last, but I did not think of renewing the acquaintance, for reasons which my reader cannot have forgotten if he recollects our quarrel when I had to dress her as an abbé. I was on the point of going away when she happened to see me and called me. I went up to her, and, not wishing to be known by anyone, I whispered to her that my name was Farusi. Manzoni informed me that I was speaking to her excellency, Madame Querini. "I know it," I said, "through a letter which I have received from Venice, and I beg to offer my most sincere congratulations to Madame." She heard me and introduced me to Count Spada, creating me a baron on the spot. He invited me most kindly to come to his box, asked me where I came from, where I was going to, etc., and begged the pleasure of my company at supper for the same evening.

Ten years before, he had been Juliette's friend in Vienna, when Maria Theresa, having been informed of the pernicious influence of her beauty, gave her notice to quit the city. She had renewed her acquaintance with him in Venice, and had contrived to make him take her to Bologna on a pleasure trip. M. Manzoni, her old follower, who gave me all this information, accompanied her in order to bear witness of her good conduct before M. Querini. I must say that Manzoni was not a well-chosen chaperon.

In Venice she wanted everybody to believe that Querini had married her secretly, but at a distance of fifty leagues she did not think such a formality necessary, and she had already been presented by the general to all the nobility of Cesena as Madame Querini Papozzes. M. Querini would have been wrong in being jealous of the count, for he was an old acquaintance who would do no harm. Besides, it is admitted amongst certain women that the reigning lover who is jealous of an old acquaintance is nothing but a fool, and ought to be treated as such. Juliette, most likely afraid of my being indiscreet, had lost no time in making the first advances, but, seeing that I had likewise some reason to fear her want of discretion, she felt reassured. From the first moment I treated her politely, and with every consideration due to her position.

I found numerous company at the general's, and some pretty women. Not seeing Juliette, I enquired for her from M. Manzoni, who told me that she was at the faro table, losing her money. I saw her seated next to the banker, who turned pale at the sight of my face. He was no other than the so-called Count Celi. He offered me a card, which I refused politely, but I accepted Juliette's offer to be her partner. She had about fifty sequins, I handed her the same sum, and took a seat near her. After the first round, she asked me if I knew the banker; Celi had heard the question; I answered negatively. A lady on my left told me that the banker was Count Alfani. Half an hour later, Madame Querini went seven and lost, she increased her stake of ten sequins; it was the last deal of the game, and therefore the decisive one. I rose from my chair, and fixed my eyes on the banker's hands. But in spite of that, he cheated before me, and Madame lost.

Just at that moment the general offered her his arm to go to supper; she left the remainder of her gold on the table, and after supper, having played again, she lost every sequin.

I enlivened the supper by my stories and witty jests. I captivated everybody's friendship, and particularly the general's, who, having heard me say that I was going to Naples only to gratify an amorous fancy, entreated me to spend a month with him and to sacrifice my whim. But it was all in vain. My heart was unoccupied; I longed to see Lucrezia and Thérèse, whose charms after five years I could scarcely recollect. I only consented to remain in Cesena the four days during which the general intended to stay.

The next morning as I was dressing I had a call from the cowardly Alfani-Celi; I received him with a jeering smile, saying that I had expected him.

The hair-dresser being in the room Celi did not answer, but as soon as we were alone he said,——

"How could you possibly expect my visit?"

"I will tell you my reason as soon as you have handed me one hundred sequins, and you are going to do so at once."

"Here are fifty which I brought for you; you cannot demand more from me."

"Thank you, I take them on account, but as I am good-natured I advise you not to shew yourself this evening in Count Spada's drawing-rooms, for you would not be admitted, and it would be owing to me."

"I hope that you will think twice before you are guilty of such an ungenerous act."

"I have made up my mind; but now leave me."

There was a knock at my door, and the self-styled Count Alfani went away without giving me the trouble of repeating my order. My new visitor proved to be the first *castrato* of the theatre, who brought an invitation to dinner from Narici. The invitation was curious, and I accepted it with a smile. The *castrato* was named Nicolas Peritti; he pretended to be the grandson of a natural child of Sixtus V.; it might have been so. I shall have to mention him again in fifteen years.

When I made my appearance at Narici's house I saw Count Alfani, who certainly did not expect me, and must have taken me for his evil genius. He bowed to me with great politeness, and begged that I would listen to a few words in private.

"Here are fifty sequins more," he said; "but as an honest man you can take them only to give them to Madame Querini. But how can you hand the amount to her without letting her know that you have forced me to refund it? You understand what consequences such a confession might have for me."

"I shall give her the money only when you have left this place; in the mean time I promise to be discreet, but be careful not to assist fortune in my presence, or I must act in a manner that will not be agreeable to you."

"Double the capital of my bank, and we can be partners."

"Your proposal is an insult."

He gave me fifty sequins, and I promised to keep his secret.

There was a numerous attendance in Narici's rooms, especially of young men, who after dinner lost all their money. I did not play, and it was a disappointment for my pretty hostess, who had invited me only because she had judged me as simple as the others. I remained an indifferent witness of the play, and it gave me an oppor-

tunity of realizing how wise Mahomet had been in forbidding all games of chance.

In the evening after the opera Count Celi had the faro
bank, and I lose two hundred sequins, but I could only
accuse ill luck. Madame Querini won. The next day
before supper I broke the bank, and after supper, feeling
tired and well pleased with what I had won, I returned
to the inn.

The following morning, which was the third day, and
therefore the last but one of my stay in Cesena, I called
at the general's. I heard that his adjutant had thrown
the cards in Alfani's face, and that a meeting had been
arranged between them for twelve o'clock. I went to
the adjutant's room and offered to be his second, assuring him that there would be no blood spilt. He declined
my offer with many thanks, and at dinner-time he told
me that I had guessed rightly, for Count Alfani had left
for Rome.

"In that case," I said to the guests, "I will take the
bank to-night."

After dinner, being alone with Madame Querini, I told
her all about Alfani, *alias* Celi, and handed her the fifty
sequins of which I was the depositary.

"I suppose," she said, "that by means of this fable
you hope to make me accept fifty sequins, but I thank
you, I am not in want of money."

"I give you my word that I have compelled the thief
to refund this money, together with the fifty sequins of
which he had likewise cheated me."

"That may be, but I do not wish to believe you. I
beg to inform you that I am not simple enough to allow
myself to be duped, and, what is worse, cheated in such
a manner."

Philosophy forbids a man to feel repentance for a good deed, but he must certainly have a right to regret such a deed when it is malevolently misconstrued, and turned against him as a reproach.

In the evening, after the performance, which was to be the last, I took the bank according to my promise: I lost a few sequins, but was caressed by everybody, and that is much more pleasant than winning, when we are not labouring under the hard necessity of making money.

Count Spada, who had got quite fond of me, wanted me to accompany him to Brisighetta, but I resisted his entreaties because I had firmly resolved on going to Naples.

The next morning I was awoke by a terrible noise in the passage, almost at the door of my room.

Getting out of my bed, I open my door to ascertain the cause of the uproar. I see a troop of *sbirri* at the door of a chamber, and in that chamber, sitting up in bed, a fine-looking man who was making himself hoarse by screaming in Latin against that rabble, the plague of Italy, and against the inn-keeper who had been rascally enough to open the door.

I enquire of the inn-keeper what it all means.

"This gentleman," answers the scoundrel, "who, it appears, can only speak Latin, is in bed with a girl, and the *sbirri* of the bishop have been sent to know whether she is truly his wife; all perfectly regular. If she is his wife, he has only to convince them by shewing a certificate of marriage, but if she is not, of course he must go to prison with her. Yet it need not happen, for I undertake to arrange everything in a friendly manner for a few sequins. I have only to exchange a few words with the chief of the *sbirri,* and they will all go away. If you

can speak Latin, you had better go in, and make him
listen to reason."

"Who has broken open the door of his room?"

"Nobody; I have opened it myself with the key, as is
my duty."

"Yes, the duty of a highway robber, but not of an
honest inn-keeper."

Such infamous dealing aroused my indignation, and I
made up my mind to interfere. I enter the room, although I had still my nightcap on, and inform the gentleman of the cause of the disturbance. He answers with
a laugh that, in the first place, it was impossible to say
whether the person who was in bed with him was a
woman, for that person had only been seen in the costume of a military officer, and that, in the second place,
he did not think that any human being had a right to
compel him to say whether his bed-fellow was his wife
or his mistress, even supposing that his companion was
truly a woman.

"At all events," he added, "I am determined not to
give one crown to arrange the affair, and to remain in
bed until my door is shut. The moment I am dressed,
I will treat you to an amusing *dénouement* of the comedy. I will drive away all those scoundrels at the point
of my sword."

I then see in a corner a broad sword, and a Hungarian
costume looking like a military uniform. I ask whether
he is an officer.

"I have written my name and profession," he answers,
"in the hotel book."

Astonished at the absurdity of the inn-keeper, I ask
him whether it is so; he confesses it, but adds that the
clergy have the right to prevent scandal.

"The insult you have offered to that officer, Mr. Land-lord, will cost you very dear."

His only answer is to laugh in my face. Highly en-raged at seeing such a scoundrel laugh at me, I take up the officer's quarrel warmly, and asked him to entrust his passport to me for a few minutes.

"I have two," he says; "therefore I can let you have one." And taking the document out of his pocket-book, he hands it to me. The passport was signed by Cardinal Albani. The officer was a captain in a Hungarian regi-ment belonging to the empress and queen. He was from Rome, on his way to Parma with dispatches from Cardi-nal Albani Alexander to M. Dutillot, prime minister of the Infante of Parma.

At the same moment, a man burst into the room, speaking very loudly, and asked me to tell the officer that the affair must be settled at once, because he wanted to leave Cesena immediately.

"Who are you?" I asked the man.

He answered that he was the *vetturino* whom the cap-tain had engaged. I saw that it was a regular put-up thing, and begged the captain to let me attend to the business, assuring him that I would settle it to his hon-our and advantage.

"Do exactly as you please," he said.

Then turning towards the *vetturino*, I ordered him to bring up the captain's luggage, saying that he would be paid at once. When he had done so, I handed him eight sequins out of my own purse, and made him give me a receipt in the name of the captain, who could only speak German, Hungarian, and Latin. The *vetturino* went away, and the *sbirri* followed him in the greatest con-sternation, except two who remained.

"Captain," I said to the Hungarian, "keep your bed

until I return. I am going now to the bishop to give him an account of these proceedings, and make him understand that he owes you some reparation. Besides, General Spada is here, and . . ."

"I know him," interrupted the captain, "and if I had been aware of his being in Cesena, I would have shot the landlord when he opened my door to those scoundrels."

I hurried over my toilet, and without waiting for my hair to be dressed I proceeded to the bishop's palace, and making a great deal of noise I almost compelled the servants to take me to his room. A lackey who was at the door informed me that his lordship was still in bed.

"Never mind, I cannot wait."

I pushed him aside and entered the room. I related the whole affair to the bishop, exaggerating the uproar, making much of the injustice of such proceedings, and railing at a vexatious police daring to molest travellers and to insult the sacred rights of individuals and nations.

The bishop without answering me referred me to his chancellor, to whom I repeated all I had said to the bishop, but with words calculated to irritate rather than to soften, and certainly not likely to obtain the release of the captain. I even went so far as to threaten, and I said that if I were in the place of the officer I would demand a public reparation. The priest laughed at my threats; it was just what I wanted, and after asking me whether I had taken leave of my senses, the chancellor told me to apply to the captain of the *sbirri*.

"I shall go to somebody else," I said, "reverend sir, besides the captain of the *sbirri*."

Delighted at having made matters worse, I left him and proceeded straight to the house of General Spada, but being told that he could not be seen before eight o'clock, I returned to the inn.

The state of excitement in which I was, the ardour with which I had made the affair mine, might have led anyone to suppose that my indignation had been roused only by disgust at seeing an odious persecution perpetrated upon a stranger by an unrestrained, immoral, and vexatious police; but why should I deceive the kind reader, to whom I have promised to tell the truth; I must therefore say that my indignation was real, but my ardour was excited by another feeling of a more personal nature. I fancied that the woman concealed under the bed-clothes was a beauty. I longed to see her face, which shame, most likely, had prevented her from shewing. She had heard me speak, and the good opinion that I had of myself did not leave the shadow of a doubt in my mind that she would prefer me to her captain.

The door of the room being still open, I went in and related to the captain all I had done, assuring him that in the course of the day he would be at liberty to continue his journey at the bishop's expense, for the general would not fail to obtain complete satisfaction for him. He thanked me warmly, gave back the eight ducats I had paid for him, and said that he would not leave the city till the next day.

"From what country," I asked him, "is your travelling companion?"

"From France, and he only speaks his native language."

"Then you speak French?"

"Not one word."

"That is amusing! Then you converse in pantomime?"

"Exactly."

"I pity you, for it is a difficult language."

"Yes, to express the various shades of thought, but in the material part of our intercourse we understand each other quite well."

"May I invite myself to breakfast with you?"

"Ask my friend whether he has any objection."

"Amiable companion of the captain," I said in French, "will you kindly accept me as a third guest at the breakfast-table?"

At these words I saw coming out of the bed-clothes a lovely head, with dishevelled hair, and a blooming, laughing face which, although it was crowned with a man's cap, left no doubt that the captain's friend belonged to that sex without which man would be the most miserable animal on earth.

Delighted with the graceful creature, I told her that I had been happy enough to feel interested in her even before I had seen her, and that now that I had the pleasure of seeing her, I could but renew with greater zeal all my efforts to serve her.

She answered me with the grace and the animation which are the exclusive privilege of her native country, and retorted my argument in the most witty manner; I was already under the charm. My request was granted; I went out to order breakfast, and to give them an opportunity of making themselves comfortable in bed, for they were determined not to get up until the door of their room was closed again.

The waiter came, and I went in with him. I found my lovely Frenchwoman wearing a blue frock-coat, with her hair badly arranged like a man's, but very charming even in that strange costume. I longed to see her up. She ate her breakfast without once interrupting the

officer who was speaking to me, but to whom I was not
listening, or listening with very little attention, for I
was in a sort of ecstatic trance.

Immediately after breakfast, I called on the general,
and related the affair to him, enlarging upon it in such
a manner as to pique his martial pride. I told him that,
unless he settled the matter himself, the Hungarian captain was determined to send an express to the cardinal
immediately. But my eloquence was unnecessary, for
the general liked to see priests attend to the business of
Heaven, but he could not bear them to meddle in tem-
poral affairs.

"I shall," he said, "immediately put a stop to this
ridiculous comedy, and treat it in a very serious
manner."

"Go at once to the inn," he said to his aide-de-camp,
"invite that officer and his companion to dine with me
to-day, and repair afterwards to the bishop's palace.
Give him notice that the officer who has been so grossly
insulted by his *sbirri* shall not leave the city before he
has received a complete apology, and whatever sum of
money he may claim as damages. Tell him that the
notice comes from me, and that all the expenses incurred
by the officer shall be paid by him."

What pleasure it was for me to listen to these words!
In my vanity, I fancied I had almost prompted them to
the general. I accompanied the aide-de-camp, and introduced him to the captain who received him with the joy
of a soldier meeting a comrade. The adjutant gave him
the general's invitation for him and his companion, and
asked him to write down what satisfaction he wanted,
as well as the amount of damages he claimed. At the
sight of the general's adjutant, the *sbirri* had quickly
vanished. I handed to the captain pen, paper and ink,

and he wrote his claim in pretty good Latin for a native of Hungary. The excellent fellow absolutely refused to ask for more than thirty sequins, in spite of all I said to make him claim one hundred. He was likewise a great deal too easy as to the satisfaction he demanded, for all he asked was to see the landlord and the *sbirri* beg his pardon on their knees in the presence of the general's adjutant. He threatened the bishop to send an express to Rome to Cardinal Alexander, unless his demands were complied with within two hours, and to remain in Cesena at the rate of ten sequins a day at the bishop's expense.

The officer left us, and a moment afterwards the landlord came in respectfully, to inform the captain that he was free, but the captain having begged me to tell the scoundrel that he owed him a sound thrashing, he lost no time in gaining the door.

I left my friends alone to get dressed, and to attend to my own toilet, as I dined with them at the general's. An hour afterwards I found them ready in their military costumes. The uniform of the Frenchwoman was of course a fancy one, but very elegant. The moment I saw her, I gave up all idea of Naples, and decided upon accompanying the two friends to Parma. The beauty of the lovely Frenchwoman had already captivated me. The captain was certainly on the threshold of sixty, and, as a matter of course, I thought such a union very badly assorted. I imagined that the affair which I was already concocting in my brain could be arranged amicably.

The adjutant came back with a priest sent by the bishop, who told the captain that he should have the satisfaction as well as the damages he had claimed, but that he must be content with fifteen sequins.

"Thirty or nothing," dryly answered the Hungarian.

They were at last given to him, and thus the matter ended. The victory was due to my exertions, and I had won the friendship of the captain and his lovely companion.

In order to guess, even at first sight, that the friend of the worthy captain was not a man, it was enough to look at the hips. She was too well made as a woman ever to pass for a man, and the women who disguise themselves in male attire, and boast of being like men, are very wrong, for by such a boast they confess themselves deficient in one of the greatest perfections appertaining to woman.

A little before dinner-time we repaired to General Spada's mansion, and the general presented the two officers to all the ladies. Not one of them was deceived in the young officer, but, being already acquainted with the adventure, they were all delighted to dine with the hero of the comedy, and treated the handsome officer exactly as if he had truly been a man, but I am bound to confess that the male guests offered the Frenchwoman homages more worthy of her sex.

Madame Querini alone did not seem pleased, because the lovely stranger monopolized the general attention, and it was a blow to her vanity to see herself neglected. She never spoke to her, except to shew off her French, which she could speak well. The poor captain scarcely opened his lips, for no one cared to speak Latin, and the general had not much to say in German.

An elderly priest, who was one of the guests, tried to justify the conduct of the bishop by assuring us that the inn-keeper and the *sbirri* had acted only under the orders of the Holy Office.

"That is the reason," he said, "for which no bolts are allowed in the rooms of the hotels, so that strangers may not shut themselves up in their chambers. The Holy Inquisition does not allow a man to sleep with any woman but his wife."

Twenty years later I found all the doors in Spain with a bolt outside, so that travellers were, as if they had been in prison, exposed to the outrageous molestation of nocturnal visits from the police. That disease is so chronic in Spain that it threatens to overthrow the monarchy some day, and I should not be astonished if one fine morning the Grand Inquisitor was to have the king shaved, and to take his place.

CHAPTER XXIII

*I Purchase a Handsome Carriage, and Proceed to Parma
With the Old Captain and the Young Frenchwoman—
I Pay a Visit to Javotte, and Present Her With a
Beautiful Pair of Gold Bracelets—My Perplexities
Respecting My Lovely Travelling Companion—A
Monologue—Conversation with the Captain—Tête-à-
Tête with Henriette*

THE conversation was animated, and the young female officer was entertaining everybody, even Madame Querini, although she hardly took the trouble of
concealing her spleen.

"It seems strange," she remarked, "that you and the
captain should live together without ever speaking to
each other."

"Why, madam? We understand one another perfectly,
for speech is of very little consequence in the kind of
business we do together."

That answer, given with graceful liveliness, made
everybody laugh, except Madame Querini-Juliette, who,
foolishly assuming the air of a prude, thought that its
meaning was too clearly expressed.

"I do not know any kind of business," she said, "that
can be transacted without the assistance of the voice or
the pen."

"Excuse me, madam, there are some: playing at cards,
for instance, is a business of that sort."

"Are you always playing?"

"We do nothing else. We play the game of the Pharaoh (faro), and I hold the bank."

Everybody, understanding the shrewdness of this evasive answer, laughed again, and Juliette herself could not help joining in the general merriment.

"But tell me," said Count Spada, "does the bank receive much?"

"As for the deposits, they are of so little importance, that they are hardly worth mentioning."

No one ventured upon translating that sentence for the benefit of the worthy captain. The conversation continued in the same amusing style, and all the guests were delighted with the graceful wit of the charming officer.

Late in the evening I took leave of the general, and wished him a pleasant journey.

"Adieu," he said, "I wish you a pleasant journey to Naples, and hope you will enjoy yourself there."

"Well, general, I am not going to Naples immediately; I have changed my mind and intend to proceed to Parma, where I wish to see the Infante. I also wish to constitute myself the interpreter of these two officers who know nothing of Italian."

"Ah, young man! opportunity makes a thief, does it not? Well, if I were in your place, I would do the same."

I also bade farewell to Madame Querini, who asked me to write to her from Bologna. I gave her a promise to do so, but without meaning to fulfil it.

I had felt interested in the young Frenchwoman when she was hiding under the bed-clothes: she had taken my fancy the moment she had shewn her features, and still more when I had seen her dressed. She completed her

conquest at the dinner-table by the display of a wit
which I greatly admired. It is rare in Italy, and seems
to belong generally to the daughters of France. I did
not think it would be very difficult to win her love, and
I resolved on trying. Putting my self-esteem on one
side, I fancied I would suit her much better than the
old Hungarian, a very pleasant man for his age, but
who, after all, carried his sixty years on his face, while
my twenty-three were blooming on my countenance. It
seemed to me that the captain himself would not raise
any great objection, for he seemed one of those men who,
treating love as a matter of pure fancy, accept all circumstances easily, and give way good-naturedly to all
the freaks of fortune. By becoming the travelling companion of this ill-matched couple, I should probably succeed in my aims. I never dreamed of experiencing a
refusal at their hands, my company would certainly be
agreeable to them, as they could not exchange a single
word by themselves.

With this idea I asked the captain, as we reached our
inn, whether he intended to proceed to Parma by the
public coach or otherwise.

"As I have no carriage of my own," he answered, "we
shall have to take the coach."

"I have a very comfortable carriage, and I offer you
the two back seats if you have no objection to my
society."

"That is a piece of good fortune. Be kind enough to
propose it to Henriette."

"Will you, madam, grant me the favour of accompanying you to Parma?"

"I should be delighted, for we could have some conversation, but take care, sir, your task will not be an

easy one, you will often find yourself obliged to translate for both of us."

"I shall do so with great pleasure; I am only sorry that the journey is not longer. We can arrange everything at supper-time; allow me to leave you now as I have some business to settle."

My business was in reference to a carriage, for the one I had boasted of existed only in my imagination. I went to the most fashionable coffee-house, and, as good luck would have it, heard that there was a travelling carriage for sale, which no one would buy because it was too expensive. Two hundred sequins were asked for it, although it had but two seats and a bracket-stool for a third person. It was just what I wanted. I called at the place where it would be seen. I found a very fine English carriage which could not have cost less than two hundred guineas. Its noble proprietor was then at supper, so I sent him my name, requesting him not to dispose of his carriage until the next morning, and I went back to the hotel well pleased with my discovery. At supper I arranged with the captain that we would not leave Cesena till after dinner on the following day, and the conversation was almost entirely a dialogue between Henriette and myself; it was my first talk with a French woman. I thought this young creature more and more charming, yet I could not suppose her to be anything else but an adventuress, and I was astonished at discovering in her those noble and delicate feelings which denote a good education. However, as such an idea would not have suited the views I had about her, I rejected it whenever it presented itself to my mind. Whenever I tried to make her talk about the captain she would change the subject of conversation, or evade my

insinuations with a tact and a shrewdness which astonished and delighted me at the same time, for everything
she said bore the impress of grace and wit. Yet she did
not elude this question:

"At least tell me, madam, whether the captain is your
husband or your father."

"Neither one nor the other," she answered, with a
smile.

That was enough for me, and in reality what more did
I want to know?

The worthy captain had fallen asleep. When he awoke
I wished them both good night, and retired to my room
with a heart full of love and a mind full of projects. I
saw that everything had taken a good turn, and I felt
certain of success, for I was young, I enjoyed excellent
health, I had money and plenty of daring. I liked the
affair all the better because it must come to a conclusion
in a few days.

Early the next morning I called upon Count Dandini,
the owner of the carriage, and as I passed a jeweller's
shop I bought a pair of gold bracelets in Venetian fili-
gree, each five yards long and of rare fineness. I intended them as a present for Javotte.

The moment Count Dandini saw me he recognized
me. He had seen me in Padua at the house of his
father, who was professor of civil law at the time I was
a student there. I bought his carriage on condition that
he would send it to me in good repair at one o'clock in
the afternoon.

Having completed the purchase, I went to my friend,
Franzia, and my present of the bracelets made Javotte
perfectly happy. There was not one girl in Cesena who
could boast of possessing a finer pair, and with that
present my conscience felt at ease, for it paid the ex-

pense I had occasioned during my stay of ten or twelve days at her father's house four times over. But this was not the most important present I offered the family. I made the father take an oath to wait for me, and never to trust in any pretended magician for the necessary operation to obtain the treasure, even if I did not return or give any news of myself for ten years.

"Because," I said to him, "in consequence of the agreement in which I have entered with the spirits watching the treasure, at the first attempt made by any other person, the casket containing the treasure will sink to twice its present depth, that is to say as deep as thirty-five fathoms, and then I shall have myself ten times more difficulty in raising it to the surface. I cannot state precisely the time of my return, for it depends upon certain combinations which are not under my control, but recollect that the treasure cannot be obtained by anyone but I."

I accompanied my advice with threats of utter ruin to his family if he should ever break his oath. And in this manner I atoned for all I had done, for, far from deceiving the worthy man, I became his benefactor by guarding against the deceit of some cheat who would have cared for his money more than for his daughter. I never saw him again, and most likely he is dead, but knowing the deep impression I left on his mind I am certain that his descendants are even now waiting for me, for the name of Farusi must have remained immortal in that family.

Javotte accompanied me as far as the gate of the city, where I kissed her affectionately, which made me feel that the thunder and lightning had had but a momentary effect upon me; yet I kept control over my senses, and I congratulate myself on doing so to this day. I told her, before bidding her adieu, that, her virginity being no longer necessary for my magic operations, I advised her to get married as soon as possible, if I did not return within three months. She shed a few tears, but promised to follow my advice.

I trust that my readers will approve of the noble manner in which I concluded my magic business. I hardly dare to boast of it, but I think I deserve some praise for my behaviour. Perhaps, I might have ruined poor Franzia with a light heart, had I not possessed a well-filled purse. I do not wish to enquire whether any young man, having intelligence, loving pleasure, and placed in the same position, would not have done the same, but I beg my readers to address that question to themselves.

As for Capitani, to whom I sold the sheath of St. Peter's knife for rather more than it was worth, I confess that I have not yet repented on his account, for Capitani thought he had duped me in accepting it as security for the amount he gave me, and the count, his father, valued it until his death as more precious than the finest diamond in the world. Dying with such a firm belief, he died rich, and I shall die a poor man. Let the reader judge which of the two made the best bargain. But I must return now to my future travelling companions.

As soon as I had reached the inn, I prepared everything for our departure for which I was now longing. Henriette could not open her lips without my discovering some fresh perfection, for her wit delighted me even more than her beauty. It struck me that the old captain was pleased with all the attention I shewed her, and it seemed evident to me that she would not be sorry to exchange her elderly lover for me. I had all the better right to think so, inasmuch as I was perfection from a physical point of view, and I appeared to be wealthy, although I had no servant. I told Henriette that, for the sake of having none, I spent twice as much as a servant would have cost me, that, by my being my own servant, I was certain of being served according to my taste, and I had the satisfaction of having no spy at my heels and no privileged thief to fear. She agreed with everything I said, and it increased my love.

The honest Hungarian insisted upon giving me in advance the amount to be paid for the post-horses at the different stages as far as Parma. We left Cesena after dinner, but not without a contest of politeness respecting the seats. The captain wanted me to occupy the back seat near Henriette, but the reader will understand how much better the seat opposite to her suited me; therefore I insisted upon taking the bracket-seat, and had the double advantage of shewing my politeness, and of having constantly and without difficulty before my eyes the lovely woman whom I adored.

My happiness would have been too great if there had been no drawback to it. But where can we find roses without thorns? When the charming Frenchwoman uttered some of those witty sayings which proceed so naturally from the lips of her countrywomen, I could not help pitying the sorry face of the poor Hungarian, and, wishing to make him share my mirth, I would undertake to translate in Latin Henriette's sallies; but far from making him merry, I often saw his face bear a look of astonishment, as if what I had said seemed to him rather flat. I had to acknowledge to myself that I could not speak Latin as well as she spoke French, and this was indeed the case. The last thing which we learn in all languages is wit, and wit never shines so well as in jests. I was thirty years of age before I began to laugh in reading Terence, Plautus and Martial.

Something being the matter with the carriage, we stopped at Forli to have it repaired. After a very cheerful supper, I retired to my room to go to bed, thinking of nothing else but the charming woman by whom I was so completely captivated. Along the road, Henriette had struck me as so strange that I would not sleep in the second bed in their room. I was afraid lest she should leave her old comrade to come to my bed and sleep with me, and I did not know how far the worthy captain would have put up with such a joke. I wished, of course, to possess that lovely creature, but I wanted everything to be settled amicably, for I felt some respect for the brave officer.

Henriette had nothing but the military costume in which she stood, not any woman's linen, not even one chemise. For a change she took the captain's shirt. Such a state of things was so new to me that the situation seemed to me a complete enigma.

In Bologna, excited by an excellent supper and by the amorous passion which was every hour burning more fiercely in me, I asked her by what singular adventure she had become the friend of the honest fellow who looked her father rather than her lover.

"If you wish to know," she answered, with a smile, "ask him to relate the whole story himself, only you must request him not to omit any of the particulars."

Of course I applied at once to the captain, and, having first ascertained by signs that the charming Frenchwoman had no objection, the good man spoke to me thus:

"A friend of mine, an officer in the army, having occasion to go to Rome, I solicited a furlough of six months,

and accompanied him. I seized with great delight the
opportunity of visiting a city, the name of which has a
powerful influence on the imagination, owing to the
memories of the past attached to it. I did not entertain
any doubt that the Latin language was spoken there in
good society, at least as generally as in Hungary. But
I was indeed greatly mistaken, for nobody can speak it,
not even the priests, who only pretend to write it, and
it is true that some of them do so with great purity. I
was therefore rather uncomfortable during my stay in
Rome, and with the exception of my eyes my senses remained perfectly inactive. I had spent a very tedious
month in that city, the ancient queen of the world, when
Cardinal Albani gave my friend dispatches for Naples.
Before leaving Rome, he introduced me to his eminence,
and his recommendation had so much influence that the
cardinal promised to send me very soon with dispatches
for the Duke of Parma, Piacenza, and Guastalla, assuring me that all my travelling expenses would be de-
frayed. As I wished to see the harbour called in former
times *Centum cellae* and now Civita-Vecchia, I gave up
the remainder of my time to that visit, and I proceeded
there with a cicerone who spoke Latin.

"I was loitering about the harbour when I saw, coming
out of a tartan, an elderly officer and this young woman
dressed as she is now. Her beauty struck me, but I
should not have thought any more about it, if the officer
had not put up at my inn, and in an apartment over
which I had a complete view whenever I opened my
window. In the evening I saw the couple taking supper
at the same table, but I remarked that the elderly officer
never addressed a word to the young one. When the
supper was over, the disguised girl left the room, and
her companion did not lift his eyes from a letter which

he was reading, as it seemed to me, with the deepest attention. Soon afterwards the officer closed the windows, the light was put out, and I suppose my neighbors went to bed. The next morning, being up early as is my habit, I saw the officer go out, and the girl remained alone in the room.

"I sent my cicerone, who was also my servant, to tell the girl in the garb of an officer that I would give her ten sequins for an hour's conversation. He fulfilled my instructions, and on his return he informed me that her answer, given in French, had been to the effect that she would leave for Rome immediately after breakfast, and that, once in that city, I should easily find some opportunity of speaking to her.

" 'I can find out from the *vetturino,*' said my cicerone, 'where they put up in Rome, and I promise you to enquire of him.'

"She left Civita-Vecchia with the elderly officer, and I returned home on the following day.

"Two days afterwards, the cardinal gave me the dispatches, which were addressed to M. Dutillot, the French minister, with a passport and the money necessary for the journey. He told me, with great kindness, that I need not hurry on the road.

"I had almost forgotten the handsome adventuress, when, two days before my departure, my cicerone gave me the information that he had found out where she lived, and that she was with the same officer. I told him to try to see her, and to let her know that my departure was fixed for the day after the morrow. She sent me word by him that, if I would inform her of the hour of my departure, she would meet me outside of the gate, and get into the coach with me to accompany me on my way. I thought the arrangement very ingenious and

during the day I sent the cicerone to tell her the hour at
which I intended to leave, and where I would wait for
her outside of the Porto del Popolo. She came at the
appointed time, and we have remained together ever
since. As soon as she was seated near me, she made me
understand by signs that she wanted to dine with me.
You may imagine what difficulty we had in understanding one another, but we guessed somehow the meaning
expressed by our pantomime, and I accepted the adventure with delight.

"We dined gaily together, speaking without understanding, but after the dessert we comprehended each
other very well. I fancied that I had seen the end of it,
and you may imagine how surprised I was when, upon
my offering her the ten sequins, she refused most positively to take any money, making me understand that
she would rather go with me to Parma, because she had
some business in that city, and did not want to return
to Rome.

"The proposal was, after all, rather agreeable to me;
I consented to her wishes. I only regretted my inability
to make her understand that, if she was followed by
anyone from Rome, and if that person wanted to take
her back, I was not in a position to defend her against
violence. I was also sorry that, with our mutual ignorance of the language spoken by each of us, we had no
opportunity of conversation, for I should have been
greatly pleased to hear her adventures, which, I think,
must be interesting. You can, of course, guess that I
have no idea of who she can be. I only know that she
calls herself Henriette, that she must be a Frenchwoman, that she is as gentle as a turtledove, that she has
evidently received a good education, and that she enjoys
good health. She is witty and courageous, as we have

both seen, I in Rome and you in Cesena at General Spada's table. If she would tell you her history, and allow you to translate it for me in Latin she would indeed please me much, for I am sincerely her friend, and I can assure you that it will grieve me to part from her in Parma. Please to tell her that I intend to give her the thirty sequins I received from the Bishop of Cesena, and that if I were rich I would give her more substantial proofs of my tender affection. Now, sir, I shall feel obliged to you if you will explain it all to her in French."

I asked her whether she would feel offended if I gave her an exact translation. She assured me that, on the contrary, she wished me to speak openly, and I told her literally what the captain had related to me.

With a noble frankness which a slight shade of shame rendered more interesting, Henriette confirmed the truth of her friend's narrative, but she begged me to tell him that she could not grant his wish respecting the adventures of her life.

"Be good enough to inform him," she added, "that the same principle which forbids me to utter a falsehood, does not allow me to tell the truth. As for the thirty sequins which he intends to give me, I will not accept even one of them, and he would deeply grieve me by pressing them upon me. The moment we reach Parma I wish him to allow me to lodge wherever I may please, to make no enquiries whatever about me, and, in case he should happen to meet me, to crown his great kindness to me by not appearing to have ever known me."

As she uttered the last words of this short speech, which she had delivered very seriously and with a mixture of modesty and resolution, she kissed her elderly friend in a manner which indicated esteem and gratitude rather than love. The captain, who did not know why she was kissing him, was deeply grieved when I translated what Henriette had said. He begged me to tell her that, if he was to obey her with an easy conscience, he must know whether she would have everything she required in Parma.

"You can assure him," she answered, "that he need not entertain any anxiety about me."

This conversation had made us all very sad; we remained for a long time thoughtful and silent, until, feeling the situation to be painful, I rose, wishing them good night, and I saw that Henriette's face wore a look of great excitement.

As soon as I found myself alone in my room, deeply moved by conflicting feelings of love, surprise, and uncertainty, I began to give vent to my feelings in a kind of soliloquy, as I always do when I am strongly excited by anything; thinking is not, in those cases, enough for me; I must speak aloud, and I throw so much action, so much animation into these monologues that I forget I am alone. What I knew now of Henriette had upset me altogether.

"Who can she be," I said, speaking to the walls; "this girl who seems to have the most elevated feelings under the veil of the most cynical libertinism? She says that in Parma she wishes to remain perfectly unknown, her own mistress, and I cannot, of course, flatter myself that she will not place me under the same restrictions as the captain to whom she has already abandoned herself. Goodbye to my expectations, to my money, and my illusions! But who is she—what is she? She must have either a lover or a husband in Parma, or she must belong to a respectable family; or, perhaps, thanks to a boundless love for debauchery and to her confidence in her own charms, she intends to set fortune, misery, and degradation at defiance, and to try to enslave some wealthy nobleman! But that would be the plan of a mad woman or of a person reduced to utter despair, and it does not seem to be the case with Henriette. Yet she possesses nothing. True, but she refused, as if she had been provided with all she needed, the kind assistance of a man who has the right to offer it, and from whom, in sooth, she can accept without blushing, since she has not been ashamed to grant him favours with which love had nothing to do. Does she think that it is less shameful for a woman to abandon herself to the desires of a man unknown and unloved than to receive a present from an esteemed friend, and particularly at the eve of finding herself in the street, entirely destitute in the middle of a foreign city, amongst people whose language she cannot even speak? Perhaps she thinks that such conduct will justify the *faux pas* of which she has been guilty with the captain, and give him to understand that she had abandoned herself to him only for the sake of escaping from the officer with whom she was in Rome. But she ought to be quite certain that the captain does not entertain any other idea; he shews himself so reasonable that it is impossible to suppose that he ever admitted the possibility of having inspired her with a violent passion, because she had seen him once through a window in Civita-Vecchia. She might possibly be right, and feel herself justified in her conduct towards the captain, but it is not the same with me, for with her intelligence she must be aware that I would not have travelled with them if she had been indifferent to me, and she must know that there is but one way in which she can obtain my pardon. She may be endowed with many virtues, but she has not the only one which could prevent me from wishing the reward which every man expects to receive at the hands of the woman he loves. If she wants to assume prudish manners towards me and to make a dupe of me, I am bound in honour to shew her how much she is mistaken."

After this monologue, which had made me still more angry, I made up my mind to have an explanation in the morning before our departure.

"I shall ask her," said I to myself, "to grant me the same favours which she has so easily granted to her old captain, and if I meet with a refusal the best revenge will be to shew her a cold and profound contempt until our arrival in Parma."

I felt sure that she could not refuse me some marks of real or of pretended affection, unless she wished to make a show of a modesty which certainly did not belong to her, and, knowing that her modesty would only be all pretence, I was determined not to be a mere toy in her hands.

As for the captain, I felt certain, from what he had told me, that he would not be angry with me if I risked a declaration, for as a sensible man he could only assume a neutral position.

Satisfied with my wise reasoning, and with my mind fully made up, I fell asleep. My thoughts were too completely absorbed by Henriette for her not to haunt my dreams, but the dream which I had throughout the night was so much like reality that, on awaking, I looked for her in my bed, and my imagination was so deeply struck with the delights of that night that, if my door had not been fastened with a bolt, I should have believed that she had left me during my sleep to resume her place near the worthy Hungarian.

When I was awake I found that the happy dream of

the night had turned my love for the lovely creature into a perfect amorous frenzy, and it could not be otherwise. Let the reader imagine a poor devil going to bed broken down with fatigue and starvation; he succumbs to sleep, that most imperative of all human wants, but in his dream he finds himself before a table covered with every delicacy; what will then happen? Why, a very natural result. His appetite, much more lively than on the previous day, does not give him a minute's rest—he must satisfy it or die of sheer hunger.

I dressed myself, resolved on making sure of the possession of the woman who had inflamed all my senses, even before resuming our journey.

"If I do not succeed," I said to myself, "I will not go one step further."

But, in order not to offend against propriety, and not to deserve the reproaches of an honest man, I felt that it was my duty to have an explanation with the captain in the first place.

I fancy that I hear one of those sensible, calm, passionless readers, who have had the advantage of what is called a youth without storms, or one of those whom old age has forced to become virtuous, exclaim,——

"Can anyone attach so much importance to such nonsense?"

Age has calmed my passions down by rendering them powerless, but my heart has not grown old, and my memory has kept all the freshness of youth; and far from considering that sort of thing a mere trifle, my only sorrow, dear reader, arises from the fact that I have not the power to practise, to the day of my death, that which has been the principal affair of my life!

When I was ready I repaired to the chamber occupied by my two travelling companions, and after paying each of them the usual morning compliments I told the officer that I was deeply in love with Henriette, and I asked him whether he would object to my trying to obtain her as my mistress.

"The reason for which she begs you," I added, "to leave her in Parma, and not to take any further notice of her, must be that she hopes to meet some lover of hers there. Let me have half an hour's conversation with her, and I flatter myself I can persuade her to sacrifice that lover for me. If she refuses me, I remain here; you will go with her to Parma, where you will leave my carriage at the post, only sending me a receipt, so that I can claim it whenever I please."

"As soon as breakfast is over," said the excellent man, "I shall go and visit the institute, and leave you alone with Henriette. I hope you may succeed, for I should be delighted to see her under your protection when I part with her. Should she persist in her first resolution, I could easily find a *vetturino* here, and you could keep your carriage. I thank you for your proposal, and it will grieve me to leave you."

Highly pleased at having accomplished half of my task, and at seeing myself near the *dénouement,* I asked the lovely Frenchwoman whether she would like to see the sights of Bologna.

"I should like it very much," she said, "if I had some other clothes; but with such a costume as this I do not care to shew myself about the city."

"Then you do not want to go out?"

"No."

"Can I keep you company?"

"That would be delightful."

The captain went out immediately after breakfast. The moment he had gone I told Henriette that her friend had left us alone purposely, so as to give me the opportunity of a private interview with her.

"Tell me now whether you intended the order which you gave him yesterday to forget you, never to enquire after you, and even not to know you if he happened to meet you, from the time of our arrival in Parma, for me as well as for him."

"It is not an order that I gave him; I have no right to do so, and I could not so far forget myself; it is only a prayer I addressed to him, a service which circumstances have compelled me to claim at his hands, and as he has no right to refuse me, I never entertained any doubt of his granting my command. As far as you are concerned, it is certain that I should have addressed the same prayer to you, if I had thought that you had any views about me. You have given me some marks of your friendship, but you must understand that if, under the circumstances, I am likely to be injured by the kind attentions of the captain, yours would injure me much more. If you have any friendship for me, you would have felt all that."

"As you know that I entertain great friendship for you, you cannot possibly suppose that I would leave you alone, without money, without resources in the middle of a city where you cannot even make yourself understood. Do you think that a man who feels for you the most tender affection can abandon you when he has been fortunate enough to make your acquaintance, when he is aware of the sad position in which you are placed? If you think such a thing possible, you must have a very false idea of friendship, and should such a man grant your request, he would only prove that he is not your friend."

"I am certain that the captain is my friend; yet

you have heard him, he will obey me, and forget me."

"I do not know what sort of affection that honest man feels for you, or how far he can rely upon the control he may have over himself, but I know that if he can grant you what you have asked from him, his friendship must be of a nature very different from mine, for I am bound to tell you it is not only impossible for me to afford you willingly the strange gratification of abandoning you in your position, but even that, if I go to Parma, you could not possibly carry out your wishes, because I love you so passionately that you must promise to be mine, or I must remain here. In that case you must go to Parma alone with the captain, for I feel that, if I accompanied you any further, I should soon be the most wretched of men. I could not bear to see you with another lover, with a husband, not even in the midst of your family; in fact, I would fain see you and live with you forever. Let me tell you, lovely Henriette, that if it is possible for a Frenchman to forget, an Italian cannot do it, at least if I judge from my own feelings. I have made up my mind, you must be good enough to decide now, and to tell me whether I am to accompany you or to remain here. Answer yes or no; if I remain here it is all over. I shall leave for Naples to-morrow, and I know I shall be cured in time of the mad passion I feel for you, but if you tell me that I can accompany you to Parma, you must promise me that your heart will forever belong to me alone. I must be the only one to possess you, but I am ready to accept as a condition, if you like, that you shall not crown my happiness until you have judged me worthy of it by my attentions and by my loving care. Now, be kind enough to decide before the return of the too happy captain. He knows all, for I have told him what I feel."

"And what did he answer?"

"That he would be happy to see you under my protection. But what is the meaning of that smile playing
on your lips?"

"Pray, allow me to laugh, for I have never in my life
realized the idea of a furious declaration of love. Do
you understand what it is to say to a woman in a declaration which ought to be passionate, but at the same
time tender and gentle, the following terrible words:
'Madam, make your choice, either one or the other, and
decide instanter!' Ha! ha! ha!"

"Yes, I understand perfectly. It is neither gentle, nor
gallant, nor pathetic, but it is passionate. Remember
that this is a serious matter, and that I have never yet
found myself so much pressed by time. Can you, on
your side, realize the painful position of a man, who,
being deeply in love, finds himself compelled to take a
decision which may perhaps decide issues of life and
death? Be good enough to remark that, in spite of the
passion raging in me, I do not fail in the respect I owe
you; that the resolution I intend to take, if you should
persist in your original decision, is not a threat, but an
effort worthy of a hero, which ought to call for your
esteem. I beg of you to consider that we cannot afford
to lose time. The word choose must not sound harshly
in your ears, since it leaves my fate as well as yours
entirely in your hands. To feel certain of my love, do
you want to see me kneeling before you like a simpleton,
crying and entreating you to take pity on me? No,
madam, that would certainly displease you, and it would
not help me. I am conscious of being worthy of your
love, I therefore ask for that feeling and not for pity.
Leave me, if I displease you, but let me go away; for if
you are humane enough to wish that I should forget you,

allow me to go far away from you so as to make my sorrow less immense. Should I follow you to Parma, I would not answer for myself, for I might give way to my despair. Consider everything well, I beseech you; you would indeed be guilty of great cruelty, were you to answer now: 'Come to Parma, although I must beg of you not to see me in that city.' Confess that you cannot, in all fairness, give me such an answer; am I not right?"

"Certainly, if you truly love me."

"Good God! if I love you? Oh, yes! believe me, my love is immense, sincere! Now, decide my fate."

"What! always the same song?"

"Yes."

"But are you aware that you look very angry?"

"No, for it is not so. I am only in a state of uncontrollable excitement, in one of the decisive hours of my life, a prey to the most fearful anxiety. I ought to curse my whimsical destiny and the *sbirri* of Cesena (may God curse them, too!), for, without them, I should never have known you."

"Are you, then, so very sorry to have made my acquaintance?"

"Have I not some reason to be so?"

"No, for I have not given you my decision yet."

"Now I breathe more freely, for I am sure you will tell me to accompany you to Parma."

"Yes, come to Parma."

END OF VOL. I